ROBERT
GROSSETESTE

PORTRAIT OF ROBERT GROSSETESTE,
BISHOP OF LINCOLN

from British Museum MS Royal 6.E.v, 14 cent.

ROBERT GROSSETESTE

AND THE ORIGINS OF
EXPERIMENTAL
SCIENCE
1100-1700

By

A. C. CROMBIE

OXFORD
AT THE CLARENDON PRESS

OXFORD

UNIVERSITY PRESS

Great Clarendon Street, Oxford OX2 6DP

Oxford University Press is a department of the University of Oxford.
It furthers the University's objective of excellence in research, scholarship,
and education by publishing worldwide in

Oxford New York

Auckland Bangkok Buenos Aires Cape Town Chennai
Dar es Salaam Delhi Hong Kong Istanbul Karachi Kolkata
Kuala Lumpur Madrid Melbourne Mexico City Mumbai Nairobi
São Paulo Shanghai Singapore Taipei Tokyo Toronto
and an associated company in Berlin

Oxford is a registered trade mark of Oxford University Press
in the UK and in certain other countries

Published in the United States
by Oxford University Press Inc., New York

British Library Cataloguing in Publication Data

Data available

ISBN 0-19-824189-5

1 3 5 7 9 10 8 6 4 2

Printed in Great Britain
on acid-free paper by
Biddles Ltd.,
Guildford and King's Lynn

PREFACE TO THE SECOND IMPRESSION

I TAKE this opportunity offered by a photographic reprint to make two points.

First: my original purpose in writing this book was to draw attention to the framework of ideas about scientific method, explanation, etc.—and the continuity of, as well as the changes in, that framework—associated with the development of scientific thought in medieval and early modern times. If I were writing the book now both its organization and its conclusions would be somewhat different. It received its present shape largely from the order of development of my own interests and knowledge. One result is that two separate (even if related) themes, one the study of the theory and use of experiment in medieval science and the other the study of Grosseteste and his influence, are insufficiently distinguished. In consequence, the commentaries on the *Posterior Analytics* and similar writings are credited with too much influence on science, as distinct from logical and epistemological theory associated with science. Certainly some of the expressions I used about the extent of the medieval contributions to the structure and methods of research of modern experimental science now seem to me exaggerated; indeed they belong to a moment of enthusiasm provoked by the once conventional, and wholly unhistorical, view which denied any such contributions. But a book has a life of its own distinct from that of its author, and I see no reason why I should be committed for ever to expressions used in controversies of a decade ago. Clearly a book of this nature cannot be revised without being rewritten entirely—and the case is better met by writing another book. Modern science emerges most distinctively as a research movement, using methods of research and criteria of cogency which, though varying considerably according to the subject of inquiry, have sufficient in common to characterize the whole movement. The experimental method appears as the product of a union between a theoretical search for reduction to common forms of explanation and a practical demand for accurately reproducible results. A special need now is to collect and analyse the technical as well as the scientific writings throwing light on this union. I have in preparation a further study with edited texts documenting some of the answers given, at different periods in the origins of modern science, to the essential questions: what to do in research, and what to count as an adequate result and a satisfactory explanation. In the present reprint I have made a small number of corrections permitted by the method of reproduction.

Second: I should like to draw attention to some immediately relevant studies published since 1952. These are printed at the end of the Bibliography on p. 353.

A. C. C.

Oxford, September 1961

I HAVE corrected some details, included a further translation on pp. 123–4, and made some additions to the Bibliography for this new impression.

A. C. C.

Oxford, April 1970

PREFACE

OF the outstanding characteristics of the Western intellectual tradition, those whose influence in all departments of life and thought has been most far-reaching in its cumulative effect have been the insistence on logical coherence and on experiential confirmation. Both are found well developed in Greek philosophy, especially in the philosophy of Aristotle and his followers, and it is to this insistence that we must attribute what success Greek natural science achieved. The very much greater success of modern science is the result of a very much more effective combination of logic and mathematics with experiment. In the pages that follow I have tried to show how that combination was brought about by the interests and genius of the peoples who entered into the Classical intellectual inheritance during the so-called Dark Ages and Middle Ages, and how the interests and methods then established are essentially continuous with those in evidence since the seventeenth century.

The plan of the book has formed itself round the materials that I have been led to study. I have tried to show first how the particular intellectual and practical interests of Western thinkers, especially from the twelfth century, led them to ask particular kinds of question about the natural world, in consequence of which they came to create the modern experimental method. In the thirteenth century the Oxford school, with Robert Grosseteste as its founder, assumes a paramount importance: the work of this school in fact marks the beginning of the modern tradition of experimental science. The first half of the book is devoted to Grosseteste and the Oxford school; the second deals with their influence on the spread of the experimental method in Western Christendom and with its history down to Newton. A special place in the interests of Oxford was taken by the study of optics and of the rainbow. I have therefore used the history of these subjects as practical examples of the experimental method in operation.

To several scholars with whom I have discussed various aspects of this story I wish to record my thanks: to the Very Rev. Dr. D. A. Callus, O.P., who read through the whole typescript and guided me through several difficult problems; to Professor Herbert Dingle and the Rev. Professor David Knowles, F.B.A., who read sections of the book and gave me invaluable assistance in many other ways; to Professor H. Butterfield, Mr. J. Crompton, Sir Maurice

Powicke, F.B A., Dr. F. Sherwood Taylor, and Professor G. H. von Wright, who also read sections of the book; to the Rev. J. C. Wey, C.S.B., who helped me to transcribe some passages from a manuscript; to the Rev. Dr. Kenelm Foster, O.P., Dr. C. H. Josten, and Mr. D. J. Lake, who read the proofs; and to Mr. C. J. G. de Hoghton, who made the index of names.

To the authorities of a number of Libraries I am indebted for special services most generously given: to Dr. R. W. Hunt, Keeper of Western MSS in the Bodleian Library, and to the Librarian of Merton College, Oxford, for kindly supplying photostats of manuscripts; to the Rev. M. H. Laurent, O.P., Scriptor of the Vatican Library, for supplying photostats and providing information about manuscripts; to the Chief Librarian of the Oeffentliche Bibliothek der Universität Basel for supplying the photographs which I have reproduced from Theodoric of Freiberg's *De Iride*, and for checking a number of passages in the manuscript; to the Director of the British Museum for kindly allowing me to reproduce three photographs taken by the Department of Manuscripts from a manuscript of Roger Bacon's *Opus Maius*; to the Director of the Biblioteca Nazionale di S. Marco, Venice, for supplying photostats; and to the Director of the Universitätsbibliothek Erlangen for supplying microfilms. The collections of sources preserved in all these libraries, except those of Basel and Erlangen, I have been privileged to examine personally, as I have those of the University Library and of Peterhouse, Cambridge: the courteous and efficient service provided by these organizations has done much to mitigate the drudgery inseparable from any long piece of research.

I gratefully acknowledge also the generous assistance given me from the Central Research Fund of the University of London towards two journeys to Italy, in default of which substantial sections of the book could never have been written.

The staff of the Clarendon Press must claim my special thanks for the efficient and kindly manner in which they have dealt with many delicate problems involved in printing.

Finally, I dedicate this book to the memory of my father, William David Crombie, who first taught me the beginning of wisdom.

A. C. C.

DEPARTMENT OF HISTORY AND PHILOSOPHY OF SCIENCE
UNIVERSITY COLLEGE, LONDON, 1952

CONTENTS

LIST OF ILLUSTRATIONS

Note on *Abbreviations, Latin Spelling, and 'fact'.*

A KEY to the abbreviations of titles of journals and collections is printed on pp. 320–1. References in footnotes to internal divisions of some works, for example Roger Bacon, *Opus Maius*, Pars v, Pars i, Distinctio iii, Capitulum 3, are given in the form: *Opus Maius*, v. i. iii. 3.

In Latin quotations I have used the spelling of the source quoted. When quoting from manuscripts and early printed books I have expanded contractions into the common medieval form (e.g. 'que', not 'quae'), but when quoting from a modern edition I have followed the spelling of the edition.

The word 'fact' I have used without distinction to mean either 'an observed occurrence (or regularity)' or 'a statement describing an observed occurrence (or regularity)'.

I

Introduction

(1)

THE history of science shows that the most striking changes are nearly always brought about by new conceptions of scientific procedure. The task demanding real genius is the revision of the questions asked, the types of explanation looked for, the criteria for accepting one explanation and not another. Underlying the conception of scientific explanation accepted, for example, by Galileo, Harvey, and Newton, was the theory of formal proof developed by the Greek geometers and logicians. The distinctive feature of scientific method in the seventeenth century, as compared with that in ancient Greece, was its conception of how to relate a theory to the observed facts it explained, the set of logical procedures it contained for constructing theories and for submitting them to experimental tests. Modern science owes most of its success to the use of these inductive and experimental procedures, constituting what is often called 'the experimental method'. The thesis of this book is that the modern, systematic understanding of at least the qualitative aspects of this method was created by the philosophers of the West in the thirteenth century. It was they who transformed the Greek geometrical method into the experimental science of the modern world.

The outstanding scientific event of the twelfth and early thirteenth centuries was the confrontation of the empiricism long present in the West in the practical arts, with the conception of rational explanation contained in scientific texts recently translated from Greek and Arabic. The question put to Western natural philosophers by these texts was: How is it possible to reach with the greatest possible certainty true premises for demonstrated knowledge of the world of experience, as for example the conclusions of Euclid's theorems are demonstrated? This they attempted to answer within the framework of the conception that 'natural science' was a special part of a single philosophical activity concerned with the search for reality and truth. The whole activity, according to the classification of philosophical knowledge deriving from Aristotle, comprised the three divisions of natural science (or 'physics'), which studied the causes of change in material things; mathematics, which was the science of abstract quantity; and metaphysics, which was concerned with being or existence as such, with necessary characteristics of reality which gave principles that were assumed by every science.

For the Greeks these divisions were distinctions either between different kinds of subject-matter in the same world (as for Aristotle himself) or between wholly different worlds (as for Plato). The contrast between Greek and modern science is emphasized by the fact that the natural philosophers of thirteenth-century Christendom, inspired partly by Arabic commentators, saw them primarily as distinctions of method. For this reason they looked upon the question put by the Greek texts as an invitation to work out the methods of investigation and principles of explanation that were appropriate in the concrete problems of astronomy, optics, chemistry, or zoology classified under the broad heading 'natural science'. In some of these problems they already had a practical interest. The thirteenth-century theory of experimental science was an attempt to define clearly the questions to be asked under this heading, to distinguish them from those asked on the one hand in mathematics and logic and on the other in metaphysics and theology, and to show how to reach appropriate answers.

All ages of rapid scientific progress are in fact forced to concern themselves with the basic principles employed, and as understanding of these increases in precision so can their range of application be extended. To anyone familiar with the recent work on the logical analysis of the foundations of science there will be no temptation to underestimate the difficulty of the task that Latin Christendom set itself. Any lingering doubts will be quickly dispelled when it is realized not only that many of the problems which modern analysis seeks to solve are precisely the problems tackled in the thirteenth and fourteenth centuries, but also that many of the answers given at that remote time were precisely those which have been rediscovered only recently after long neglect.

Briefly, the object of the experimental method worked out between Robert Grosseteste and William of Ockham was to discover and define the conditions necessary and sufficient to produce the experimental facts. Moreover, it was recognized that a theory defining those conditions could never be certain; it was 'sufficient to save the appearances' but it was not 'necessarily true' in the sense of being a necessary conclusion from the analysis of the experimental facts and therefore unique and final.

In the seventeenth century, when metaphysics had fallen into decay and science was rapidly becoming a visible and overwhelming success, it was perhaps natural that the debt to an earlier age which hedged its conclusions about with so many qualifications should often have been forgotten. Indeed it required the crude and uncompromising virility of the *buccinatores novi temporis* to take the new science out of the worn framework of the traditional metaphysics which they inherited with it. If their next action was to try to reverse the position and to place metaphysics in a scientific framework, if they thought it possible to carry the methods and conclusions of triumphant science into subjects where they could bring only a new confusion based upon another misunderstanding, doubtless that was the price that the dying remnant they had vanquished taught them to exact.

Nevertheless, the conception of the logical structure of experimental science held by such prominent leaders as Galileo, Francis Bacon, Descartes, and Newton was precisely that created in the thirteenth and fourteenth centuries. They inherited also the concrete contributions made to particular sciences during the same period. The unfolding of natural science by the application of the experimental-mathematical method since the seventeenth century has shown us with a new precision the character of science among the philosophical disciplines, and has given new currency to old distinctions made when that method was first devised.

(2)

The Greek science which stimulated this thirteenth-century work on method was dominated by the desire to discover the enduring and intelligible reality behind the constant changes perceived through the senses. This was a metaphysical question and the answer to it already perfected before Plato was the metaphysical conception of 'substance' as the identity persisting through change.

This conception of substance was brought into the realm of logical discourse through the idea of geometrical demonstration or proof, the great methodological discovery of the Greeks which has occupied an essential place in all ideas of scientific explanation ever since. It meant, broadly speaking, that a particular fact was explained when it could be deduced from general principles which related it to other facts. For example, particular facts about triangles, such as that the three internal angles add up to two right angles, were explained by

Euclid by deducing them from his definition of a triangle as a figure bounded by three straight lines, together with the definition of a straight line and a few axioms or rules of inference. The Greeks tried to express all their science in this form of deductions from indemonstrable first principles. Geometry was the model not only for their astronomy, optics, and mechanics, but also for their biology and medicine.[1]

When this conception of explanation was applied, not to abstract entities like triangles, but to the world of experience, the object of science was to show that the observed effects followed from the 'nature' or 'substance' of a physical thing, just as the properties of triangles followed by deduction from the definition of a triangle. So in order to explain some particular physical fact it had to be shown that it could be deduced from the definition of some substance. This definition would include everything about the thing, its relations as well as its qualities, size, shape, &c. Thus, logically speaking, the definition was the *theory* of which the particular fact was a necessary consequence, while in the real world the substance defined was the *cause* of the observed fact or sequence of change.[2]

This conception of substance as the real identity persisting through and causing change has been the chief metaphysical term in the relations between science and metaphysics in the Western world since before Plato, though the conceptions of substance held by individual natural philosophers have differed widely in important details. Plato himself, in his Pythagorean allegory, the *Timaeus*, conceived of substance as mathematical form which gave order to the disorderly movements of chaos.[3] Number and extension formed the being of things and caused the world to arise by the penetration of number, and of geometrical figures reducible to number, into the χώρα or indefinite matrix of 'first matter'. The influence of this conception is seen throughout the Augustinian-Platonist tradition in the Middle Ages, and in such seventeenth-century scientists as Galileo, Kepler, and Descartes.

Aristotle, on the other hand, held that qualitative differences could not be deduced simply from differences in mathematical struc-

[1] Cf. F. M. Cornford, *Laws of Motion in the Ancient World*, 'Greek philosophy and modern science'; R. G. Collingwood, *Idea of Nature*. For a general account of Greek science see A. Reymond, *Sciences exactes et naturelles dans l'antiquité gréco-romaine*; P. Brunet et A. Mieli, *Histoire des sciences: Antiquité*; A. Rey, *Science dans l'antiquité*.
[2] Cf. Sir Thomas L. Heath, *Euclid's Elements*, pp. 143 sqq.
[3] *Timaeus*, 27C–32C; 48E–58C. See F. M. Cornford, *Plato's Cosmology*.

ture and that other essential attributes besides mathematical ones must be included in the definition of a substance.[1] Moreover, he said that number and geometry could give no information about the efficient and other causes *producing* the movement; these could become known only through knowledge of the concrete substance undergoing the change. Mathematics explicitly abstracted from such knowledge, which was the province of the independent science of 'physics'.

These two conceptions, the Platonic (or Pythagorean) and the Aristotelian, the mathematical and the qualitative, were the poles about which later conceptions of substance tended to gather. But all conceptions of substance shared in common the assumption that there was a real world to be discovered behind observed facts and behind scientific theories regarded simply as mathematical or logical constructions from which the facts could be deduced.

Already among the ancient Greek astronomers, however, a distinction had arisen between theories that were 'true' and theories that simply 'saved the appearances'.[2] Plato had held that it was characteristic of the substance of heavenly bodies to move with uniform circular motion, and he put to the mathematicians the problem of finding the particular uniform circular motions that must be taken as hypotheses in order to save the appearances presented by the planets. This distinction between 'physical' and mathematical theories was discussed by a long series of later Greek writers including Aristotle, Posidonius, Ptolemy, Proclus, and Simplicius.[3] Some maintained

---

[1] *Physics*, ii. 2, 193^{b}23 sqq.; *Metaphysics*, E. 1, 1025^{b}30 sqq., Z. 10, 1036^{a}2 sqq., 11, 1036^{b}32 sqq., K. 4, 1061^{a}30 sqq., M. 1–3, 1076^{a}8–1078^{b}5, N. 6, 1092^{b}26–1093^{b}29. Cf. *Physics*, ii. 1, 192^{b}9 sqq., iii. 1, 200^{b}10 sqq., vi. 1, 231^{a}20 sqq. See W. D. Ross, *Aristotle*, 3rd ed., pp. 66 sqq., and Sir Thomas Heath, *Mathematics in Aristotle*, pp. 1 sqq. See below, p. 91, n. 2.

[2] For a full history of this distinction see P. Duhem, 'Essai sur la notion de théorie physique de Platon à Galilée', *Annal. philos. chrétienne*, vi (1908).

[3] 'Naturalis quidem contemplationis est considerare de substantia coeli, astrorum, vi, qualitate, generatione et corruptione, et per haec de magnitudine, figura, et ordine demonstrare potest. At astrologia de tali quidem nullo nititur dicere, demonstrat inquam ordinem coelorum, quae mundum revera statuit. . . . Verum prorsus Astrologi non interest cognoscere quid sit quiescens natura, et quae moveantur, sed suppositiones et postulata introducens, videlicet eorum quae sunt alia stare, alia vero moveri, considerat quae videntur in coelo nonnullis prius statutis postulatis.' (Simplicii *Comm. Phys. Auditu*, ii. 2, Comm. 12, Parisiis, 1544, f. 71^v.) He discussed the astronomical theories of Eudoxus and Callippus, Aristotle, Heraclides of Pontus, Ptolemy, and Hipparchus. 'Propositum enim est quo supposito salvari possint apparentia. Nihil igitur mirum si alii ex aliis suppositionibus conati sunt salvare apparentia.' Simplicii *Comm. de Coelo*, i, Comm. 11, Venetiis, 1563, p. 13^a (Greek text ed. J. L. Heiberg in *Comm. Arist. Graeca*, vii, p. 32;

that the 'physicist' (or metaphysician) could discover principles by means of which he could discern, among several geometrical theories all of which saved the appearances, the true theory that conformed with the nature of things. Others asserted that the purpose of an astronomical theory was simply to save the appearances and nothing more, and Ptolemy said that if it came to a choice the simplest theory should be used.[1]

Implicit in these Greek discussions was the idea that, granted logical coherence, the 'criterion of truth' for scientific, as distinct from metaphysical or, in Aristotle's sense, 'physical', theories was simply that they should 'save the appearances'. Scientific theories were simply logical or mathematical constructions erected for no other purpose than to correlate observed facts. The scientific explanation of the facts was simply that they could be deduced from the theory. Such a theory made no statements about existence, about substances or causes; these were left for metaphysical theories which contained, over and above the experimentally verifiable statements of scientific theories, additional postulates about existence. An example of a metaphysical theory in science is Plato's assumption that it was the nature of celestial substance to move with uniform circular motion.

Perhaps because for the Greeks this distinction between science and metaphysics was one between either two worlds or two kinds of subject matter, they did not adequately consider some fundamental methodological problems involved in the method of experimental verification on which the distinction was by implication based. These problems were entailed by the Greek conception of scientific explanation itself, of geometrical demonstration applied to the world of experience. The first problem was how to investigate as exhaustively as possible and to generalize the various correlations of facts present in a given situation, so that possible theories might be suggested from which demonstration could proceed. The second problem was how, among several possible theories, to distinguish between true and false, or complete and defective. The first is the problem of induction, the second the problem of experimental verification and falsification.

Greek science, in fact, was and remained rather a science of de-

commentary on Aristotle's *De Caelo*, i. 2, 269ª9). See also, in the 1563 edition, ii, Comm. 20, pp. 147^b–148^a (on Arist. 288ª13), Comm. 30 and 31, pp. 156–8, Comm. 42, pp. 169^b–170^a (on Arist. 292^{b}10); Duhem, *Annal. philos. chrétienne*, vi (1908) 137–9.

[1] Cf. L. O. Kattsoff, 'Ptolemy and scientific method', *Isis*, xxxviii (1947) 18 sqq.; below, p. 85, n. 4.

monstrative proof than a science of inductive and experimental investigation. The basic doctrine, formulated by Plato and Aristotle[1] and carried to its consequences by Euclid, was that science could be established deductively by starting from certain irreducible postulates, which could not themselves be proved but were grasped by intuition; they could not be overthrown or even modified or limited by any result of scientific investigation. Among these were the laws of logic and the axioms of geometry.

In accordance with this doctrine, the Greeks aimed at using a strictly axiomatic method for all scientific problems. When setting out to explain something, their first task was to look for premisses from which to deduce it. They began, as described by Plato, with certain assumptions or 'hypotheses', and 'making these their starting-point, they proceed to travel through the remainder of the subject and arrive at last, with perfect unanimity, at that which they have proposed as the object of investigation'.[2] Typical examples are the writings of Euclid on optics, of Archimedes on mechanics, and of Ptolemy on optics and astronomy.[3] Each treatise begins with a clear statement of postulates; from these, in a series of theorems, are deduced statements describing the phenomena in question, the conclusions of earlier theorems helping to form the premisses of later ones; the deduction constitutes the explanation.

This method was effective provided that the premisses for the demonstration were fairly obvious and could be accurately formulated. Often they were based on simple experiments. The main defect of the method was that it contained no procedures for dealing with problems involving many variables. As a result, the Greeks formed the habit of basing theories about complicated phenomena on casual and commonsense observation.

Only Aristotle himself and some of his followers in the Lyceum and in Alexandria, in particular Theophrastus and Strato, and certain medical writers, seriously discussed the inductive and experimental side of science. Aristotle seems to have derived his empirical attitude from his medical training, and he excelled as a practical bio-

---

[1] *Posterior Analytics*, ii. 19, 100ᵇ5 sqq.; see below, pp. 26, 57, 71 sqq. See also Ross, *Aristotle*, 3rd ed., pp. 40 sqq., 54 sqq.; Aristotle's *Prior and Posterior Analytics*, ed. W. D. Ross, pp. 47–51, 674–8; E. W. Beth, 'Critical epochs in the development of the theory of science', *Brit. J. Philos. Science*, i (1950) 27 sqq. See below, pp. 26 sqq.

[2] *Republic*, vi. 510.

[3] See Duhem, *Origines de la statique*, i. 11; cf. Reymond, *Sciences exactes et naturelles dans l'antiquité*, p. 189. See below, pp. 52, 97, 118.

logist. His logic of science was to become the starting-point for the medieval and modern theory of experimental science. Strato carried out some very intelligent experiments to verify the theory that air consisted of particles moving in a vacuum. Erasistratus, a follower of Strato, and Galen and other members of the medical school of Alexandria, carried out experiments on respiration, the movements of the blood, the function of nerves, metabolism, and other physiological problems. Galen also discussed in great detail certain important aspects of induction. Ptolemy experimentally verified the law of reflection of light and measured the angles of refraction between air and water with various angles of incidence.[1]

The Greek axiomatic method provided both Arabic and Western philosophers with their conception of scientific explanation, and these first Greek steps with induction and experiment introduced them to the problems involved in the search for the theories at which the method aimed.

(3)

Various aspects of the contribution made in medieval Christendom to the development of natural science have been brought to light by scholars during the last half-century, and as a result of their work the importance of that contribution has gradually become appreciated. The existence of a mature and accurate experimental science in the thirteenth and fourteenth centuries has been shown beyond doubt by the publication of such texts as Petrus Peregrinus of Maricourt's *Epistola de Magnete* and Theodoricus Teutonicus de Vriberg's *De Iride et Radialibus Impressionibus*.[2] But students of medieval science have concentrated hitherto almost entirely on the addition of facts and development of concepts in the particular sciences,[3] in astronomy, optics, magnetics, statics, and dynamics, in

[1] See G. Senn, 'Über Herkunft und Stil der Beschreibungen von Experimenten im Corpus Hippocraticum', *AGM*, xxii (1923) 217 sqq., *Biologische Forschungsmethode in der Antike*; Heidel, *Heroic Age of Science*; Brunet et Mieli, *Histoire des sciences: Antiquité*, pp. 321 sqq., 552 sqq., 817 sqq., 871 sqq.; W. H. S. Jones, *Philosophy and Method in Ancient Greece, Medical Writings of Anonymus Londinensis*, p. 127; B. Farrington, *Greek Science*, ii; I. M. Bocheński, *Logique de Théophraste*. See below, pp. 25-28, 74-77, 83, 91, 133.

[2] For bibliographical details see G. Sarton, *Introduction to the History of Science*, ii. 1030 sqq., iii. 704 sqq. See below, pp. 204 sqq., 233 sqq. Two outstanding thirteenth-century biological works to be set beside these physical writings are Albertus Magnus's *De Animalibus*, hrg. von H. Stadler; and *The Herbal of Rufinus*, ed. L. Thorndike and F. S. Benjamin Jr.

[3] See in particular Duhem, *Orig. statique*, *Théorie physique*, *Léonard de Vinci*,

trigonometry, in the mathematical treatment of the 'latitude of forms', of limits and of infinity, and in botany, zoology, and medicine. Students of medieval logic were the first to draw attention to the definite methodological framework within which scholastic thinking took place, but they have devoted their attention almost entirely to general philosophy.[1] What has not been generally appreciated is the methodological framework within which research into natural science was carried out. Yet it was in fact only within that framework,[2] within the system of a theory of experimental science, that the positive contributions to the special sciences got their validity in the later Middle Ages and survived into the seventeenth century and modern times.

The experimental method was certainly not completed in all its refinements in the thirteenth or even in the fourteenth century. Nor was the method always systematically practised. The thesis of this book is that a systematic theory of experimental science was understood and practised by enough philosophers for their work to produce the methodological revolution to which modern science owes its origin. With this revolution appeared in the Latin West a clear understanding of the relation between theory and observation on which the modern conception and practice of scientific research and explanation are based, a clear set of procedures for dealing with physical problems.

The most important improvement made subsequently to this scholastic method was a change, general by the seventeenth century,

Système du monde, Mouvement absolu et mouvement relatif; C. B. Boyer, *Concepts of the Calculus*; and A. Maier, *Problem der intensiven Grösse in der Scholastik, Impetustheorie der Scholastik, An der Grenze von Scholastik und Naturwissenschaft, Vorläufer Galileis im 14. Jahrhundert*; R. Dugas, *Histoire de la mécanique*. For a general account of medieval science, with bibliography, see A. C. Crombie, *Augustine to Galileo*. For a general bibliography of medieval science see Sarton, *Introduction*, iii. 1872 sqq. and i–iii, *passim*.

[1] For a good account of medieval philosophy see E. Gilson, *Philosophie au moyen âge*, 2e éd. For a general bibliography see M. D. Knowles, 'Some recent advance in the history of medieval thought', *CHJ*, ix (1947) 22 sqq. See also F. Ueberweg, *Grundriss der Geschichte der Philosophie*, ii, 'Die patristische und scholastische Philosophie', 11th ed., revised by B. Geyer.

[2] Recent writers who have made a start in studying the logic of natural science in the Middle Ages are A. Mansion, 'L'Induction chez Albert le Grand', *RNP*, xiii (1906) 115 sqq., 246 sqq.; Duhem, *Annal. philos. chrétienne*, vi (1908); R. Carton, *Expérience physique chez Roger Bacon*; and J. H. Randall, 'The development of scientific method in the school of Padua', *JHI*, i (1940) 177 sqq. Randall has said that 'The transformation of the demonstrative proof of causes into a method of discovery is precisely the achievement of the Paduan theory of science' (p. 186) in the fifteenth century, but as will be shown in what follows this was done two centuries earlier in Oxford.

from qualitative to quantitative procedures. Special apparatus and measuring instruments increased in range and precision, controls were used to isolate the essential factors in complicated phenomena, systematic measurements were made to determine the concomitant variations and render problems capable of mathematical statement. Yet all these were advances in existing practices. The outstanding original contribution of the seventeenth century was to combine experiment with the perfection of a new kind of mathematics and with a new freedom in solving physical problems by mathematical theories, of which the most striking are those of modern dynamics.[1]

What seems to be the first appearance of a clear understanding of the principles of modern experimental science is found in the writings of the English logician, natural philosopher, and scholar, Robert Grosseteste (*c.* 1168–1253); and with his followers, particularly in Oxford, the new methodology made rapid progress.

This new tinge to modern minds is a vehement and passionate interest in the relation of general principles to irreducible and stubborn facts. All the world over and at all times there have been practical men, absorbed in 'irreducible and stubborn facts'; all the world over and at all times there have been men of philosophic temperament who have been absorbed in the weaving of general principles. It is this union of passionate interest in the detailed facts with equal devotion to abstract generalisation which forms the novelty of our present society.[2]

The strategic act by which Grosseteste and his thirteenth- and fourteenth-century successors created modern experimental science was to unite the experimental habit of the practical arts with the rationalism of twelfth-century philosophy.

Grosseteste appears to have been the first medieval writer to recognize and deal with the two fundamental methodological problems of induction and experimental verification and falsification which arose when the Greek conception of geometrical demonstration was applied to the world of experience. He appears to have been the first to set out a systematic and coherent theory of experimental investigation and rational explanation by which the Greek geometrical method was turned into modern experimental science. As far as is known, he and his successors were the first to use and exemplify such a theory in the details of original research into concrete

[1] Below, pp. 303 sqq.
[2] A. N. Whitehead, *Science and the Modern World*, Ch. 1.

problems. They themselves believed that they were creating a new science and in particular that they were creating a new methodology. Much of the experimental work of the thirteenth and fourteenth centuries was in fact carried out simply to illustrate this theory of experimental science, and all their writings show this methodological tinge. The eventual result of this attempt to understand how to correlate facts by theories in an accurate practical discipline was to show that in science the only 'criteria of truth' were logical coherence and experimental verification. The metaphysical question about *why* things happen, which was answered in terms of substance and causes, in terms of *quod quid est*, gradually gave place to the scientific question about *how* things happen, which was answered simply by a correlation of the facts by any means, logical or mathematical, that was convenient.

Grosseteste was in a position to dominate the beginnings of the thirteenth-century methodological revolution for several reasons. First, he lived at a point of time when, as a result of a century of literary research and translation, most of the important Greek and Arabic scientific writings had just been brought into effective contact with the new environment of active Western technology. At least since the time of Bede Western scholars had shown an interest in getting the kind of results for which some technical knowledge and even manual skill was necessary. These practical interests encouraged the asking of questions to which an experimental answer was possible. Even where no actual experiments were performed, a theoretical empiricism showed itself in a long tradition of 'thought experiments'. The new translations, of which the Greek and Arabic originals had so conspicuously failed to produce a thoroughgoing experimental science in the classical and Mohammedan worlds, provided Western Christendom with the beginnings of a method of rational explanation of empirical facts.

The encouragement of a rational inquiry into the nature of things had been implicit in St. Augustine's rational theology,[1] which had long predisposed Western Christendom to value the natural world as sacramental and symbolic of spiritual truths. Already by the early twelfth century Adelard of Bath,[2] and other philosophers who had

[1] For the background to St. Augustine see H. I. Marrou, *St. Augustin et la fin de la culture antique.*

[2] For Adelard of Bath see C. H. Haskins, *Mediaeval Science*, 2nd ed., pp. 20 sqq.; L. Thorndike, *History of Magic and Experimental Science*, ii. 19 sqq.

come under the influence of the new translations, had begun to
realize that the study of 'natural causes' had a legitimate interest of
its own quite apart from its didactic value.[1] Moreover, they pointed
out that there could be no conflict between explanations in terms of
natural causes and explanations in terms of Divine Providence, because the two types of explanation were expressed in languages
which had nothing in common, were in fact the products of different
methods of approach. This was an important step in the detachment
of science from metaphysics. The point at issue is shown clearly by
Adelard's *Quaestiones Naturales* in which, in the course of an
imaginary conversation, Adelard's 'nephew' asserts that a certain
natural event could be explained only as 'a wonderful effect of the
wonderful Divine Will'. Adelard replies by saying that it was
certainly the Creator's will that it should happen, 'but it is also not
without a natural reason',[2] and that this was open to human investigation. 'I do not detract from God', he said, 'for everything that is, is
from him and because of him. But [nature] is not confused and without
system and human science should be given a hearing on those points
which it has covered.'[3] The same emphasis on natural causes is seen
in the cosmological speculations, arising out of an attempt to give a
rational explanation of the events described in the first chapters of
Genesis, that were the chief preoccupation of the twelfth-century
school of Chartres. William of Conches and Thierry of Chartres tried
to use explanations *secundum physicas rationes*.[4]

The pursuit of rational explanations was made possible by the
Greek idea of geometrical demonstration itself, which, after being
lost to the West during the Dark Ages, had been fully recovered by
the twelfth century with the translation of Aristotle's logical works
and of Euclid's geometry.[5] This idea catalysed the whole range of

---

[1] 'Ce qui manque au xiie siècle pour poser une réalité concrète sous ce monde de
symboles, c'est la conception d'une nature ayant une structure en soi et une intelli-
gibilité pour soi, si faible soit-elle. Nous sommes à la veille du jour où cette conception
va se former, et c'est à la physique aristotélicienne que le xiiie siècle la devra.' Gilson,
Philos. au moyen âge, p. 343.

[2] '*Nepos*. Quaero itaque, qua ratione herbae a terra nascantur . . . cui id, nisi mirabilis
divinae voluntatis mirabili effectui imponas? *Adelardus*. Voluntas quidem creatoris est, ut
a terra herbae nascantur. Sed eadem sine ratione non est' *Quaestiones Naturales*, C. 1,
hrg. von M. Müller.   [3] Ibid., C. 4.

[4] The physical speculations of these writers were dominated by Plato's *Timaeus*,
though William of Conches was also influenced by Lucretius. See Chalcidii *Timaeus . . .*,
ed. F. W. A. Mullach; Duhem, *Syst. monde*, iii. 87 sqq., 184 sqq., v. 236 sqq.; A.
Clerval, *Écoles de Chartres*, p. 241; J. M. Parent, *Doctrine de la création dans l'école de
Chartres*; Thorndike, *History of Magic*, ii. 50 sqq.   [5] See below, pp. 30 sqq.

philosophical thinking, from theology to science, and perhaps without it modern science would never have been born. Moreover, the Platonic metaphysics which dominated twelfth-century thought, and which remained in favour in the English school, had always contained the possibility of mathematical explanations. In Platonism there was the 'conviction that the basis of any satisfactory physical science must be sought in mathematics', and the 'sense of the *provisionality* of all results attained in physical science and the consequent necessity of systematic and accurately registered experimentation if we are to be duly acquainted with the "appearances" to be "saved" by scientific theory'.[1] The chief vehicle for this Platonic metaphysics was St. Augustine's rational theology. Grosseteste was able to give Augustinian-Platonism a twist which turned the inquiry for God in things into the first systematic experimental investigation of things. Beginning with a Neoplatonic 'metaphysics of light' which led him to believe that light was the first 'corporeal form', that is, the substantial basis of spatial dimensions and the first principle of motion, he concluded that the laws of light were the basis of a scientific explanation of the physical world.[2] He proceeded therefore to make a detailed study of optics and with it to illustrate his theory of science.

As a beginning for his theory of science Grosseteste took the double, inductive-deductive procedure described by Aristotle in his *Posterior Analytics*.[3] He found the inductive side illustrated by the writings of the medical school and the deductive side illustrated by the writings of Euclid, Ptolemy, and others on geometry, optics, and astronomy. The classifications of science deriving from Aristotle described optics, astronomy, and music as *mathematica media*, sciences in which mathematics was used to *correlate* observed facts, as distinct on the one hand from pure mathematics and on the other from 'physics' in Aristotle's sense as the science of the *causes* of change in material things. Thus optics was particularly well suited to be a medium in which to exemplify the methodological principles of experimental science and in which the distinctive character of scientific explanation, of mathematical demonstration applied to the world of experience, could become clear.

Besides the advantages of the period of history in which he lived,

---

[1] A. E. Taylor, *Platonism and its Influence*, p. 50. Cf. the papers by M. B. Foster, *Mind*, N.S. xliii (1934), xliv (1935), xlv (1936).

[2] See below, pp. 104 sqq.   [3] See below, pp. 25-26.

Grosseteste was favoured also by unusual opportunities to make his influence felt. For a long period he was in a position to exert a decisive influence over the intellectual interests of the young University of Oxford, and he became the effective founder of a distinguished school of scientific thought. After him there developed at Oxford a characteristic interest both in the methods and implications of experimental investigation and scientific explanation in general and in the special experimental and mathematical sciences, a tradition that may be traced through the works of Roger Bacon, John Pecham, Duns Scotus, William of Ockham, Thomas Bradwardine, John of Dumbleton, and other less known writers. The contribution made by this Oxford school was first and foremost to methodology, and in particular to the study of the relation between theory and experience, of the use of induction and experiment in scientific investigation, of the relation of mathematical to 'physical' and metaphysical explanations, and of the problem of certainty in the study of the world known through the senses. The characteristic science in which these methodological ideas were put into practice was optics. With Grosseteste, Oxford became the first centre of the methodological revolution with which modern science began.

On the Continent, Grosseteste's influence may be traced with certainty in several writers, and there is evidence to suggest that the methodology of the Oxford school exerted a decisive influence on European science as a whole. The achievements of Paris during the thirteenth and fourteenth centuries were no doubt to a large extent the result of an independent reaction to the new translations from Greek and Arabic, and with Albertus Magnus, the next important writer after Grosseteste to make a systematic study of the theory of science, Paris soon took at least an equal place beside Oxford on the European stage. There was, however, a continuous exchange of ideas and men between the two Universities, and at least in some cases, for example that of Albertus Magnus himself, it is certain that the theory of experimental science developed at Oxford was responsible for similar work at Paris and its dependent schools. But whether this theory of science took its origin uniquely in Oxford or, as seems more probable, it was the product of a more general European response, in which Oxford took the lead, to the new ideas coming from classical Greece and medieval Islam, there is no doubt that from the time of Grosseteste the experimental science which has ever since been an essential part of the Western world began to appear in centre after centre. It is found from the end of the thirteenth century in the Germanies and in the medical schools of Padua and other north Italian towns. There it was taken up in the fifteenth and sixteenth centuries by Leonardo da Vinci and the Italian physiologists and mathematical physicists. And so it went to Galileo, William Gilbert, Francis Bacon, William Harvey, Descartes, Robert Hooke, Newton, Leibniz, and the world of the seventeenth century.

II

Empiricism and Rationalism in
Twelfth-Century Science

(1)

THAT the habit of experiment and an appreciation of the value of empirical evidence had existed in Western Christendom from an early date is shown by the state of the practical arts.[1] Not only had a continuous empirical and manual tradition survived the collapse of the Roman Empire and subsequently given rise to one of the most remarkable periods of technical innovation ever seen, but at least since the time of Bede in the seventh century Western scholars had been interested in practical knowledge and had taken an active part in getting it.

In the so-called Dark Ages that followed the collapse of the Roman Empire in the West much technical knowledge was lost, but from as early as the ninth century new techniques began to be introduced. By the ninth and tenth centuries the heavy Saxon wheeled plough and an improved system of crop rotation had come into use in northern Europe. This was followed by advances in the use of non-human power which at first were chiefly connected with agriculture[2] and its products, and later were extended to other industries. The invention of a new method of harnessing and the introduction of the nailed horseshoe in the ninth and tenth centuries made it possible to use draft-animals to pull heavy weights, and the

---

[1] For a general account of medieval technology see Lynn White Jr., 'Technology and invention in the Middle Ages', *Speculum*, xv (1940) 141 sqq., which contains a useful bibliography; and Crombie, *Augustine to Galileo*, i, Ch. 4 and bibliography at end. The first to make much of this aspect of life in the Latin West in the Middle Ages was Lefebvre des Noëttes: see his article 'La "Nuit" du moyen âge et son inventaire', *Mercure de France*, ccxxxv (1932) 572 sqq. Various aspects of medieval technics are discussed also by F. M. Feldhaus, *Technik der Vorzeit, der Geschichtlichen Zeit und der Naturvölker, Technik der Antike und des Mittelalters*; A. P. Usher, *History of Mechanical Inventions*; A. Uccelli *et alii*, 'La Storia della Tecnica', in *Enciclopedia Storica delle Scienze*, ii, *Tecnica dal Medio Evo ai Nostri Giorni*; R. J. Forbes, *Man the Maker*; and the more popular L. Mumford, *Technics and Civilization*. For technics in Antiquity there are H. Diels, *Antike Technik*, 3e Aufl., and A. Neuburger, *Technical Arts and Sciences of the Ancients*.

[2] *Cambridge Economic History*, ed. J. H. Clapham and Eileen Power, i.

introduction of the watermill and the windmill allowed the effective use of water-power and wind-power by the end of the twelfth century. Following the introduction of these new sources of power came the invention of new power-driven machinery for industrial purposes and the development of devices—driving wheels, cams, cranks, and geared wheels—for transmitting and controlling power and for converting rotary into reciprocal motion. The crank seems to have been unknown in the Ancient World and to have made its first appearance only after the Germanic invasions. By the twelfth century the rotary motion of the water-wheel was being converted to operate trip-hammers for fulling[1] and other processes, and by the fourteenth century the same mechanism was being used for forge-hammers. In the thirteenth century, if a device sketched by the French architect Villard de Honnecourt[2] represents something actually used, water-wheels were used for driving saws for cutting wood, and water-driven saw-mills certainly existed in the fourteenth century. By the early fourteenth century water-wheels were being used to drive forge-bellows for blast-furnaces, and by the fifteenth century water-wheels and horse-driven wheels were used for pumping and hoisting in mines and for driving iron-rolling mills and wire-drawing mills.

This mechanization of mining and metallurgy, which made possible the production of metals on a comparatively large scale, led to the refinement of empirical techniques for such processes as casting bells of the required pitch, and gun-making. Attention to finishing processes made it possible to produce such instruments of precision as the astrolabe, the compass, and the mechanical clock; recognition of the need to control the alloy used led to the development of assaying, which made metallurgists familiar with the balance and laid the foundations of quantitative chemistry. A particular triumph of metallurgical skill was the introduction, in the fourteenth century, of cast movable metal type in place of the wood-cuts and block-printing which had appeared in the West in the twelfth and thirteenth centuries.

The same inventiveness is seen not only in these applications of power and metallurgical skill, but also in many other aspects of

[1] This brought about a small industrial revolution in the English cloth trade; see E. M. Carus-Wilson, 'An industrial revolution in the 13th century', *Econ. Hist. R.* xii (1941) 39 sqq.

[2] Villard de Honnecourt, *MS fr. 19093 der Pariser Nationalbibliothek*, ed. H. R. Hahnloser.

medieval technics: in architecture, in which entirely new problems of construction were faced as early as the eleventh century; in the glass industry, to whose credit is the production of stained glass windows in the twelfth century[1] and of spectacles at the end of the thirteenth; in the development of such small machines and machine-tools as the spinning-wheel, pole-lathe, and brace-and-bit, which appear to be medieval inventions; and in the arts as in painting and music. The gains thus made were never lost and as a result Western Christendom as early as the thirteenth century was not only using techniques unknown to the Romans, but also had thoroughly developed a mentality interested in finding exact experimental answers to practical questions. The most important result of this mentality was that it encouraged precision and measurement, and this is seen very clearly in the writings of some scholars on practical questions.

It is sometimes said that one of the reasons for the failure of classical science is that theoretical speculation remained to a large extent divorced from the experimental habit, the former being the occupation of philosophers and the latter developing only among menials working in the practical arts. In the Middle Ages there is much evidence to show that by the time of Robert Grosseteste, in the early thirteenth century, scholars had long been interested in practical scientific problems. Medicine was studied in the earliest Benedictine monasteries and in the eleventh century, with the revival of Western medicine in Salerno, began a long series of practical treatises which, in the twelfth century, included the so-called *Antidotarium Nicholai* on drugs, the *Anatomia Porci* describing the public dissection of a pig, and the *Practica Chirurgica* of Roger of Salerno, the first great Western surgeon.[2] Another long series of treatises was written on the preparation of pigments and other chemical substances, the earliest known manuscript dating from the eighth century. Early in the twelfth century Adelard of Bath produced an edition of an early Latin treatise on practical chemistry, the *Mappae Clavicula*, which con-

---

[1] The glass industry was stimulated by the new developments in architecture in the twelfth century, large windows having been made possible by the Gothic arch and vaulting; see E. E. Viollet-le-Duc, *Dictionnaire raisonné de l'architecture française*, ix. 373 sqq.

[2] On early medieval medicine see J. F. Payne, *English Medicine in Anglo-Saxon Times*; Sir T. C. Allbutt, *Historical Relations of Medicine and Surgery*; J. J. Walsh, *Medieval Medicine*; K. Sudhoff, *Handbuch der Geschichte der Medizin*; C. and D. Singer, 'The origin of the medical school of Salerno, the first European university' in *Essays presented to Karl Sudhoff*; G. W. Corner, *Anatomical Texts of the Earlier Middle Ages*; L. C. MacKinney, *Early Mediaeval Medicine*.

tains the first known account of the distillation of alcohol, and his contemporary, Theophilus the Priest, included in his *Diversarum Artium Schedula* accurate accounts of a large number of practical processes, including the making of bells and of glass.[1] Music, a practical art of which the theory formed part of the medieval *quadrivium*, was also the subject of a series of practical treatises beginning in the tenth century with several works on an early form of harmony.[2] Even magic became a practical art which contributed to the formation of the experimental habit.[3]

Perhaps the most significant collection of treatises in which the practical interests of early medieval scholars can be seen is that concerned with practical mathematics and measurement.[4] From the time when Bede wrote on arithmetic and on the calendar[5], scholars had been interested in measurement. The Latin mathematics which survived into the Dark Ages was concerned largely with such questions as surveying land[6] and calculating the date of Easter and with problems arising in commerce.[7] The desire for an accurate calendar was the chief reason for the early medieval interest in astronomy, and when the astrolabe was introduced from the Arabs it was immediately recognized as a measuring instrument which could be used to correct old and inaccurate data.[8] This form of learning

[1] P. E. M. Berthelot, *Chimie au moyen âge*; R. J. Forbes, *Art of Distillation*; R. P. Johnson, 'Compositiones variae from Codex 490, Biblioteca Capitolare, Lucca, Italy', *Illinois Stud. Lang. Lit.* xxiii (1939) 3 sqq.; Theophilus Presbyter, *Schedula Diversarum Artium*, ed. by Albert Ilg. For general accounts of medieval chemistry see J. A. Stillman, *Story of Early Chemistry*, and F. Sherwood Taylor, *The Alchemists*.

[2] G. Reese, *Music in the Middle Ages*.

[3] Thorndike, *History of Magic*, i–ii. See, for example, i. 738–9, on occult remedies recommended in the *Regimen Salernitanum*; and ii. 110 sqq. on Bernard Silvester's book of geomantic tables which he entitled *Experimentarius*.

[4] Cf. F. Sherwood Taylor, 'Mediaeval scientific instruments', *Discovery*, xi (1950) 282 sqq.; Gunther, *Early Science in Oxford*, ii.

[5] His *De Loquela per Gestum Digitorum* or *De Indigitatione* is the main source of knowledge of medieval 'finger reckoning'. The *De Temporum Ratione* was an important contribution to chronology and it also contained observations on the tides and other phenomena; see Bedae *Opera de Temporibus*, ed. C. W. Jones, and Sarton, *Introduction*, i. 510–11.

[6] P. Tannery, *Mémoires scientifiques*, v. *Sciences exactes au moyen âge*, pp. 79 sqq., 204 sqq.; A. van der Vyver, 'L'Évolution scientifique du haut moyen âge', *Archeion*, xix (1937) 12 sqq.

[7] M. Cantor, *Geschichte der Mathematik*, i–ii; G. Libri, *Sciences mathématiques en Italie*.

[8] On twelfth-century astronomy see Duhem, *Syst. monde*, iii. 164–230, and Haskins, *Mediaeval Science*, pp. 82 sqq., 327 sqq. For two early twelfth-century astronomical observers, Walcher of Malvern and Petrus Alfonsi, see Haskins, pp. 113 sqq., and Thorndike, *History of Magic*, ii. 68–71. On Walcher see also J. K. Wright, 'Notes on the knowledge of latitudes and longitudes in the Middle Ages', *Isis*, v (1923) 83 sqq.

was of sufficient official importance for Canute, Earl Harold, and William the Conqueror to appoint Lotharingian astronomers and mathematicians to ecclesiastical positions in England.[1]

The recording of the hours of the day was another form of measurement that had attracted the interest of the educated from an early date. Water-clocks which were adjusted nightly by taking observations of the Pole Star are known to have been used for regulating the canonical hours as early as the tenth century, when Gerbert is said to have made such a clock for the monastery at Magdeburg.[2] The invention, at the end of the thirteenth century, of the mechanical clock, itself a triumph of mechanical skill in the interlocking of parts to produce an accurate, automatically controlled result, was simply the last of a series of time-keepers.

Maps that were something more than mere symbolic representations of the world and could give an accurate measure of position also interested some early medieval scholars. The earliest extant portolan maps or 'compass charts' date only from the end of the thirteenth century, but it is probable that they were in use much earlier, perhaps as early as the eleventh century.[3] The magnetic compass itself was discussed by Alexander Neckam at the end of the twelfth century.[4] Later, in the mid-thirteenth century, Matthew Paris was to produce some recognizable maps of England[5] and Petrus Peregrinus was to conclude his scientific account of magnetism with a description of the lodestone as a measuring instrument.[6]

As was natural when an inferior scientific culture was absorbing a superior one, most of the additions to scientific knowledge in the West before the thirteenth century came through literary sources, and it was precisely because of the active interest of scholars in

[1] M. C. Welborne, 'Lotharingia as a center of Arabic and scientific influence in the XI century', Isis, xvi (1931) 188 sqq.

[2] Usher, History of Mechanical Inventions, p. 152.

[3] Sarton, Introduction, i. 767; C. R. Beazley, Dawn of Modern Geography, ii. 470, and iii. 515 sqq.; K. Kretschmer, Italienische Portolane des Mittelalters; for a discussion of recent work see R. Almagià, 'Quelques questions au sujet des cartes nautiques et des portulans d'après les recherches récentes', Actes du ve congrès internat. d'hist. des sciences, pp. 140 sqq.

[4] See Alexander Neckam, De Naturis Rerum, C. 98, ed. T. Wright, p. 183, and De Utensilibus, ed. T. Wright, pp. 96 sqq.; Thorndike, History of Magic, ii. 190.

[5] Four Maps of Great Britain by Matthew Paris about 1250. For later medieval cartography see the references given by Sarton, Introduction, ii. 1047 sqq., iii. 181 sqq., 762 sqq., 1140 sqq., 1591 sqq.

[6] Petri Peregrini Maricurtensis De Magnete, hrg. von G. Hellmann. See below, pp. 204 sqq.

practical science that this knowledge was made available. It was chiefly for their practical knowledge that Western scholars from the time of Gerbert at the end of the tenth century first took an interest in Arabic learning. In the twelfth century, when the outstanding form of scholarship was the work of translation from Greek and Arabic into Latin, a large proportion of the translations were treatises on the abacus, the astrolabe, and other astronomical instruments, and on Arabic numbers, medicine, and chemistry.[1]

Early in the twelfth century this practical tendency began to affect the teaching of the seven liberal arts, which were extended and specialized so as to include various kinds of technical knowledge.[2] Of particular interest is the conception of the origin of the sciences put forward by Hugh of St. Victor (d. 1141) in his *Didascalicon de Studio Legendi*, or *Eruditionis Didascalica*, the most influential of the treatises on the liberal arts using exclusively Latin sources. He said that the sciences had been developed first as a set of customary usages in response to human needs before being reduced to formal rules. Man, he said, preserved himself by imitating nature. For example, he made his own clothes while nature clothed the tree with bark, the fish with scales, the shell-fish with a shell, and so on. Man could imitate nature because of his reason, 'but how the work of the artificer imitates nature is by long and burdensome pursuit of particulars'.[3] Then, in discussing the origin of the sciences, which, following a modification of the tradition of Aristotle and Boethius,[4]

[1] Haskins, *Mediaeval Science*, pp. 114-15, 120; J. W. Thompson, 'The introduction of Arabic science into Lorraine in the tenth century', *Isis*, xii (1929) 184 sqq.; Welborne, *Isis*, xvi (1931) 188 sqq.; J. Drecker, 'Hermannus Contractus über das Astrolab', *Isis*, xvi (1931) 200 sqq.; Sarton, *Introduction*, i and ii, *passim*; A. van de Vyver, 'Les Premières Traductions latines (xe-xie siècles) de traités arabes sur l'astrolabe', *Ier congrès internat. géog. hist.*, ii, *Mémoires*, pp. 266 sqq., 'Les Plus Anciens Traductions latines médiévales (xe-xie siècles) de traités d'astronomie et d'astrologie', *Osiris*, i (1936) 665, and in *Archeion*, xix (1937) 17-18. See also below, pp. 35-36.

[2] See M. Clagett, 'Some general aspects of physics in the Middle Ages', *Isis*, xxxix (1948) 30 sqq.

[3] *Erudit. Didas.* i. 10 (*PL*, clxxvi) 747. There is a more recent edition of *Didascalicon* by C. H. Buttimer.

[4] The Aristotelian-Boethian division of the sciences was into theoretical and practical sciences, the former being further subdivided into theology (or metaphysics), mathematics (including the *quadrivium*: arithmetic, music, geometry, astronomy), and physics, and the latter into ethics, economics, and politics. This classification was used by Cassiodorus (*Institutiones*, ii. 3, ed. R. A. B. Mynors, p. 110). The alternative to this was the so-called 'Platonic' classification used in various forms by the Stoics, Academics, and Epicureans and passed to the Latin West by Augustine and Isidore of Seville, who divided the sciences into physics, ethics, and logic. The Aristotelian-Boethian classification was the one that became usual by the thirteenth century but it became much

he divided into theory, practice, mechanics, and logic,[1] he said:

> It is not to be thought that before the invention of logic, that is the science of discourse, there were no discussions and men did not exchange speech. Earlier there were common discourses and literature, but the doctrine of discourses and literature had not yet been made into an art and as yet no precepts for speaking correctly or for disputing had been given, for all the sciences were in the state of use rather than of art. But then men thought that use could be converted into art and that what had been vague and unrestrained before could be restrained by certain rules and precepts. So they began, as has been said, to reduce to an art custom which had grown up in part by accident, and in part naturally, correcting what had a distorted use, supplementing what had too little and cutting down what had too much, and in other ways from particulars prescribing certain rules and precepts.[2]

In this way, Hugh said, following the Greek tradition which he got from Isidore,[3] geometry first arose among the Egyptians because they had to measure the land after the Nile had flooded its banks.[4] 'Mechanics', the 'adulterine' science or the science of providing for those things which are necessary because of the weakness of the human body, had a similar origin. In 'mechanics' Hugh included seven sciences, the manufacture of cloth and arms, navigation, agriculture, hunting, medicine, and theatrical science, of which three pertained to the extrinsic and four to the intrinsic needs of the body.[5]

The same practical tendency in twelfth-century education is shown by the list of books recommended for study at Chartres, which is given in the *Heptateuchon* of Thierry of Chartres (d. *c.* 1155), another work on the seven liberal arts. A prominent place in the syllabus was occupied by geometry and arithmetic, most of the works recommended being on surveying and measurement; others were on practical astronomy and medicine.[6] The same practical

elaborated by further sub-divisions. For an account of this subject see L. Baur's ed. of Dominicus Gundissalinus, *De Div. Philos.*, pp. 349 sqq.; M. Grabmann, *Geschichte der scholastischen Methode*; R. W. Hunt, 'The introductions to the "Artes" in the twelfth century' in *Studia Mediaevalia R. J. Martin*, pp. 85 sqq.

[1] *Erudit. Didas.* ii. 2 (*PL*, clxxvi) 752.   [2] Ibid. i. 12 (*PL*, clxxvi) 750.

[3] Isidori Hispalensis *Etymologiarum*, iii. 10, ed. W. M. Lindsay, i.

[4] *Erudit. Didas.* ii. 10 (*PL*, clxxvi) 755. Hugh went on in C. 14, col. 756: 'Geometria tres habet species: planimetriam, altimetriam, cosmimetriam', showing that he regarded it as a practical subject; see below, p. 31, n. 2.   [5] Ibid. ii. 21 (*PL*, clxxvi) 760.

[6] The works recommended for the study of geometry included practical treatises by Isidore, Frontinus, Columella, Gerbert, and other writers, and the anonymous *De mensuris in lineis, in superficiebus, in solidis, in liquidis, in ponderibus, in temporibus*, though

emphasis is found in a list of textbooks in use in Paris at the end of the twelfth century.[1] In the thirteenth century the encyclopaedias of writers like Albertus Magnus and Roger Bacon[2] were to contain a large amount of accurate information about astronomy, the calendar, the compass, chemistry, agriculture, and other practical matters and this interest was to be carried on in the fourteenth century by such writers as Pietro dei Crescenzi, Giovanni da San Gimignano, and Konrad Kyeser.[3] In the universities also an interest in such practical mathematical subjects as optics and astronomy, and in medicine, was maintained.[4]

This attention by twelfth-century scholars to technical problems was not simply the expression of a literary interest or of an abstract desire for power over nature such as was found in works on magic and was to be expressed by Roger Bacon.[5] Scholars took an active part in practical science, and the experimental habit was certainly present among those who used the astrolabe, who surveyed and practiced medicine. Natural philosophers like Adelard of Bath appear also to have performed experiments.[6] Moreover, even those writers who did approach technics and science as literary men and

two anonymous works on *Definitiones geometriae* were also recommended. The last may possibly refer to the *Excerptum de Geometria* edited by Mynors in his Cassiodori *Institutiones*, pp. 169 sqq.; it consists mainly of *definitiones* from Euclid's books. Ptolemy's *Planisphere* and works by Al-Khwarizmi, and the eleventh-century medical corpus of works by Haly Abbas, Isaac Israeli, and other writers translated by Constantine the African, were also taught in Chartres. See A. Clerval,'L'Enseignement des arts libéraux à Chartres et à Paris dans la première moitié du xiie siècle d'après l'*Heptateuchon* de Thierry de Chartres', *Congrès scient. internat. cath.* ii. 277 sqq. and *Écoles de Chartres*, pp. 220 sqq.

[1] *Sacerdos ad Altare Accessurus*, Cambridge MS Gonville and Caius 385 (605), 13 c., ff. 7–61; see Haskins, *Mediaeval Science*, pp. 356 sqq.

[2] See below, p. 139, n. 3, p. 192, n. 5; Thorndike, *History of Magic*, ii; M. de Bouard, 'Encyclopédies médiévales', *Rev. quest. hist.* cxii (1930) 258 sqq.; Crombie, *Augustine to Galileo*, Ch. 4.

[3] Sarton, *Introduction*, iii. 811 sqq., 920 sqq., 1550 sqq., 1866.

[4] H. Rashdall, *Universities*, 2nd ed. by F. M. Powicke and A. B. Emden, i. 75–86, 233–53, 435–50, ii. 18, 81, 119–28, 243–5, iii. 152–60; L. Thorndike, *University Records*, pp. 64 sqq., 279 sqq. Cf. H. Suter, 'Die Mathematik auf den Universitäten des Mittelalters', in *Festschrift der Kantonsschule in Zürich*, pp. 39 sqq.

[5] Cf. Crombie, *Augustine to Galileo*, i. 68–71.

[6] e.g. the experiment with a clepsydra described in Adelard of Bath's *Quaest. Nat.* c. 58. The experiment showed that if a vessel of water with a hole in the top and several holes in the bottom were suspended in air, no water would fall from it so long as the hole at the top remained closed. This contradicted Aristotle's theory of natural place and Adelard explained it by the 'universal continuity of nature', saying that the water could not move down unless there were opportunity for the air to move in from above and maintain contact with it; see Thorndike, *History of Magic*, ii. 37–39.

knew little of the practical side, recognized at least in theory that natural science rested on a basis of experience: 'nihil est in intellectu quod non prius fuerit in sensu.' Such a theoretical empiricism is characteristic of the tradition of 'thought experiments' which persisted till the seventeenth century. A good example is the method, described in the late twelfth-century *Practica Geometriae* ascribed to Hugo Physicus[1] (d. 1199), for determining the depth of the sea by dropping overboard a weight with a float attached. When the weight hit the bottom it would release the float, and the method involved the measurement of the interval of time between the release of the weight and the reappearance of the float. The author suggested that this should be done with an astrolabe, but it would be impossible to measure such small intervals of time with this instrument,[2] and in fact the author had copied the whole 'experiment' from an earlier literary source. Yet, however uncritical such twelfth-century writers were as to what constituted empirical evidence, and however lacking they may have been in the habit of experiment, they still recognized the need for experiment.[3]

(2)

What these practical writers of the twelfth century chiefly lacked, even when they habitually practised observation, was, in fact, not an empirical attitude but the ability to transcend the rule-of-thumb methods[4] of the practical crafts and to construct a theoretical science offering rational explanations of the facts of experience. This was necessary even for the pursuit of utilitarian ends.

The construction of such a theoretical science was made possible by an event in philosophical history which at first had very little to do with natural science as a practical discipline. This was the grasp of the idea of theoretical scientific explanation, which was made first

[1] Tannery, 'Practica Geometriae', *Mém. scient.* v. 206–7. On another 'thought experiment', by Roger Bacon, see Duhem, 'Roger Bacon et l'horreur du vide', in *RBE*, p. 262.

[2] Nicholas of Cusa suggested using a clepsydra or water-clock for measuring the time, when describing the same method two and a half centuries later in his *Idiota*, iv, 'De Staticis Experimentis'. The method itself had a long history, being suggested again in the seventeenth century by Robert Hooke.

[3] As Tannery said of the author of the *Practica Geometriae*: 'il voit bien qu'il faut expérimenter, mais il ne sait point s'y prendre, ou ne pense qu'à des expériences impossibles.' Op. cit., p. 207.

[4] Cf. below, p. 31, n. 2.

by logicians of the early twelfth century who expounded the *logica vetus*, or 'old logic' based on the first two books of Aristotle's *Organon*, Porphyry's *Isagoge*, and Boethius's commentaries,[1] and later by logicians of the mid-twelfth century who were able to make use of Aristotle's *Posterior Analytics*. What these logicians did was to recognize the distinction between experiential knowledge of a fact and rational or theoretical knowledge of the cause of the fact, by which they meant knowledge of some prior principles from which they could deduce and so explain the fact. This distinction[2] between experience of a fact and demonstrative explanation had been expounded by Boethius,[3] who was then the guide in logic, but it derived ultimately from Aristotle.

According to Aristotle, scientific investigation and explanation was a twofold process, the first inductive and the second deductive. The investigator must begin with what was prior in the order of knowing, that is, with facts observed through the senses, and he must ascend by induction to generalizations or universal forms or causes which were most remote from sensory experience, yet causing that experience and therefore prior in the order of nature. The second process in science was to descend again by deduction from these universal forms to the observed facts, which were thus explained by being demonstrated from prior and more general principles which were their cause.[4] As Aristotle put it, 'Knowledge of the fact differs

---

[1] The study of the 'old' or 'Boethian' logic had been revived at the end of the tenth century by Gerbert; see Duhem, *Syst. monde*, iii. 164 sqq.; A. van der Vyver, 'Les Étapes du développement philosophique du haut moyen âge', *Rev. belge philol. hist.* viii (1929) 425 sqq. As distinct from this, the *logica nova* was constituted during the second half of the twelfth century by the addition of the remaining four books of Aristotle's *Organon*, the most important for the logic of science being the *Post. Anal.*, and of Gilbertus Porreta's *Liber de Sex Principiis* (below, p. 34).

[2] St. Augustine had discussed this distinction, but in the course of a philosophical search for certainty, which he found only in rational knowledge of the eternal ideas of which mathematical entities were examples; see *De Libero Arbitrio*, ii. 8 (*PL*, xxxii) 1251–3.

[3] Boethii *In Isagogen Porphyrii Commenta*, i. 9, edited by G. Schepss and S. Brandt, pp. 157–8. Germane to the same question is the philosophical problem of the nature of universals, the medieval controversy over which arose at the end of the eleventh century out of Boethius's commentary on the *Isagoge* of Porphyry. Boethius asked what is the relation of universals to the individual material things that exemplify them and to the human mind that knows them. The subsequent debate over realism and nominalism and their alternatives had an important influence on the development of certain concepts in natural science.

[4] The idea that the order of demonstration was the order of nature came from Plato. Aristotle said that the order of discovery was the reverse of the order of demonstration.

from knowledge of the reason for the fact',[1] and he held scientific knowledge to be knowledge of the 'reason for the fact'. 'We suppose ourselves to possess unqualified scientific knowledge of a thing, as opposed to knowing it in the accidental way the sophist knows, when we think that we know the cause on which the fact depends, as the cause of that fact and of no other and, further, that the fact could not be other than it is.' This kind of knowledge was obtained by demonstration; and

the premisses of demonstrative knowledge must be true, primary, immediate, more knowable than and prior to the conclusion, which is further related to them as effect to cause. . . . The premisses must be the cause of the conclusion, more knowable than it, and prior to it; its causes, since we possess scientific knowledge of a thing only when we know its cause; prior, in order to be causes; antecedently known, this antecedent knowledge being not our mere understanding of the meaning, but knowledge of the fact as well. Now 'prior' and 'more knowable' are ambiguous terms, for there is a difference between what is prior and more knowable in the order of being and what is prior and more knowable to man. I mean that objects nearer to sense are prior and more knowable to man; objects without qualification prior and more knowable are those further from sense. Now the most universal causes are furthest from sense and particular causes are nearest to sense, and they are thus exactly opposed to one another.[2]

The model of scientific knowledge, in which effects could be shown to follow necessarily from their causes as conclusions from premisses, Aristotle held to be mathematics, and where mathematics could be used in the natural sciences their conclusions were also exact and necessary.[3] When an investigator was seeking scientific knowledge or explanation of a fact, that is, knowledge of the 'principles, conditions or elements' that caused the fact, Aristotle said:

The natural way of doing this is to start from the things which are more knowable and obvious to us and proceed towards those which are clearer and more knowable by nature; for the same things are not 'knowable relatively to us' and 'knowable' without qualification. So in the present inquiry we must follow this method and advance from what is more obscure by nature, but clearer to us, towards what is more clear and more knowable by nature. Now what is to us plain and obvious at first is rather

---

[1] *Post. Anal.* i. 13, 78ᵃ22; see Aristotle's *Prior and Post. Anal.* ed. Ross, p. 552.
[2] *Post. Anal.* i. 2, 71ᵇ9 sqq.; cf. ii. 2, 90ᵃ1 sqq., *Topics*, vi. 4, 141ᵃ25 sqq. and 105ᵃ13.
[3] *Post. Anal.* i. 7, 75ᵇ15 sqq.; C. 9, 76ᵃ12 sqq.; C. 13, 78ᵇ32 sqq. See below, pp. 56 sqq., 91 sqq.

confused masses, the elements and principles of which become known to us by later analysis . . . for it is a whole that is best known to sense-perception.[1]

Of the inductive process by which the investigator passed from sensory experience of particular facts or connexions to a grasp of the prior demonstrative principles that explained them, Aristotle gave a clear psychological account. The final stage in the process was the sudden act by which the intuitive reason or νοῦς, after a number of experiences of facts, grasped the universal or theory explaining them, or penetrated to knowledge of the substance causing and connecting them.[2]

Another version of this distinction between empirical and rational knowledge which had an influence on the twelfth-century logicians, and was to have an even greater influence in the thirteenth century, was the distinction made by the Greek physician Galen between the *via experimenti* and the *via rationis*. This distinction Galen made in various of his works but most clearly when discussing the different schools of medicine in the second century A.D. The Empirical School had held that it was impossible to arrive at generalizations that did not mislead, so that in preparing compound medicines it was necessary to be purely empirical; it did not matter how medicines produced their effects but what the effect was, not how we digested but what was digestible. The Dogmatic School had held, on the contrary, that the best method was to proceed by deduction from existing theory. Galen himself held that only by a combination of the two methods could the best results be obtained.[3] He referred to effects or symptoms as 'signs', and he said that it was necessary first to argue inductively from these signs to the causes that produced them, and then, with this knowledge of causes, to administer medicines rationally to cure diseases. His ideas were first made known to the Latin

---

[1] *Phys.* i. 1, 184ᵃ16 sqq. Cf. *Metaph.* A. 1, 981ᵃ2–6.

[2] *Post. Anal.* i. 31, 87ᵇ26 sqq.; C. 34, 89ᵇ10 sqq.; ii. 19, 99ᵇ15 sqq. On Aristotle's scientific method see A. Edel, *Aristotle's Theory of the Infinite*, Ch. 7; Ross, *Aristotle*, 3rd ed., pp. 38 sqq.; Aristotle's *Prior and Post. Anal.* ed. Ross, pp. 47–75, 598–9, 609,673–8; R. McKeon, 'Aristotle's conception of the development and the nature of scientific method', *JHI*, viii (1947) 3 sqq.; E. W. Beth, 'Critical epochs in the development of the theory of science', *Brit. J. Philos. Science*, i (1950) 27 sqq. Cf. H. Scholz und H. Schweitzer, *Die sogenannten Definitionen durch Abstraktion.* See above, p. 7.

[3] See *De Sectis*, CC. 7–9; *Ars Medica*, C. 1; *De Methodo Medendi*, i. 3–4, ii. 7, iii. 1, 2, 7, in Claudii Galeni *Opera Omnia*, ed. C. G. Kühn. See also the important, recently discovered text, known only in the Arabic version: Galen, *On Medical Experience*, ed. with English translation by R. Walzer. See below, pp. 76 sqq.

West through the translations and writings of Constantine the African (d. 1087), a prominent member of the Salerno school of medicine.[1]

These same two movements in science, from experience to theory, effect to cause, composite particular to simple universal, and from theory to experience, cause to effect, simple universal to composite particular, were respectively designated also by the terms *resolutio* and *compositio* used by certain Latin writers. These words were in fact translations respectively of the Greek ἀνάλυσις (analysis) and σύνθεσις (synthesis), which had been used by Greek geometers to designate the corresponding movements in mathematical reasoning.[2] Galen had used the same terms in his *Ars Medica*[3] but, before the translation of this work into Latin, Chalcidius in his commentary on Plato's *Timaeus* had defined the combined *resolutio-compositio* as the proper method of philosophical research.[4] Boethius also translated ἀνάλυσις as *resolutio* and he went on to oppose the *resolutoria* to the *topica* as two phases of philosophical method, of which the first was 'judicativa veritatis' and the second 'inventiva veritatis'.[5] Thirteenth-

---

[1] Constantine translated into Latin from Arabic Galen's *Ars Medica*, also known as the *Microtegni* or simply *Tegni*, and made a Latin summary from Arabic of Galen's *Meth. Med.*, also known as the *Therapeutica* or *Megategni*. This summary was printed in *Omnia Opera Ysaac*, Lugduni, 1515, ff. 189ᵛ sqq. (See F. Wüstenfeld, *Übersetzungen arabischer Werke in das Lateinische*, p. 19.) It contains a characteristic passage on the study of disease: 'eam cum experimento invenire investigamus. . . . Sicut enim experimentum sine ratione est debile, sic et ratio non iuncta experimento fallax est. . . . Experimento autem necessarium est longum tempus cum tentatione rei.' (*Megategni*, iii, f. 190ᵛ.) Constantine also translated several of the medical writings of the Jewish doctor Isaac Israeli (d. *c.* 932) himself (Wüstenfeld, op. cit., p. 17; Sarton, *Introduction*, i. 640). In another characteristic passage Isaac discussed the roles of 'experience and reason' in determining the use of diets and herbs: Isaaci Iudaei *De Diaetis Univ. et Partic.*, i. 2, Basileae, 1570, pp. 11-12.

A similar distinction in terms of practice and theory was made by the Persian, Haly Abbas or 'Ali ibn 'Abbas (d. 994), one of the greatest Arabic medical writers, whose *Liber Regalis* Constantine translated under the name *Pantegni*. This was printed in full in *Omnia Opera Ysaac*, Lyons, 1515; and the *pars theorica* was printed in Basel in 1539 in Constantini Africani *Summi in Omni Philosophia*: see *De Communibus Medico Cognitu Necessariis Locis*, i. 1, p. 4. See Sarton, *Introduction*, i. 677; Haskins, *Mediaeval Science*, pp. 132, 374.

[2] See L. Brunschvicg, *Étapes de philos. math.* 3ᵉ éd., pp. 43-105; Heath, *Euclid's Elements*, pp. 137-42; H. Hankel, *Gesch. Math. in Altertum und Mittelalter*, pp. 137-50; H. G. Zeuthen, ibid., pp. 92-104. Cf. Newton, below, pp. 317-18.

[3] See below, p. 76, n. 7.

[4] Chalcidii *Comm. Timaeum Platonis*, ccc, cccii, ed. Mullach, pp. 245ᵇ, 246ᵃ. See the important article by L. M. Régis, 'Analyse et synthèse dans l'œuvre de Saint Thomas', in *Studia Mediaevalia R. J. Martin*, pp. 303 sqq.

[5] *De Differentiis Topicis*, i (*PL*, lxiv) 1173. See also *In Topica Ciceronis Commentaria*, i (*PL*, lxiv) 1044, 1047. For the argument from species to genera by the method of com-

century writers tended to identify Boethius's *via judicii* with *resolutio* and his *via inventionis* with *compositio*.[1] The ninth-century philosopher John Scot Erigena was another translator and philosopher who used the terms *resolutio* and *compositio*. For the latter he used also *divisio* and in *De Divisione Naturae* he built upon this double process the whole structure of his ontology.[2] In the twelfth century the terms *resolutio* and *compositio* do not seem to have been widely used by philosophers, but in the thirteenth century they became one of the starting-points of the analysis of scientific method which began with Grosseteste.[3]

An early twelfth-century logician who showed a clear understanding of the distinction between empirical knowledge of a fact and rational knowledge of the cause of the fact was Peter Abelard (1079–1142). Abelard did not know Aristotle's *Posterior Analytics*[4] and he was making use only of the *logica vetus*, but he shows signs of having been acquainted with at least some of the translations or writings of the medical school. Some of his contemporaries had read works by Constantine the African and other members of the Salerno school and it seems probable that Abelard made use of some of the same sources.[5]

Some sciences are concerned with action, others with understanding; that is, some consist in constructing things, others in analysing compound things. For many people are practiced in action but have little scientific understanding; they have tested the healing power of medicines and are good at healing because of their experience alone, but they do not know much about the natural causes. For they know which herbs are useful for healing which diseases because they learn this by experience, but the reason why the herbs have this power they do not study; they know the

parison, see *Isagog. Porph. Comment.* i. 11, ed. Schepss and Brandt, p. 166. See also the references given by Régis, op. cit., pp. 307–8. Cf. below, pp. 62–64, 75.

[1] For Albertus Magnus and St. Thomas Aquinas on this see Régis, op. cit., pp. 309, 311–13. Cf. below, pp. 75 sqq.; p. 193.

[2] Régis, op. cit., pp. 308–9.

[3] Below, pp. 54, 61 sqq.

[4] Haskins, *Mediaeval Science*, p. 226; van der Vyver, *Rev. belge philol. hist.* viii (1929), 450 sqq. See also M. Grabmann, *Bearbeitungen und Auslegungen der Aristotelischen Logik*. Abelard knew neither Aristotle's *Posterior Analytics*, except perhaps by name, nor his *Physics*, which was not translated into Latin till the end of the twelfth century.

[5] Adelard of Bath in his *De Eodem et Diverso*, hrg. von H. Willner, p. 33, refers to an occasion 'cum a Salerno veniens in Graecia maiore' he questioned a Greek doctor on the cause of a magnet's attracting iron; William of Conches had read Constantine (Thorndike, *History of Magic*, ii. 53); and Thierry of Chartres also knew Constantine's translations (see above, p. 22, n. 6).

powers of herbs and the natures of infirmities because they are practised
in the practical science, but they are not instructed in the theoretical.
(But beasts and all the other irrational animals are very sound in practice
but are ignorant of natures and causes, as for example the dog brings
about its own cure by licking its wound. Bees also nature has taught with
wonderful subtlety to make honey, which is beyond human skill.) Many
people on the other hand have understanding but not practical ability,
and these can impart knowledge to others but cannot put it into practice
themselves. The man of understanding is he who has the ability to grasp
and ponder the hidden causes of things. By hidden causes we mean those
from which things originate, and these are to be investigated more by
reason than by sensory experiences.[1] . . . Whence Virgil's judgement:[2]
Happy the man who has been able to discover the causes of things.[3]

The causes that Abelard sought in nature were the necessary
causes of metaphysics,[4] causes that could be the start of certain
demonstration, and his attitude to them was one of extreme rationalism. He was so far empirical as to hold that to know is to affirm as
existing together what exists together in reality, the universal being
a *nominum significatio* signifying that coexistence, so that the event is
the cause of the truth of the proposition.[5] He even held that demonstrations in geometry might be confirmed by experience.[6] But he
maintained that causes were to be investigated more by reason than
by sensory experience, and he concentrated on the deductive side of
science. Even so empirical a natural philosopher as Adelard of Bath
held that the senses, though necessary for investigating the particular
and concrete, gave not truth but opinion,[7] and when he castigated
those who slavishly followed authority it was not to urge them to
observe but to urge them to reason.[8]

Such extreme rationalism was in fact part of a general intellectual
movement in the twelfth century, and in several different subjects
philosophers tried to arrange knowledge as a system of deductions
like mathematics, starting from indemonstrable, necessary first

[1] A reference to Boethius follows: cf. above, p. 28, n. 5; *PL*, lxiv. 1044.

[2] *Georgics*, Lib. ii, l. 490.

[3] Petrus Abaelardus, *Logica 'nostrorum petitioni sociorum'*, *Glossulae super Porphy-
rium*, hrg. von B. Geyer, pp. 505–6.

[4] *Logica 'ingredientibus'*, *Glossae super Praedicamenta Aristotelis, De Priori*, hrg. von
B. Geyer, p. 293.

[5] Ibid.   [6] Ibid., p. 289.

[7] 'O perversa rerum conversio, cum nihil ratione certius, nihil sensibus fallacius . . .',
he said in *De Eodem et Diverso*, hrg. von Willner, p. 13. 'Unde nec ex sensibus scientia,
sed opinio oriri valet. Hinc est, quod familiaris meus Plato sensus irrationabiles vocat.'

[8] *Quaest. Nat.* C. 6, hrg. von Müller, pp. 11–12.

principles and proceeding to the proposition to be demonstrated. Anselm, Richard of St. Victor, Abelard, Gilbertus Porreta and others tried to formulate theology according to this mathematical-deductive method.[1] Contemporary mathematics[2] scarcely lived up to

[1] Here Boethius was the chief inspiration: see prologue to De Hebdomadibus (Quomodo substantiae in eo quod sint, bonae sint) (PL, lxiv) 1311. He tried to deduce a theological argument from self-evident propositions (cf. also De Differentiis Topicis, i, PL, lxiv. 1176). Typical of this rationalism is the Theologicae Regulae of Alain de Lille (c. 1128–1202), in which he held that theological truth should be deduced from indemonstrable first principles based on faith, for: 'Omnis scientia suis nititur regulis velut propriis fundamentis . . . Theoremata vero geometrarum regulae sunt. . . . Suas etiam maximas habet astronomia' and 'theologia . . . habet regulas digniores' (PL, ccx) 621. See M. Baumgartner, Philosophie des Alanus de Insulis, pp. 27 sqq.; also on Alain's interest in astronomy see Duhem, Syst. monde, iii. 223 sqq. On the introduction of logic and rational methods into theology and other subjects see M. Grabmann, Scholastische Methode; J. de Ghellinck, 'Dialectique et dogme aux xe–xiie siècles', in Festgabe zum 60. Geburtstag Clemens Baeumker, Le Mouvement théologique du xiie siècle, 2e éd.; C. H. Haskins, Renaissance of the Twelfth Century; J. Cottiaux, 'La Conception de la théologie chez Abélard', Rev. d'hist. ecclés. xxviii (1932) 247 sqq., 533 sqq., 788 sqq.; G. Paré, A. Brunet et P. Tremblay, Renaissance du xiie siècle; M. D. Chenu, 'Un Essai de méthode théologique au xiie siècle', RSPT, xxiv (1935) 258 sqq., Théologie comme science au xiiie siècle, 2e éd.

[2] After the time of Gerbert there had been a revival of interest in geometry and arithmetic, as in logic. (See the recent article by H. P. Lattin, 'The eleventh century MS Munich 14436: Its contribution to the history of co-ordinates, of logic, of German studies in France', Isis, xxxviii, 1948, pp. 205 sqq.) In arithmetic an elementary idea of treatment of theoretical problems based on the properties of numbers had been preserved in Boethius's De Arithmetica (PL, lxiii), which was based on Nicomachus, and in Cassiodorus's Institutiones; and knowledge was acquired of how to make calculations with the abacus, on which Gerbert, Adelard of Bath and other authors wrote treatises (cf. above, pp. 19 sqq.; also S. Gandz, 'The origin of the Ghūbar numerals', Isis, xvi, 1931, pp. 393 sqq.). But in geometry the main source of knowledge in the eleventh and early twelfth centuries, a collection which passed under the name of Boethius, contained his translation only of certain of Euclid's definitions, axioms, and postulates, and the proofs of the first three theorems of Book i of the Elements. The rest of the work was an interpolated description of the use of the abacus and of practical surveying methods (see Euclidis Geom. Lib. ab Boethio translati, PL, lxiii; Tannery, Mém. scient. v. 92, 97 sqq.; Heath, Euclid's Elements, p. 92; A. van der Vyver, 'L'Évolution scientifique du haut moyen âge', Archeion, xix, 1937, p. 13). Though they knew the theorems of Book i, the geometers of this time lacked all idea of geometrical demonstration. They were able to make use of the conclusions of Euclid for practical instruments but showed no ability to prove them. Sometimes geometrical reasoning was concluded by an appeal to experience and, for instance, the squaring of the circle was regarded as an experimental fact based on cutting up pieces of parchment (Tannery, Mém. scient. v. 88–89, 90–93; cf. Abelard, above, p. 30, n. 6). Even towards the end of the twelfth century geometry remained a practical science using the conclusions of Greek geometers but not attempting to demonstrate those conclusions (ibid. 206–7), though the whole of Euclid's Elements had by then been translated, the principal version being that made by Adelard of Bath from Arabic (Heath, op. cit., pp. 93 sqq.; Haskins, Mediaeval Science, pp. 24–25; van der Vyver, Rev. belge philol. hist. viii, 1929, p. 425, n. 2). It was, however, in Euclid's works that later natural philosophers such as Alexander Neckam (see below, p. 41) and

this ideal, and until towards the end of the twelfth century geometry in fact remained a purely practical science of which the exponents were able to use some of the conclusions of the Greek geometers for such practical purposes as surveying and astronomy, but showed no ability to demonstrate those conclusions. But these twelfth-century philosophers, true to the tradition of Plato and St. Augustine, regarded the mathematical method as the scientific method. Scientific knowledge they held was knowledge that could be demonstrated rationally from true first principles. The senses were deceitful; only reason could give truth.

Typical of this attitude was that of Hugh of St. Victor when in his *Didascalicon* he discussed the relation of mathematics to physical science. 'Mathematics', he said, 'is known as theoretical science' (*doctrinalis*). It considered abstract quantity, that is, as Boethius and Cassiodorus had said, quantity as such separated by the intellect from matter and from other accidents and treated only by reason.[1] This separation was brought about by theory (*doctrina*) and was not so in nature.[2]

The proper function of mathematics is to deal clearly by means of reason with confused actually existing things. For instance, in the actuality of things no line exists apart from surface and solidity . . . but reason considers the line purely *per se* without surface or thickness. And this belongs to mathematics not because it is or can be so in things, but because reason often considers the acts of things not as they are, but as they can be, not in themselves but as they might appear to reason itself. Considered in this

above all Robert Grosseteste (see below, pp. 52 sqq.) saw an example of a science which demonstrated its conclusions from prior and better-known principles, such as Aristotle had described in the *Post. Anal.* See also Cantor, *Gesch. Math.* i, for twelfth-century mathematics, and ii for the change brought about early in the thirteenth century by Leonardo Fibonacci of Pisa, Jordanus Nemorarius, Sacrobosco, and others.

[1] See ref. above, p. 22, n. 1, for Hugh's classification of theoretical science into metaphysics, mathematics, and physics. This division of the theoretical sciences occurs in Boethius's *De Trinitate*, C. 2 (*PL*, lxiv) 1250. Boethius himself derived it from Aristotle: see *Phys.* ii. 1, 2, 192^{b}6–194^{a}19; *Metaph.* K. 3, 1061^{a}30–^{b}11; Ross, *Aristotle*, pp. 68 sqq., 156 sqq. Aristotle said that the entities considered by physics had a separate substantial existence but were subject to change, the entities considered by mathematics existed only as distinguishable aspects of concrete things but were free from change, and the entities considered by metaphysics or theology had both a separate existence and were free from change. Cf. above, p. 5, n. 1. On Hugh see Grabmann, *Scholastische Methode*, ii. 229 sqq.; and on some other twelfth- and early thirteenth-century classifications of science, ibid., pp. 28–54.

[2] *Erudit. Didas.* ii. 4 (*PL*, clxxvi) 753. Hugh quoted a passage from Cassiodorus's *Institutiones*, ii. 21, ed. Mynors, p. 130. He went on in ii. 7, col. 755, to quote the definition of 'quantitas abstracta' given by Boethius in his *De Arith.* i. 1 (*PL*, lxiii) 1081.

way continuous quantity [e.g. length] is said to increase to infinity: for such is the liveliness of reason that it divides every length in length, breadth in breadth, &c.[1]

Of the four mathematical sciences, two dealt with discontinuous quantity. Arithmetic considered discontinuous quantity or multitude *per se*, as for instance 3, 4, and other numbers; music considered the relations of discontinuous quantities to each other, as for instance double, one-and-a-half, one-and-a-third, and so on.[2] The other two mathematical sciences dealt with continuous quantity, geometry considering space only and astronomy considering motion in space and time.[3] Geometry and astronomy thus considered the same thing, continuous magnitude, but from a different point of view.[4]

Physics (*physica* or *physiologia*), Hugh said, was the theoretical discourse considering natural things[5]; it

investigates the causes of things in their effects and the effects from their causes.[6] . . . The proper function of physics is to attend in an unmixed manner to things which are actually mixed, for the acts of the bodies of the world are not pure but are compounded from the acts of pure bodies, which, though they are not formed purely as such, physics considers as such. . . .[7]

But, he added, asserting his extreme rationalism:

It should not be passed over that only physics deals properly with things; all the others [*sc.* logic and mathematics] deal with the concepts of things. . . . And because logic and mathematics are prior in the order of learning to physics and, in a certain manner, function for it like tools

---

[1] *Erudit. Didas.* ii. 18 (*PL*, clxxvi) 758.

[2] Ibid., C. 7, 'De quadrivio' (*PL*, clxxvi) 755.

[3] Ibid., C. 15 (*PL*, clxxvi) 757.

[4] This distinction was to become important in the thirteenth-century discussions of the relation of mathematics to physics, though Hugh did not bring out the notion of the hierarchy of the sciences as Boethius had done. In a discussion of the mathematical sciences in his *De Arith.* i. 1 (*PL*, lxiii) 1079 sqq., Boethius said that the more abstract sciences of arithmetic and geometry were prior and necessary to the less abstract sciences of music and astronomy, respectively, to which they bore the relation of genus to species. This conception of superior and subordinate sciences Boethius got from Aristotle's *Post. Anal.* i. 13, 78^{b}32 sqq.

[5] *Erudit. Didas.* ii. 17 (*PL*, clxxvi) 758. A useful discussion of the meaning of the word 'physics' in the twelfth and thirteenth centuries has been given by M. Clagett, 'Some general aspects of physics in the Middle Ages', *Isis*, xxxix (1948) 29 sqq.

[6] *Erudit. Didas.* ii. 17 (*PL*, clxxvi) 757.

[7] Ibid. ii. 18, col. 758. Physics thus tries to isolate the principles behind the appearances of things.

about which anyone must first learn before he gives his attention to the study of physics, it was necessary that these sciences put their consideration not in the actual state of things, where experience is deceitful, but in reason alone where there is firm truth; and then with reason as the guide they could descend to experience of things.[1]

The problem that their ideal of a mathematical-deductive method then raised for these philosophers, when considering physical things, was how to arrive at the original principles from which the demonstration proceeded, at true causes from which the effects were seen necessarily to follow. The need for the induction of first principles[2] from experience, before using those principles as the start of a deductive demonstration, had been vaguely recognized by Gilbertus Porreta (c. 1076-1154), one of the leaders of the school of Chartres, in his commentary on Boethius's *De Hebdomadibus*.[3] But a clear understanding of this dual inductive-deductive procedure of science came only when the Latin translation of Boethius's own original source, the *Posterior Analytics* of Aristotle, began to be read and mastered during the second half of the twelfth century.[4] John of Salisbury, a pupil of Gilbertus's[5] who had read this work of Aristotle, gave in his *Metalogicon* (1159) a clear account of Aristotle's conception of induction, emphasizing the psychological aspects as Aristotle had done.

A science must first know the principles and from these infer the consequence that follows from the necessary connexion of the premisses involved, and it must do this by close reasoning, pressing on, so to speak, step by step so that there may not be, owing to lack of necessary sequence, any hiatus which may prejudice demonstrative science. For not every science is a demonstrative science, but that only which proceeds from premisses that are true, primary and immediate. . . . Thus common conceptions of the mind come first, then self-evident propositions, and from these arise demonstrative science. But it is important to consider whether these known things are more knowable in nature or to us, for those nearest

---

[1] *Erudit. Didas.* ii. 18, col. 758-9.

[2] This was the induction by abstraction of universals from experience of singulars, described in Aristotle's *Post. Anal.* (see above, p. 27). Aristotelian logic also included another kind of induction by enumeration, as described in the *Prior Anal.* ii. 23, 68^{b}15 sqq., 27, 70^{a}3 sqq.; see Aristotle's *Prior and Post. Anal.* ed. Ross, pp. 47-51, 481-502. These two forms of induction were often discussed together in the Middle Ages; see A. Mansion, *RNP*, xiii (1906) 115 sqq., 246 sqq.

[3] Gilberti Porretae *Comm. Quomodo substantiae bonae sint* (*PL*, lxiv) 1316; Pelster, *Scholastik*, xx-xxiv (1949) 401-3.   [4] Haskins, *Mediaeval Science*, pp. 223 sqq.

[5] Clerval, *Écoles de Chartres*, p. 180. There were a number of English scholars at Chartres at that time. See also Grabmann, *Scholastische Methode*, ii. 451.

to sense are more knowable to us, while the remoter, namely the universals, are more knowable simply and in nature. . . . For common conceptions get their validity by induction from particulars, for it is impossible to arrive at universals without induction, because, as [Aristotle] says, the things that are said to exist as a result of abstraction, we come to know by induction. But induction is impossible to those who have no sense. But sense has to do with particulars, and it is impossible to acquire knowledge of them either from universals, save by induction, or by induction without sense. Thus from sense arises memory, from often repeated memories of many things, empirical knowledge, and from empirical knowledge comes science or art.[1]

Such a psychological treatment of induction was no guide for the experimental scientist, and it was in fact Robert Grosseteste, writing half a century later, who made the first thorough logical analysis of the inductive and experimental procedures of practical science.

(3)

The reason why Grosseteste was able to approach the problems of induction and demonstration with experimental science in mind was that during the second half of the twelfth century the attention of philosophers had been directed towards natural science by the large number of Greek and Arabic scientific works that were becoming available in Latin.[2] By the end of the twelfth century not only the *Analytics*, but also the *Physics*, *De Generatione et Corruptione*, *De Anima*, *Parva Naturalia*, and the first four books of the *Metaphysics* of Aristotle had been translated into Latin from the Greek, and the *De Caelo* and the first three books of the *Meteorologica* had been translated from the Arabic. During the same period Latin versions from either Greek or Arabic, and sometimes from both, were made

[1] Ioannis Saresberiensis, *Metalogicon*, iv. 8, ed. C.C. J. Webb, pp. 172-4. Cf. above, p. 26.
[2] For details of these translations see M. Alonso Alonso, 'Homenaje a Avicena en su milenario. Las traducciones de Juan González de Burgos y Salomón', *Al-Andalus*, xiv (1949) 291 sqq., and below, p. 37, n. 1; H. Bédoret, 'Les Premières Traductions tolédanes de philosophie. Œuvres d'Alpharabi', *RNP*, xli (1938) 80 sqq., '. . . Œuvres d'Avicenne', ibid., pp. 374 sqq., 'L'Auteur et le traducteur du *Liber de Causis*', ibid., pp. 519 sqq.; Duhem, *Orig. statique*; M. Grabmann, *Lateinische Aristoteles-Übersetzungen* and above, p. 29, n. 4; Haskins, *Mediaeval Science*; G. Lacombe, *Aristoteles Latinus*; Sir J. E. Sandys, *History of Classical Scholarship*, 3rd ed.; Sarton, *Introduction*; F. Van Steenberghen, *Aristote en Occident*.; M. Steinschneider, *Europäische Übersetzungen aus dem Arabischen*; G. Théry, 'Notes indicatrices pour s'orienter dans l'étude des traductions médiévales', in *Mélanges Joseph Maréchal*, ii. 296 sqq.; Ueberweg–Geyer, *Geschichte der Philosophie*, ii; S. D. Wingate, *Mediaeval Latin Versions of the Aristotelian Scientific Corpus*; F. Wüstenfeld, *Übersetzungen arabischer Werke in das Lateinische*. Cf. A. Mieli, *Science arabe*; M. Meyerhof, 'Von Alexandrien nach Bagdad', *SP.AWB*, 1930. pp. 389 sqq. See Crombie, *Augustine to Galileo*, i. 54-67.

of the *Elements*, *Optics*, and *Catoptrics* of Euclid, *De Speculis Comburentibus* (*Liber Tidei de Speculo*) of Diocles, part of the *Conics* of Apollonius, the *Almagest* and *Optics* of Ptolemy, several late Greek fragments on statics then attributed to Euclid, the pseudo-Aristotelian *De Vegetabilibus* or *De Plantis*, and numerous works by Hippocrates and Galen. During the first two decades of the thirteenth century Latin versions were made of the remaining books of Aristotle's *Metaphysics* and of his *Generation*, *Parts*, and *History of Animals*, which together went under the name *De Animalibus*. Versions of other Greek works followed later in the thirteenth century.

Scientific works of Arabic origin which had been translated into Latin by 1200 included the *Liber Alchorismi*, *Algebra*, and astronomical tables of Al-Khwarizmi, the *Liber Almansoris* and *Liber Continens* of Rhazes, the *De Ortu Scientiarum* and *De Scientiis* of Alfarabi, the *Liber Regalis* of Haly Abbas, the *De Aspectibus* and *De Umbris et de Diversitate Aspectum* of Alkindi, the *Optics* of Alhazen, the *De Motu Accessionis et Recessionis* and *Liber Charastonis*, a work on the Roman balance, of Ibn Thabit, the *Canon Medicinae* and commentaries on Aristotle by Avicenna, and the pseudo-Aristotelian *De Causis et Proprietatibus Elementorum*. In 1217 Alpetragius's *Liber Astronomiae* was translated and by about 1230 the commentaries on Aristotle by Averroës had become available in Latin.[1]

This new learning included practical treatises on astronomy, medicine, and chemistry as well as theoretical works like Aristotle's *Physics* and Euclid's *Optics*, and it brought about an increase in practical, observational science, usually with some useful purpose in view. It soon became necessary for the pursuit of utilitarian ends themselves to understand precisely how theory and practice or experience were related to each other. During the half-century before Grosseteste began to write, natural philosophers became increasingly aware of this need, though at first they were too much occupied with collecting and digesting the new material to be able to make any important contributions to methodology.

The first writer to make a systematic exposition of such of this new learning as was available to him was the Spaniard, Dominicus Gundissalinus (*fl. c.* 1140), who was the first in the Latin West to

---

[1] For a general account of Arabic philosophical influence see G. Quadri, *Philosophie arabe dans l'Europe médiévale*. See also Mieli, op. cit.; A. M. Goichon, *Philosophie d'Avicenne*; Léon Gauthier, *Ibn Rochd* (*Averroès*). Also of interest is G. Vajda, *Pensée juive du moyen âge*. See also *Avicenna, Scientist and Philosopher*, below, p. 351.

take up the Arabic tradition of the classification of the sciences. In his *De Divisione Philosophiae*, which was based largely on the treatises by Alfarabi known in Latin as *De Ortu Scientiarum* and *De Scientiis*,[1] though also on traditional Latin sources, Gundissalinus discussed the relation between the sciences as to both their subject matter and the means of knowing them. He accepted a form of the traditional Aristotelian division of the sciences into theoretical and practical.[2] The theoretical sciences he subdivided into physics, which considered material things in change; mathematics, which considered entities abstracted from matter but existing only in material things and therefore subject to change; and metaphysics or theology, which considered entities which were both abstracted from matter and free from change.[3] The practical sciences he subdivided into politics, or the art of civil government; the art of family government, which included giving instruction in the liberal and mechanical arts; and ethics, or the art of self-government. The 'fabrile or mechanical arts' were those concerned with making out of matter something useful to man. The matter they used might be from living things as, for instance, wood, wool, linen, or bones, or from dead things as, for instance, gold, silver, lead, iron, marble, or precious stones. Through the mechanical arts resources were acquired which provided for the needs of the family.[4] For each of the sciences Gundissalinus gave the definition, genus, material, species, parts, use (*officium*), aim, instrument, practitioner (*artifex*), etymology, and order in which it should be studied.[5]

Physics, or 'natural science', he defined as 'the science considering only things unabstracted and with motion',[6] the science which 'considers bodies only in so far as they are changed and transformed'.[7]

[1] For Alfarabi see Sarton, *Introduction*, i. 628–9; and Alpharabius, *De Ortu Scientiarum*, hrg. von C. Baeumker. For the influence of Alfarabi and other writers on Gundissalinus, see Baur's ed. of Dominicus Gundissalinus, *De Div. Philos.*, pp. 164 sqq.; A. González Palencia, *Alfarabi, Catálogo de las Ciencias*; H. G. Farmer, *Al-Farabi's Arabic-Latin Writings on Music*; Bédoret, *RNP*, xli (1938) 80 sqq.; M. A. Alonso, 'Notas sobre los traductores toledanos Domingo Gundisalvo y Juan Hispano', *Al-Andalus*, viii (1943) 155 sqq., 'Las fuentes literárias de Domingo Gundisalvo', ibid. xi (1946) 159 sqq.

[2] 'Una consistit in sola cognicione mentis, altera in execucione operis.' *Div. Philos.* Prologus, p. 11.

[3] Ibid., pp. 14–15, 19–43, 103; cf. above, p. 22, n. 1; p. 32, n. 1. Gundissalinus differed slightly from Aristotle in his definition of mathematical entities.

[4] Ibid., pp. 16, 139–40.

[5] On the Latin origin of this division see Hunt, in *Studia Mediaevalia R. J. Martin*, p. 87.   [6] *Div. Philos.*, p. 19.   [7] Ibid., p. 20.

Physics was 'first for us because with us form is apprehended simultaneously with matter by the senses, before form is apprehended without matter by the intellect'.[1] It was a 'universal science' because it contained under it several 'particular sciences', namely, medicine,[2] the science of judgements, necromancy, the science of images, agriculture, navigation, the science of mirrors, and alchemy.[3] The use of physics was 'to consider natural bodies and accidents which have no being except through those bodies',[4] and its aim was to make change in natural bodies intelligible by showing the causes that brought it about. 'This science provides knowledge of natural bodies through observation of their sensible aspects, and proof from their intelligible aspects. It provides knowledge of the matter and form of a natural body and of the moving agent and of the end on account of which it acts. . . . The instrument of this art is the dialectical syllogism, which is based on what is true and probable. . . . The practitioner is the natural philosopher who, proceeding rationally from the causes of things to the effects and from effects to causes, seeks out principles.'[5] Such principles were the four Aristotelian causes in natural things, 'the constituents of which are not perceptible to sense, and the being of which constituents is verified for us only by reasoning and demonstration'.[6] He concluded by saying that physics should be studied after logic.

The office of logic, Gundissalinus said, was on its theoretical side discovery (*inventio*) and judgement (*iudicio*) and on its practical side division (*divisio*), definition and reasoning (*ratiocinacio*). Reasoning he divided into dialectic (*dialectica*), which proceeded from probables; demonstration, which proceeded from self-evident propositions and of which definition was an integral part; and sophistical reasoning, which proceeded from what appears to be and is not. The principal instruments of logic were the syllogism and induction, and

---

[1] *Div. Philos.*, pp. 19–20.

[2] He distinguished between practical and theoretical medicine (ibid., pp. 84, 218 sqq.) and gave the following account of the different Greek sects: 'Empirici vero experienciam solam sectantur; Logici experiencie racionem adiungunt; Methodici nec elementorum racionem observant, nec tempora nec etates, set solas morborum substancias et ideo remansit in usu et auctoritate sola racionalis.' Ibid., p. 89. See above, p. 27.

[3] Ibid., p. 20; cf. Thorndike, *History of Magic*, ii. 79–80.

[4] *Div. Philos.*, pp. 23–24. This was copied from Alfarabi. See *De Scientiis*, in Alpharabii *Omnia Opera*, Paris, 1638, p. 28. González Palencia (op. cit., pp. xii, 106, 157) has re-edited this text and published also Gerard of Cremona's translation of *De Scientiis*.

[5] *Div. Philos.*, 'Scientia naturalis', p. 27.

[6] Ibid., p. 26. This was copied almost word for word from Alfarabi's *De Scientiis*; see Alpharabii *Opera Omnia*, p. 30; González Palencia, op. cit., p. 107.

others were enthymeme and example, though he did not explain how to use these instruments.[1]

Mathematics Gundissalinus defined as the science of abstract quantity considering such entities as lines, surfaces, circles, and triangles, which were found only in material things but were not themselves material.[2] 'Abstraction is concerned with the form of things however apprehended.' The instrument of mathematics was the demonstrative syllogism, and of its premisses, as of the demonstrative sciences in general, 'some are derived from the senses as, for instance: "all fire heats" and "all snow is white" and such like; and others are derived from reason, as, for instance: "every whole is greater than its part" and such like.'[3] Mathematics was a universal science 'because it contains under itself seven arts, which are arithmetic, geometry, music, and astronomy, the science of aspects [i.e. optics], the science of weights, and the science of mathematical devices'.[4] Each of these sciences consisted of a theoretical part which studied basic principles, and a practical part in which those principles were put to use.[5] Thus arithmetic, on its theoretical side, considered the theory of numbers in the abstract and, on its practical side, the counting and reckoning of material things, as in commerce by means of an abacus. Theoretical music considered proportions and harmonies in the abstract and practical music was concerned with the production of sound by voice or instruments. Theoretical geometry considered lines, surfaces, and

---

[1] *Div. Philos.*, pp. 75–77. These come from the *Prior Anal.* See in particular ii. 23, 24, 27 and Aristotle's *Prior and Post. Anal.*, ed. Ross, pp. 47–51, 481–502.

[2] Ibid., pp. 222 sqq. On this cf. Alfarabi who held that apart from God all that exists is accidents and substance, the former known only by the five senses and the latter only by reason. Substance was capable of being divided into parts and figures, and these were the subject of mathematics (*De Ortu Scient.* hrg. von Baeumker, pp. 17–18, 20; cf. González Palencia, op. cit., pp. 97, 106, 145, 157).

[3] *Div. Philos.*, pp. 28–32.

[4] Ibid., pp. 31–32. Cf. Alfarabi on the notion of the necessity, to some sciences, of others which provided their demonstrative principles. He said that moving substance could be measured and that the measurement of the movement of heavenly bodies was the task of astronomy, which would be impossible without geometry and arithmetic (*De Ortu Scient.*, hrg. von Baeumker, pp. 18–19; cf. also *De Scientiis*, in Alpharabii *Opera Omnia*, p. 14; González Palencia, op. cit., pp. 97, 145). The original source of this was Aristotle's theory of the subordination of some sciences to others, as of astronomy and optics to geometry or music to arithmetic (*Post. Anal.* 75^{b}14 sqq., 76^{a}9 sqq., 78^{b}32 sqq., 87^{a}31 sqq.).

[5] *Div. Philos.*, pp. 90–124. Much of his account is taken word for word from Alfarabi's *De Scientiis*; see Alpharabii *Opera Omnia*, pp. 14–27; González Palencia, op. cit., pp. 97–98, 145–8.

volumes in the abstract, and practical geometry was concerned with the measurement of bodies, as in measuring heights or in surveying.[1] Astrology and astronomy considered the position and motion of the heavenly bodies by means of the astrolabe and other instruments and were to be read after geometry. The science of weights considered the basic principles of the balance and of instruments by which heavy things were lifted and carried. The science of 'mathematical devices' turned the principles of the other mathematical sciences to useful purposes, as for stone-masonry, for instruments for measuring and lifting bodies, for musical and optical instruments, and for carpentry and other mechanical arts. Of particular interest is Gundissalinus's account of optics (*de aspectibus*) as illustrating the relation of a more abstract to a more concrete science.[2] This account he copied almost word for word from Alfarabi's *De Scientiis*.[3]

Other writers on natural science in the late twelfth and early thirteenth centuries showed an increasing acquaintance with the scientific works of Ptolemy, Euclid, Galen, Aristotle, Alkindi, Avicenna, and other Greek and Arab writers. They were interested in searching for principles and causes of observed things, though their approach to a theory of science was unsystematic and they were still primarily concerned with collecting the new learning and with its immediate practical applications.[4] Typical of this line of approach were the attitudes taken in discussions of scientific questions by a number of Englishmen of this time. Roger of Hereford, in an outline of study in the preface to his *Compotus* (1176), showed a conscious interest in explanatory principles in physics and astronomy, but his primary concern was the practical problem of calculating dates. Daniel of Morley, who may have studied at Hereford some

---

[1] He repeated the story about geometry being discovered in Egypt; cf. *Div. Philos.* p. 110 and above, p. 22.

[2] *Div. Philos.*, pp. 112 sqq., 123.

[3] Alpharabii *Opera Omnia*, pp. 18–20. Clagett, *Isis*, xxxix (1949) 31–35 has given an English translation of Alfarabi's passage on this from an Arabic text and has drawn attention to Gundissalinus's debt to him. See also Baur, op. cit., pp. 256 sqq.; González Palencia, op. cit., pp. xii, 99 sqq., 148 sqq.

[4] See Duhem, *Syst. monde*, v. 233 sqq.; Haskins, *Mediaeval Science*, pp. 113 sqq.; A. Birkenmajer, 'Le Rôle joué par les médecins et les naturalistes dans la réception d'Aristote aux xiie et xiiie siècles', *Pologne au vie congrès internat. sciences hist.*, pp. 1 sqq.; S. d'Irsay, 'Les Sciences de la nature et les universités médiévales', *Archeion*, xv (1933) 216 sqq.; R. W. Hunt, 'English learning in the late twelfth century', *Trans. Roy. Hist. Soc.* 4 Ser. xix (1936) 19 sqq.; D. A. Callus, 'Introduction of Aristotelian learning to Oxford', *PBA*, xxix (1943) 229 sqq.

time before 1187,[1] introduced a discussion of the four Aristotelian elements and causes as *principia* into a work on natural operations,[2] but his main interest was to expound everything he had learnt in Toledo. Alexander Neckam (1157–1217), who taught at Oxford, showed himself familiar with the new logic of Aristotle, with Euclid and the idea of geometrical demonstration, and with Galen, Isaac Israeli, and the Salerno school of medicine where Urso of Lodi and Maurus had introduced some logical precision into medical teaching; but Neckam was also primarily a collector[3] interested in the new learning and in such practical inventions[4] as the mariner's compass and glass mirrors. His friend and younger contemporary, Alfred of Sareshel, who may have worked for a time at Hereford,[5] showed, in his *De Motu Cordis* (before 1217), which was addressed to physicians, an even wider knowledge of Aristotle's scientific writings and of the medical works of Hippocrates, Galen, and various Arab authors. He was acquainted with the new logic, and he referred to the middle term of the syllogism as the cause of the conclusion or event,[6] to Galen's experiments on the thorax[7] and to the use of 'experience and reason';[8] but he too was more interested in expounding the new learning than in a systematic theory of science. Other writers teaching in Oxford during the first decade of the thirteenth century also expounded the 'new Aristotle'; Edmund of Abingdon lectured on the *Sophistici Elenchi*, a Master Hugh on the *Posterior Analytics*, John of London on certain Avicennian theories and on astronomy and meteorology, and John Blund on the *libri naturales*.[9]

[1] J. C. Russell, 'Hereford and Arabic science in England about 1175-1200', *Isis*, xviii (1932) 14 sqq.; see also C. Singer, 'Daniel of Morley, an English philosopher of the xiith century', *Isis*, iii (1920-1) 263 sqq.; Thorndike, *History of Magic*, ii. 171 sqq.

[2] K. Sudhoff, 'Daniels von Morley *Liber de naturis inferiorum et superiorum*, nach der Handschrift Cod. Arundel 377 des Britischen Museums zum Abdruck gebracht', *AGNT*, viii (1918) 14 sqq.

[3] *De Utensilibus*, ed. T. Wright, pp. 96 sqq.; Alexander Neckam, *De Naturis Rerum*, ed. Wright, pp. 283-307; Thorndike, op. cit., ii. 188 sqq.; cf. Hunt, *Trans. Roy. Hist. Soc.* 4 Ser. xix (1936) 19 sqq.; Birkenmajer, *Pologne au vi^e congrès internat. sciences hist.*, pp. 2 sqq.; Callus, *PBA*, xxix (1943) 235 sqq.

[4] Here he showed the same utilitarian interest that had characterized his twelfth-century predecessors and stood in contrast with the learned of Antiquity. Then, as he said, the liberal arts had been the monopoly of free men, the mechanical or adulterine arts being for the ignoble (*De Naturis Rerum*, ii. 21; cf. Cassiodorus, *Institutiones*).

[5] J. C. Russell, *Isis*, xviii (1932) 18 sqq.

[6] 'Medii inventio rei dicit causam', Alfredus de Sareshel, *De Motu Cordis*, C. 1, 1, hrg. von C. Baeumker, p. 5. [7] Ibid., C. 6, 8, p. 24. [8] Ibid., C. 7, 12, p. 30.

[9] Cf. Sarton, *Introduction*, ii. 582; Callus, *PBA*, xxix (1943) 240 sqq., *Oxoniensia*, x (1945) 43.

Another British writer of this period who occupied a prominent position in various continental centres of learning showed that the same tendencies were to be found in those centres. Michael Scot (d. *c.* 1235), the translator of Alpetragius's *Liber Astronomiae*,[1] of Aristotle's zoological works, which went under the title *De Animalibus*, and of other works from Arabic,[2] wrote during his Spanish period a classification of science, the *Divisio Philosophiae*, based largely on Gundissalinus.[3] This work has been preserved only in fragments in Vincent of Beauvais's *Speculum Doctrinale*. In it Scot divided knowledge in the usual Aristotelian manner into *theoretica*, comprising *naturalis*, *mathematica* or *doctrinalis*, and *divina*; and *practica*, which he divided into three groups of arts corresponding to each of the three theoretical sciences. The first group consisted of such arts as medicine, agriculture, alchemy, the study of mirrors, and navigation, 'which are related to that part of theoretical science which is called physics (*naturalis*) and belong to it as the practical side of it'.[4] The second group consisted of practical arts related to mathematics (*doctrinalis*), 'such as business concerned with money, carpentry, the crafts of the smith and the mason, weaving, shoemaking, and many others of the same kind which look to mechanics and are as it were the practical side of that'.[5] Scot thus envisaged some definite connexion between the theoretical and practical sciences, but he never explained what this connexion might be, though in his later Sicilian period at the court of Frederick II he shared his imperial patron's inclination to put opinions to the test of experiment.[6]

It was to this connexion between theory and practice or experience that Grosseteste devoted his attention, and in view of the scientific interests shown by British writers[7] it is not surprising that the need

[1] In this translation he opened the controversy between the 'mathematical' astronomy of Ptolemy and the 'physical' astronomy of Aristotle; see below, pp. 96 sqq.

[2] The most important other works were Aristotle's *libri naturales* with Averroës's commentaries; see Sarton, *Introduction*, ii. 579 sqq.

[3] Haskins, *Mediaeval Science*, p. 279.

[4] See Baur's edition of Gundissalinus, *Div. Philos.*, p. 399; cf. pp. 364 sqq.

[5] Ibid., p. 399. In another, different division of the practical arts Scot distinguished these as *vulgares*, belonging to *vulgus et viles homines*, as opposed to *civiles*, which included *linguae*, *morales*, &c. and belonged to *civiles homines et honestos* (ibid.).

[6] Haskins, op. cit., pp. 242 sqq., 289 sqq.; Thorndike, op. cit. ii. 307 sqq. In his *Phisionomia*, Paris, 1515, C. 17, Scot showed a slight acquaintance with the kind of inductive procedures used in medicine, referring to 'Signa probabilia quibus ad oculum et intellectum scitur mulier sit gravida masculi vel femelle'; but the reasoning which followed this statement was trite.

[7] Another British writer of the early thirteenth century who showed an interest in

for a systematic theory of experimental science should have received early recognition in Oxford. Grosseteste's contribution was to unite the two twelfth-century traditions of technology and logic.[1] From the almost pure empiricism of such practical sciences of the twelfth century as practical mathematics, astronomy, and medicine, and the almost pure rationalism of the theoretical speculations in contemporary philosophy on scientific method, he produced a science in which he tried to show the principles according to which the world of experience could be experimentally investigated and rationally explained.

natural science was Alexander of Hales (d. 1245), a prominent teacher in Paris. The authorship and date of the *Summa Theologica* attributed to Alexander of Hales are complex problems which have not yet been solved, but the text as it stands suggests that the author was a rational theologian in the tradition of Anselm and the school of St. Victor. The *Summa* is much concerned with the problem of certitude in knowledge of natural things. It includes a discussion of the natural sciences in which it is said that all science and art begins with experience: 'Omnis humana scientia est acquisita per inventionem vel doctrinam. . . . Omnis scientia et ars per experientiam accidit: experientia enim fecit artem' (*Summa*, i, Tr. Introd., Quaest. 1, C. 2, Quaracchi, 1924, i. 4). The *Summa* shows also the Augustinian tendency to think in mathematical terms and includes a section on measurement (ibid. ii, Inquis. 1, Tr. 1, Sect. 2, Q. 1, Memb. 1, 'De mensura, numero et pondere', Quaracchi, 1928, ii. 38). But the author's interest in these questions was chiefly in seeing how they were related to theology, and this attitude was in fact characteristic of Paris before Albertus Magnus turned his attention both to experimental science and to scientific methodology. See F. Picavet, *Hist. gén. et comp. philos. médiévales*, 2e éd., pp. 204 sqq.; M. de Wulf, *Hist. Mediaeval Philos.*, 3rd English ed., ii. 71 sqq., 99 sqq.

[1] Roger Bacon in his *Compendium Studii*, C. 8, claimed that Grosseteste 'prae aliis hominibus scivit scientias' (*Opera Quaedam Hactenus Inedita*, ed. J. S. Brewer, p. 472). Grosseteste seems to have been the first to develop a mature theory of science but he was not, of course, the first to read and teach the new science, even at Oxford. On the state of science in Oxford at this time see d'Irsay, *Archeion*, xv (1933) 216 sqq.; Hunt, *Trans. Roy. Hist. Soc.* 4 Ser. xix (1936) 19 sqq.; Callus, *PBA*, xxix (1943) 229 sqq. For the parallel influence of Aristotle in Paris see Van Steenberghen, *Siger de Brabant*, ii, 'Siger dans l'histoire de l'aristotélisme', and *Aristote en Occident*. See also A. Forest, F. Van Steenberghen, M. de Gandillac, *Le Mouvement doctrinal du xie au xive siècle*.

III

Grosseteste's Writings on Theory of Science

(1)

ROBERT GROSSETESTE[1] was born probably before 1170, possibly in 1168. He probably received his early education first at Lincoln, then at Oxford. His name appears for the first time in a charter of Hugh, Bishop of Lincoln, probably 1186–9, where he is described as *magister*. He was in the household of William de Vere, Bishop of Hereford, not later than 1198, during which time Giraldus Cambrensis described him as skilful in determining causes and in securing and maintaining bodily health, which has been construed as pointing to a knowledge of law and medicine. After leaving Hereford he may have resumed teaching at Oxford, but his career there would have been interrupted by the *suspendium clericorum*[2] from 1209 till 1214, during which time he probably went to study theology in Paris. Soon after the resumption of lectures in Oxford in 1214 Grosseteste became *Magister scholarum* or Chancellor of the University, probably the first or one of the first Chancellors. In 1229 he was Archdeacon of Leicester, but he was at Oxford in 1229–30, and from then till his election to the see of Lincoln in 1235 he was first lecturer to the Franciscans at Oxford. During his episcopate he attended the

---

[1] For the details of what is known of Grosseteste's life see S. Pegge, *Life of Robert Grosseteste*; F. S. Stevenson, *Robert Grosseteste*; E. Wickersheimer, 'Robert Grosseteste et la médecine', *3ᵉ Congrès hist. art de guérir*; J. C. Russell, 'The preferments and "Adiutores" of Robert Grosseteste', *Harvard Theol. Rev.* xxvi (1933) 161 sqq., 'Phases of Grosseteste's intellectual life', ibid. xliii (1950) 93 sqq., 'Richard of Bardney's account of Robert Grosseteste's early and middle life', *MH*, ii (1944) 45 sqq.; D. A. Callus, 'The Oxford career of Robert Grosseteste', *Oxoniensia*, x (1945) 42 sqq., 'The Summa Theologiae of Robert Grosseteste', in *Studies in Mediaeval History presented to F. M. Powicke*, pp. 180 sqq. For further details of his relations with his contemporaries see Adae de Marisco *Epistolae*, ed. J. S. Brewer; Roberti Grosseteste *Epistolae*, ed. H. R. Luard; and the chronicles of Thomas of Eccleston, Nicholas Trivet, and Matthew Paris. For a general account of his scientific work see L. Baur, *Die Philosophie des Robert Grosseteste*; Duhem, *Syst. monde*, iii. 277 sqq., 397 sqq., v. 341 sqq. For a general account of his philosophy see D. E. Sharp, *Franciscan Philos. at Oxford*, pp. 1 sqq.; E. Gilson, *Philos. au moyen âge*, pp. 469 sqq.

[2] Rashdall, *Universities*, iii. 3 sqq.

Council of Lyons in 1245. He died in 1253 and was buried at Lincoln.

Grosseteste set out his theory of science at length in his commentary on the *Posterior Analytics* of Aristotle and made further additions in his commentary on the *Physics*; and he put his methodological ideas into practice in his separate writings on optics, physics, and astronomy.[1] The dates of his writings are not always easy to determine.

[1] A complete list, which requires some revision, of Grosseteste's known scientific writings is given by S. H. Thomson, *The Writings of Robert Grosseteste*, 1940. These are discussed also by L. Baur in his edition of *Die philosophischen Werke des Robert Grosseteste*, 1912. This is cited below as: Baur, 1912. There are several manuscripts and early printed editions of the commentary on the *Posterior Analytics*. I have used the editions published in Venice in 1494 and 1514. This work is cited below as *Comm. Post.*, folio references being to the edition of 1494. There is an apparently earlier edition, lacking date and publisher's imprint, but dated 1475? in the British Museum Catalogue. I have used the edition of the *Summa Linconiensis super Octo Libris Physicorum Aristotelis* published in Venice in 1500. On the genuineness of this work see S. H. Thomson, 'The *Summa in VIII Libros Physicorum* of Grosseteste', *Isis*, xxii (1934) 12 sqq.; it is simply an abstract of Aristotle's *Physics*. For the *Commentarius in VIII Libros Physicorum Aristotelis* I have used MS 295, ff. 120–31ᵛ, 136–45ʳ (*c.* 1325) in the Library of Merton College, Oxford and MS Digby 220, ff. 84–105ʳ (15 c.) in the Bodleian Library. The two manuscripts differ slightly. This work is cited below as *Comm. Phys.* On Grosseteste's authorship of it see Baur, 1912, pp. 19*–24*; A. Pelzer, 'Les Versions latines des ouvrages de morale conservés sous le nom d'Aristote en usage au xiiiᵉ siècle', *RNP*, xxiii (1921) 397–8, n. 1; Thomson, op. cit., 1940, pp. 82–3; Callus, *Oxoniensia*, x (1945) 45–47. The end of this commentary, somewhat abbreviated, passed as a separate treatise under the name of *De Finitate Motus et Temporis* and was printed in Baur's edition of 1912. Some of Grosseteste's scientific opuscula were published early in the sixteenth century (see Thomson, op. cit., 1940, pp. 82–120 and Sarton, *Introduction*, ii. 585; below, p. 278). There is an English translation of one work by G. C. Riedl, *Robert Grosseteste on Light* (*De Luce*). Where possible, I have used Baur's edition, which contains most of his important scientific and philosophical writings. Certain of these I have checked against MSS, namely, *De Lineis, Angulis et Figuris*; *De Natura Locorum*; and *De Iride*. (See Bibliography, p. 326.) I have used also S. H. Thomson's improved text of *De Cometis et Causis Ipsarum* published in *Isis*, xix (1933) 21 sqq., and the text of the *Compotus*, ed. by R. Steele as an appendix to Rogeri Baconi *Opera Hactenus Inedita*, vi. 217 sqq. I have also consulted the text of the *Kalendarium* published by A. Lindhagen; and the unpublished *Hexaëmeron*, Brit. Mus. MS Royal 6. E. v, 14 c., and *De Universitatis Machina*, Cambridge Univ. Lib. MS Ff. 6. 13, 13 c. S. H. Thomson published a fragment of a text which he believed to be by Grosseteste, *Quaestiones in De Caelo et Mundo Aristotelis*, in his article 'The *De Anima* of Robert Grosseteste', *NS*, vii (1933) 218 sqq.; cf. Thomson, *Writings of Rob. Grosseteste*, pp. 66–67, 86, 90, and Lacombe, *Aristoteles Latinus*, p. 53. This attribution has been controverted by D. A. Callus, 'Philip the Chancellor and the *De Anima* ascribed to Robert Grosseteste', *MRS*, i (1941) 105 sqq. See also Callus, 'The *Summa Duacensis* and the Pseudo-Grosseteste's *De Anima*', *RTAM*, xii (1946) 225–9. Franceschini suggested that Grosseteste translated from the Greek, Books i–iii of Aristotle's *De Caelo*, adding explanatory notes: see his *Roberto Grossatesta, Vescovo di Lincoln, e le sue Traduzioni Latine*. In a recent reexamination of this problem D. J. Allan has shown that there is little doubt that Grosse-

It seems probable that the commentary on the *Posterior Analytics* was one of his earlier works, begun if not completed while he was still a Master of Arts[1] and before his writings on special scientific questions. The Latin version of the *Posterior Analytics* which Grosseteste used for his commentary was the common version from Greek then attributed to Boethius,[2] but he cited other translations, including possibly one from the Arabic, and also the commentary by Themistius;[3] all of these had been translated during the twelfth century. If Trivet's assertion that Grosseteste wrote this commentary when he was still a Master of Arts is true, then the date of it must be before 1209, when the Masters and Scholars of Oxford were dispersed; unless he lectured later in Arts in Paris, for which there seems to be no evidence. But if some zoological information mentioned in the commentary on the *Posterior Analytics*[4] was derived from Michael Scot's translation of Aristotle's *De Animalibus*, then the date of this part of the commentary would have to be advanced till after 1217–20, the probable dates between which this translation was made.[5] Trivet did not say that Grosseteste com-

teste translated from the Greek, Book ii of the commentary on *De Caelo* by Simplicius and the beginning of Book iii (Oxford MS Balliol 99, 14 c.). This translation included Aristotle's text. Grosseteste translated also Aristotle's Book i, though it cannot yet be decided whether he translated Simplicius's commentary on this book: see Allan's 'Mediaeval versions of Aristotle, *De Caelo*, and of the Commentary of Simplicius', *MRS*, ii (1950) 82 sqq. This translation was evidently made after Grosseteste wrote the shorter works published by Baur in 1912, for these show no special interest in *De Caelo*. The *Quaestiones* discussed by Thorndike and Callus show no knowledge of this version (Allan, op. cit., pp. 86–87, 117–18). For Grosseteste as a translator from Greek see Rashdall, *Universities*, iii. 240, n. 1; below, p. 136, n. 2.

[1] Callus, *Oxoniensia*, x (1945) 45. Trivet said explicitly: 'Qui, cum esset magister in artibus, super librum Posteriorum compendiose scripsit.' (*Annales*, ed. T. Hog, p. 243.) He added: 'Tractatus etiam de Sphaera et de Arte compoti, multaque alia in philosophia utilia, edidit'. This commentary remained popular till the end of the Middle Ages.

[2] It is very improbable that this version was by Boethius. In the last quarter of the twelfth century there were three translations of the *Posterior Analytics*, two from Greek, and one from Arabic. Grosseteste used the 'versio communis' beginning: 'Omnis doctrina et omnis disciplina intellectiva. . . .' See Lacombe, *Aristoteles Latinus*, pp. 47–49; van der Vyver, *Rev. belge philol. hist.* viii (1929) 426; Haskins, *Mediaeval Science*, pp. 223–41; L. Minio-Paluello, *Revista di Filosofia Neo-Scolastica*, xlii (1951) 222–37.

[3] Grosseteste said: 'Littera autem aliarum translationum et sententia Themistii neutri praedictarum sententiarum videtur concordare.' (*Comm. Post.* i. 10, f. 9ᵛ.) See Baur, 1912, pp. 18*–19*; Thomson, *Writings of Rob. Grosseteste*, p. 84.

[4] See below, p. 65, n. 2, p. 67, n. 3.

[5] Haskins, *Mediaeval Science*, pp. 273–8; Sarton, *Introduction*, ii. 579–80; Lacombe, *Aristoteles Latinus*, pp. 80–81. Wingate's (*Mediaeval Latin Versions*, p. 76) attempt to give an earlier date to Scot's translation is based on some citations by Alexander Neckam (d. 1217) but, as Dr. R. W. Hunt has shown in a dissertation deposited in the Bodleian Library, Oxford, these citations were not from *De Animal.* I am much indebted to Dr.

pleted his commentary while he was a Master of Arts, but only that he 'wrote compendiously' on the *Posterior Analytics*. It was quite common for an author to spread his commentary on a work over several years and possibly that is what Grosseteste did with this one.[1] In any case the commentary on the *Posterior Analytics* was written certainly before the commentary on the *Physics*, in which it is mentioned,[2] and almost certainly before *De Lineis* and *De Iride*.[3] Other points in favour of an early date of composition are the frequent citations from Euclid's *Elements*[4] and the absence of reference to Averroës.[5]

The shorter works on optics and astronomy, and the commentary on the *Physics*, Grosseteste most probably composed between 1215 and 1235.[6] Thomson regards *De Luce seu de Inchoatione Formarum* and *De Motu Corporali et Luce*, in which Grosseteste expounded his 'light metaphysics', as early works, being written perhaps between 1215 and 1220. *De Luce* seems to be the object of a reference in the commentary on the *Physics* where, during a discussion of a point about infinity which is discussed in detail in *De Luce*, the statements

Hunt for permission to read his dissertation. Some of the subjects discussed by Grosseteste (below, pp. 65–67) are found only in the *De Animal.* and are not mentioned in other possible sources, viz. Pliny's *Natural History*, Avicenna's *Canon Medicinae*, Alfred of Sareshel's *De Motu Cordis* and *De Plantis*, or in the translations of *De Anima* and *Parva Naturalis*.

[1] Grosseteste's tentative remarks about the Divine Ideas (below, p. 128, n.3) suggests that he wrote this part of his commentary late enough to have heard of this theory but before it had become fully mastered in the West. The problem of the date of the commentary will be solved only when a thorough examination has been made of all the manuscript evidence.

[2] In a discussion of definition in his *Comm. Phys.* Grosseteste referred to a fuller discussion of the subject in 'conclusion xi' of his *Comm. Post.*; see below, p. 55, n. 3.

[3] See below, pp. 50–51. Cf. also, below, pp. 112, n. 6.

[4] Cf. below, pp. 95, 113. Other works mentioned in *Comm. Post.* include Aristotle's *Prior Anal.* (below, p. 56, n. 1, p. 84, n. 4), *Topics* (below, p. 54), *Phys.* (*Comm. Post.* i. 10, f. 9rb; 17, f. 19^r; ii. 3, f. 27rb; below, p. 58, n. 3, p. 71), *De Anima* (*Comm. Post.* i. 19, f. 20^v–21^r) and *Metaph.* In *Comm. Post.* ii. 2, f. 24rb Grosseteste said: 'et dico, quod esse demonstratur de quomodolibet nisi sit substantia, quia de substantia prima que per se est, et quo est sua essentia, non scitur per causam quia ipsa est. Et hoc intellegit Aristoteles hic per demonstrare, scilicet, per causam scire. Demonstratur tamen in metaphysicam per effectum de causa prima quia ipsa est.' This may refer to E. 1, Λ. 6–7 or Z. 1, which were first translated shortly before 1210 (Lacombe, *Aristoteles Latinus*, p. 62); see below, p. 63, n. 5. In *Comm. Post.* Grosseteste cited also Euclid's *Catoptrics* and Ptolemy's *Almagest*; see below, pp. 95, 129. Cf. Wingate, *Mediaeval Latin Versions*, pp. 71, 77–78.

[5] Below, p. 48, n. 4.

[6] See Thomson, *Writings of Rob. Grosseteste*, pp. 82–120. But the *Compotus Minor* shows that as late as 1244, the year of its composition, Grosseteste could still undertake scientific work (Thomson, p. 97). See also below, p. 50, n. 3.

are made: 'sicut alibi diximus' and 'hoc alibi probatum est'.[1] *De Motu Corporali* seems to be the object of a reference in *De Lineis, Angulis et Figuris seu de Fractionibus et Reflexionibus Radiorum*, where other, presumably earlier, works are cited 'quae pertinent ad totum universum et partes eius absolute' and 'aliis, quae motum rectum et circularem sequuntur'; these Baur[2] held to be *De Sphaera, De Motu Corporali et Luce* and *De Motu Supercaelestium*. The problem whether Grosseteste's *De Sphaera* was written before or after Sacrobosco's *De Sphaera* is a subject of controversy to which there seems to be no definite answer, but it seems probable that both works were written between 1215 and 1230 and perhaps about 1220.[3] The absence of reference to Averroës, the Latin translation of whose commentaries began to come into circulation about 1230,[4] agrees with the supposition that *De Sphaera* was written before that date. Thomson has suggested that *De Universitatis Machina* was perhaps an early draft for *De Sphaera*.[5] For the *Compotus Correctorius*, which is presumably the work which Trivet[6] coupled with *De Sphaera*, Thomson suggests the date 1215-29.[7] It was written explicitly to correct the *Kalendarium* and an earlier *Compotus*,[8] and in a later *Compotus Minor* written in 1244 Grosseteste once more brought his calculations up to date.[9] *De Motu Supercaelestium* contains a possible reference to Averroës,[10] and may therefore be later than 1230. A reference in *De Generatione Stellarum* to 'Aristoteles in XVIII de animalibus'[11] would place his work after 1217-20, and the absence of reference to Averroës perhaps places it before 1230. To *De Cometis et Causis Ipsarum* a more precise date can perhaps be given from Grosseteste's reference in it to a comet 'que nuper apparuit', which

---

[1] See below, p. 100, n. 3; cf. *De Luce*, Baur, 1912, pp. 52-54; below, p. 108.

[2] Baur, 1912, pp. 79*, 60.

[3] Ibid., p. 64*; Thomson, op. cit., pp. 115, 119; L. Thorndike, *The Sphere of Sacrobosco*, pp. 10-15. Cf. Sarton, *Introduction*, ii. 584.

[4] Baur, 1912, pp. 10 sqq.; R. de Vaux, 'La Première Entrée d'Averroès chez les Latins', *RSPT*, xxii (1933) 193 sqq.; Callus, *PBA*, xxix (1943) 264.

[5] Thomson, op. cit., pp. 118-19. Cf. Thorndike, op. cit., pp. 64-66.

[6] See above, p. 46, n. 1.

[7] Thomson, op. cit., p. 96. This date agrees with the absence of reference to Averroës, though other Arab writers on astronomy are mentioned. Cf. *Compotus Fratris Rogeri*, ed. Steele (*Opera Hactenus Inedita*, vi) p. xxi.

[8] *Compotus . . . Roberti Grosse Capitis*, ed. Steele, op. cit., pp. 212, 214 *et passim*.

[9] Thomson, op. cit., pp. 94-97, 106.

[10] Baur, 1912, p. 94. Grosseteste refers in this work also to 'Aristoteles in XII Metaphysicae' (pp. 94, 100).

[11] Baur, 1912, p. 32.

may have referred to Halley's comet which would have been due in 1222.[1]

The commentary on the *Physics* would appear to have been written during the latter part of Grosseteste's scholastic career at Oxford. The text of the *Physics* which he used was the current Latin translation from the Greek,[2] and the commentary itself, in contrast with that on the *Posterior Analytics* which was full and systematic, was simply a series of marginal glosses on points that interested him.[3] The use of Averroës[4] would place this commentary after about 1230; and the last year in which Grosseteste could have composed it at Oxford, as it seems probable that he did, was 1235. Callus suggests that Grosseteste may have gone on writing it for several years, and the date 1230–5[5] would be consistent with its contents and with the parallels with the *Hexaëmeron*.[6] The quotations from Averroës in the *Summa in VIII Libros Physicorum Aristotelis*[7] would place this work also after about 1230.

De Lineis seems to belong to the period *c.* 1230–5, together with *De Natura Locorum* and other optical works with which it seems to be organically connected. In *De Lineis* there is a reference to 'Commentator super tractatum de sono'[8] and in *De Natura Locorum* there is a reference to 'Commentator . . . super secundum Caeli et Mundi'.[9] The subjects under consideration are discussed, respectively, in

---

[1] Thomson, *Isis,* xix (1933) 19 sqq. Cf. E. Franceschini, 'Intorno ad alcune opere di Roberto Grossatesta, *Aevum*, viii (1934) 529–33; H. C. Plummer, *Nature*, cl (1942) 249 sqq.

[2] This version began: 'Quoniam quidem intelligere et scire . . . opinamur' (Lacombe, *Aristoteles Latinus*, p. 51). It was translated from the Greek about 1170.

[3] Cf. Callus, *Oxoniensia*, x (1945) 46–47.

[4] *Comm. Phys.*, MS Digby 220, ff. 104ᵛ sqq.; Merton 295, ff. 144ʳ sqq.; cf. Baur, 1912, pp. 102 sqq.

[5] Callus, *Oxoniensia*, x (1945) 47.

[6] *Idem*, p. 59, places the *Hexaëmeron*, which is a systematic commentary on the six days of creation and deals extensively with cosmological subjects, during the last years of Grosseteste's scholastic career at Oxford or the first of his episcopate; cf. G. B. Phelan, 'An unedited text of Robert Grosseteste', in *Hommage à M. de Wulf*, Louvain, 1934; J. T. Muckle, 'The Hexameron of Robert Grosseteste', *MS*, vi (1944) 151 sqq., 'Robert Grosseteste's use of Greek sources in his Hexameron', *MH*, iii (1945) 33 sqq. Grosseteste's habit of using his scientific knowledge when expounding theological works is shown also in his commentaries on the psalms, in which he quoted Aristotle's *De Animal.* and the pseudo-Aristotelian *De Veget.* and often dwelt on points of natural history. See Callus, op. cit., pp. 67, 71.

[7] Venetiis, 1500, f. 1ᵛ. Cf. Thomson, *Writings of Rob. Grosseteste*, p. 83.

[8] Baur, 1912, pp. 62–63.

[9] Ibid., p. 69. A. Birkenmajer, in *Pologne au viᵉ congrès internat. sciences hist.* p. 14, said that Averroës's commentary on *De Caelo* was first cited by William of Auvergne in *De Universo*.

Averroës's commentaries on *De Anima* and *De Caelo*,[1] and if, as seems probable, it was he who was meant by 'Commentator', then these treatises must have been written after about 1230. This conclusion is supported by the mention in *De Natura Locorum* of 'Avicennam quarto de animalibus'[2], that is Michael Scot's translation of *Avicenne Abbreviatio de Animalibus*, which was made between 1220 and 1232 and probably nearer the latter date.[3]

The organic connexion between *De Natura Locorum* and *De Lineis* is indicated both by their contents and by the manuscript evidence;[4] possibly they originally formed a single work. The contents of the two treatises show quite plainly that *De Natura Locorum* was composed after *De Lineis*. The former work is prefaced by what seems to be a summary of a much fuller discussion in *De Lineis* of the power of geometry in understanding natural operations through 'lines, angles and figures'.[5] Later on reference is made to other matters discussed in *De Lineis*, for example, to the theory that 'linea recta brevior magis facit ad actionem',[6] to the classification of different kinds of rays and the variation in their power,[7] and to two rules concerning refraction by which Grosseteste argues 'per regulam unam' and 'per secundam regulam'. These rules he attempted to establish in *De Lineis*.[8]

---

[1] Aristotelis *De Anima cum* Averrois *Commentariis*, ii. 4, Venetiis, 1551, vi, f. 143^r (*De Anima*, ii. 8, 420^{a}1); *De Caelo cum* Averrois *Commentariis*, ii. iii. 1, Venetiis, 1550, iv, f. 59 (*De Caelo*, ii. 7, 289^{a}34). It is plain from the context that Grosseteste was not referring to Avicenna's *De Anima* or *De Caelo et Mundo* (Avicenne *Opera*, Venetiis, 1508). In another passage, however, after Grosseteste had referred to 'Aristoteles dicit secundo de vegetabilibus', the phrase 'Commentator dicit ibidem' may have referred to Alfred of Sareshel; Baur, 1912, p. 68. Cf. Roger Bacon, *Opus Maius*, iv. iv. 3, ed. Bridges, i. 133; Wingate, *Mediaeval Latin Versions*, p. 71.

[2] Baur, 1912, p. 66.

[3] Wingate, *Mediaeval Latin Versions*, pp. 84–85; Haskins, *Mediaeval Science*, pp. 273–9; Lacombe, *Aristoteles Latinus*, pp. 80–81. In *De Impressionibus Aëris seu de Prognosticatione* Grosseteste gave an account of a theory of tides which he discussed also in *De Nat. Loc.* (see below, p. 112, n. 7). *De Prognost.* appears to have been written in 1249 for, as Thorndike (*Sphere of Sacrobosco*, p. 14) has pointed out, it contains a reference in the present tense to 15 April in that year, and references in the future tense to July of 1249 and also of 1255 (Baur, 1912, pp. 49–50). Cf. Thomson, *Writings of Rob. Grosseteste*, p. 103.

[4] *De Nat. Loc.* follows immediately after *De Lineis* in all seven of the pre-sixteenth-century MSS in which both occur; see Thomson, *Writings of Rob. Grosseteste*, pp. 108, 110; Baur, 1912, pp. 78*–83*.

[5] Baur, 1912, pp. 59–60, 65–66; see below, p. 110.

[6] Ibid., pp. 61, 66; see below, p. 86.

[7] Ibid., pp. 67, 69; see below, pp. 112, 120.

[8] Ibid., pp. 63, 71; see below, pp. 121, 122.

De Iride seu de Iride et Speculo[1] seems also to be connected in some way with *De Lineis*, for it seems to presuppose conclusions already discussed in that work. The law of reflection is referred to as known in *De Iride*,[2] whereas a fairly full demonstration of it is attempted in *De Lineis*.[3] Knowledge of the phenomenon of refraction is also presupposed in *De Iride*, in which attention is confined to an attempt to demonstrate the quantitative law;[4] refraction is discussed at length in *De Lineis*.[5] This seems to suggest that *De Iride* also belongs to the period *c.* 1230–5[6] along with *De Lineis* and *De Natura Locorum*. These three works, with *De Colore*, comprise the body of Grosseteste's contribution to optics. *De Colore* contains a reference to Averroës[7] so that this treatise also probably belongs to the last years of Grosseteste's scholastic career at Oxford and, as it resumes a discussion on the nature of colours which forms the last part of *De Iride*, it may have been a continuation of this work.[8]

Another piece of evidence supports the conclusions already reached about the probable order in which Grosseteste composed his works. There are several points of similarity between the optical treatises and the commentary on the *Posterior Analytics*, in which many optical examples are given.[9] One of the most important methodological ideas occurring in both is that mathematical science can often provide the reason (*propter quid*) for factual knowledge acquired in physical science. This idea is mentioned in *De Lineis*[10] and in *De Iride*[11] as if it were already familiar, and in fact it came from

---

[1] G. Hellmann, 'Zur Optik des Robertus Linconiensis', *BM*, ii (1901) 443–4, suggested that this work, together with *De Luce* and *De Colore*, originally formed one large work on optics, but it seems very unlikely that this was the case; see Baur, 1912, p. 79*, n. 3; Thomson, op. cit., p. 107.

[2] Baur, 1912, pp. 74–75; see below, p. 123.

[3] Ibid., p. 62; see below, p. 119.

[4] Ibid., pp. 74–75; see below, p. 123.

[5] Ibid., p. 63; see below, pp. 120–2.

[6] A reference in *De Iride* to 'Aristoteles . . . in libro de animalibus' (Baur, 1912, p. 73) would place it at least later than 1217–20; cf. below, p. 114, n. 1.

[7] Ibid., p. 78. Therefore it cannot be 'shortly before 1220', as Thomson (*Writings of Rob. Grosseteste*, p. 93) suggests.

[8] For the MSS of these two works see ibid., p. 106.

[9] Cf. *Comm. Post.* i. 8, f. 8ʳ (see below, pp. 95 sqq.) with Baur, 1912, pp. 60–61, 62, 74–75 (see below, pp. 86, 119, 123); and *Comm. Post.* ii. 4, f. 29ᵛ (see below, pp. 113–15) with Baur, 1912, pp. 51–52, 63, 75–77 (see below, pp. 106 sqq., 120, 125 sqq.). Also see below, p. 112, n. 6.

[10] Baur, 1912, pp. 59–60; see below, p. 110.

[11] Ibid., p. 72; see below, p. 117.

Aristotle's *Posterior Analytics*. In his commentary[1] on this work Grosseteste discussed it at length and illustrated it with optical examples, whereas in the optical treatises he took it for granted. This supports the idea that Grosseteste developed his methodological ideas first and later put them into practice in the examination of particular physical problems.

(2)

The conception of science which Grosseteste, like his twelfth-century philosophical predecessors, learnt from Aristotle[2] was one in which there was a double movement, from theory to experience and from experience to theory. When discussing the opening statement of the *Posterior Analytics*, in which Aristotle said that all instruction by way of argument proceeded from already existing knowledge, which might be used as the start for either syllogistic or inductive reasoning according to what it was, Grosseteste said: 'There is a double way with already existing knowledge and knowledge, namely, from the more simple to the composite, and the reverse', from principles and from the effect.[3] Scientific knowledge of a fact was had, he held, when it was possible to deduce the fact from prior and better known principles which were its cause.[4] This meant, in effect, relating the fact to other facts in a deductive system.[5] Such knowledge he found exemplified in Euclid's *Elements*.[6]

Scientific knowledge, properly speaking, was thus demonstrative knowledge of things through their causes, and its instrument was the

---

[1] Cf. *Comm. Post.* i. 2, f. 3ʳ, 12, f. 11ʳᵇ ᵛ, f. 11ᵛᵇ–12ʳ, 8, f. 8ʳ, ii. 4, f. 29ᵛ; see below, respectively, pp. 53, 91 sqq., 95 sqq., 113 sqq.

[2] Above, pp. 25–26.

[3] 'Est autem precognitionis et cognitionis duplex via, scilicet, a simplicioribus in composita vel e converso. . . . Utraque enim per prius nota faciunt doctrinam. Dividitur etiam precognitio in duas partes per ea que precognoscuntur de precognitis que, scilicet, sunt duo, scilicet, esse de principiis et quid est quod dicitur de passione.' (*Comm. Post.* i. 1, f. 2ʳᵇ.) The more simple meant universals or principles and the composite meant physical objects; see below, p. 55.

[4] 'Demonstratio est syllogismus faciens scire. . . . Demonstrativa scientia est ex veris primis et immediatis prioribus et notioribus et causis conclusionis. . . . Scientia autem premissarum est efficiens sicut origo scientie conclusionis, scientia enim premissarum in anima videtur generare scientiam conclusionis.' *Comm. Post.* i. 2, f. 3ʳ.

[5] Above, pp. 3 sqq.

[6] See Heath, *Euclid's Elements*, pp. 129, 146. Euclid begins with a statement 'De principiis per se notis' and of postulates ('Petitiones sunt quinque') and axioms ('Communes animi conceptiones sunt hee'): *Liber Elementorum* Euclidis, i, Venetiis, 1482, f. 2. This is Adelard of Bath's translation revised by Campanus of Novara. For Adelard's version unrevised see Euclidis *Elementa*, Brit. Mus. MS Roy. 15. A. xxvii, 12 c.

demonstrative syllogism, which established the connexion between premisses and conclusion, or causes and their effects, through the middle term. By this means effects were shown to follow from their causes, as conclusions from premisses. This led to an examination of the distinction between knowledge of a fact (the 'that', *quia*) and knowledge of the reason for the fact, its cause (the 'wherefore', *propter quid*).[1] Grosseteste said he would call 'syllogism *quia*[2] everything which shows through the effect, and syllogism *propter quid* everything which shows through the cause'.[3] He went on:

> Science acquired by demonstration is acquired through a cause of the thing known, which may be either a proximate cause or a non-proximate cause. What is acquired through the proximate cause is called science *propter quid* and this is most appropriately called science, and demonstration by which this science is acquired is most properly called demonstration. But that which is acquired through any cause but the proximate is said to be science since it is said to be science *per posterius*, and the demonstration by which this is acquired is *per posterius* demonstration. But science *propter quid* and science *quia* acquired of the same subject differ in two different ways, for science *quia* is acquired either not through a cause or through a non-proximate cause.[4]

The object of Grosseteste's science, which, like Aristotle's, was a search for reality and truth, was thus to discover and define the 'form' or universal or 'nature', in the sense of principle (*principium*), ἀρχή, origin, cause of behaviour and source of understanding, which could become the start of demonstration. Definition was necessary

[1] See above, pp. 25-26. For Arab discussions of this subject see C. von Prantl, *Gesch. der Logik*, ii. 317 (Alfarabi), 372 (Algazali), 359 (Avicenna), 385 (Averroës); and on Grosseteste, ibid., 1867, iii. 89.

[2] Cf. below, n. 4.

[3] 'dicatur syllogismus quia omnis qui ostendit per effectum et syllogismus propter quid omnis qui ostendit per causam.' *Comm. Post.* i. 6, f. 6ᵛ.

[4] This was a gloss on the text (Aristotle, 78ᵃ22): 'Sed quia differt et propter quid scire.' (*Comm. Post.* i. 12, f. 11ʳᵇ ᵛ.) The two forms of *scientia quia* here distinguished refer to *Post Anal.* i. 13, where Aristotle is contrasting scientific knowledge of the 'reason for the fact' (τὸ διότι) with scientific knowledge of the 'fact' (τὸ ὅτι). The first form is illustrated by the proof: What does not twinkle is near, planets do not twinkle, therefore they are near. 'This syllogism, then, proves not the reason for the fact but only the fact; since they are not near because they do not twinkle, but, because they are near, do not twinkle' (78ᵃ37-38). This can be rearranged to follow the causal order of demonstration *propter quid* by making the cause, 'nearness', the middle term: The planets are near, hence they do not twinkle. The other form of *scientia quia* is demonstration in which the middle term is more general than major or minor and does not exhibit the proximate cause. Aristotle's illustration is: What can breathe is an animal, no wall is an animal, therefore no wall can breathe. Grosseteste used both these illustrations.

before demonstration could begin because all effects were considered as attributes of some substance, and the cause of an effect was shown when the effect could be predicated as an attribute of a defined substance.

Aristotle's intention here being to complete the method (*artem*) by which all uncertainties become known, he must show us the method by which we may know what the nature of a thing is, that is, the method of defining, discovering and stabilizing the definitions of definable things. And this method is very different from that discussed in the Topics and in the Method of Definition (*in methodo diffinitiva*),[1] as will be plain enough from what follows. . . . . All demonstration is through a middle term which is the definition. Therefore, in order to have actual demonstration, it is necessary actually to have the definition of the thing under examination, which, if this definition were unknown, would be discovered only by the *method* of definition; so that for the method of demonstration to be complete the method of definition must be added as part of it. Therefore, since the things known are four like the questions,[2] and as in an investigation we do not stop until we understand what the nature of a thing is (*quid est*) or why it is (*propter quid est*) (but what the nature of a thing is and the reason why it is, are the same), we must know where we should stop in an investigation. Where we stop is at the middle term considered not only as the definition itself, but in the causal reasons according to which it is ordered to the caused thing being investigated. . . .[3] After he has explained the demonstrative method Aristotle teaches us at the end of this book how to put it into practice, because he shows us how from many sensibles (*ex multis sensibilibus*) are acquired memories and from memories empirical knowledge (*experimenta*) and from empirical knowledge a universal which is a principle of science, and with this discovery of principles begins the work of demonstration. These having been discovered through the science and method discussed in this book, we are now in a position to examine and complete the special demonstrative sciences.[4]

[1] This and another reference a few lines down to 'hic libro de diffinitione' may refer to a work by Isaac Israeli; cf. J. T. Muckle, 'Isaac Israeli *Liber de Definicionibus*', *AHDLMA*, xi (1938) 299 sqq. For an analysis of the treatment of definition in the *Topics* see Ross, *Aristotle*, pp. 56–59.

[2] Aristotle had said: 'The kinds of question we ask are as many as the kinds of things which we know. They are in fact four: (1) Whether the connexion of an attribute with a thing is a fact, (2) What is the reason for the connexion, (3) Whether a thing exists, (4) What is the nature of the thing.' *Post. Anal.* ii. 1, 89ᵇ21–25.

[3] Cf. Albertus Magnus's 'duplex resolutio, resolutio scilicet rei conclusae in principia et causas per quas concluditur, et syllogismi collecti iam et constituti in principia formalia'. *Priorum Anal.* i. i. 1 (*Opera*, ed. Petrus Jammy, i) 290a. See Régis, in *Studia Mediaevalia R. J. Martin*, pp. 311–12; above, p. 28; below, p. 193.

[4] *Comm. Post.* ii. 1, f. 21ʳ.

As the end of this quotation shows, Grosseteste held that in order to reach the definition of the form, human beings must begin with sensory experience, that is, with already existing knowledge derived from effects. What was prior and more intelligible in the order of nature was not prior in the order of knowing, and to reach the universals prior in the order of nature human beings must pass upwards from the particulars of sense which were prior for man.[1] Aristotle had said, '. . . it is the whole object that is best known to sense-perception'.[2] So, as Grosseteste put it in his *Commentarius in VIII Libros Physicorum Aristotelis*:

The natural way for us to arrive at knowledge of principles is to go from . . . whole objects which follow from the principles, to the principles themselves. . . . The way of knowledge is . . . from confusedly known whole complete objects . . . into the parts by which it is possible to define the whole object itself, and from the definition to return to determinate knowledge of the whole object. . . . (For a further discussion of this see the same book of the *Posterior Analytics*, conclusion xi.)

He added:

Every thing which is to be produced is already described and formed in some way in the agent, whence the 'nature' as an agent has the natural things which are to be produced in some way described and formed within itself, so that this description and form itself . . . is called knowledge of this 'nature'. . . .[3]

---

[1] See above, pp. 25–26. The Latin translation of Aristotle, 72ª1–4, occurs in *Comm. Post.* i. 2, f. 2vb–3^r.

[2] 'Totum enim secundum sensus notius est', Latin version of Aristotle's *Phys.* i, 1. 184ª25, in *Expositio* Sancti Thome *super Libros Physicorum*, i. 1, Venetiis, 1500. Cf. above, p. 26.

[3] The whole passage runs as follows: 'Cum scire et intelligere adquirantur ex principiis, ut sciantur et intelligantur naturalia primo determinanda sunt universalium principia. Via autem innata nobis ad perveniendum in principiorum cognitionem est ex intentionibus universalibus ad ipsa principia et ex totis que constant ex ipsis principiis. In notitiam namque prime materie et prime forme pervenitur ex hiis universalibus intentionibus materia et forma que sunt communes ad omnem materiam et omnem formam, et iterum ad notitiam passionum materie et forme pervenitur ex intentione huius nominis mobile. Primo namque accipitur intentio huius nominis confuse, accipitur enim solummodo primo quid est quod dicitur per vocabulum. Deinde per divisionem pervenitur in partes integrantes ipsam, materiam scilicet et formam, et ex earum notitia acquisita reditur ad perfectam notitiam mobilis ex suis principiis. Per divisionem universalium in species et totorum que constant ex principiis in partes pervenitur in ipsa principia. Universalia namque notiora sunt intellectui, et tota accepta secundum quid est quod dicitur per vocabulum notiora sunt ipsis principiis, licet totorum cognitio perfecta posterior sit cognitione principiorum. Sicut ergo generaliter est via cognitionis ex totis universalibus confusis in species magis determinatas, etiam ex totis integralibus acceptis confuse (intentione solum dicente quid significatur per vocabulum) in partes ipsas per quas diffinire potest ipsum totum et diffinitione redire in determinatam cognitionem totius. Sic est in

This progress of inductive knowledge from the objects of sensory experience to the principles that were their causes, that is, from effects to causes, which in any investigation must precede the opposite process of demonstration from causes to effects, was very clearly expounded by the early fourteenth-century writer, Walter Burley, in his commentary on this passage of Grosseteste:

To discover the causes of natural things it is necessary to proceed from confusedly known effects, as for example from composite substances, to knowledge of principles and causes. . . . To discover the principles, causes and elements of natural things it is necessary to proceed from knowledge of the whole things produced by the principles. And this . . . is to proceed from what is more knowable to us and less knowable in the order of nature, to what is less knowable to us and more knowable in nature, but confused; that is, the whole things produced by the principles themselves are more knowable to us than the principles themselves and less knowable in nature. . . . Discovery (*Inveniens*) is the method by which we reach knowledge of principles from knowledge of whole things; because, by the division of the composite whole produced by the principles according to the principles themselves, we reach knowledge of the principles. . . . But . . . it is to be noted according to Averroës[1] that . . . in mathematics the same things are

hac scientia specialiter via ad cognoscendum principia ex universalibus ad ipsa principia et ex totis que constant ex principiis confuse accepti. (De hoc quere plus ab eodem libro posteriorum conclusionem xi). Omne agens aliquo modo habet in se descriptum et formatum opus operandum, unde natura agens habet per modum aliquem descripta et formata in se naturalia fienda, ipsa ergo descriptio et formatio in ipsa natura fiendarum rerum antequam fiant notitia nature dicitur. Perfecta autem opera nature in ipsa natura descriptionem habent expressiorem forme quam partes perfectorum, et ideo perfecta sunt notiora nature, id est in ipsa natura expressius descripta. Partes tamen sunt descripte in ipsa natura propinquius ipsi nature et sic sunt notiores nature, id est in ipsa natura propinquius descripte, utpote in motu manus scribentis est figura littere scribende et expressior est in ipso motu manus tota litere figuratio quam partiales figurationes. Proprie tamen partiales figurationes motui ipsi sunt propinquiores. Ratio huius est quod sensus comprehendit confuse.' (MS Digby 220, f. 84ʳ; Merton 295, f. 120ʳ.) The reference to 'lib. posteriorum' is to Grosseteste's *Comm. Post.* ii. 2, f. 23ᵛ, where he discussed the 'methodus diffinitiva'. See below, p. 63, n. 5.

[1] Averroës said 'sunt modi omnium doctrinarum trium generum demonstrationum' (*Interpretis* Averrois *in Libros Physicorum*, Prooemium, Venetiis, 1550, iv, f. 3ʳ). He made a threefold distinction between demonstration *of sign* or *of being (quod est)*, in which we start from effects to arrive 'per viam inducentem' at causes, proceeding 'de propositionibus acceptis ex rebus posterioribus in esse que sunt notiores et manifestiores apud nos, ad conclusiones priores in esse que sunt notiores et manifestiores apud naturam et latentiores apud nos' (i. 1, f. 4ᵛ); demonstration *propter quid* or *of cause* in which we proceed from what is first in nature but not first for us; and demonstration *simpliciter* or *of cause and being* in which, as in mathematics, the causes are first both for us and in the order of nature; below, pp. 59–60 (cf. Randall, *JHI*, i., 1940, pp. 187–8). He discussed the same points in his *Posteriorum Resolutoriorum Magna Commentaria*, i. 2, Venetiis, 1550, i, ff. 130ᵛ–131ᵛ and *De Coelo cum Averrois Commentariis*, ii. ii, Q. 5, Comm. 35, v,

more knowable to us and in nature, whence in mathematics the definitions and demonstrative causes are more knowable both in nature and to us. . . . But in natural science, to acquire knowledge of the causes of natural things, it is necessary to proceed from what is more knowable to us and less knowable in nature, to what is more knowable in nature and less knowable to us, and the same applies to divine science, that is metaphysics, because there it is necessary to go from effects to the cause and from the posterior to the prior. . . . But in natural science the procedure is not always from the less knowable to the more knowable in nature, but only in the first process, when knowledge of the causes of natural things is being sought; in the second process, where the argument goes from knowledge of the causes to knowledge of the effects, it goes from the more knowable to the less knowable in nature. For this reason . . . Averroës said that there is a double process in natural science: one is from effect to cause, the other from cause to effect; the first goes from the less knowable to the more knowable in nature, and the second is the converse of this; and this is what Grosseteste (*Linconiensis*) means here.[1]

Grosseteste accepted Aristotle's psychological account of how universals were abstracted from many experiences of singulars and grasped by the *virtus intellectiva* or νοῦς, though he held that in this act the mind was assisted by Divine illumination.[2] These universals or forms, in themselves and as causes, he held to be principles of being and as such to exist *in re* in particular things, where they were that 'through which particular things are what they are'.[3] As known and as the start for demonstration he held that forms were principles of knowing existing *post rem* in the mind after being abstracted from particular things. The human intellect thus produced principles which were 'principles of knowing conclusions when it orders them to conclusions. But in themselves and apart from anything we do with them they are principles of being.'[4]

f. 56[r]. Grosseteste referred to Averroës's commentary on the *Physics* in his own *Commentarius* (MS Digby 220, f. 104[v]) but he evidently did not know Averroës when he wrote his *Comm. Post.* Aristotle had discussed demonstration from signs, from effects to causes, in his *Prior Anal.* ii. 27, 70[a]3 sqq. Grosseteste referred to this work in *Comm. Post.* i. 2, f. 2vb, i. 17, f. 18[r], and ii. 2, f. 23[r].

[1] Gualteri Burlei *In Physicam Expos. et Quaest.* i, Text. com. 2, Venetiis, 1501, f. 6[v].

[2] 'Virtus intellectiva est id secundum quod aliquid est principium primum et sine medio acceptum. Quia ut superius dictum est lux spiritualis per se visibilis a mentis aspectu est hec natura.' *Comm. Post.* ii. 6, f. 31[vb]. Cf. below, p. 71; Aristotle, *Post. Anal.* ii. 19, 99[b]15 sqq.; below, p. 130.

[3] Below, p. 128, n. 3.

[4] 'Non est autem certior habitus quam scientia nisi intellectus, erit igitur intellectus principium scientie et principium principiatis et principium acceptivum principiatorum. Non est enim intellectus effectivus principiorum nisi forte dicatur quod efficit ea que

The nature of things themselves, Grosseteste held, introduced a hierarchy of degrees of certainty with which these *principia essendi* might be known, that is become *principia cognoscendi* in the human mind. The nature of things, as subjects of knowledge, led to the differentiation of the sciences of physics, mathematics, and metaphysics.

The form [he said] is threefold. One is that which in terms of being and for purposes of study (*secundum esse et considerationem*) is in matter, and is that which the natural philosopher studies. The second is that which the mathematician studies, which is abstracted from motion and from matter, not in terms of being but for the purposes of study. . . . The third is that which the metaphysician studies, which is abstracted from matter and motion both in terms of being and for purposes of study, of which kind are the intelligences and other separate substances, for example God and the soul and suchlike.[1]

As to the possibility of knowing these three kinds of form, he said:

The grasping of certainty is dependent not only on the nature of the demonstration, but also on that of the things on which the demonstration is erected.[2] Science generally speaking is the comprehension of truth, and erratic contingent happenings (*contingentia erratica*) are known in this way. Science properly so called is the comprehension of the truth of those things which always or very frequently behave in one given manner (*semper vel frequentius uno modo se habent*), and in this way some contingent natural things are known, of which there can be demonstrative knowledge generally speaking.[3] But what is more appropriately called science is the

sunt principia esse principia cognoscendi conclusiones cum ordinat ea ad conclusiones. In se autem sine nostra ordinatione sunt principia essendi.' *Comm. Post.* ii. 6, f. 31vb.

[1] *Summa* Linconiensis *Physicorum*, f. 1^v.

[2] *Comm. Post.* ii. 6, f. 31vb. Demonstrative science as understood by the Greeks was necessarily drawn from universal and necessary premisses, and therefore could not refer to corruptible things (cf. Aristotle, *Post. Anal.* i. 8, 75^{b}20 sqq.). How then could there be a true science of natural things? Aristotle said because at any time there were always examples of such things, e.g. snow, somewhere, and Plato because they existed in eternal examplars (cf. Duhem, *Syst. monde*, v. 345 sqq.). Grosseteste said the eternal exemplars existed in the Divine Mind (see below, pp. 128 sqq.).

[3] From this it followed that 'chance and luck' were not subjects for science. In his *Comm. Phys.* Grosseteste, following Aristotle, said: 'Quia physici est causas physicorum cognoscere, casus autem et fortuna multorum physicorum videntur esse cause, ideo de hiis considerat. . . . Hec autem diffinitio casualium, scilicet casualia esse que nec semper nec frequenter uno modo accidunt, est diffinitio exponens nomen solum et diffinitio nota [per se] non demonstrabilis, et supponitur quod hec sit intentio nominis, sive sint casualia sive non. Quod autem talia sint que nec semper nec frequenter uno modo accidunt docet sensus et experientia et est propositio et principium experimentale sensibile. . . . Fortuna est cum accidentaliter evenit aliquid et preter intentionem nec sepe nec semper ex concursu causarum per se et preter intentionem agentium.' (MS Digby 220, f. 89^v; Merton 295, f. 125rb.) Grosseteste discussed the same point in *Comm. Post.* i. 18, f. 19^r, concluding: 'Dicit ergo quod re que est a casu non est scientia demonstrativa, et

comprehension of the truth of those things which always behave in one given manner, and in mathematics both the premisses and the conclusions are known in this way. But since the truth is that which is, and the comprehension of truth is the comprehension of that which is, the being of that which depends on something is known only through that on which it depends. It is clear that what is most appropriately called knowing is to understand that which immutably is, through understanding that from which it has its immutable being, and that is through understanding the immutable cause in being and in causing. Therefore to know simply and most appropriately is to understand the unchanging cause of a thing in itself, and unchanging in causation . . . and this knowledge is the most special goal of this [metaphysical] science and is acquired by demonstration most properly so called.[1]

Of the three divisions of science corresponding to these different subjects of knowledge, Grosseteste said that physics was uncertain because there could be only probable knowledge of changeable natural things, and that purely human knowledge of metaphysics was uncertain because of the remoteness from sense and the subtlety of the eternal forms;[2] in metaphysics there was no certainty apart from Divine illumination.[3] Mathematics was the only certain science for the unaided human intellect.[4] In mathematics he held that complete certainty was possible because the premisses of mathematical

quia res que est a casu nec est necessaria sicut res divine et mathematice, que semper sunt uno modo, neque est frequenter eveniens sicut naturales. Sed res casualis est extra necessitatem simpliciter et extra necessitatem naturalem, que non est necessitas simpliciter sed cum circumscriptione impedimenti. Hec . . . manifesta est in phisica Aristotelis.' This is a gloss on Aristotle's *Post.Anal.* i. 30, 87^b19-27. Cf. D. M. Balme, 'Greek science and mechanism. I. Aristotle on nature and chance', *Classical Quart.* xxxiii (1939) 129 sqq.; 'II. The atomists', ibid. xxxv (1941) 23 sqq.

[1] *Comm. Post.* i. 2, f. 2vb.

[2] 'Ea vero que sunt in logicis et in metaphisica propter remotionem eorum a sensu et subtilitatem nature sue subterfugiunt intellectum et speculantur velut a longe et non discernuntur eorum subtiles differentie. Et hic speculatio velut longinqua et indiscretio parvarum differentiarum causa est frequentis deceptionis in illis. Similiter in naturalibus est minor certitudo propter mutabilitatem rerum naturalium. Et has tres, scilicet, logicam, metaphisicam, et naturalem vocat Aristoteles rationales, quia propter parvitatem certitudinis illarum comprehensionis quodammodo versatur in his rationaliter magis et probabiliter quam scientifice, licet in his sit scientia et demonstratio sed non maxime dicta. In solis enim mathematicis est scientia et demonstratio maxime et particulariter dicta.' *Comm. Post.* i. 11, f. 10^v. Cf. ibid. i. 6, f. 6rb; *De Artibus Liberalibus*, Baur, 1912, p. 1. [3] See below, pp. 128 sqq.

[4] On the knowledge of Plato, particularly of the *Timaeus*, in the Middle Ages see C. Baeumker, 'Der Platonismus im Mittelalter', in *Studien und Charakteristiken zur Geschichte der Philosophie*, pp. 139 sqq.; R. Klibansky, *Continuity of the Platonic Tradition*. Grosseteste's Platonism is obvious. His thought is an amalgam of the old Augustinianism and the new Aristotelianism.

demonstrations were both self-evident and as immediately clear to us as the facts demonstrated. For example, the axiom 'things that are equal to the same thing are equal to one another', or the definition of a triangle as a figure bounded by three straight lines, were both self-evident and as immediately clear to us as the conclusion of the theorem which showed that the three internal angles of a triangle equalled two right angles. As Walter Burley summarized Averroës, 'in mathematics the same things are more knowable to us and in nature'. But in physics this was not the case. The first knowledge we had of the world of experience was the bare observation of particular facts; the causes or principles that explained them were not self-evident or immediately apparent and could be reached only by in-ductive argument. As Aristotle had put it, these principles were prior in the order of demonstration, because they were the premisses from which the observed facts could be demonstrated, and they were prior in the order of nature because, as existents, they were the real causes of the facts.[1] But in the order of knowing they were reached only by argument from the observed facts, and in the course of this inductive argument from observed particulars to general principles it was always possible for uncertainty to enter because in the world of experience things did not always behave exactly in a uniform manner. So, whereas mathematical demonstrations were certain and necessary because their premisses were indisputable, demonstrations in physics were at best only probable because their premisses were only probable.

To the methods of investigation appropriate to the aspect of reality and truth that was the subject of physics, and to the explana-tory principles that might be given to physics by mathematics and by metaphysics, Grosseteste devoted the most original and historically important part of his theory of natural science.[2] These three subjects will now be considered in turn.

[1] Above, pp. 4, 25.
[2] Grosseteste said: 'Dispositiones autem quantitatis sunt communes omnibus scientiis mathematicis, quia omnis mathematica circa quantitates est. Et etiam disposi-tiones quantitatis sunt communes scientie naturali eo quod naturalis subiicit corpus quantum mobile, et . . . philosophie prime quia philosophia prima stabilit quantitatem et dispositiones eius proprias communes. . . . Dyalectica etiam communicat in principiis cum omnibus aliis scientiis, quia ipsa habet viam ad omnium principia si egent aliquo modo explanationis, et ipsa etiam syllogisat ex principiis omnium. Eius etenim est problema construere vel destruere probabiliter, et eiusdem principiis communibus utitur demon-strator inquantum non sunt necessaria. . . . Et licet . . subiectum metaphysice sit com-mune ad omnia subiecta aliarum scientiarum, tamen ipsa non demonstrat nisi per se inherentia subiecto suo, et non descendet ut demonstret proprias passiones de subiectis inferioris nisi per modum scientie subalternantis. . . .' Comm. Post. i. 10, ff. 9ᵛ-10ʳ.

IV

Induction, and Verification and Falsification in Natural Science

(1)

KNOWLEDGE of changing physical things was the least certain scientific knowledge, and physics, or natural science (*naturalis*), the least certain science. Nevertheless, there was in the study of physical things, as Grosseteste put it, 'science and demonstration, though not in the strictest sense'.[1] It was possible to arrive at a probable knowledge of the causal necessities or laws, belonging to the form, according to which natural things behaved. Such laws were suspected when certain phenomena were seen to be frequently correlated.[2] It was the function of natural science to discover and define as accurately as possible the form that could give rise to demonstration, as the middle term of a syllogism, and so to knowledge of the causes (*propter quid*) of observed effects. Of the logical requirements for making such a definition, and for distinguishing between true and false forms, Grosseteste made an elaborate study. His method involved two distinct procedures: first, a combination of induction[3] and deduction, which he called 'resolution and composition',[4] for arriving at definitions; and secondly, what he called verification and falsification. By relating these logical methods to scientific practice Grosseteste made the first moves towards the creation of modern experimental science.

A definition of itself, Grosseteste pointed out, did not give knowledge of causes because, as Aristotle[5] had said, a definition asserted nothing about existence. The assertion of the existence of the thing defined was, in fact, an additional postulate which did not alter the definition. 'Definition does not make known what the thing is but

---

[1] *Comm. Post.* i. 11, f. 10ᵛ; see above, p. 59, n. 2.

[2] See above, p. 58.

[3] On the two meanings of 'induction' in the Middle Ages, see above, p. 34, n. 2.

[4] For the origin of these terms see above, p. 28; below, p. 75.

[5] *Post. Anal.* ii. 7, 92ᵇ4–39, i. 10, 76ᵃ31 sqq., 1, 71ᵃ11 sqq.; see Aristotle's *Prior and Post. Anal.* ed. Ross, pp. 504-6, 538 sqq. Cf. Heath, *Euclid's Elements*, pp. 143 sqq.; J. S. Mill, *System of Logic*, i. 8.

only what the name signifies, that is, what the thing signified is according to its existence in the intellect, whether it has existence in nature or not.'[1] For example, in geometry definitions of circles and triangles were used with perfectly definite meanings without regard to whether or not there were any existing circles and triangles. He went on:

such definitions are assigned, when [Aristotle] assigns defining causes, not because the thing signified may possibly exist nor because the defined thing may be an actuality, but simply so that they may make understood the meaning of the name. And it is always permissible after such a definition to inquire the cause on account of which the thing is, because the definition as such does not give the cause of the thing.[2]

In the investigation of the world of experience, the problem was, first, to find a nominal, non-causal definition describing the empirical connexion between the events observed, and then to see whether this definition could exhibit the cause of the attributes predicted of a defined subject.[3] This programme Grosseteste attempted to fulfil by the method of 'resolution and composition', which he saw as the practical means by which the two movements in science, from experience to theory and from theory to experience, might be related.

Grosseteste derived the basis of his method of resolution and composition from Aristotle's discussion of definition[4] and he followed Aristotle in reversing what would seem to be the logical order of considering them. Aristotle had shown, first, how to pass from the non-causal[5] to the causal definition, from which demonstration began, and only after that how to reach the non-causal definition itself. Following this order Grosseteste treated composition before resolution. The first of these procedures, composition, passed from general to particular, and the second, resolution, from particular to general.[6] Composition began with what was most universal and simple, that is the *genus*, and descended by the addition of differentiating attributes to what was most particular and composed of the greatest number of

---

[1] 'est diffinitio non explicans quid est res sed solum quid significat nomen, hoc est quid res significata est secundum esse quod habet apud intellectum, sive habeat esse in natura sive non.' (*Comm. Post.* ii. 2, f. 24^r.) A similar point was made by St. Thomas Aquinas in his distinction between essence and existence.

[2] Ibid., f. 24^{vr}. Cf. i. 1, f. 2^v.

[3] See above, p. 53; below, p. 68, n. 3.

[4] *Post. Anal.* ii. 13, 96^{a}20–97^{b}40; see below, p. 75. Cf. above, pp. 25 sqq.

[5] Cf. above, p. 53, nn. 3, 4.   [6] Cf. above, p. 55.

differentiae, that is the lowest species defining the particular object itself.[1] Resolution ascended from the most particular and composite, that is particular objects, to the most universal and simple genus to which they belonged.[2] The following is a translation of Grosseteste's description of his method; his meaning will be clarified by the examples that follow:

The method of definition is the method of discovering what the thing under consideration is by means of the definition of that thing in so far as it makes it known. This method involves two procedures, one being by composition and the other by resolution. Aristotle teaches first the method of arriving at the definition by composition, because this method is like a progression from the more universal and simple[3] to the more composite. The method of resolution is the opposite of that. The method of definition by the first way may be treated in a few words as follows. First, one must consider and understand to what genus the thing to be defined belongs. Next the genus should be divided according to its nearest dividing *differentiae*[4] and one of the two *differentiae* should be joined to the genus, the *differentia*, namely, under which the thing to be defined falls. Then the combined genus and *differentiae* should be divided again according to its nearest *differentiae*, one of which, as was said above, should be joined with the whole as already divided; and the division must be made in this way further according to the nearest substantial *differentiae*, of which one should be added to the whole as already divided till the whole aggregate becomes convertible with the thing to be defined, though each of the parts of that aggregate has a wider application.[5]

---

[1] The *infima species* or *species specialissima*. Cf. above, p. 55.

[2] *Comm. Post.* ii. 4, f. 29ʳ. 'In his itaque singularibus stat prima cognitio sensitiva et ascendit ab his cognitio donec perveniat in simplicia universalia. Et in hoc similiter manifestum est quoniam universalia primo composita sicut et simplicia ex inductione a sensibilibus facta nobis sunt manifesta.' *Comm. Post.* ii. 6, f. 31ᵛ.

[3] These universals were prior in the order of nature: 'De duabus scientiis que eriguntur super res abstractas illa est certior que erigitur super res simpliciores quam ea que erigitur super res compositiores, et hec patet . . . quia res simpliciores sunt priores nature.' *Comm. Post.* i. 17, f. 18ᵛ.

[4] Those first in the scale descending from the genus. As Grosseteste said: 'Docens ergo Aristoteles hanc artem primo demonstrat quam primo accipiendum est genus rei diffiniende et ea que consequenter sunt posterius in descendendo sub ipso genere donec aggregatum ex his sit convertibile cum re diffinienda cum tamen quelibet partium totius aggregati sit in plus.' *Comm. Post.* ii. 4, f. 29ʳᵇ.

[5] *Comm. Post.* ii. 4, f. 27ᵛᵇ. The example Grosseteste gave was Aristotle's definition of the 'triad' (*Comm. Post.* ii. 4, f. 27ᵛ-28ʳ; cf. Aristotle, *Post. Anal.* ii. 13, 96ᵃ27 sqq.). Grosseteste also gave as an example the definition of man as 'animal rationale mortale'. As he said: 'diffinitio sive quod quid erat esse est composita ex his propriis que intrant in quiditatem et est convertibile; hec autem demonstratis propriis que intrant in quiditatem hominis que collecta sunt convertibile cum homine sunt in eo quod quid est in homine,

The method of definition by the way of composition being known, [he went on] Aristotle teaches how to hunt for the definition by the way of resolution, that is by taking first the more composite things, that is inferiors, and ascending from them by division to the more simple superiors. This method is as follows. One must consider first the things to which the name to be defined applies and take from among those things those which are least differentiated, namely, those which are least differentiated according to species and which have the greatest likeness in their accidents. And one must consider what these undifferentiated things have that is common according to the name to be defined. Secondly, one must consider other things which are of the same species as the former but have a greater accidental difference with the first group than the first group have among themselves. And one must consider what is common according to the name to be defined in the second group of things. And thirdly, one must consider what is common according to the name to be defined between the second group of things and the first group. If now everything has been included to which the name to be defined applies, and if they agree in the way described in one common formula (*in unam rationem communem*) according to the name to be defined, then that common formula, thus reached by ascending, will be the definition of the name under consideration.[1]

Grosseteste's meaning can be seen in the method adopted by a series of later writers, beginning with Roger Bacon, in the attempt they made to find the 'common formula' or 'common nature' of the colours of the spectrum.[2] The investigation began, following the resolutive method, with the collecting of particular 'composite' phenomena[3] in which the colours of the spectrum were seen; each phenomenon was then resolved into its constituent attributes and the attributes common to more than one phenomenon noted. For instance, the colours of the spectrum were found in rainbows, in sprays,

---

ut verbi gratia animal rationale mortale. . . .' (*Comm. Post.* ii. 2, f. 23ᵛ.) It is possible that Grosseteste knew the discussion of definition in Aristotle's *Metaph.* Z. 10–12, H. 6 (see above, p. 47, n. 4). Grosseteste was aware of the pitfalls which Aristotle had pointed out in this method of division, e.g. when the genus was more naturally divided into more than two sub-genera, and of the necessity of selecting proximate sub-genera in the right order; cf. *Comm. Post.* ii. 4, f. 29ʳᵇ, and Aristotle, 98ᵃ1 sqq., and below, pp. 65–66. See also Aristotle, *Prior Anal.* i. 31, 46ᵃ31 sqq., which Grosseteste knew (see above, p. 56, n. 1); *Post. Anal.* ii. 5–7; and Aristotle's *Prior and Post. Anal.* ed. Ross, pp. 397–8, 618 sqq., 653 sqq.

[1] 'Cognita sic arte diffiniendi per viam compositionis, consequenter docet Aristoteles venari diffinitionem per viam resolutionis. . . .' *Comm. Post.* ii. 4, f. 29ʳ.

[2] Below, pp. 124 sqq. and the sections on the study of the rainbow by Roger Bacon, Albertus Magnus, Witelo, Theodoric of Freiberg, and Themon Judaei.

[3] Above, p. 55.

in light passed through a spherical glass flask filled with water or through a prism or a hexagonal crystal, in iridescent feathers, &c. It was found that the colours seen in rainbows, sprays, and spherical flasks had in common that they were associated with transparent spheres or drops in which the different colours were refracted through different angles, and that the colours always formed a circle or part of a circle. The colours produced by prisms and hexagonal crystals had in common that they were refracted through different angles, but they differed from the members of the first group by not being circular. The colours produced by iridescent feathers had in common (and thereby differed from both previous groups) that they had not been refracted but reflected and that they changed in a special manner with changing incidence of light. The 'common nature' of the first two groups was: 'colours produced by differential refraction'. The 'common nature' of all three groups was provided by a hypothesis, supposing that both refraction and reflection by a dense medium weakened white light so that it absorbed different degrees of darkness from the medium and thereby became differentiated into the different colours of the spectrum: 'colours produced by the weakening of white light'. This common nature was the nominal or formal definition[1] of the genus, 'colours of the spectrum'.

If, as sometimes happened, the phenomena that were the subject of the investigation were in fact radically heterogeneous, this would be discovered in the course of resolution, for then not one but two or more common formulae or natures would be reached. For instance, in the case of bone in the animal kingdom, vertebrate bone, fish spine, and the cuttlebone of the squid did not all belong to one univocal genus 'bone'.[2]

The purpose of the opposite order of argument followed in the

---

[1] Below, p. 68, n. 3.

[2] 'Item quedam diffinibilium sunt que non habent genus unum univocum nominatum, sed habent commune ambiguum analogum innominabile. . . . Quia quod est os in animali gressibili hoc est spina in pisce: et hoc est sepion in malacte. Est autem malacte animal omne mollis carnis cuius creatio est ex cartilagine tamen et cuius creationem posuit natura inter carnem et nervum: ut sit molle sicut caro: et habeat extensionem sicut nervus: et est in tali animali membrum conveniens spinis piscium: et illud membrum dicitur sepion. Sepia vero animal est marinum.' (*Comm. Post.* ii. 4, f. 29^v.) By 'nervis' Grosseteste meant cartilage: 'in nervis est robur motuum, in ossibus vero est robur sustentativum' (ibid.). Cf. Aristotle's *Hist. Animal.* iv. 1, 524^{b}25 and *Part. Animal.* ii. 8, 654^{a}20, 9, 654^{b}28, 655^{a}20. Grosseteste was clearly making use of information from these sources. See above, pp. 46–47.

compositive method was to show how any of the particular phenomena with which resolution began could be reconstituted theoretically from the definition and its cause thereby shown. Grosseteste's
description of this method can also be exemplified from the work of
his successors on the rainbow. The genus, 'colours of the spectrum',
of which this phenomenon was a member, could be divided first, for
example, according to whether the colours were produced by refraction or reflection, the rainbow being an instance of 'colours produced
by differential refraction'. This species could then be divided according to the medium producing the colours, so a further *differentia* was
added to the definition of the rainbow: 'colours produced by differential refraction in spherical drops'. By a further division the definition
could acquire yet another *differentia*: 'colours produced by differential refraction in spherical drops in large numbers'. And so on, until
the aggregate of *differentiae* defined specifically, that is became equivalent to (or convertible with), the rainbow itself. This aggregate of
differentiae showed the cause, in the sense of the conditions necessary
and sufficient to produce a rainbow.

And we will find . . . not only the definition itself but also the cause of the
differentiae posited in the definition of the thing to be defined. . . . As has
been said above, we will build up the definition from division and we will
have the cause by reason of which every *differentia* is in the thing defined.
For, because of the divided genus, the dividing *differentia* is in the thing
defined, for the genus is the cause and root from which spring the
differentiae and species.[1]

By means of this 'method of definition' Grosseteste showed how
it was possible to discover the form, formal definition, or 'formal
cause' of the events or attributes observed. For 'the definition, or
what the thing was, is compounded from those properties which
enter into the quiddity, and is convertible',[2] and the 'quiddity' or
nature of the thing was the reason for the empirical connexions of
facts.[3] The definition of this 'form' or 'nature' could then become the
middle term in a demonstrative syllogism. The 'method of definition' was the method by which 'we acquire certain vision of the sub-

---

[1] *Comm. Post.* ii. 4, f. 29rb. The propositions might have to be rearranged in the
causal order: e.g. the definition of thunder is 'the extinction of fire in a cloud' and the
continuous noise is caused by the extinction of fire, not vice versa. See above, p. 53, nn. 3,
4; below, p. 69.

[2] *Comm. Post.* ii, 2, f. 23^{v}; above, p. 63, n. 5. Cf. Aristotle, *Post. Anal.* 96^{a}34: 'for
this synthesis must be the substance of the thing'.

[3] Cf. Aristotle, *Post. Anal.* 90^{a}15 and above, pp. 53–54.

stance of a thing';[1] 'by which the nature of the thing (*quid est*) is known and the demonstrative middle term reached, and for showing the rational causes in accordance with which the middle term is ordered which provides the reason (*propter quid*) for the conclusion investigated'.[2]

An example which Grosseteste himself gave of his method of discovering the causal definition was his attempt to find the 'common nature' of horned animals and the cause of the attribute 'having horns'. He began by making a survey of horned animals, and he noted that 'having horns' was always associated with the absence of teeth in the upper mandible and the presence of more than one stomach.[3] He then went on to survey the distributions of these three attributes in the animal kingdom and he found that their distributions did not coincide. All animals with only one row of teeth had more than one stomach, but some such animals had no horns, for example, the doe and the camel. He noted, however, that horned animals used their horns as a means of protection against their enemies, and that the animals which had only one row of teeth but no horns had some other means of preserving their lives. For example, the doe was preserved by its rapid flight and the camel by its large body. Horns were found, in fact, in those animals which had only one row of teeth and no other means of preservation. So he came to the formal definition:

If therefore we wish to define this accidental natural thing 'having horns' (*habens cornua*), we will say that 'having horns' is 'not having teeth in the upper mandible in those animals to which Nature does not give other means of preservation in place of horns', and we reach this definition by the division of the accidental natural thing into co-accidents. For we say that, of those animals lacking teeth in the upper mandible, some have horns and some not; and those which lack horns are those to which Nature has given other means of preservation in place of horns, and those which have horns are those to which Nature has not given any other means of preservation.[4]

---

[1] *Comm. Post.* ii. 4,f . 29rb. This was the case 'in geometria ubi describuntur figure similes et in scientia naturali in qua cognoscitur quid sit similitudo qualitatum naturalium'. Cf. Aristotle, *Metaph.* Z. 5, 1031^{a}12: 'definition is the formula of the essence'.

[2] Comm. Post. ii. 1, f. 21^r.

[3] Cf. Aristotle, *Post. Anal.* 98^{a}15 sqq. Grosseteste's discussion of the problem shows that he was making use of information from Aristotle's *Hist. Animal.* ii. 1, 501^{a}12 and *Part. Animal.* iii. 2, 662^{b}35–664^{a}13, 14, 674^{a}27–^{b}17; see above, pp. 46–47.

[4] *Comm. Post.* ii. 4, f. 29^v. Another example of a common cause reached by the method of definition was the following cause of deciduousness in plants (cf. Aristotle,

This formal definition summarized the discovered connexion between the facts of the case and showed 'what is' (*quid est*). It showed the 'common nature' of horned animals. But to show the complete cause (*propter quid*) of the attribute 'having horns' it was necessary to show not only what the facts were but how they came about. A complete causal definition, according to Grosseteste, must include all four Aristotelian causes.[1] As he put it:

Aristotle said, 'Because we believe we know when we know the cause.' Now there are four causes. One is the formal, which reveals the being of the thing. Another is the material, which must be, in order that the form can exist. The third is the efficient, which is the first principle of motion. The fourth is the final, on account of which the thing comes to be. This being so, I say that all of these four causes can be used in demonstration because they can form the middle term of a syllogism. . . .[2] Thus we have four genera of causes and from these, when they exist, there must be a caused thing in its complete being. For a caused thing cannot follow upon the being of any other cause except these four, and that alone is a cause from whose being something else follows. Therefore there is no other cause beyond these, and so there is in these genera a number of causes that will be sufficient.[3]

99^a23 sqq.): 'folia fluere in plus est quam vitis et quam ficus, sed non est in plus quam omnes arbores que conveniunt in una ratione secundum quam rationem fiunt primum et universale subiectum eius quod est folia fluere. Sed de illo subiecto convertibiliter dicitur. Similiter medium eius primum erit diffinitio fluendi folii, et hoc medium primum erit medium in aliis que sunt sub subiecto primo, quoniam illa conveniunt in ratione una subiecti primi. Est autem medium et ratio eius quod est folio fluere succum densari in contactu seminis.' *Comm. Post.* ii. 5, f. 30^v.

[1] And to say that a thing existed *in potentia* was to say that all its four causes existed *in potentia*; see *De Potentia et Actu*, Baur, 1912, p. 127.   [2] *Comm. Post.* ii. 3, f. 26rb.

[3] *De Statu Causarum*, Baur, 1912, p. 121. The last sentence implies the principle of 'sufficient reason' which Leibniz was to use in a different setting as part of the foundation of his system. The use of the four causes in definition Grosseteste elaborated further in his discussion of the *diffinitio formalis* and the *diffinitio materialis*, a distinction which he derived from Arab sources (cf. Prantl, *Gesch. der Logik*, ii. 312 on Alfarabi and iii. 88–89 on Grosseteste). He said that since there were four causes the definition might be taken from any of them. Formal definitions were taken from the formal and final causes, material definitions from the material and efficient causes, and formal definitions stood to material definitions in the relation of theoretical principles to realizable conclusions. 'Iam igitur habemus duas diffinitiones, scilicet, diffinitiones formales que sunt principia et media demonstrativa, et diffinitiones materiales que sunt conclusiones demonstrate.' (*Comm. Post.* ii. 2, f. 25^{rb, v}; cf. Aristotle, 93^b21 sqq., 94^a20 sqq.) He went on to point out that the formal definition was nominal and the composite formal-and-material definition real, for 'esse autem duplex est, in se, scilicet, et in intellectu. . . . Igitur de duabus diffinitionibus nunc ultimo dictis, una [the formal definition] est diffinitio nominis et alia [the compound definition] est diffinitio demonstrationis propter quid est', for 'diffinitio composita est idem cum demonstratione quia causa et diffinitio idem, licet differant in modo, quia differt dicere propter quid tonat et quid est tonitruum'. And he

In the example under consideration, Grosseteste said: 'The cause of having horns is not having teeth in both jaws, and not having teeth in both jaws is the cause of having several stomachs.'[1] He held that animals with only one row of teeth could not masticate the food properly on first taking it and therefore needed an extra stomach into which it could be received and later regurgitated into the mouth for rumination, after which it could pass to another stomach to be digested. The possession of several stomachs was therefore a direct consequence of the lack of teeth in the upper mandible, and only animals without the upper row of teeth had several stomachs. The material and efficient cause of the horns found in some animals lacking upper teeth Grosseteste held to be that the hard earthy matter that would, in other animals, go to form teeth in the upper mandible was deflected to the top of the head to form the horns.[2] The final cause of horns was that they were a means of protection. Where they were unnecessary for this purpose, as in the doe and the camel, no horns were formed. In the camel, in fact, the hard earthy matter formed a hard cartilage in place of the upper teeth because it ate hard thorny food.

This Aristotelian distinction of types of cause meant in practice that in any scientific investigation two general types of question were asked. The first question led to the formal definition as, for example, 'that "having horns" is "not having teeth in the upper mandible in those animals to which Nature does not give other means of preservation in place of horns" '. The second question led to the elucidation of the rearrangements of material parts that took place in time in order to bring about the consequences required by the formal definition. In the example just quoted this was done by the deflection of hard earthy matter from the teeth to form horns. Another example given by Aristotle and Grosseteste was thunder. The formal definition of thunder was 'the extinction of fire in a cloud'.[3] This led to the

added, 'Diffinitio autem formalis dicitur ostendere quod quid erat esse; eo quod forma est vere essentia ipsius rei et dat esse proprie. Materia autem dat proprie potentiam essendi.' f. 26^r.

[1] 'Habere autem cornua causa est non habendi dentes utrobique, et non habere dentes utrobique causa est habere ventres plures.' *Comm. Post.* ii. 4, f. 29^v.

[2] *Comm. Post.* ii. 4, f. 29^v.

[3] 'Tonitruum est extinctio ignis in nube . . . manifestum est quod per se notum est tonitruum esse sonus in nubibus, unde demonstrari non potest. Sed non patet quod tonitruum sit extinctio ignis in nube nisi his qui noverent generationem tonitrui et quoniam sit sonus extincto igne in humido. . . .' *Comm. Post.* ii. 2, f. 25vb. Cf. Aristotle, 93^{b}8 sqq., 94^{a}2 sqq.

question: What are the material and efficient causes of thunder? Grosseteste gave an account[1] of how thunder was produced by the dry vapours (the material of wind) compressed inside the moist vapours of clouds. Owing to the compression these dry vapours burst out of the cloud and in their violent exit they became rarefied and caught alight. The flame was extinguished by the moist vapours, which in the process were themselves heated and rarefied. This rarefied vapour, as it rushed through the surrounding denser vapour and was reflected from the denser surfaces, made the sound of thunder.

A further point which Grosseteste discussed with regard to causes which preceded their effects in time (that is, in general, material and efficient causes) was the question, in what sense the middle term contained the cause. As Aristotle[2] had pointed out, no problem arose in the case of the formal cause or definition, because this was always compresent with that whose cause it was. But where two events, which were apparently related as cause and effect, succeeded each other in a time-*continuum*, there might be an infinite number of intermediate events between the cause and its effect. Grosseteste followed Aristotle in proposing the logical doctrine that, of two such events, only the occurrence of the earlier could be inferred from the later, and not vice versa. That is, it was possible to argue that because a certain event had happened, therefore an earlier event (its cause) must have happened; but it was impossible to argue that because one event had happened, therefore another, later event would happen. Grosseteste said:

Aristotle inquires whether [events] succeed each other continuously in time, so that a completed caused event [effect] immediately follows the completed cause and a future effect the future cause, and whether the earlier completed cause is continuous with that which is caused. If these do not follow each other immediately, but are interrupted so that there is an intermediate time between completed cause and completed effect, the syllogism will always be taken from the effect and not from the cause. . . . It is clear that the completed effect will not follow the completed cause, because in the intermediate time the cause already exists but it is untrue to say that the effect exists, and the same argument applies in the case of other times.[3] Therefore the cause which is the middle term of the syllogism bringing in its effect is the definition and total cause (*tota causa*

---

[1] The source of most of this is Aristotle's *Meteor.* ii. 9, 369[a]10 sqq.

[2] *Post. Anal.* ii. 12, 95[a]10–[b]37; cf. Aristotle's *Prior and Post. Anal.* ed. Ross, pp. 648–52.   [3] e.g. with two future events.

completa) of it; as shown above, such a cause must be generated simultaneously with its effect . . . and the future cause with the future effect and similarly in other cases. Therefore it is clear that if there is an interval between completed cause and completed effect . . . the effect will not follow the cause. But that there must be an interruption Aristotle shows because, as is pointed out in *Physics*,[1] a completion is the end of becoming and of movement, and is a single completion in an indivisible instant. But becoming is divisible to infinity, like movement. For in every movement there is an infinite number of movements going on and completed, and similarly in becoming there is an infinite number of things in process of becoming and things that have come to be, just as in a unit of time there is an infinite number of instants, and in lines of points. Therefore, as points are not contiguous with points nor lines with points, so neither is an event contiguous with another event nor is an event contiguous with a process of becoming. Therefore events which are not contemporaneous must in reality come one after the other and must have a time-interval between them. But in events which are not contemporaneous the middle term of a syllogism may be used as a cause; that is, when cause and effect are separated by an intermediate time, the syllogism may be taken from the effect.[2]

The method of 'resolution and composition' which Grosseteste described for inquiring into the causes of observed effects gave an outline of an orderly programme of procedure when embarking upon a scientific problem. It showed how to describe and classify the facts of the case and how to arrange them so that the empirical connexion between events could be seen. But Grosseteste knew that there was a logical hiatus between asserting a formal definition, or generalization stating the regularity actually observed, and asserting a theory stating a universal and causal connexion.[3] To leap this gap in the logical process of induction he envisaged an act of intuition or scientific imagination, corresponding to Aristotle's *νοῦς*, by which the mind reflecting on the classification of facts produced by induction suddenly grasped a universal or principle or theory explaining the connexion between them. For example, resolution showed the empirical connexion between horns, upper teeth, and number of

[1] This problem is discussed at length by Aristotle in *Phys.* iv. 10–14, 217[b]30 sqq. and vi. 231[a] sqq., and by Grosseteste in *Comm. Phys.* iv and vi, MS Digby 220, ff. 96[v]–98[vb], 100[r]–101[rb]; Merton 295, ff. 136[r]–138[vb], 140[rv].   [2] *Comm. Post.* ii. 3, f. 27[rb].

[3] This was different from the analogous problem arising because, except in the trivial case where a complete enumeration of all the facts could be given, the generalization reached by resolution was based only on a sample. This logical gap could be crossed by assuming the principle of uniformity, as Duns Scotus pointed out; below, pp. 168 sqq.; cf. p. 85. Cf. Aristotle, *Prior. Anal.* ii. 23, 68[b]9–36; cf. above, p. 34, n. 2.

stomachs as described by the formal definition of 'having horns' (see below, pp. 305–6). But from knowledge of that empirical generalization it required a leap to make the statement: 'The *cause* of having horns is not having teeth in both jaws, and not having teeth in both jaws is the cause of having several stomachs', *because of* the movements of earthy matter in the head and the requirements of digestion. Another example discussed by Grosseteste was that of the eclipse. After observing eclipses and examining the relations of the heavenly bodies involved the observer suddenly said: 'It's a shadow!'[1] Other examples of resolution followed by a leap of scientific imagination are found in the inquiry into the cause of the rainbow made by Grosseteste and his followers.[2] Such theories as these fulfilled the principal object of science, which was to provide demonstrated knowledge of as wide as possible a variety of facts. The special means of doing this was to assert that all the facts could be deduced from the relations between a limited and usually small number of defined factors, for example the movements of earthy matter in the head, or of sunlight passing through droplets of water. The special merit of Grosseteste's theory of science was that he recognized clearly that although causal theories of this kind could not be inferred from the facts they served to explain but could only be suggested by them, nevertheless they could be tested by deducing from them consequences not included in the original generalization and then carrying out observations or experiments to see if these consequences did in fact happen. The following passage gives a good account both of Grosseteste's conception of the intuitive act by which causal theories were reached and of how he was led to his method of experimental isolation of true causes, or verification and falsification. It is a gloss on Aristotle's *Post. Anal.* i. 18, 81ª37 sqq., and as it summarizes the most important elements in Grosseteste's theory of knowledge it is worth quoting as a whole.

He [*sc.* Aristotle] said therefore that when some sense is lacking some part of knowledge is also lacking. . . . Since the senses apprehend singulars,

---

[1] Grosseteste said of the example given by Aristotle (*Post. Anal.* i. 31, 87ᵇ27 sqq.) of finding the cause of the eclipsing of the moon: 'ex multiplici visione terre interposite possible est nobis venari universale . . . huius universale quod sic venatur ex multis sensibilibus dicitur simpliciter causam cuius non queritur causa alia . . . ipsam sic venatum est principium scientie.' *Comm. Post.* i. 18, f. 19ʳᵇ. Cf. above, p. 53, n. 3, p. 57, below, p. 170. Another example is that of scammony, below, p. 74.

[2] A good seventeenth-century example is the formulation of the principle of inertia in mechanics.

when a particular sense is lacking the apprehension of a particular set of singulars is also lacking, and therefore, since induction is made from singulars, when a particular sense is lacking the induction will be lacking which is taken from the singulars which the missing sense apprehends. . . . But I say that it is possible to have some knowledge without the help of the senses. For in the Divine Mind all knowledge exists from eternity, and not only is there in it certain knowledge of universals but also of all singulars. . . . Similarly, intelligences receiving irradiation from the primary light see all knowable things, both universals and singulars, in the primary light itself. Moreover, the Divine Mind, in the reflection of Its intelligence upon Itself, knows the very things which come after Itself, because it is Itself their cause. Therefore, those who are without any senses have true knowledge.

Similarly, the highest part of the human soul, which is called the intelligence and which is not the act of any body and does not need for its proper operation a corporeal instrument—this intelligence, if it were not obscured and weighed down by the mass of the body, would itself have complete knowledge from the irradiation received from the superior light without the help of sense, just as it will have when the soul is drawn forth from the body, and as perhaps those people have who are free from the love and the imaginings of corporeal things.

But because this purity of the eye of the soul is obscured and weighed down by the corrupt body, all the powers of this rational soul born in man are laid hold of by the mass of the body and cannot act and so in a way are asleep. Accordingly, when in the process of time the senses act through many interactions of sense with sensible things, the reasoning is awakened mixed with these very sensible things and is borne along in the senses to the sensible things as in a ship. But the functioning reason begins to divide and separately consider what in sense were confused. For example, vision confuses colour, size, shape and body, and in its judgment these are all taken as a unity. But the functioning reason separates colour from size and shape and body, and again shape and size from corporeal substance, and so by division and abstraction it comes to knowledge of corporeal substance having size, figure and colour. But the reasoning does not know this to be actually universal except after it has made this abstraction from many singulars, and has reached one and the same universal by its judgement taken from many singulars.

This, therefore, is the way by which the abstracted universal is reached from singulars through the help of the senses; clearly the experimental (*experimentale*) universal is acquired by us, whose mind's eye is not purely spiritual, only through the help of the senses. For when the senses several times observe two singular occurrences, of which one is the cause of the other or is related to it in some other way, and they do not see the connection between them, as, for example, when someone frequently notices that the eating of scammony happens to be accompanied by the discharge of red bile and does not see that it is the scammony that attracts and withdraws the red bile, then from constant observation of these two observable things he begins to form a third, unobservable thing, namely, that scammony is the cause that withdraws the red bile. And from this perception repeated again and again and stored in the memory, and from the sensory knowledge from which the perception is built up, the functioning of the reasoning begins. The functioning reason therefore begins to wonder and to consider whether things really are as the sensible recollection says, and these two lead the reason to the experiment, namely, that scammony should be administered after all other causes purging red bile have been isolated and excluded. But when he has administered scammony many times with the sure exclusion of all other things that withdraw red bile, then there is formed in the reason this universal, namely, that all scammony of its nature withdraws red bile; and this is the way in which it comes from sensation to a universal experimental principle.[1]

*　*　*　*　*　*　*　*

Before discussing Grosseteste's theory of experimental verification and falsification it is an interesting problem to try to discover the sources of his ideas on induction. Undoubtedly Grosseteste was brought to see the relevance, to practical science, of the previous century's efforts in logic by being able to read a number of the most important works of Graeco-Arabic scientific learning. Though in fact those parts of that corpus which he knew contained no systematic theory of experimental science, they contained examples of experimental science, and these must have drawn his attention to the need for a systematic methodology. The chief sources he used for his theory of induction seem to have been, besides Aristotle's works, some Arabic medical and logical writings based on Aristotle and Galen.[2]

The practical idea which Grosseteste got from Aristotle was Aristotle's own practical contribution to the problem of induction raised by his distinction between demonstration *quia* and *propter*

---

[1] 'Cum enim sensus apprehendit duo singularia pluries, quorum alterum est alteri causa vel alio modo ad ipsum comparatum, et ipsam comparationem mediam non apprehendit, ... ex frequenti visione horum duorum visibilium incipit estimare tertium invisibile, scilicet, quod scammonea est causa educens coleram rubeam. ... convertunt rationem ad experientiam, scilicet, ut det comedere scamoneam cum circumscriptione et ablatione aliarum causarum purgantium coleram rubeam. Cum autem dederit frequenter scamoneam cum certa circumscriptione ablationis aliarum rerum educentium coleram rubeam, formatur apud rationem hoc universale quod scamonea omnis secundum se educit coleram rubeam.' *Comm. Post.* i. 14, ff. 13vb–14rb. Cf. below, pp. 129–30.

[2] Cf. above, pp. 7, 25–29.

quid. This was a method of combined division and generalization which he set out in his *Posterior Analytics*[1] for arriving at nominal or non-causal definitions. The object of Aristotle's method of definition was, first, to define a species already confusedly recognized as belonging to a given genus. His method was to enumerate a collection of attributes essential to the species to be defined which were severally of wider extent than this species, but collectively coextensive with it and therefore defining it. In making such a collection of attributes he held that the method of division, by which the genus containing the species to be defined was divided according to successive, mutually exclusive pairs of *differentiae*, was a valuable guide in placing the attributes that were to form the parts of the definition in the right order and in showing when the definition of a species was complete. After the genus had been completely divided into its species, the definition of the genus could be reached by noting the common elements in the definitions of its constituent species,[2] for these alone were essential to the genus. Definitions so reached could then become the start of demonstration, for 'the nature of the thing and the reason for the fact are identical'.[3] In this way the definition revealed the cause of the attributes observed.

The terms 'resolution' and 'composition' Grosseteste no doubt knew from the writings of Boethius and other medieval Latin writers,[4] but in his use of these methods he is closer to the medical school. That Grosseteste had studied medicine himself has been inferred from two lines of evidence, first from external references and secondly from his own writings.[5] Grosseteste's name was connected with a knowledge of medicine by Giraldus Cambrensis,[6] Richard of Bardney,[7] in a manuscript of *De Secretis Mulierum* attributed to

[1] ii. 13, 96ᵃ20–97ᵇ40; cf. *Comm. Post.* ii. 4, f. 27ᵛ. See Ross, *Aristotle*, pp. 49–53; Aristotle's *Prior and Post. Anal.* ed. Ross, pp. 387, 653–4; *Topics*, i. 18, 108ᵇ.

[2] 'Compositis enim ex athomis convenientia ex diffinitionibus erunt manifesta' as it ran in the Latin text of Aristotle, 96ᵇ22; *Comm. Post.* ii. 4, f. 28ʳᵇ.

[3] *Post. Anal.* ii. 2, 90ᵃ15.

[4] Above, pp. 28–29. Grosseteste was certainly very familiar with Boethius's writings and it is probably safe to conjecture that so scholarly a person would be familiar also with the writings and translations of Chalcidius and John Scot Erigena.

[5] See Rob. Grosseteste *Epistolae*, ed. Luard, p. xxxii, and *Dict. Nat. Biog.* xxiii. 275 sqq.; F. S. Stevenson, *Robert Grosseteste*, pp. 12–13; E. Wickersheimer, 'Robert Grosseteste et la médecine', *3ᵉ Congrès hist. art guérir*, in which most of the evidence is summarized; Callus, *Oxoniensia*, x (1945) 44–45.

[6] Giraldus Cambrensis, *Opera*, ed. J. S. Brewer, i. 249; see above, p. 44.

[7] Richardi Monachi Bardeniensis *Vita Roberti Grosthed*, C. 19, 'De Studiis Grosthede in Oxoniam', in Henry Wharton, *Anglia Sacra*, ii. 332.

Albertus Magnus,[1] and in a fourteenth-century manuscript in the British Museum on the medicinal value of herbs which adds 'Grosthede' after various items.[2] Grosseteste himself referred to subjects connected with medicine in several of his letters,[3] in one letter speaking of curing a companion of quartan fever while on a voyage,[4] and he shows his familiarity with medicine in several of his other writings.[5] Some of his references show a knowledge that could have been obtained only by a detailed study of the subject.[6]

The original medical source of the method of resolution and composition was Galen himself. In the prologue of his *Tegni (Techne)* or *Ars Medica* Galen said that there were three *doctrinae* or methods of procedure in medicine: by resolution, by composition, and by definition.[7] Galen spoke also of the necessity of being led by the signs or symptoms of disease to the cause before it is possible, from knowledge of the cause, to prescribe a cure.[8] Grosseteste could hardly have

[1] Tr. 1, C. 2; see Wickersheimer, op. cit., p. 260, n. 7.

[2] MS. Sloane 3468, 14c., ff. 43ᵛ, 47ª, 50ᵛ, 53ʳ, 55ᵛ, 57ʳ, 60ʳᵛ, 61ᵛ, 64ʳ. See Thorndike, *History of Magic*, ii. 447–8.

[3] Rob. Grosseteste *Epistolae*, ed. Luard, pp. 50, 53, 64, 75, 162, 166, 187, 320, 403, 426.

[4] Ibid., p. 334.

[5] Baur, 1912, pp. 5–7, 22, 25, 36, 59, 66, 71 (where he refers to a 'urinale', a medical word for a flask, which he used filled with water for optical experiments; see below, p. 122), 72 (where he refers to Hippocrates), 78, 90–91, 114–15.

[6] e.g. in a short text on favourable and unfavourable days published by Wickersheimer, op. cit., p. 4. There are several medical passages, which have not been noticed by previous historians, in *Comm. Post.* Of interest is the following commentary on the passage in Aristotle's *Post. Anal.* (ii. 12, 96ª1 seq.) on the cycle of water from moist earth to cloud to rain and back to earth: 'Verumtamen secundum veritatem terra primo erat madidando dico depluta: irigatione aquarum venientium a mari magno per meatus occultos sicut sanguis a corde veniens per venas et arterias irrigat totum corpus animalis.' (*Comm. Post.* ii. 3, f. 27ᵛ.) Another medical passage is the commentary on an illustration of Aristotle's, that the Scythians had no flute-players because they had no vines. (*Comm. Post.* i. 12, f. 11ᵛ.) There are further medical passages in i. 7, f. 7ᵛ, i. 12, f. 12ʳ (see below, p. 92), i. 14, ff. 13ᵛ–14ʳ (see above, pp. 73–74), and i. 18, ff. 18ᵛ.

[7] Galeni *Liber Tegni cum Commento* Hali, MS Vat. Pal. Lat. 1102, *c.* 1300 (?), f. 117; Galieni *micro Tegni cum commento* Hali Rodoham, Venetiis, 1487, f. 151ʳ. See also *Ars Medica*, Prologue, ed. Kühn, i. 305–6, *De Locis Affectis*, i. 6, ed. Kühn, viii. 60 sqq.; *De Sophismatis*, ed. Kühn, xiv. 583. In his *De Febrium Differentiis* (i. 2, ed. Kühn, vii. 273, 275–6, 282, 352) Galen spoke of resolving a fever into its genus and *differentiae*, these giving its cause. This latter work was translated into Latin by Burgundio of Pisa (d. 1193); see Haskins, *Mediaeval Science*, p. 208.

[8] 'In actionibus vero prius quidem corporum cognitio ex signis manifesta est; postea vero et earum causarum inventio' (*Tegni*, C. 1, MS Vat. Pal. Lat. 1102, f. 119ʳ). See *Ars Medica*, C. 1, ed. Kühn, i. 308; above, p. 27. The causes of health and disease depended on the balance of the four humours, itself depending on the balance of the four elements and qualities, and cures depended on restoring this balance, if disturbed, by drugs with the appropriate qualities; cf. *Comm. Post.* i. 12, f. 12ʳ: see below, p. 92. In his *De*

studied medicine without coming across Galen's *Tegni*, though he never mentioned it in his scientific writings. This work had been translated from the Arabic into Latin by Constantine the African and again by Gerard of Cremona, and it was recommended (in Constantine's translation) for study in Paris at the end of the twelfth century[1] and, one may presume, also in Oxford.[2]

Gerard of Cremona translated Galen's *Tegni* along with the commentary by the eleventh-century Egyptian doctor, 'Ali ibn Ridwan or Haly Rodohan.[3] There is no direct evidence that Grosseteste knew this commentary, though Gerard's translation was certainly well known by the end of the thirteenth century and probably by a much earlier date.[4] However, in it Haly brought the method of 'resolution and composition' into relation with Aristotle's treatment of the dual inductive-deductive movement involved in reaching definitions, in a way that suggests Grosseteste's own treatment of the subject. In commenting on the beginning of the prologue[5] to Galen's *Tegni*, Haly said:

In all science which follows a definite order there are three orders of procedure. . . . One of them is that which is carried out by the way of conversion and resolution; in it you set up in your mind the thing at which you are aiming, and of which you are seeking scientific knowledge, as the end to be satisfied. Then you examine what lies nearest to it, and the nearest to that without which the thing cannot exist; nor are you finished till you arrive at the principle which satisfies it. . . . The second follows the way of composition and is the contrary of the first way. In it you begin with the thing at which you have arrived by the way of resolution, and then

Methodo Medendi, which was also translated by Burgundio of Pisa, Galen gave many examples of his method; see especially i. 3, ii. 2, iii. 1, ed. Kühn, x.

[1] See Haskins, *Mediaeval Science*, pp. 369, 374; above, p. 28, n. 1.

[2] It was recommended in an Oxford statute before 1350; see *Statuta Antiqua Universitatis Oxoniensis*, ed. S. Gibson, pp. ciii, 41; Rashdall, *Universities*, iii. 156.

[3] Sarton, *Introduction*, i. 729, ii. 343; Haskins, *Mediaeval Science*, p. 14. This is the translation cited above, p. 76, n. 7. Randall (*JHI*, i, 1940, p. 187) has confused Gerard's translation with Constantine's and the commentary of Haly Rodohan with that of Haly Abbas; cf. above, p. 28, n. 1.

[4] e.g. it was known to Pietro d'Abano who in 1310 indicated the history of the terms 'resolution and composition' in his *Conciliator*, Diff. iii. i, viii, Introductio, Prop. iii. 2 and iv, Venetiis, 1504. Cf. Randall, loc. cit.

[5] Above, p. 76, n. 7. In the 1487 ed. some of Haly's commentary is reprinted as Galen's text, and Randall, loc. cit., follows the fifteenth-century editor in this confusion. The correct distinction between text and commentary is made in MS Vat. Pal. Lat. 1102. The text as indicated there corresponds to the Greek and Latin of Kühn's edition and to the Latin of another fifteenth-century commentary in which Haly's commentary is mentioned: Turisani *Commentum Microtegni*, Venetiis, 1498, f. 2ʳᵇ.

return to the very things resolved, and put them together again in their proper order, until you arrive at the last of them. . . .[1] All demonstrations are carried out in these two methods: demonstration *propter quid* is effected by composition and demonstration *quia* by resolution. . . . And the third follows the way of resolving the definition. . . .[2]

Another writer from whom Grosseteste may have got an idea of the method of 'resolution and composition' was the ninth-century Arab philosopher, doctor and mathematical scientist Alkindi.[3] In his

[1] The same two methods corresponded respectively to 'analysis' and 'synthesis' as used by some Greek geometers; see above, p. 28; and cf. Newton, below, pp. 317–18. Galen himself held it to be the ideal of medicine to be able to deduce its conclusions from indemonstrable first principles after the model of mathematics (*Meth. Med.* i. 4, ed. Kühn, x. 33–34, 36–37).

[2] 'In omnibus doctrinis que currunt secundum ordinem incessus sunt secundum tres ordines. . . . Una earum est que fit secundum viam conversionis et solutionis, et est ut statuas rem ad quam intendis et cuius inquiris scientiam in mente tua secundum finem complementi eius. Et deinde consideres in propinquiori, et propinquiori ex eo sine quo non stat illa res; neque completur usquequo pervenias ad principium complementi eius. Hec est una specierum doctrinarum que currunt secundum ordinem, et est illa que nominatur dissolutio per conversionem. Quidam vero posuerunt ei exemplum dicentes: in ea corpus est compositum ex membris, et membra sunt composita ex humoribus, et humores ex cibis, et cibi ex elementis. Hoc autem exemplum non convenit sententie Galeni neque convenit sententie antiquorum quod est quia dissolutio per conversionem est secundum hunc ordinem et modum. Accipe quesitum et solve ipsum in subiectum quod est in eo et predicatum, et considera consequentiam subiecti, deinde consequentia predicati, et attrahe per illud ratiocinationem eius. Et si invenis in aliqua propositionum ratiocinationis eius locum considerationis i.e. dubitationis, solve etiam iterum illam propositionem, et non cesses facere hoc semper usquequo descendas et devenias ad principia artis et scientias cognitas. Et geometre quidem et auctores scientiarum sciunt hunc modum doctrine. Et Aristoteles quidem iam posuit ipsum in analeticis, id est in libro posteriorum. . . . Et secunda doctrina est secundum viam compositionis et secundum contrarietatem semite prime. Et est ut incipias a re ad quam tu pervenisti per viam dissolutionis et conversionis, et deinde redi in illis rebus et compone eas ad invicem usquequo pervenias ad postremum earum. . . . Et demonstrationes quidem omnes fiunt in his duabus doctrinis; demonstratio autem propter quid fit per compositionem, et demonstratio quia fit per dissolutionem. . . . Et tertia fit per viam dissolutionis diffinitionis . . . et est ut accipias diffinitionem quesiti et dividis partes eius, et aspicias in unamquamque partium eius et partium particularium eius, et compleas consideratione tua totum cuius intellectu indiges in quesito.' *Liber Tegni cum Commento* Hali, MS Vat. Pal. Lat. 1102, f. 117; ed. 1487, ff. 151ʳ–152ʳ: this edition has 'quare' instead of 'propter quid' above; the terms were used synonymously. After saying that 'In hoc autem libro nos utimur doctrina que fit ex dissolutione diffinitionis', Haly went on to discuss the distinction between 'substantive' and 'notional' definitions: 'Diffinitio substantialis est que determinat rem diffinitam per res essentiales, et diffinitiones nominate notiones sunt descriptiones. Et differentia quidem inter diffinitionem et descriptionem est quod in diffinitione ponitur genus rei et adiungitur cum differentia aut cum differentiis que discernunt essentiam diffiniti ab aliis. Et in descriptione ponitur genus rei et adiungitur cum proprietatibus aut accidentibus que discernunt descriptum ab aliis, et non per rem essentialem.' MS Vat. Pal. Lat. 1102, f. 118ʳ; ed. 1487, f. 152ʳ.

[3] See below, p. 117, n. 2.

Liber Introductiorius in Artem Logicae Demonstrationis, which was translated by Gundissalinus and John of Spain,[1] Alkindi described a fourfold dialectical method for arriving 'at knowledge of the certainty of things' by 'division and resolution, definition and demonstration'.[2] By division and resolution, he said, the investigator broke up the composite thing,[3] e.g. a physical object, into its parts, so that it could be assigned to its species. By combining the species the definition of the genus might then be reached and this, as the causal definition, might finally become the start of demonstration.[4] In another work, *De Aspectibus*, Alkindi spoke of 'resolution and composition'.[5] These terms were used also by Averroës.[6]

Another important medical writer whom Grosseteste knew was Avicenna, and in his *Canon Medicinae* Avicenna gave a set of seven rules for discovering the powers of medicines, which were a precise guide for practical experimentation. They were taken partly from Galen.[7] Grosseteste referred in his *De Natura Locorum* to 'Avicennam quarto de animalibus et primo artis medicinae', in support of the statement 'quod loca mundi sola sub tropicis et prope sunt combustiva et loca sub aequinoctiali temperata et temperatissima'.[8] The second reference seems to be to the first book of the *Canon*,[9] where the same subject is discussed. In that work, after saying that medicine was the science of understanding the causes of health and disease and that science was acquired only through knowledge of causes and principles,[10] Avicenna went on to say that the properties

---

[1] *Philosophische Abh. Al-Kindi*, hrg. von A. Nagy, p. xv.

[2] *Liber Introductiorius*, i, hrg. von Nagy, p. 41.

[3] Ibid., p. 45.

[4] Ibid., pp. 44–45. Geometry was his model demonstrative science, as in the *Almagest* and in Euclid (ibid., pp. 49, 53, 58).

[5] *De Aspectibus*, Section 14, ed. A. A. Björnbo and S. Vogl in *Alkindi, Tideus und Pseudo-Euklid. Drei optische Werke*, p. 23. See below, p. 117, n. 2.

[6] Averroës said that definition was necessary before demonstration from causes could begin. The method of arriving at a definition was by 'via divisionis et via compositionis'. *Post. Resol. Comm.* ii. 8, Venetiis, 1552, i, f. 223ᵛᵇ. See above, p. 56, n. 1.

[7] Cf. Galen, *De Simplicium Medicamentorum*, ii. 9, 21, ed. Kühn, xi. 485, 518; *De Compositione Medicamentorum*, vii. 4, ed. Kühn, xiii. 960–2.

[8] Baur, 1912, p. 66. Grosseteste also referred to Avicenna in *De Motu Corp.*, Baur, 1912, p. 91. Avicenna was popular in Oxford early in the thirteenth century (Callus, *PBA*, xxix, 1943, pp. 249–51).

[9] Avicennae *Canon Medicinae*, Lib. i, Fen i, Doctrina iii, C. 1, Venetiis, 1608, p. 12ᵇ, 40; i. ii. ii. 8, p. 103ᵃ, 30. For Avicenna's influence see above, p. 35, n. 2; p. 36, n. 1.

[10] *Canon*, i. i. i. 1, p. 7. In his *Logica* (Pars. i) Avicenna discussed Aristotle's method of discovering the 'common nature' by division (Avicenne *Opera*, Venetiis, 1508, ff. 7–8) and in his *Sufficientia* (i. 1, ff. 13ʳ sqq.), or commentary on the *Physics*, he spoke as Aristotle had done of passing from whole composite things, which the senses apprehended,

(*virtutes*) of medicines were to be known by two methods, by experiment and by reasoning. In laying down the conditions for a reliable experimental investigation of the causes of the effects of medicines administered to cure diseases in man, Avicenna was in effect trying to relate these effects to the chemical constitution of the medicine, as this was then understood: that is, to the proportions of the four primary qualities which they possessed. It was thought, for example, that a medicine which reduced the excess of heat in a fevered person must have a cold nature. Avicenna's rules may be summarized as follows:[1]

1. The medicine must be free from any extraneous, accidental quality, as, for example, from the heat retained by heated water which by nature was cold.

2. The experimentation must be done with a simple and not a composite disease, for in the latter case it would be impossible to infer from the cure what was the curing cause in the medicine.

3. The medicine must be tested with two contrary types of disease, because sometimes a medicine, for example scammony, cured one disease *per se* by its 'complexion', or complement of qualities, and another *per accidens*. It could not be inferred, simply from the fact that it cured a certain type of disease, that a medicine necessarily had a given quality.

4. The quality (*virtus*) of the medicine must correspond to the strength of the disease. For example, there were some medicines whose 'heat' was less than the 'coldness' of certain diseases, so that they would have no effect on them. The experiment should therefore be done first with a weaker type of disease and then with diseases of gradually increasing strength.

5. The time of action must be observed so that essence and accident be not confused. For example, heated water might temporarily have a heating effect because of an acquired extraneous accident, but after a time it would return to its cold nature.

to simple principles which the intellect apprehended. Averroës spoke of Avicenna's opinion 'quod posteriora composita ex rebus prioribus non constant esse essentialia rebus prioribus nisi cum constituerit causa propter quam constat posterius ex priori.' (*Post. Resol. Comm.* i. 13, Venetiis, 1550, i, ff. 158vb, 159^r.) On the translation of these works into Latin see H. Bédoret, 'Les Premières Versions tolédans de philosophie. Œuvres d'Avicenne', *RNP*, xli (1938) 374 sqq.

[1] '... Isti ergo sunt canones, quos observare oportet in cognitione virtutum medicinarum ex via experimenti.' (Avicennae *Canon Medicinae*, ii. i. 2, Venetiis, 1608, i. 246.) He went on to speak of the *via rationis* which depended on the theory of the four qualities and elements (ibid., C. 3, p. 247). See Crombie, in *Avicenna . . .*, below, p. 351.

6. The effect of the medicine must be seen to occur constantly or in many cases, for if this did not happen it was an accidental effect.[1]

7. The experimentation must be done with the human body, for testing a medicine on a lion or a horse might not prove anything about its effect on man.[2]

Grosseteste's reference to scammony, in the passage quoted from his commentary on the *Posterior Analytics*,[3] suggests that when writing he might have had this section of Avicenna's *Canon* in mind.

(2)

The reason why Grosseteste held that in natural science the theories of causes reached by resolution and 'intuition'[4] had to be tested by further observation or experiment before they could be regarded as true, was that he held that these were only theories of *possible* causes and that the same effect might have more than one possible cause. As he put it:

Can the cause be reached from knowledge of the effect with the same certainty as the effect can be shown to follow from its cause? Is it possible for one effect to have many causes? If one determinate cause cannot be reached from the effect, since there is no effect which has not some cause, it follows that an effect, when it has one cause, may have another, and so that there may be several causes of it.[5]

In natural science, he said, the inductive, resolutive method was aimed at bringing to light causes that were hidden 'from us', and it was usually impossible to reach a complete definition of the cause[6] of an experienced effect because it was usually impossible to exhaust

---

[1] 'Et sexta est, ut observetur processus operationis eius secundum assiduationem aut secundum plurimum; nam si non fuerit ita, tunc processio operationis ab ea est per accidens; quoniam res naturales procedunt a principiis suis, aut semper, aut secundum plurimum.' (*Canon Medicinae*, ed. cit. i. 246.)

[2] For similar conditions described in the second half of the thirteenth century by Petrus Hispanus and Jean de Saint-Amand, see Thorndike, *History of Magic*, ii. 508–13.

[3] Above, p. 74. [4] Above, pp. 71–74.

[5] 'An ex causato sequatur causa sua sicut ex causa sequitur causatum. An contingat unius plures esse causas. Si enim ex causato non sequitur causa una determinata, cum non sit causatum quin habeat causam aliquam, sequitur quod causatum cum habeat causam unam sequitur etiam quod habeat causam aliam, et ita quod illius sint plures cause.' (*Comm. Post.* ii. 5, f. 30rb.) Cf. Aristotle, *Post. Anal.* ii. 16–18, 98^{a}35–99^{b}14; Ross, *Aristotle*, p. 53. In *De Calore Solis*, Baur, 1912, p. 80 (below, p. 87, n. 1) and *De Motu Corp.* ibid., p. 90 (below, p. 107) Grosseteste envisages the possibility of establishing a 1 : 1 relation between cause and effect. This question of the truth of theories was an important issue in astronomy from the thirteenth century down to the time of Newton: see Duhem, *Annal. philos. chrétienne*, vi (1908), and below, pp. 96 sqq.

[6] Whether formal, material, efficient, or final.

all the possibilities.[1] Here Grosseteste drew a distinction between natural science and mathematics in which, he said, the premisses of demonstrations were both self-evident and indisputable, and as immediately clear to us as the conclusions;[2] and, moreover, of the abstracts subjects like triangles and circles with which geometry dealt, it was possible to give complete definitions.[3] In mathematics, therefore, there was no fundamental difference between arguing by 'composition' from premisses to conclusion and arguing the other way round by 'resolution',[4] and mathematical theorems certainly required no empirical verification.

But in natural science, Grosseteste held, in order to distinguish the true cause from other possible causes, at the end of 'composition' must come a process of experimental verification[5] and falsification. A theory reached by resolution and intuition was, as he pointed out, capable of yielding by deduction consequences beyond the original

---

[1] Complete definition would be possible only when complete enumeration was possible; see above, pp. 71, n. 3; below, pp. 168 sqq.

[2] Above, pp. 59–60; cf. pp. 56–57, and below, pp. 91 sqq.

[3] 'In utroque modo predicto essendi vel dicendi per se alterius de altero habet hoc ipsum per se duos modos, quia cum duo sic se habent ad invicem quod a quiditate unius est quiditas alterius, aut ita est quod neutri aliquid superadditur quod sit non causa vel causatum respectu alterius, aut alteri aliquid superadditur quod est non causa vel non causatum respectu alterius. Sicut enim, verbi gratia, a tota quiditate trianguli egreditur tota quiditas habitus trium angulorum equalium duobus rectis, et nihil est in triangulo quod non sit causa respectu habitus trium angulorum, &c., neque est aliquid in habitu trium angulorum, &c., quod sit non causatum respectu trianguli. . . .' *Comm. Post.* i. 4, f. 4vb.

[4] 'In doctrinis autem est facilior et brevior resolutio usque ad principia quam in dyalecticis vel in aliis, igitur in his maior certitudo et error minor. Quia autem in doctrinis per resolutionem possit facilius perveniri a conclusione ad principia prima patet quia in doctrinis magis convertuntur termini, quia in his non recipitur accidens medium, sed diffinitiones sunt media. In convertibilibus autem facilis est resolutio, in dyalecticis autem sumitur accidens plus et non convertibile.' (*Comm. Post.* i. 11, f. 10vb.) 'Alia ratio quod facilior sit resolutio etiam in mathematicis est quia in dyalecticis sunt plura media proximo inferentia eandem conclusionem. In mathematicis autem ad unam conclusionem non est nisi unicum medium, unde in mathematicis a conclusione in sua principia non est nisi via unica. . . . In mathematicis vero non querit resolvens nisi unum solum medium proximum ad unum conclusionem quod est causa et diffinitio, et hec via resolutionis in mathematicis manifesta est ex via compositionis.' (*Comm. Post.* i. 11, f. 11^r.) Cf. Themistius, to whom Grosseteste referred on f. 10^r: 'nam causa per signum semper ostenditur, signum per causam non semper ostenditur. Quemadmodum itaque non omnes causae cum effectibus suis reciprocant, ita nec omnia quae reciprocant effectus et causae sunt, quia fieri potest in eiusdem causae plura indicia sint, quae invicem recurrent. Causae huius, quod quis febriat signa sunt arteriae creber pulsus et intentus calor. Signa haec mutuo se asserunt, sed de neutro syllogismus quamobrem ducitur: de utroque syllogismus ut sit, componitur.' Themistii *Paraphrasis in Post. Anal.* i. 29, Basileae, 1533, p. 38.

[5] 'per modum verificationis.' *Comm. Post.* i. 1, f. 2rb.

facts on which the induction was based. 'For when the argument proceeds by composition from principles to conclusions, . . . it may proceed to infinity by the addition of the minor extreme under the middle term.'[1] On the basis of these consequences controlled experiments were arranged by which false causes could be eliminated. The investigator could then entertain as the true cause that which was left after all the other possibilities had been eliminated, as, for example, he came to hold the proposition 'that all scammony of its nature withdraws red bile'.[2] An example which Grosseteste gave was in his commentary on Aristotle's statement that necessary truth[3] was obtained from premisses designating attributes that belonged essentially to their subject. Grosseteste said: 'If anything that is cut or wounded dies and this is not due to some further cause such as disease but to this mortal cut or wound, then this wound is *per se* the cause of the death.'[4]

Aristotle and Galen themselves had recognized in principle the necessity for experimental verification and falsification. Aristotle said that scientific theories were acceptable only if the consequences that followed from them were verified in the facts of sense perception: 'credit must be given rather to observation than to theories, and to theories only if what they affirm agrees with the observed facts'.[5] He pointed out also that the objection that could be raised against a proposition asserted as having one characteristic of necessary truth, a proposition asserted as true in every instance, was an instance in which this proposition was not true.[6] Galen said that

---

[1] *Comm. Post.* i. 11, f. 11ʳ. Cf. Aristotle, *Post. Anal.* i. 12, 78ᵃ14 sqq. Grosseteste added: 'non comprehenduntur omnes actu ab intellectu creato potentie finite, sed solum ab intellectu increato potentie infinite.' (f. 11ʳᵇ); cf. Galileo, *Dialogo sopra i Due Massimi Sistemi*, i, ed. naz. (*Opere*, vii) 128, Salusbury's translation, p. 86.

[2] See above, p. 74.

[3] 'Since the object of pure scientific knowledge cannot be other than it is, the truth obtained by demonstrative knowledge will be necessary.' (*Post. Anal.* i. 4, 73ᵃ21 sqq.) Such knowledge referred to an attribute that belonged to every instance of its subject and belonged essentially and as such.

[4] *Comm. Post.* i. 4, f. 4ᵛ. The illustration was Aristotle's (73ᵇ14–15).

[5] *De Gen. Animal.* iii. 10, 760ᵇ31. Cf. *Post. Anal.* i. 31, 88ᵃ12–17, *Phys.* 262ᵃ17–19, *De Gen. et Corrupt.* 325ᵃ13–16, 331ᵇ24–6, 336ᵇ15–17, *Meteor.* 334ᵃ5–8, *De Motu Animal.* C. 1, 698ᵃ11–16, *De Gen. Animal.* 740ᵃ4–5, 788ᵇ17–20, *Metaph.* 1054ᵃ26–9.

[6] *Post. Anal.* i. 4, 73ᵃ33. In his discussion of the cause of comets Aristotle began by showing that two theories postulated by previous writers were contradicted by the observations: 'Enough has been said, without further argument, to show that the causes brought forward to explain comets are false.' (*Meteor.* i. 6, 344ᵃ4; cf. *Meteor. cum Averrois Expos.* i. 3–4, Venetiis, 1550, v, ff. 183ʳ–184ᵛ.) Cf. Aristotle's discussion of the cause of the Milky Way, *Meteor.* i. 8, 345ᵃ11 sqq.

truth discovered by logic must be confirmed by experience.[1] Following Galen, Avicenna made an acute analysis of certain of the conditions to be observed in experimentally isolating causes.[2]

Grosseteste's contribution was to emphasize the importance of *falsification*[3] in the search for true causes and to develop the method of verification and falsification into a systematic method of experimental procedure. He set out his method first in a theoretical form in a commentary on Aristotle's account of the mode of hypothetical reasoning by *reductio ad impossibile*.[4] Referring to Aristotle's distinction of ostensive negative demonstration from *reductio ad impossibile*, he said:

Ostensive demonstration is that which concludes directly to that which is in question. *Reductio ad impossibile* is that which, when something the opposite of that which is in question has been assumed, concludes with some other proposition directly to a known and manifest impossibility, from the opposite of which the investigator is led back to the original proposition in question. But there is a difference between ostensive demonstration and *reductio ad impossibile*, because the former proves from things prior in the order of nature but the latter from things posterior in the order of nature. When things prior in nature are better known to the intellect of the person making the demonstration the process is carried out ostensively; but when posterior things are better known to his intellect then the demonstration is carried out *per impossibile*. . . . If we want to demonstrate *per impossibile* that not all[5] B is A, it could be assumed that all B is A and also that all C is B and so that all C is A. But this may be manifestly impossible, so that it will be impossible for all B to be A and necessary that not all[5] B is A. . . . It is clear therefore that in demonstration carried out *per impossibile* the showing of the original thing in question is carried out by means of things posterior to it in the order of nature. . . . And there is in the contrary, falsely supposed in predicate or subject, a connecting term by which something is implied to be which is impossible in the nature of things.[6]

---

[1] e.g. 'longa nostra experientia confirmatam concipio' (*Meth. Med.* vi. 6, ed. Kühn, x. 455); 'quae vero per rationem separata sunt, experientia confirmantur' (*De Compos. Medicam.* vi. 7, ed. Kühn, xiii. 887).

[2] See above, pp. 80–81.

[3] His method corresponded to what Francis Bacon was to call 'exclusion': *Novum Organum*, ii. 8; below, pp. 301–2.

[4] *Post. Anal.* i. 26, 87ᵃ. He discussed the subject also in *Prior Anal.* i. 23 and ii. 17. Grosseteste referred to this latter work in *Comm. Post.* i. 17, f. 18ʳ.

[5] The logic demands that 'nullum' in the Latin text be translated 'not all'.

[6] *Comm. Post.* i. 17, f. 18ʳ. Grosseteste discussed *reductio ad impossibile* also in *Comm. Post.* i. 10, giving examples of its use by Euclid and also 'in multis demonstrationibus ducentibus ad impossibile tam naturalibus quam mathematicis quam moralibus' (f. 9ʳᵇ).

This clearly supposed a method of choosing between alternative hypotheses by deducing consequences from them and falsifying the hypotheses whose consequences were impossible either logically or because of what things are.

In its application to natural science Grosseteste based his method of verification and falsification on two assumptions about the nature of reality. (*a*) The first was the principle of the uniformity of nature, meaning that forms are always uniform in their operations. As he put it in *De Generatione Stellarum*: 'Res eiusdem naturae eiusdem operationis secundum naturam suam effectivae sunt. Ergo si secundum naturam suam non sunt eiusdem operationis effectivae, non sunt eiusdem naturae.'[1] In support of this principle he quoted 'Aristoteles II *de Generat.*: "idem similiter se habens non est natum facere nisi idem" '; 'the same cause, provided it remains in the same condition, cannot produce anything but the same effect.'[2]

(*b*) The second assumption Grosseteste made was that of the principle of economy, or *lex parsimoniae*. This also he derived from Aristotle,[3] who stated it as a pragmatic principle.[4] Commenting on Aristotle's text, Grosseteste said:

He gave another example in his gloss on Aristotle's *Physics* (242^{b}20 sqq.), in which he tried to prove that there was not an infinite succession of movers, because if there were this would imply that an infinite movement occurred in finite time. 'Secundo oportet quod motores secundum localem motum non abibunt in infinitum, sed est prima causa motus, et hoc ostendit per impossibile. Sed prima eius ostensio non est necessaria, sed ad faciendum eam necessariam addit quod movens est cum moto et non distat a moto. . . . Et si motores abeant in infinitum necesse est corpus contiguari corpori donec aggregatur corpus continuum vel contiguum in infinitum et tunc accipitur inconsequens, scilicet infinitum motum esse in tempore finito, unde igitur demonstratum est quod motores corporales non essent in infinitum.' *Comm. Phys.*, MS Digby 220, ff. 101$^{rb, v}$; Merton 295, f. 141rb.

[1] Baur, 1912, p. 32; translated below, p. 88.

[2] Aristotle, *De Gen. et Corrupt.* ii. 10, 336^{a}27 sqq. This principle is implied by the meaning given to cause by Aristotle (98^{a}35 sqq.) and by Grosseteste; cf. above pp. 81–82.

[3] 'fit enim demonstratio dignior, aliis existentibus eisdem, aut ex minoribus questionibus aut suppositionibus aut propositionibus. Si enim note sint similiter cognoscere velocius per hec est, hoc autem appetibilius est.' Latin text of Aristotle (86^{a}33-6) in *Comm. Post.* i. 17, f. 17vb.

[4] Ptolemy in the *Almagest* (iii. 4 and xiii. 2, Venetiis, 1515) had made use of the principle of economy as a pragmatic principle when deciding between different theories accounting for the motion of the heavenly bodies; see L. O. Kattsoff, *Isis*, xxxviii (1947) 18 sqq. Averroës in his commentary on the *Metaphysics* (xii. ii. 4, Comm. 45, Venetiis 1552, viii, f. 154vb) had put it forward as a real principle of nature. Grosseteste knew the *Almagest*, which he cited in his *Comm. Post.* (e.g. i. 17, f. 18rb) and other works (e.g. *De Sphaera*, Baur, 1912, p. 25), and when he was writing *De Lineis* and the other optical treatises he knew other commentaries of Averroës, though whether he knew this one is not certain (see above, pp. 47–51; *De Colore*, Baur, 1912, p. 78). As a logical principle

That is better and more valuable which requires fewer, other circumstances being equal, just as that demonstration is better, other circumstances being equal, which necessitates the answering of a smaller number of questions for a perfect demonstration or requires a smaller number of suppositions and premisses from which the demonstration proceeds. For if one thing were demonstrated from many and another thing from fewer equally known premisses, clearly that is better which is from fewer because it makes us know more quickly, just as universal demonstration is better than particular because it produces knowledge from fewer premisses. Similarly in natural science, in moral science, and in metaphysics the best is that which needs no premisses[1] and the better that which needs the fewer, other circumstances being equal.[2]

But Grosseteste, again like Aristotle, held the *lex parsimoniae* to be also a real, objective principle of nature. As he said in his *De Lineis*, when speaking of the propagation of 'virtue' or power:

Power from natural agents may go by a short line, and then is its activity greater. . . . But if by a straight line then its action is stronger and better, as Aristotle says in Book V of the *Physics*,[3] because nature operates in the shortest way possible. But the straight line is the shortest of all, as he says in the same place.[4]

And in *De Iride* he said in justification of his law of refraction of light: 'Et idem manifestavit nobis hoc principium philosophiae naturalis, scilicet quod "omnis operatio naturae est modo finitissimo, ordinatissimo, brevissimo et optimo quo ei possibile est".'[5]

based on a conception of reality, such as it was for Grosseteste, the principle of economy became a commonplace for later Franciscan philosophers at Oxford in the thirteenth and fourteenth centuries, as for instance for Richard of Middleton, Duns Scotus, and William of Ockham, though later medieval astronomers used it purely pragmatically within the limitations of 'saving the appearances' (Duhem, *Annal. philos. chrétienne*, vi, 1908, pp. 277 sqq.). Even Galileo and Newton seem to have regarded the validity of the principle as resting on the nature of the world. See below, pp. 308–9, 317, n. 3.

[1] i.e. where there is immediate perception of truth without the need for discursive reasoning.

[2] 'melior est demonstratio, aliis circumstantiis paribus existentibus, que eget paucioribus questionibus quas oportet absolvi ad hoc ut ipsa demonstratio sit perfecta, vel paucioribus suppositionibus et propositionibus ex quibus demonstratur.' *Comm. Post.* i. 17, f. 17vb.

[3] *Metaph.* v. 6 is probably meant. This (1016^{a}12 sqq.) is quoted by Grosseteste a few lines down. Cf. below, p. 145.

[4] Baur, 1912, pp. 60–61; cf. *De Nat. Loc.* ibid., p. 66.

[5] Baur, 1912, p. 75; translated below, p. 123. He justified the law of reflection by the same principle; see below, p. 96. Cf. also *De Differentiis Localibus*, Baur, 1912, p. 85, where the principle 'natura movens via brevissima movens est' is used to prove that bodies return to their natural place by the shortest route, this being a diameter. See also Baur, *Philos. Rob. Grosseteste*, p. 100.

Beginning with these assumptions about reality Grosseteste's method was to distinguish between possible causes 'by experience and reason'. He made deductions from rival theories, rejected those theories which contradicted either the facts of experience or what he regarded as an established theory verified by experience, and used those theories which were verified by experience to explain further phenomena. This method he explicitly put into practice in his *opuscula* on various scientific questions, where the theories with which he began were sometimes original though usually taken from such previous authors as Aristotle, Ptolemy, or various Arabic naturalists. Good examples are his discussions of the nature of stars and of comets.[1]

[1] Cf. Baur, ibid., pp. 63 sqq. Other examples can be found in his other scientific works, e.g. in *De Sphaera* (Baur, 1912, pp. 13 sqq.) where Grosseteste quoted observations by Ptolemy, Thabit, and other astronomers in discussing such theoretical points as the rotundity of the earth, the precession of the equinoxes, &c.; and as Baur (*Philos. Rob. Grosseteste*, p. 29) notes he appealed to experience rather than to the proofs given by Aristotle in *De Caelo* (ii. 4, 286^{b}10 sqq., 14, 296^{a}25 sqq.) to establish the sphericity of the universe. Grosseteste said: 'Quod autem coelum sit sphaericum, patet per apparentiam in visu', and the observation he quoted was that all the stars revolved round one fixed star (the Pole Star) in circles, which were smaller the nearer they were to this star. Ptolemy had used somewhat different observations to prove the same point (*Almagestum*, i. 3, Venetiis, 1515). In *De Calore Solis* (Baur, 1912, pp. 79–84) Grosseteste put forward an original theory of heat based on the principle that 'omnis enim passionis univocae est causa univoca'. He showed that heat could be generated by three possible causes, by a hot body, by motion, and by the concentration of rays, and that in each case heat was produced by the scattering of small particles of matter: 'In omnibus autem illis est proxima causa calidi disgregatio.' Hot bodies generated heat by a scattering of matter. Bodies in violent motion generated heat because of the tendency of their parts to scatter under the influence of opposing forces; the greater the tendency the greater the heat: 'Et illud maxime patet ratione et experimento.' Bodies in natural motion downwards generated heat for the same reason, because the different parts of the body were prevented by those lateral to them from converging on the centre of the earth. The concentration of rays generated heat because the particles of matter (e.g. air) incorporated with the rays passing through a dense medium were violently scattered when the rays met in a point. He concluded: 'Sic ergo patet, quod in his tribus generibus calidum inest causa univoca.' Going on to consider the heat of the sun, Grosseteste submitted each of the three possible causes to the test of experience and reason. He said that the sun could not generate heat in the same way as a hot body did, because if it did the heat would have to be transmitted to the earth by the celestial substance or quintessence, and this was impossible because the quintessence was inalterable. The motion of the sun could not generate heat either, because there was no internal tension in bodies in natural motion in a circle and there was no external resistance from the medium. Concerning one consequence of supposing that there might be such a resistance Grosseteste said: 'Sed hoc est falsum, ut patet experimento.' He was left with the theory that the sun generated heat by means of the concentration of rays, and the greater the 'incorporatio lucis cum aëre' the greater was the 'disgregatio partium aëris in collectione radiorum' and the greater the heat. He showed that this theory agreed with all the observations: 'Quod etiam patet

Concerning the nature of stars, he discussed whether this was the same as that of the spheres which bore them. He began his tract with a statement of the uniformity principle and then went on to examine the evidence.

Things of the same nature are productive of the same operations according to their nature. Therefore if the same operations are not produced by their natures they are not of the same nature. But the spheres and the stars are not productive of the same operations according to their natures. Therefore the spheres and their stars are not of the same nature.[1]

The major premiss is plain from this proposition which Aristotle made in Book II of the *De Generatione et Corruptione*: 'the same cause, provided it remains in the same condition, cannot produce anything but the same effect'. The minor premiss of this syllogism is evident thus: the sun when present is the principle of generation and when absent of corruption.[2] If therefore the sphere of the sun produced the same effect or operation as the sun, since it is always equally present everywhere in any one given region it would be always causing generation. But this is false, therefore so is the first statement [*sc.* that the sun and its sphere are of the same nature].[3]

In discussing the nature of comets he began with the statement that

those who consider and make observations on things and produce a theory from their observations without the foundation of reason necessarily fall into false opinions, and concerning the nature of comets there is a variety of theories depending on the variety of the experience which they have received through radiations and generations of fire, and through optical illusions due to the diaphanous medium.[4]

The first theory he considered was that put forward by 'those who have observed that rays of the sun falling on a mirror are reflected many times with visible radiation' and who held that the tail of the comet was produced by the reflection of the sun's radiation falling on a planet. But, Grosseteste argued, this theory was disproved by two

experimento.' Grosseteste referred twice in this work to 'de Speculis' (ibid., pp. 81, 83); see below, p. 116, n. 4. Cf. Baur, 'Der Einfluss des Robert Grosseteste auf die wissenschaftliche Richtung des Roger Bacon', in *RBE*, pp. 52 sqq, and *Philos. Rob. Grosseteste*, pp. 157 sqq.

[1] This is an example of the *modus tollens* in hypothetical reasoning.

[2] The approach and retreat of the sun during its passage along the ecliptic Aristotle had already asserted to be the cause of the seasons.

[3] *De Generatione Stellarum*, Baur, 1912, p. 32. He went on to discuss further evidence, saying of one statement 'hoc est contra experimentum et contra rationem', ibid., p. 34.

[4] *De Cometis*, ed. Thomson, *Isis*, xix (1933) 21–22; cf. Baur, 1912, p. 40. Cf. Aristotle, *Meteor.* i. 6, 342^{b}25–344^{a}4; above, p. 83, n. 6.

considerations: first, because the reflected rays would not be visible unless they were associated with a transparent medium of a terrestrial, not a celestial, nature; and secondly, because 'the tail of the comet is not always extended in the opposite direction to the sun, whereas all reflected rays would go in the opposite direction to the incident rays at equal angles'.[1]

The second theory was that put forward by those who had observed that a 'concentration of many rays' would set inflammable things on fire, and who held that comets were produced by such rays coming together in the highest air and there igniting the inflammable vapours. But, he said, 'this theory is falsified'[2] because the rays must come from the planets, since if they came from the fixed stars the flame they produced would never change. But the planets moved so rapidly that a concourse of rays from them could not burn for long, whereas comets were seen to remain for six months. Moreover, if the concentration of rays was produced by reflection from vapour 'as from a concave mirror or through concentration as by passing through a spherical transparent medium', this sub-lunary vapour would neither retain its shape long nor follow the daily movements of the heavens, whereas all comets did both.

The third theory was based on the observation that 'many things close together may seem to be continuous when seen from a distance', from which analogy a comet was held to be an aggregation of several neighbouring planets. But, he said, this was false because comets did not always appear in the path of the planets.[3]

The fourth theory was based on the observation that the intervening transparent medium might distort the shape of a thing seen through it, from which it was concluded that a comet was an optical illusion of the sun, or of some other body, produced by rising vapour. But against this theory, he said, might be brought the same arguments from the properties of such vapour as were brought against the second theory.

Such were the theories advanced by those who based their ideas on observations alone without considering 'the principles of the

[1] In a treatise inspired by the comet of 1264, Aegidius of Lessines (1247–1316) made the following reference to Grosseteste's criticism of this first theory: 'expositio Lincolniensis fundatur super exemplum experimentale de resplendentia radiorum solis quando cadunt super corpus speculare sicut super specula seu super aquam.' Thorndike, *Latin Treatises on Comets*, p. 109; cf. pp. 2, 77–82, 87–92, 117–20, 156, 161–2.

[2] 'Ista opinio falsificatur.' Op. cit., ed. Thomson, p. 22; Baur, 1912, p. 41.

[3] Comets are not always in the ecliptic whereas planets are.

special sciences'.[1] The first such principle Grosseteste took was the Aristotelian one that there was no change except in position in the celestial region, from which it followed that comets must be sublunary. After some further discussion, each assertion being tested by reference to 'experience or reason', he advanced the theory that comets were produced by sublimated fire separated from its terrestrial nature by 'virtus celestis' descending from the fixed stars or planets and drawing up the comet as a magnet drew iron. Each comet was associated with a particular planet. Hence he came to the definition: 'A comet is sublimated fire assimilated to the nature of one of the seven planets.'[2] This theory he then used to explain various further phenomena.

Of particular interest is Grosseteste's treatment of optics and astronomy. These sciences introduced in a concrete form the problem of the relationship between the mathematical and physical aspects of theories postulated to provide the reason for observed facts. The use of mathematics made it possible to correlate concomitant variations in a protracted series of observations made with measuring instruments. A mathematical theory could give a formal description of what was observed to happen, and the truth of the mathematical theory depended only on the accuracy with which these facts could be deduced from it. But a mathematical theory gave no account of the material and efficient, to say nothing of the final, causes of change, and Grosseteste followed Aristotelian tradition in holding that no explanation of any set of occurrences was adequate which did not take account of at least the first two of these types of cause. A complete explanation would in fact have to include all four causes.[3]

[1] 'Hec ergo sunt opiniones de natura talium apparitionum quas possibile est ut performet sibi animus experimentis in rebus naturalibus cum non profundaverunt cum eis rationes scientiarum specialium.' Op. cit., ed. Thomson, p. 23.

[2] Ibid., p. 24. Hence the astrological significance of comets: Thorndike, *History of Magic*, ii. 446–7.

[3] Cf. above, p. 68.

V

Mathematical Physics

(1)

MATHEMATICS could often provide the reason for occurrences in
the world of experience, Grosseteste held, because although the subject that mathematics studied was abstract quantity,[1] mathematical
entities actually existed as quantitative aspects of physical things.
In fact 'quantitative dispositions are common to all mathematical
sciences . . . and to natural science'.[2] Therefore, as Aristotle[3] had
said, the different branches of mathematics logically subordinated
to themselves different physical sciences concerned with physical
things. The superior mathematical science then provided knowledge
of the reason for facts provided by the lower physical science.

Another way in which science *propter quid* and science *quia* differ is that
in which one kind of knowledge is acquired through one science and the
other kind through another. Such sciences, of which one gives knowledge
propter quid and the other knowledge *quia* about the same thing, are those
which have such a relationship to each other that one is subordinating
(*subalternans*) and the other subordinated (*subalternata*). For example, the
science that is concerned with the study of radiant lines and figures falls
under geometry, which is concerned simply with lines and figures; the
science of constructing machines, as architecture and other mechanical
arts, falls under the science of the figures of bodies; the science of harmonies falls under arithmetic; and the science which sailors use to direct

---

[1] Aristotle had said in *Metaph.* K. 3, 1061ª30 sqq. that 'the mathematician investigates
abstractions, for before beginning his investigation he strips off all the sensible qualities,
e.g. weight and lightness, hardness and its contrary, and also heat and cold and the other
sensible contrarieties, and leaves only the quantitative and continuous, sometimes in one,
sometimes in two, sometimes in three dimensions, and the attributes of these *qua*
quantitative and continuous, and does not consider them in any other respect, and
examines the relative positions of some and the attributes of these, and the commensur-
abilities and incommensurabilities of others, and the ratios of others; but yet we posit
one and the same science of all these things—geometry.' Grosseteste several times
referred to the *Metaph.* (e.g. above, p. 47, n. 4; Baur, 1912, pp. 61, 94, 120) and a lost
commentary on that work is attributed to him; Stevenson, *Rob. Grosseteste*, pp. 43 sqq.,
Baur, 1912, p. 46. See also above, pp. 58–60, 81–82; below, pp. 129 qq.

[2] Above, p. 60, n. 2; cf. *Phys.* ii. 2, 193ᵇ23 sqq.; above, p. 5, n. 1.

[3] Cf. Aristotle, *Post. Anal.* i. 7, 75ᵇ14; 9, 76ª9 sqq.; 13, 78ᵇ32 sqq.; 27, 87ª31 sqq.
See also *Post. Anal.* i. 9, 76ª10–12; 12, 77ᵇ5–10; 13, 79ª1–15; 27–28, 87ª31–ᵇ4; ii. 15,
98ª24–29; Heath, *Mathematics in Aristotle*; and Ross, *Aristotle*, pp. 68 sqq.

the course of ships by the appearance of the stars is subordinate to astronomy.

But not all pairs of sciences, of which one is subordinating and the other subordinate to it, have one kind of relationship to each other, because [only] some of them are in general univocally united in one name and in one principle in the name. Indeed some are not united in one name. But where the subordinating and subordinate sciences are in general united in one name and in one principle (*ratio*) in the name, they are such that the subject of the subordinate science is made from the subject of the subordinating science by a superadded condition, but so that these two subjects remain the same in substance and one remains predicable of the other, as number-related sound is number-related. When, therefore, the subject of the subordinate science receives the name and definition of the subject of the subordinating science, then both the subordinate science receives the name and definition of the subordinating science and, in general, they are said to be univocal in the name of the subordinating science. I say in general that the subordinate science appropriates a condition which does not destroy the application of the name of the subordinating science, but permits it to be preserved, as naval science and mathematical astronomy are both called astronomy. Similarly harmony in sound and mathematical harmony are both called harmony. But when the subject of the subordinating science cannot be predicated of the subject of the subordinate science, then both are not united in the name of the superior science, as harmony is not called arithmetic, for the subject of arithmetic is simply number, but as receptive of absolute dispositions and not as referred to something else. But when with number are joined dispositions referred to something else, making one compound thing, then the subject of music is formed. For the subject of music is not number between which there is relation, but the compound formed from number and relation, and since number is not predicated of this compound, the part is not predicated of its whole. Nor is it to be supposed that the subject of the subordinating science is always directly predicable of the subject of the subordinated science, for arithmetic subordinates to itself the tenth part of geometry, but not simply or because lines and surfaces are numbers, but when number descends into the subject of the subordinated science in some way the two sciences produce something in the nature of number. . . . Similarly, the science of the elements descends into the science of medicine, of which the subject is the human body as regards restoring it to health and removing health from it, but not the human body as being itself an element but as being composed of elements. Therefore, with such sciences of which one is under the other, the superior science provides the reason (*propter quid*) for that thing of which the inferior science provides the fact (*quia*).

But one must know that an inferior science always adds the condition by which it appropriates to itself the subject and also the characteristics of the superior science, and they are in the conclusions of the subordinate science like two natures, namely, the nature which it receives from the superior and its own nature which it superadds of itself. And so the superior science does not speak of the causes of the thing that is super-added—and sometimes the inferior science speaks of the causes and some-times not—but the superior science treats of the causes of the subject which the inferior science receives from it. And so the subordinating science treats of the causes of a conclusion that has been appropriated into the subordinate science, and it does this not in itself but in its universal, for the conclusion of an inferior science is in the superior science only as in its universal. For this reason mathematicians very often know the reason for a conclusion of an inferior science, but they do not know the fact, because they do not know the cause of the conclusion in itself but in the universal and from the mathematical aspect. And these sciences are sub-ordinate to mathematics which consider forms existing in the subject, but not as being in the subject but as abstract. The inferior sciences appro-priate these forms in some way to the subject; just as a science sometimes subordinates, sometimes is subordinated, so the same science may be sub-ordinated to one and subordinate another to itself. For example, optics falls under geometry, and under optics falls the science concerned with the rays of the sun refracted in a concave watery cloud. It is optics that provides the causes of the rainbow simply speaking, that is according to the condition of radiation which optics appropriates over and above the geometrical subject.[1]

[1] 'Sciendum autem quod scientia inferior semper addit conditionem per quam appropriat sibi subiectum et passiones superioris scientie et sunt in conclusione scientie subalternate sicut nature due, natura scilicet quam accipit a superiori et natura propria quam superaddit proprii. Itaque superadiecti causas non dicit scientia superior et quando-que dicit eas causas scientia inferior et quandoque non, illius vero quod accipit scientia inferior a superiori causas dicit scientia superior. Unde conclusionis appropriate in scientia subalternata causas dicit scientia subalternans non in se sed in suo universali. Non enim est conclusio scientie inferioris in scientia superiori nisi sicut in suo univer-sali. Propter hoc ipsi mathematici multotiens noscunt propter quid conclusionis in-ferioris scientie: nec tamen noverunt quia, quia non noscunt causam conclusionis in se sed in universali et ex parte ea, qua mathematica est.   Et hec scientie subalternate mathematice sunt que considerant formas existentes in subiecto, non tamen utuntur eis secundum quod sunt in subiecto sed secundum quod sunt abstracte.' (*Comm. Post.* i. 12, ff. 11vb-12^{r}; cf. Aristotle, 78^{b}31 sqq.) Resuming the same subject in *Comm. Post.* i. 18, f. 18^{r}, Grosseteste said: 'Et quia nihil scitur nisi ex principiis propriis et immediatis ad hoc quod sit scientia una, oportet ut habeat principia propria unificata in unitate subiecti unius ex quibus demonstret. . . . Et signum quod he sint conditiones scientie unius est quod cum per viam resolutionis pervenitur in immediata, ipsa immediata inveniuntur unita in genere uno et proximo cum partibus demonstratis et cum per se accidentibus demonstratis. Scientia autem est subalternata alteri cuius subiectum addit conditionem super subiectum subalternantis, que conditio non est totaliter exiens a natura subiecti

These two [mathematics and physics, Grosseteste went on in his *Commentarius in VIII Libros Physicorum Aristotelis*] have much common ground and because of this a physicist can easily make the mistake of thinking that mathematical being is physical being and that physical being is mathematical being; and so that he [Aristotle] himself will not in this science [physics] suppose something purely mathematical to be a demonstration on the assumption that it is physical, or omit something physical on the ground that it is mathematical, he subtly shows the difference between physics and mathematics so that it may be possible to distinguish what belongs to this science and what not. And so I say that there are three things, namely, physical body, magnitudes which belong to physical bodies, and accidents of magnitudes purely speaking. Mathematicians abstract magnitudes from motion and matter and have as subjects abstract magnitudes, and from these they demonstrate accidents which are *per se* accidents of magnitudes. But the physicist does not demonstrate *per se* accidents of magnitudes as belonging simply to magnitudes, but he demonstrates the figured magnitudes of physical bodies as belonging to physical bodies in so far as they are physical. Certainly the astronomer demonstrates the figured magnitudes of physical bodies, but not as belonging to them as physical bodies. For he does not show that the moon is spherical, considering the moon as a natural body, but it is enough for him to show that the moon is spherical, either as an effect or a cause of sphericity. The cause of sphericity simply speaking transcends nature. So the astronomer is on common ground with the physicist both in the subject and in the predicate of the conclusion, but the physicist demonstrates the predicate to belong to the subject by nature, whereas the astronomer does not care whether it belongs by nature or not. What, therefore, is the predicate for the physicist, is abstracted as the subject for the pure mathematician, though the subject and predicate are the same for the astronomer and the physicist. Hence, to the subject of pure mathematics are added the natural accidents making a composite physico-mathematical subject, and the mathematical accident of a composite subject of this kind is demonstrated as belonging to it on account of the natural accident of the subject. For example, from a line and a radiation is compounded a radiant line, and from it are demonstrated the accidents and forms of lines which belong to it as radiation. For this reason this is more physical than mathematical, and perhaps astronomy in certain parts of its conclusions is like this.[1]

subalternati, sed extra assumitur, velut radiositas non est natura totaliter exiens a natura magnitudinis sed extra assumpta.'

[1] 'Multis communicent hii duo [sc. mathematici et physici] et propter communicationem cito posset errare physicus putans quod mathematici est physici esse et quod physici est mathematici esse, ne ipse in hac scientia aliquid pure mathematicum assumat ad demonstrandum velud esset physicum vel aliquod physicum omittat velud esset mathematicum, differentiam physici et mathematici subtiliter ostendit, ut possit dino-

Precisely how he regarded the relationship between mathematics and physics in explaining natural occurrences Grosseteste made clear when he discussed the law of reflection, knowledge of which he got from Euclid's *Catoptrica*, Theorem 1.[1] Of this law Grosseteste said:

It is demonstrated in optics that every two angles, of which the ray incident with a mirror makes one and the reflected ray the other, are two equal radiant angles, and this conclusion has the following geometrical proof: in every two triangles of which one angle of one is equal to one angle of the other and the sides containing the equal angles are proportionals, the remaining angles belonging to them are equal. This proof, in as much as it is simply geometrical, abstracts from the radiant and non-radiant triangles, angles and sides, but since it comes in a demonstrative syllogism the above conclusion is appropriated in optics for the radiant triangles, angles and sides in this manner [an attempted geometrical proof follows]. . . . Therefore, every two angles of which the ray incident with the mirror makes one, and the reflected ray the other, are two equal radiant angles. And so it is clear that in the subordinate science, as much as in the subordinating science, the middle term so taken in the syllogism has led to the extreme term. But the syllogism of the inferior science differs from the syllogism of the superior science in this, that the syllogism of the inferior science is a syllogism *quia*, but the syllogism of the superior science is a syllogism *propter quid*, which is clear in the above example. For the

scere que ad hanc scientiam pertinent et que non. Dico itaque quod tria sunt, corpus scilicet physicum, magnitudines que accidunt corporibus physicis, et accidentia magnitudinum pure. Mathematici magnitudines abstrahunt a motu et a materia et subiciunt magnitudines abstractas et de hiis demonstrant accidentia per se magnitudinibus. Physicus vero non demonstrat per se accidentia magnitudinibus de magnitudinibus in quantum accidunt simpliciter magnitudinibus, sed de corporibus physicis demonstrat magnitudines figuratas secundum quod accidunt corporibus physicis ex parte ea qua physica sunt. Astrologus vero de corporibus physicis demonstrat magnitudines figuratas sed non in quantum eis ex parte qua corpora physica sunt. Non enim ostendit spericum accidere lune ex ea parte qua luna est corpus naturale, sed sufficit ei ostendere lunam est spericam aut per effectum aut per causam spericitatis. Causa spericitatis simpliciter naturam transcendit. Astrologus ergo et in subiecto et in predicato conclusionis demonstrate communicat cum physico, sed physicus demonstrat predicatum accidere subiecto per naturam, astrologus vero non curat an accidat a natura an non. Quod itaque physico est predicatum hoc abstractum est pure mathematico subjectum, astrologo vero et physico idem subiectum et predicatum. Propterea subiectis pure mathematicis superadduntur accidentia naturalia et fit subiectum compositum ex mathematico et naturale, et demonstratur accidens mathematicum de tale subiecto composito secundum quod accidit ei propter accidens naturale quod est in subiecto, utpote ex linea et radiositate componitur linea radiosa et demonstrantur ex ea accidentia et figurationes linee que accidunt ei ex parte radiositate et propter hoc magis physicum quam mathematicum est hoc, et forte astrologia in quibusdam conclusionibus suis est huic simile.' MS Digby 220, f. 88ᵛ; Merton 295, f. 124ᵛ. Cf. Aristotle's *Phys.* ii. 2, 193ᵇ23 sqq. This passage possibly owes something to Simplicius: see above, p. 5, n. 3, p. 45, n. 1.

[1] See below, p. 116, n. 4.

cause of the equality of the two angles made on a mirror by the incident ray and the reflected ray is not a middle term taken from geometry, but is the nature of the radiant energy generating itself according to the rectilinear progress, which, when it is generated on an obstacle having in itself this kind of spiritual nature, becomes there as a principle regenerating itself along a path similar to that along which it was generated. For, since the operation of nature is finite and regular,[1] the path of regeneration must (*necesse est*) be similar to the path of generation, and so it is regenerated at an angle equal to the angle of incidence.[2]

Thus geometry could provide the 'reason for the fact' in the sense that it could be used to describe what happened, could correlate the concomitant variations in the observed effects as, for example, between the angles of incidence and reflection.[3] But geometry could not provide knowledge of the efficient and other causes producing that movement. Geometry, in fact, was concerned explicitly with abstractions from such causes, knowledge of which could be obtained only by taking into account the physical nature of things or, in other words, the nature of the substance undergoing change. To give a complete explanation of the movement of light in reflection it was therefore necessary to know not only the formal, geometrical description of the movement, but also the physical nature of light which was the cause of that movement.[4]

In astronomy, which Grosseteste said was 'in certain parts of its conclusions' like optics, the main problem was to arrive at a theory which gave both satisfactory mathematical and satisfactory physical reasons for the same observed facts.[5] Of the astronomical theories

---

[1] Cf. above, p. 86; below, pp. 118, 123.

[2] 'Causa namque equalitatis duorum angulorum . . . non est medium sumptum ex geometria, sed eius causa est, natura radiositatis sese generantis. . . .' *Comm. Post.*i . 8, f. 8r.

[3] Thomson (*Writings of Rob. Grosseteste*, pp. 30 sqq.) has drawn attention to Grosseteste's early interest in Arabic mathematics, as seen in the matter copied in his own hand in 1215-16. This included *Algorismus* Jordani *tam in Integris quam in Fraccionibus Demonstratus*, Jordanus *de Fraccionibus*, Thabit *de Proporcionibus*, and various astronomical tables and similar works.

[4] Averroës made the same distinction in discussing the halo and its circular shape. *Meteor. Expos.* iii. i. 2, Venetiis, 1550, v, f. 205vb. In this he cited Alhazen.

[5] On this problem in the Middle Ages see Duhem, *Annal. philos. chrétienne*, vi (1908) 129 sqq. and *Syst. monde*, iii–iv. Grosseteste's main contributions to geometrical astronomy are contained in *De Sphaera*, *De Prognost.*, *De Motu Supercael.*, and the *Compotus* which have been printed, and *De Universitatis Machina* which has not. He said 'Magnitudo enim mobilis est subiectum astronomi' (*Comm. Post.* i. 11, f. 10rb), and 'Intentio nostra in hoc tractatu est describere figuram machinae mundanae et centrum [et situm] et figuras corporum eam constituentium et motus corporum superiorum et figuras circulorum suorum'. *De Sphaera*, Baur, 1912, p. 11.

known to Grosseteste, the Ptolemaic system was able to 'save the appearances' by means of the mathematical devices of epicycles and eccentrics, but it contradicted several of the fundamental physical principles of the Aristotelian system which, it was generally held, gave the only satisfactory explanation of the causes of the heavenly movements. It was essential to the Aristotelian system to consider the spheres bearing the heavenly bodies as concentric. Grosseteste used the Ptolemaic epicycles and eccentrics as devices to follow the movements of the planets as measured with instruments, to construct tables and to fix the length of the year,[1] though he said the Arab astronomer Alpetragius had saved the appearances with a modified Aristotelian system without using epicycles and eccentrics.[2] Grosseteste said of these devices in his *Compotus*, a work in which he made an important contribution to research on the reform of the calendar:[3] 'These modes of celestial motion are possible, according to Aristotle, only in the imagination, and are impossible in nature, because according to him all nine spheres are concentric.'[4]

Ptolemy's theory that the sphere of the fixed stars had two motions, one being that producing the daily rising and setting of the

[1] Baur, *Philos. Rob. Grosseteste*, pp. 41 sqq. This, and the lunar cycle, were the main problems in the reform of the calendar.

[2] 'facte sunt considerationes in instrumentis super modum motuum celestium. . . . Modus igitur verificandi quantitatem anni et kalendarium. . . .' *Compotus*, ed. Steele, p. 217; cf. Duhem, *Syst. monde*, iii. 282; Baur, op. cit., pp. 51–52.

[3] 'Compotus est scientia numerationis et divisionis temporum.' (*Compotus*, ed. Steele, p. 213.) Grosseteste was the first Latin writer to make a systematic attempt to bring about the reform that was put into effect only by Pope Gregory XIII in 1582. For Grosseteste's work on the calendar see F. Kaltenbrunner, *Vorgeschichte der Gregorianischen Kalenderreform*; Baur, 1912, pp. 60* sqq., *Philos. Rob. Grosseteste*, pp. 46–63; Duhem, *Système du monde*, iii. 277 sqq.; Grosseteste, *Kalendarium*, ed. Lindhagen; *Compotus*, ed. Steele, pp. vii sqq. Trivet (*Annales*, ed. Hog, p. 243) mentioned *De Sphaera* and *De Arte Compoti* among Grosseteste's most famous works, and the large number of MSS of these works is evidence of their popularity (Thomson, *Writings of Rob. Grosseteste*, pp. 95, 115). Grosseteste possibly influenced Sacrobosco (see above, p. 48) and certainly influenced Campanus of Novara (*Compotus*, ed. Steele, p. xxi; Duhem, *Syst. monde*, iii. 281, iv. 49 sqq.), Roger Bacon (Baur, in *RBE*, pp. 45 sqq.; Duhem, op. cit., pp. 397 sqq.) and Pierre d'Ailly (Stevenson, *Robert Grosseteste*, pp. 46–47; Thorndike, *History of Magic*, ii. 444, 644 sqq.), and he was quoted by several fourteenth-century writers such as John of Eschenden (Thorndike, op. cit., iii. 120, 325 sqq., 330), and Thomas Werkwoth (Thorndike, *Isis*, xxxix, 1948, p. 213). Four editions of *De Sphaera* were printed between 1508 and 1531 (Sarton, *Introduction*, ii. 585).

[4] *Compotus*, ed. Steele, p. 217. Averroës had also supported Aristotle against Ptolemy on 'realist' grounds in his commentary on *De Caelo*, a work to which Grosseteste referred in *De Nat. Loc.*, Baur, 1912, p. 69. See *De Coelo cum* Averrois *Commentariis*, ii. ii. Q. 2, Comm. 32, and Q. 5, Comm. 35, Venetiis, 1550, v. Cf. *Metaph. cum* Averrois *Commentariis*, xii. ii. 4, Comm. 45, Venetiis, 1552, viii. See Duhem, *Mouvement abs. et rel.*

stars, and the other a proper motion which accounted for the precession of the equinoxes,[1] Grosseteste criticized for contradicting
principles which he held to be fundamental to reality.[2] Nevertheless,
for practical purposes he used the Arab astronomer Thebit's version
of this proper motion; and he knew that certain observations, such
as the varying apparent diameter of the moon,[3] could be explained
by Ptolemy's system but not by Aristotle's concentric spheres. In
fact, he remained puzzled about how to reconcile the mathematical
devices for 'saving of appearances' which the Ptolemaic theory provided most satisfactorily, with the explanation of the cause of movement for which Aristotle's principles were most satisfactory. As he
said: 'It is suggested that the motions of the planets in latitude and
longitude are shown by means of their eccentrics and the motions
of progression and retrogradation by means of epicycles: how can
these different appearances be saved with one simple mover?'[4] In
practice he went on using both theories, adopting each where it was
the more satisfactory. He followed 'Ptolémée lorsqu'il voulait faire
œuvre d'astronome, et s'attacher à la doctrine des sphères homo-
centriques lorsqu'il se proposait d'être métaphysicien'.[5]

   This distinction between mathematical and physical subjects
Grosseteste used also in his *Commentarius in VIII Libros Physicorum
Aristotelis* to try to determine the meaning that could be given to the

----

[1] *Compotus*, C. 1; *De Sphaera*, Baur, 1912, 25–27; cf. Baur, *Philos. Rob. Grosseteste*,
pp. 43 sqq.

[2] 'Sed quomodo erit hoc', he said, 'cum motor [sc. the *primum mobile*] non sit nisi
unus, et a motore uno non proveniat nisi motus unus? Videtur enim, quod motus unus
simplex non moveat nisi motu uno simplici, et quod non proveniant ab eo motus duo
neque motus oppositi.' (*De Motu Supercael.*, Baur, 1912, p. 99.) This criticism was
based on the principle of contradiction and the non-inherence of contradictory attributes
in one substance at the same time. Cf. *De Motu Corp.*, Baur, 1912, p. 90 and below,
p. 202; and Duhem, *Mouvement abs. et rel.*

[3] See *De Sphaera*. On Grosseteste and Alpetragius see P. Duhem in *Fragment inédit
de l'Opus Tertium de Roger Bacon*, pp. 134–7.

[4] *De Motu Supercael.*, Baur, 1912, p. 99.

[5] Duhem, *Syst. monde*, iii. 397; cf. above, pp. 5–6; below, pp. 201 sqq. A common
attitude to astronomical hypotheses at the end of the thirteenth century was that
expressed by St. Thomas Aquinas: '. . . ad aliquam rem dupliciter inducitur ratio. Uno
modo, ad probandum sufficienter aliquam radicem: sicut in scientia naturali inducitur
ratio sufficiens ad probandum quod motus caeli semper sit uniformis velocitatis. Alio
modo inducitur ratio, non quae sufficienter probet radicem, sed quae radici iam positae
ostendat congruere consequentes effectus: sicut in astrologia ponitur ratio excentricorum
et epicyclorum ex hoc quod, hac positione facta, possunt salvari apparentia sensibilia
circa motus caelestes: non tamen ratio haec est sufficienter probans, quia etiam forte alia
positione facta salvari possent.' *Summa Theol.* i. xxxii. 1 (*Opera Omnia*, iv) 350. See
also his *Comm. de Caelo et Mundo*, ii. viii. 6 (lectio xi) (*Opera Omnia*, iii) 163–4.

concepts of vacuum and infinite space. He said that vacuum was like mathematical space, and he pointed out that a cube placed in a vacuum would not displace anything, as it would displace air or water in a space already containing those fluids.[1] Space 'as it was imagined by mathematicians'[2] could be thought of as empty or infinite in extent only because it was not the same as real space.

In these demonstrations one should imagine the vacuum either as a concave surface filled with nothing or as space filled with nothing, and if space thus imagined existed it would contain no local differences, especially if the space were infinite. So in a vacuum which is imagined as infinite there cannot be local differences, both on account of its infinity, and also because of the fact that the vacuum, if it exists, would have no nature but a privation, and therefore it can have no natural differences.[3]

Mathematicians were at liberty to think of space in this way for their own purposes and the geometer could not be accused of being false because he used abstract concepts not realised in physical fact.[4] But, Grosseteste said, the space of the real physical world must be considered as full, that is a *plenum*, because in fact a vacuum could have no physical existence.[5]

Mathematics, then, was an instrument for describing happenings in the world of experience. Essential to this use of mathematics was measurement, which meant performing operations which resulted in a number. Commenting on Aristotle's definition of time as the 'number of movement in respect of before and after',[6]

---

[1] 'Vacuum videtur esse stans et manens sicut spatium mathematicum. Cum enim quis ponit cubum ubi prius sint aqua vel aer vel aliud corpus illud corpus recedet et oportet recedens esse equale corpori cubi intranti nisi forte corpus recedens coeat propter condensationem. Si autem cubus intrat vacuum, vacuum non recedit nec recedit cubo intranti sicut recedit aer vel aqua. . . .' *Comm. Phys.* iv, MS Digby 220, f. 96rb; Merton 295, f. 131vb.   [2] Cf. below, p. 106, n. 2.

[3] 'Oportet in hiis demonstrationibus ymaginari vacuum sive superficiem concavam nullo repletam sive spatium nullo repletum, et in spatio sic ymaginato si esset nulle essent differentie locales, precipue si esset spatium infinitum. Sic in vacuo quod ymaginatur infinitum non possent esse differentie locales, tum propter infinitatem cum propter hoc quod vacui nulla esset natura sed privatio si esset, nec potest habere differentias naturales.' *Comm. Phys.* iv, MS Digby 220, f. 96rb; Merton 295, f. 131vb.

[4] *Comm. Post.* i. 9, f. 9^r; Aristotle, *Post. Anal.* 76^{b}40 sqq.

[5] 'ymaginatio ponit spatium infinitum et si spatium infinitum sit extra celum sicut dicit ymaginatio et si est repletum corpore infinitum est; si est vacuum sequitur ut post patebit quod sit plenum quia locum esse vacuum est impossibile et ita quod infinitum sit.' (*Comm. Phys.*, MS Digby 220, f. 91vb; Merton 295, f. 127^v.) Cf. Aristotle, *Phys.* iii. 4, 203^{b}25 sqq. Grosseteste said: 'Ostensum est quod non est corpus infinitum in augmento.' MS Digby 220, f. 93^r; Merton 295, f. 128^v.

[6] Aristotle, *Phys.* iv. 11, 220^a 24–25. The commentary on time begins with 217^{b}30.

Grosseteste pointed out that by using this definition rates of local motion and other kinds of change[1] could be measured and compared, just as magnitudes of bodies could be compared by measuring lengths.[2] But, he said, associated with all measurement was an inescapable inaccuracy which sprang from the nature of things and which made all human measurement conventional. As it was put in the clear summary of Grosseteste's views[3]

[1] 'Ostendit quod non solum motus localis sed omnis motus et omne mobile in quantum huiusmodi in tempore est, et ad omnem motum consequitur velocius vel tardius. . . .' *Comm. Phys.* iv, MS Digby 220, f. 98vb; Merton 295, f. 138^v.

[2] '. . . hic sit diffinitio temporis: tempus est numerus motus secundum prius et posterius; . . . tempus . . . habet comparationem ad motum sicut mensura ad illud quod per illam mensuratur. . . . [After a reference to 'Boethius . . . geometrie' he went on]: Tempus autem sic dicitur numerus motus sicut linee rationales et magnitudines rationales dicuntur numeri corporum que ipse magnitudines metiuntur secundum numeratas magnitudines et positas mensuras. Linea enim cubiti vel bicubiti numerus dicitur aliquis, qui secundum ipsius linee mensuram positam numeratur et dimetitur; sic secundum mensuras positas in tempore numeratur et metitur motus. Sicut natura facit lineas rationales per comparabilitatem determinatam in naturam, sic facit tempora ut rationalia per commensuratam mensuris temporalibus determinatis in natura.' *Comm. Phys.* iv, MS Digby 220, f. 96^{vab}; Merton, 295, f. 136rb.

[3] 'In diffinitione tamen temporis supra posita que ut puto explicat solam intentionem nominis, puto tempus dici numerum quo numeratur motus et metitur . . . Sed cum linea numeretur numerus est quo numeretur. Ponamus enim solam unicam lineam esse, et intelligamus eam abstractam ab omni materia. Hec iam metiri potest non per aliam lineam nec ad longum quia non est alia dimensio longitudinis ab ipsa nec per ipsam metiri potest. Quomodo enim per se ipsam scietur quam longa sit aut quam brevis sit; quomodo enim posset sciri de linea unius cubiti per se ipsam tantum quod ipsa esset unius cubiti? Si enim dicatur quod ipsa posset metiri per suam partem aliquotam, quomodo scietur de illa parte aliquota quanta sit? Si enim non sciatur determinata magnitudo illius partis aliquote, non scietur magnitudo totius per numerationem illius partis aliquote, non enim scio de tota linea quanta sit quia scio quod eius tertia pars est in ipsa ter. Sed si scirem quanta esset illa tertia, scirem quantum esset totum. Unde igitur scietur et metietur mensura linee unice? Unde aut quomodo mensuravit natura in intentione sua quantam voluit, aut oportuit facere primam lineam quam fecit, aut quomodo mensuravit? Non enim dici potest quod mensuravit eam corpore naturali subiecto. Similiter intelligamus unicum motum tantum, ut motum diurnum primi celi, et circumscribatur penitus omnis alius motus. Quero quomodo scietur an iste motus sit velox vel tardus et quomodo scietur an una revolutio sit facta in brevi tempore aut longo? Unde metietur tempus huius motus unici hec difficilia sunt valde ad que vix pervenit humanus intellectus. Credo tamen, sicut alibi diximus, quod unus numerus infinitus ad alium numerum infinitum se potest habere in omni proportione numerali et non numerali. Aliquis enim infinitus duplus est ad alium numerum infinitum et triplus et sic secundum ceteras species proportionis, et etiam aliquis numerus infinitus se habet ad alium sicut diameter ad costam, et hoc alibi probatum est. Et iterum audacter dico quod omnis numerus infinitus ipsi domino totius sapientie non est numerus infinitus plus quam binarius est infinitus; est illi finitus numerus infinitus collatus ex omnibus paribus, et similiter omnis numerus infinitus collatus ex omnibus imparibus et similiter omnes numeri infiniti qui infinities dividi possunt. Sicut enim que vere in se finita sunt, nobis sunt infinita, sic que vere in se infinita sunt, illi sunt finita. Iste

made by the fourteenth-century Franciscan Scotist, William of Alnwick:[1]

he said that one infinity is greater than another infinity and that there are more instants in a greater time than in a less and more points in a greater

autem omnia creavit numero pondere et mensura et iste est mensurator primus et certissimus. Iste numeris infinitis sibi finitis mensurat alias lineas quas creavit; numero aliquo infinito toto sibi et finito mensurat lineam cubitem, et numero infinito duplo lineam bicubitem, et numero infinito subduplo lineam semicubitem; et unus est numerus infinitus punctorum omnium linearum unius cubiti quo numero certissime et finitissime mensurat omnes lineas unius cubiti. Quomodo ergo mensuratur et numeratur primo linea prima mensurata? Puto quod numero infinito punctorum illius linee finite tamen mensuratur alius numerus, qui numerus punctorum non est in aliqua alia linea maiori vel minori, sed in maiori est maior numerus infinitus punctorum et in minori minor. Per hunc modum mensurandi non potest mensurare nisi ille cui numeri infiniti finiti sunt et cui unus numerus infinitus est magnus et alius parvus. Unde si nullo creato est infinitum finitum nullum creatum sic mensurat. Et certum autem est quod nostre intelligentie non est infinitum finitum sed potius econtrario. Unde predicto modo mensurare non possumus, sed lineam aliquam, quam predicto modo mensuravit mensurator primus, supponimus nobis primam mensuram, illam non metientes sed per illam ceteras maiores et minores omnes ei commensurabiles metientes et numerantes. Prima igitur mensura quam mensurat, mensurat simpliciter universalissime et certissime linea et numerus infinitus punctorum qui sunt in ista linea. Deinde aliquam mensuratam supponimus nos ipsam non metientes, quia nobis non est hic possibile, sed statuentes nobis istam mensurandi principium; et quia linea non potest actu separata esse a conditionibus materialibus per accidens dicimus mensurare materialia per materialia. Per se tamen non mensuramus nisi magnitudines et per ipsas magnitudines, et si intellectus non divideret inter materiam et ipsas magnitudines crederet quod per se metiretur materialia et per ipsa materialia, utpote non divideretur lineam a ligno, crederet quod per se metiretur lignea linea aut ligno. Hoc modo puto esse de tempore: factor temporis numeris infinitis sibi tamen finitis eternaliter antequam essent tempora omnia tempora et maiora et minora mensuravit. Tempus quod mensurat unam revolutionem celi mensuratur a factore temporis numero infinito instantium indivisibilium que sunt in illo tempore, et duplum tempus duplo numero infinito instantium et subduplum subduplo, et tempus illi commensurabile numero infinito; illi numero commensurabili potest enim numerus infinitus ad infinitum esse penitus incommensurabile. Et potuit sicut ordinasse si voluisset factor omnium quod una revolutio celi perficeretur in duplo maiori vel in duplo minori tempore quam nunc compleatur ut metitus est ipse tempus quo voluit unam revolutionem fieri aut per motum aut per spatium secundum sicut predictum est.' *Comm. Phys.* iv, MS Digby 220, ff. 96vb–97rb; Merton 295, ff. 136^{v}–137^{r}. The reference 'sicut alibi diximus', is to *De Luce*; below, p. 108, above, p. 47. Cf. also *Comm. Post.* i. 11, f. 11^{r}; i. 15, ff. 14^{r}–15^{v}.

[1] I translate the passage from Anneliese Maier, 'Die Anfänge des physikalischen Denkens im 14. Jahrhundert', *Philos. Nat.* i (1950) 32–34, and A. Pelzer, *RNP*, xxiii (1921) 397–8. It comes from William of Alnwick's *Determinationes* (MS Vat. Pal. Lat. 1805, f. 9^{rv}, 10^{v}), and William was actually relating an argument which Henry of Harclay adduced against him from Grosseteste's *Comm. Phys.* in a disputation on the question 'Utrum in maiori quantitate continua sint plures partes in potentia quam in minori.' Henry of Harclay was Chancellor of Oxford from 1312 to 1317, and according to Callus (*Oxoniensia*, x, 1945, pp. 45–46) the disputation took place in 1316–17; see also F. Pelster, 'Heinrich von Harclay, Kanzler von Oxford, und seine Quaestionen', *Miscellanea Ehrle*, i. 328 sqq. William of Alnwick, who was 42nd regent-master of the

magnitude than in a less. Whence he said that the primary measure of time, by which Nature has first measured the quantity of time, cannot be any quantity of time known to us, for that is not measured by itself and therefore it is measured by something else. Therefore the primary measure, as he said, is a certain infinite multitude of instants contained in time, for it is the prerogative of number to give the primary and minimum, though not of the *continuum*. And God, who knows that multitude, measures other times by the replication of it, because the same proportions can be found between infinite as between finite numbers, as for example double and half and the like. And therefore one time, which contains more infinite instants than another, is greater than it. Whence, after long investigation of the measure of lengths and times, he concluded: 'One' is the infinite number of points in all lines of one cubit's length, by which number God most certainly and definitely (*certissime et finitissime*) measures all lines of one cubit's length. . . . Later he said: The time that measures one move- ment of the sky or one revolution of it is measured by means of the infinite number of indivisible instants which are in that time, and twice the time by twice the infinite number of instants and half by half the number. . . . But to reach a precise and distinct measure of a continuous quantity the proportion of the numeral parts to the whole is not sufficient. For we do not know the quantity of any line because we know that it con- tains four of its four parts or five of its five parts, because we know this of every quantity of whose measure we are, however, ignorant. For it is necessary to know the quantity of its parts, which it is impossible to know except by means of some simple and indivisible part of it. Therefore there is no perfect measure of continuous quantity except by means of indi- visible continuous quantity, for example by means of a point, and no quantity can be perfectly measured unless it is known how many indi- visible points it contains. And since these are infinite, therefore their number cannot be known by a creature but by God alone, who disposes everything in number, weight and measure.

The point Grosseteste was making was that it was humanly im- possible to measure a *continuum* by means of the number of its primary and minimal parts, as, for example, 'when they say that the primary line measured is measured and numbered by some certain infinite number of points'. To continue William of Alnwick's summary:

This is impossible because that line is divisible to infinity into divisible parts, which is the truth and which they themselves concede when they

Oxford Franciscan house, made his *Determinationes* at Bologna in 1323: Pelzer, loc. cit.; Maier, loc. cit.; see also Little, *AFH*, xix (1926) 872–3; Maier, *Vorläufer Galileis*, pp. 161–8.

say that it is the prerogative of number to give the primary and minimum, though not of the *continuum*. . . . Again, referring to their statement about any line, which the first Measurer has measured in the aforesaid manner, we suppose ourselves that the primary measure does not measure that line but, by means of it, other greater and less lines, all commensurable with it, which it measures and we measure: this, I say, is not to teach how to measure but how to err. For how are we to know the number or quantity of that line which the first Measurer has measured? That quantity he reveals to no man, nor can we measure the line by means of infinite points, because they are neither known nor determined (*finita*) to us, as they are to God by whom they are comprehended. Whence this method of measuring is for us as uncertain as the first.

To overcome this difficulty in the practice of mathematical physics it was necessary to use conventional units of measurement. As another fourteenth-century follower of Grosseteste, the Oxford scholar Walter Burley, was to put it, 'to this state of incertitude I say that since the *continuum* is divisible to infinity, therefore in a *continuum* there is no primary and unique measure according to Nature, but only according to the institution of men'.[1] The mathematical physicist must measure magnitudes of all kinds by means of 'prima et minima mensura secundum institutionem'. Thus Grosseteste mentioned the finger and span and the cubit as units of measurement of length[2] and 'one revolution of the heavens' as a measure of time.[3] These units allowed the mathematical physicist to carry on with the practical problem of describing the world of experience.

The solution was, however, a pragmatic one. From the inherent uncertainty of the descriptions that mathematicians could give of the world of experience there was at a more fundamental level no escape. As the fourteenth-century French physicist, Jean Buridan, was to express it: 'It is to be noted that we cannot measure natural motions

[1] Gualteri Burlei *In Physicam Expos. et Quest.* iv, Text. com. 102, Venetiis, 1501, f. 133vb. Of the measurement of time Burley said: '. . . tempus est quasi quedam linea successionis . . . hoc nomen tempus significat uno modo durationem habentem prius et posterius absolute, alio modo significat durationem mensuratam . . . et reductam ad certum numerum, quoniam annus est duratio duodecim mensium, et mensis est duratio quatuor hebdomadarum, dies autem duratio 24. horarum . . . utputa ad unum determinatûm numerum ut linea decem palmarum habet rationem mensure.' (f. 133^{r}.) Cf. Maier, *Philos. Nat.* i (1950) 34. For Burley, see below, p. 186. In the section from which these quotations are taken Burley several times cited 'Linconiensem' on time, measurement, infinity, &c.(e.g. ff. 129^{v}, 133^{v}). He was referring to *Comm. Phys.*; above, p. 100, n. 3.

[2] Above, p. 100, n. 2.

[3] Above, p. 100, n. 3. On units of time measurement in the Middle Ages cf. Thorndike, *History of Magic*, iii. 123 sqq.; Grosseteste's *Compotus*, ed. Steele, pp. 290–7.

absolutely precisely and punctually, that is according to the manner of mathematical considerations. We cannot know by means of a balance if a pound of wax is precisely equal to a pound of lead, for there could be an excess of so small a quantity that we might not be able to detect it.'[1]

(2)

Besides the general consideration outlined above, Grosseteste had a special reason for believing that it was impossible to understand the physical world without mathematics, even though the principles that geometry could give to physics were not sufficient completely to define ontological natures and real causes. This opinion he based on his metaphysical conceptions about the nature of reality. He held light to be the first corporeal form[2] and the first effective principle of movement by which the operations or 'becoming' of natural things were caused. He held that the characteristic property of light was its ability to propagate itself instantaneously[3] in straight lines in all directions without loss of substance, and that in this way light had generated the universe. In the beginning of time God had created out of nothing unformed matter (*materia prima*) and light (*lux*) which, by autodiffusion, had produced the dimensions of space and then all subsequent beings.[4] For this reason Grosseteste believed that the study of optics was the key to the understanding of the physical world; and it was impossible to study optics without geometry, for light behaved according to geometrical laws.

This 'metaphysics of light' Grosseteste seems to have derived from earlier Neoplatonic sources.[5] The pseudo-Aristotelian *Liber de*

---

[1] Johannis Buridani *Quest. super Phisic.* iv, Q.14, Parhisiis, 1509, f. 81rb. In the same question he discussed the use of a clock: 'etiam per horologium mensuramus motum solis diurnum sciendo quot gradus in horologio signati correspondent uni hore et quot nocti et quot diei. . . .' (f. 80^{v}).

[2] *forma corporeitatis.*

[3] See below, p. 106. Cf. Aristotle, *De Anima*, ii. 418^{b}20; *De Sensu*, C. 6, 446^{b}27. This theory was rejected by Roger Bacon, who said that the propagation of light and other 'species' took time. See below, pp. 146 sqq.

[4] 'Lux ergo, quae est prima forma in materia prima creata, seipsam per seipsam undique infinities multiplicans et in omnem partem aequaliter porrigens, materiam, quam relinquere non potuit, secum distrahens in tantam molem, quanta est mundi machina, in principio temporis extendebat.' (*De Luce*, Baur, 1912, p. 52.) Cf. *De Statu Causarum*, Baur, 1912, pp. 120 sqq.; *Hexaëmeron*, MS Roy. 6. E. v, f. 147vb.

[5] For an account of Neoplatonic 'light metaphysics' see C. Baeumker, *Witelo*, pp. 357–467. For a discussion of Grosseteste's 'light metaphysics' see ibid., pp. 392 sqq., 413–14, 682; Baur, 'Das Licht in der Naturphilosophie des Robert Grosseteste', in *Festschrift Georg v. Hertling*, pp. 42–55, *Philos. Rob. Grosseteste*, pp. 76 sqq.; Duhem,

Causis[1] had given a terse account of the conception, deriving from Plotinus, of causality as an emanation: Plotinus had said that things had the power of exteriorizing themselves and so produced their effects as fire produced heat. The eleventh-century Spanish Jew, Avicebron, in his *Fons Vitae*, which Grosseteste also probably knew, had put forward the idea that all causal action followed the pattern of light. He said that *vires et radii* emanated from all substances, and that in addition in man animal *vis* flowed into the body from the rational *virtus*, as light flowed from the sun into the air, and that the power of an emanation decreased with distance from its source. In this manner form actualized the potency of the universal *continuum* of matter.[2] Other aspects of this Neoplatonic philosophy were added by Christian writers. St. Augustine had spoken of God as infinite incorporeal light and the source of incorporeal and corporeal created light, the latter being the noblest among bodies.[3] Pseudo-Dionysius had made an analogy between the emanation of goodness from God and of the light from the sun.[4] St. Basil, in his *Hexaëmeron*, had discussed a theory according to which the light described in *Genesis* before the sun and stars had been actually created three days before those luminaries, a theory of which Grosseteste made use in his own *Hexaëmeron*. Certain of his ideas Grosseteste may also have got from the school of Chartres and from William of Auvergne and Alexander of Hales.[5]

Implicit in this Neoplatonic philosophy of light there was perhaps always the possibility of expressing events in terms of mathematics, and certainly some Neoplatonic philosophers showed a strong liking

---

Syst. monde, v. 343 sqq.; Ueberweg–Geyer, *Gesch. der Philos.* ii. 371 sqq.; Sharp, *Franciscan Philos. at Oxford*, pp. 18 sqq.; C. K. McKeon, *Summa Philosophiae of the Pseudo-Grosseteste*, pp. 89 sqq., 157 sqq.

[1] *Liber de Causis*, ed. Steele (*Opera Hactenus Inedita Rogeri Bacon*, xii. 161 sqq.). See H. Bédoret, 'L'Auteur et le traducteur du *Liber de Causis*', *RNP*, xli (1938) 519 sqq. This is not *De Causis et Prop. Elem.*, above, p. 36.

[2] *Fons vitae*, iii. 52, editit C. Baeumker: 'Essentiae substantiarum simplicium non sunt defluxae, sed vires earum et radii, haec sunt quae defluunt et effunduntur' (p. 196). 'Quo magis elongatum fuerit lumen ab origine, erit debilius et spissius' (iv. 15, p. 245). See also p. 16. Cf. Duhem, *Syst. monde*, v; C. K. McKeon, op. cit., pp. 53 sqq.

[3] *De Genesi ad Litteram*, v. 20 (*PL*, xxxiv) 228; *De Libero Arbitrio*, iii. 5 (*PL*, xxxii) 1279. Cf. Grosseteste's *De Luce*, Baur, 1912, p. 52; *De Intelligentiis*, ibid., pp. 112 sqq. In *Comm. Post.* i. 7, f. 7rb, Grosseteste spoke of 'lux incorruptibilis creata vel increata'.

[4] *De Divinis Nominibus*, iv (*PL*, cxxii) 1128 sqq.; D. A. Callus, 'The date of Grosseteste's translations and commentaries on Pseudo-Dionysius and the Nicomachian Ethics', *RTAM*, xiv (1947) 186 sqq.

[5] Grosseteste's use of Alexander of Hales is, however, very problematic.

for mathematics. Grosseteste, by giving his 'light metaphysics' a new physical meaning and by relating it to geometrical optics, transformed it into mathematical physics and brought it within the realm of experimental verifiability, though in this he may have been influenced by Alkindi, who had taken a similar step.[1]

According to Grosseteste, light as the first corporeal form had two essential functions in the physical world: to be the basis of extension in spatial dimensions, and to be the original physical cause of all natural movement or change. From this first corporeal form there were generated, in the production of natural things,[2] a succession of other forms becoming increasingly more specific. For example, a given animal might be considered as consisting of a hierarchy of forms, from the first corporeal form, 'light', making it a material thing, through such intermediate forms as 'animal', to the most specific form making it the particular kind of animal it was. The two essential functions of light of producing magnitude and motion Grosseteste clearly explained in the following passages.

The first corporeal form, which some call corporeity (*corporeitatem*), I hold to be light. For light (*lux*) of its own nature diffuses itself in all directions, so that from a point of light a sphere of light of any size may be instantaneously[3] generated, provided an opaque body does not get in the way. Corporeity is what necessarily follows the extension of matter in three dimensions, since each of these, that is corporeity and matter, is a substance simple in itself and lacking all dimensions.[4] But simple form in itself and in dimension lacking matter and dimension, it was impossible for it to become extended in every direction except by multiplying itself and suddenly diffusing itself in every direction and in its diffusion extending matter; since it is not possible for form to do without matter because it is not separable, nor can matter itself be purged of form. And, in fact, it is light, I suggest, of which this operation is part of the nature, namely, to multiply itself and instantaneously diffuse itself in every direction. Therefore, whatever it is that produces this operation is either light itself or

---

[1] See below, p. 117, n. 2; p. 136, n. 3.

[2] As Grosseteste said in his *Comm. Phys.*: 'a prima enim forma que lux est gignitur omnis forma naturalis substantialis et accidentalis.' (MS Digby 220, f. 86ᵛ; Merton 295, f. 122ᵛ.) 'An forte omne corpus in universitate rerum sensibile est? Non est enim corpus quod non participet luce, que per se visibile est. Sed sine hac ymaginari potest trina dimensio, sicut ymaginantur mathematici.' Digby 220, f. 93ʳ; Merton 295, f. 128ᵛ.

[3] St. Augustine had said that a visual ray travelled the vast distance to the sun and back in an instant or twinkling of an eye. *De Gen. ad Litt.* iv. 34 (*PL*, xxxiv) 319–20. Cf. below, p. 107, n. 1.

[4] i.e. body as such, *simpliciter*, is a punctual, positional substance lacking dimensionality.

something that produces this operation in so far as it participates in light, which produces it by its own nature. Corporeity is therefore either this light, or is what produces the operation in question and produces dimensions in matter in so far as it participates in this light itself and acts by virtue of this same light. But for the first form to produce dimensions in matter by virtue of a subsequent form is impossible. Therefore light is not the form succeeding this corporeity, but is this corporeity itself.[1]

One cause, in so far as it is one, is productive of only one effect. I do not rule out several efficient causes of which one is nearer and another more remote in the same order. Thus, when I say simply 'animal', I do not exclude another substance or particular substance. Hence motion, in so far as it is one, is productive of only one effect. But motion is present in every body from an intrinsic principle which is called natural. Therefore an efficient cause simply proportional to the motion is present in all bodies. But nothing is present in common in every body except primitive matter (*materia prima*) and primitive form (*forma prima*) and magnitude, which necessarily follows from these two, and whatever is entailed by magnitude as such, as position and shape. But simply through magnitude a body does not receive motion, as is clear enough where Aristotle[2] shows that everything that moves is divisible. Not, therefore, simply because of magnitude or something entailed by magnitude is a body productive of motion. Nor is primitive matter productive of motion, because it is itself passive. It is therefore necessary that motion follow simply from the primitive form as from an efficient cause. . . .

I hold that the first form of a body is the first corporeal mover. But this is light (*lux*), which as it multiplies itself and expands without the body of matter moving with it, makes its passage instantaneously through the transparent medium and is not motion but a state of change. But, indeed, when light is expanding itself in different directions it is incorporated with matter, if the body of matter extends with it, and it makes a rarefaction or augmentation of matter; for when light is itself charged with the body of matter, it produces condensation or rarefaction. So when light generates itself in one direction drawing matter with it, it produces local motion (*motus localis*); and when the light within matter is sent out and what is outside is sent in, it produces qualitative change (*alteratio*). From this it is clear that corporeal motion is a multiplicative power of light, and this is a corporeal and natural appetite.[3]

[1] *De Luce*, Baur, 1912, pp. 51–52. Some of the same points are made in the *Hexaëmeron*, MS Roy. 6. E. v, f. 147vb: e.g. 'Lux enim prior secundum locum gignit lucem sequentem et lux genita similis gignitur et est et gignit lucem sibi proximo succedentem, et illa succedens adhuc succedentem ulterius, et ita consequenter. Unde in instanti unus punctus luminis potest replere orbem lumine.'

[2] *Phys*. vi. 10, 240^{b}8 sqq.

[3] *De Motu Corporali et Luce*, Baur, 1912, pp. 90, 92; cf. below, p. 113.

The actual structure of the universe generated by the diffusion of *lux* Grosseteste tried to derive from a mathematical law correlating the intensity of *lux* with the density of the extended matter.[1] Since *lux* itself, Grosseteste held, was simple and without dimensions, it was necessary for it to multiply itself infinitely in order to generate a finite quantity: finite multiplication of a non-dimensional unit would not produce a quantity.[2] And so by infinite multiplication *lux* extended matter into dimensions of finite magnitude, the limits of which were determined by the exhaustion of the capacity of matter for further extension. The precise mathematical law governing this extension of matter Grosseteste led up to by a discussion of the proportions obtaining between infinite aggregates of finite numbers. For example, the aggregate of all (natural) numbers was infinite and was greater than the aggregate of all even numbers (which was also infinite) exactly by the aggregate of all odd numbers (which was also infinite).[3] Similarly, he said, in all numerical proportions there might be a proportion between infinite and finite, and this was the sort of proportion obtaining between the infinite multiplication of *lux* and the finite extension of matter. The precise dimensions of the universe so produced were determined by two principles, namely, that there was a constant relation between the activity of *lux* and the quantity of matter given corporeal form by spherical extension,[4] and that the intensity of this activity of *lux* varied directly with the distance from its primordial source. The resulting universe was a sphere more dense and opaque towards the centre and more rare and transparent towards the peripherae. He went on to give an account of the production of the different concentric spheres, the outermost sphere

[1] *De Luce*, Baur, 1912, pp. 52–54.

[2] In expounding this point Grosseteste introduced a discussion of atomism and summarized earlier views on the distinction between mathematical and natural points: ibid., pp. 53–54.

[3] Here, as C. K. McKeon (*Pseudo-Grosseteste*, p. 161) has pointed out, Grosseteste was posing the problem of finite and transfinite numbers, of which the successful resolution in the nineteenth century by Georg Cantor depended on the definition of an infinite class as one in which there was a 1:1 relation between the whole and the part. Cf. also A. Birkenmajer, 'Robert Grosseteste and Richard Fournival', *MH*, v (1948) 39. Cf. above, p. 100, n. 3; below, pp. 148, 174, n. 4. Galileo said that there could be no ratio between a finite and an infinite magnitude: *Due Nuove Scienze*, i (*Opere*, viii) 79 sqq. In this he agreed with Richard Swineshead, or 'Calculator' as he was called; see Boyer, *Concepts of the Calculus*, pp. 70, 115.

[4] C. K. McKeon (op. cit., p. 162) has pointed out that the upshot of Grosseteste's argument was that the intensity of action of *lux* and the cubic dimensionality of matter constituted two series related to each other as the whole series of natural numbers to some part of it.

emanating *lumen* (as distinct from the first corporeal form, *lux*) which produced the second sphere, this in its turn producing the third, and so on until all the celestial spheres and the four elementary spheres of the Aristotelian system were produced.[1]

By this *lux* as the first corporeal form Grosseteste did not, of course, mean simply visible light.[2] As an emanation or propagation of substance and power *lux* was the basis of all bodily magnitude and of all natural operations,[3] of which the manifestation of visible light was only one.[4] Every natural secondary cause, Grosseteste held, produced its effects as an efficient cause by a means (*quo est*) distinct from its essence (*quod est*), and in non-rational beings this means was an emanation of power (*virtus, species*) corresponding to a quality of the being,[5] the effect of this power on the recipient varying with the nature of the recipient. The understanding of events in the physical world depended, therefore, on the study of the propagation of this power; and since this propagation went according to geometrical laws, the study of its behaviour, though not the study of the essence

[1] 'Et sic procedit a corpore primo lumen, quod est corpus spirituale, sive mavis dicere spiritus corporalis. Quod lumen in suo transitu non dividit corpus per quod transit, ideoque subito pertransit a corpore primi coeli usque ad centrum.' (*De Luce*, Baur, 1912, p. 55.) Fire and the other elements were produced as follows: 'Et pars suprema molis huius disgregata non ad summum, sua tamen disgregatione ignis effecta, remansit adhuc materia elementorum . . . sic corpus primum multiplicatione sui luminis est omne corpus sequens.' Ibid., p. 56. Cf. above, p. 98, for metaphysical cosmology.

[2] Both *lux* and *lumen* were bodies (*corpora*) and not simply qualities; cf. Baur in *Festschrift Georg v. Hertling*, pp. 46 sqq.; *Philos. Rob. Grosseteste*, pp. 79 sqq. John Pecham (*Perspectiva Communis*, i. 60), who was influenced by Grosseteste, regarded physical light as a manifestation of a *quidditas* known only to reason; cf. Sharp, *Franciscan Philos. at Oxford*, pp. 22, 184.

[3] One of the most important functions of *lux* was to be the intermediary between spirit and matter. It was the instrument by which God produced the macrocosm of the universe, and the instrument by which the soul made contact with the physical body and the things of sense in the microcosm of man. In the second of these roles Sharp (op. cit., pp. 23, 28) has suggested that *lux* was probably Grosseteste's ingenious substitute for the immaterial *pneuma* of the Neoplatonists and the 'animal spirits' of medical writers: cf. Baur in *Festschrift Georg v. Hertling*, pp. 47–48. When light enters the eyes 'Lux igitur est per quam anima in sensibus agit et quae instrumentaliter in eisdem agit'. (*Hexaëmeron*, MS Roy. 6. E. v, f. 147vb.) Lux, by giving unity, proportion, and lustre to bodies, was also the essence of beauty (*Hexaëmeron*, f. 148^r). On the role of illumination, the analogy of physical light, in Grosseteste's treatment of the problem of certainty see below, pp. 128 sqq.

[4] 'Lux enim que est in sole gignit ex sua substantia lucem in aere, nec est aliquid novum creatum ut sit lux in aere, sed lux solum est multiplicata et propagata. Alia utique est lux in sole et alia in aere; non tamen sic penitus est alia quin aliquo modo sit unitas essentie in gignente et genita luce. Aliter enim lux genita esset totaliter de novo creata et ex nihilo.' *Comm. Post.* i. 17, f. 17^r.

[5] *De Statu Causarum*, Baur, 1912, pp. 122–3.

of *lux* itself which was the cause of the propagation, was subordinate to mathematics.

The usefulness of considering lines, angles and figures is the greatest, [he said] because it is impossible to understand natural philosophy without these. They are efficacious throughout the universe as a whole and its parts, and in related properties, as in rectilinear and circular motion. They are efficacious also in cause and effect (*in actione et passione*), and this whether in matter or in the senses, and in the latter whether in the sense of sight, where their action properly takes place, or in other senses, in the operation of which something else must be added on top of those which produce vision. . . . For all causes of natural effects have to be expressed by means of lines, angles and figures, for otherwise it would be impossible to have knowledge of the reason (*propter quid*) concerning them. This is clear in this way: a natural agent propagates its power (*virtutem*) from itself to the recipient (*patiens*), whether it acts on the senses or on matter. This power is sometimes called species,[1] sometimes a similitude, and is the same whatever it may be called; and it will send the same power into the senses and into matter, or into its contrary, as heat sends the same thing into the sense of touch and into a cold body. For it does not act by deliberation and choice, and therefore it acts in one way, whatever it may meet, whether something with sense perception or something without it, whether something animate or inanimate. But the effects are diversified according to the diversity of the recipient. For when received by the senses this power produces an operation in some way more spiritual and more noble;[2] on the other hand when received by matter, it produces a material operation, as the sun by the same power produces diverse effects in different subjects, for it cakes mud and melts ice.[3]

Hence these rules and principles and fundamentals having been given by the power of geometry, the careful observer of natural things can give the causes of all natural effects by this method. And it will be impossible otherwise, as is already clear in respect of the universal, since every natural action is varied in strength and weakness through variation of lines, angles and figures. But in respect of the particular this is even clearer, first in natural action upon matter and later upon the senses, so that the truth of geometry is quite plain.[4]

By means of mathematical aspects of *lux* Grosseteste held that it was possible to explain qualitative differences in physical powers as

[1] The propagation of light was an example of the 'multiplication' or propagation of 'species'; below, p. 118.

[2] Cf. Aristotle, *De Anima*, ii. 11–12, 424[a]5–[b]19; *De Iride*, Baur, 1912, p. 72; Baur, *Philos. Rob. Grosseteste*, pp. 97–106.

[3] *De Lineis*, Baur, 1912, pp. 59–60.

[4] *De Nat. Loc.* Baur, 1912, pp. 65–66.

arising from quantitative differences based on geometrical structure.[1] Such a view of things led him to attempt to explain the intensity of heat[2] and light[3] as due to the concentration of rays, and heat itself as a scattering of molecular parts due to movement.[4] Colour, he said, was 'light incorporated with the transparent medium', and the range of the nine principal colours from white to black was produced by the 'intension and remission' of three factors, namely, the purity of the medium from earthy matter (*puritas vel impuritas*) and the brightness (*claritas vel obscuritas*) of the light and quantity (*multitudo vel paucitas*) of the rays.[5] The purer the medium and the brighter the light and more multitudinous the rays, the nearer the colour approached white, lying beyond red at one end of the spectrum. And as these factors became less intense, so the colour produced was one nearer the blue and black end of the spectrum. That these factors accounted for the essence of colour, he said, was not only apparent to reason, but those learned in natural science and optics 'can by experiment (*per artificium*) visibly show every kind of colour they wish to'.[6]

[1] Cf. P. Duhem, *Théorie physique*; Baeumker, 'Über die Lockesche Lehre von den primären und sekundären Qualitäten', *PJ*, xxi (1908) 293 sqq.; and *De Gen. Stell.*, Baur, 1912, p. 33.

[2] *De Calore Solis*, ibid., pp. 81, 83, above, p. 87, n. 1; *De Nat. Loc.* ibid., p. 71, below, p. 123.

[3] *De Lineis*, ibid., pp. 63, 65; below, pp. 122, 112. Cf. *L'Ottica di* Claudio Tolomeo, pub. G. Govi, p. 14.

[4] See above, p. 87, n. 1.

[5] *De Iride*, Baur, 1912, p. 77; *De Coloribus*, ibid., pp. 78–79. See also *Comm. Post.* i. 19, f. 20^v, ii. 5, f. 30^v, and *Hexaëmeron*, MS Roy. 6. E. v, f. 147vb, for further remarks on colour. Aristotle, in *De Sensu et Sensibili* (C. 3, 439^a–440^b; C. 4, 442^{a}20–25), which Grosseteste cited in *De Gen. Stell.* (Baur, 1921, pp. 33–34), ascribed the formation of colours to mixtures of brightness and darkness, or white and black, in different proportions, and to the effect of impurities in the transparent medium. He discussed the same theory in *Meteor.* iii. 4, 374^a–375^a and it is found also in the peripatetic treatise, *De Coloribus*, which is included in the Aristotelian corpus (791^a–799^b). Grosseteste put forward his ideas on colour as a development of Aristotle's theory. A similar theory is found in Plato's *Timaeus*, 67C–68D. On theories of colour in Antiquity see A. Haas, 'Antike Lichttheorien', *Arch. Gesch. Philos.* xx (1907) 345 sqq., 'Die ältesten Beobachtungen auf dem Gebiete der Dioptrik', *AGNT*, ix (1922) 108 sqq. Aristotle said that there were three colours in the rainbow (red, green, and blue or violet), though a fourth colour (yellow) was also seen sometimes (*Meteor.* iii. 2, 372^{a}1–10). These three colours were 'simple' colours and according to Aristotle they could not be obtained by mixing other colours. Averroës said that there were four 'simple' colours, in Latin, *rubeus*, *croceus*, *viridis*, and *pavonaceus* (*Meteor.* iii. 3, Venetiis, 1550, v, ff. 208^v–9^v). Grosseteste cited both authors in *De Colore*, Baur, 1912, p. 78.

[6] *De Colore*, Baur, 1912, p. 79. Cf. below, p. 126. Grosseteste may possibly have been referring to Seneca's description of the production of colours similar to those in the rainbow by passing solar rays through glass prisms: 'Virgula solet fieri vitrea, striata

The concentration of light-power or virtue from the heavens on to the earth according to the laws of perspective, strength varying with distance,[1] Grosseteste held to be responsible for a number of different phenomena. They caused the differences in climate[2] observed in different parts of the globe, the growth of plants and animals,[3] the transformation of one of the four elements into another,[4] the astrological influences varying with the configurations of the planets,[5] and the rising and falling of the tides. For the last he offered two different explanations. The first was that briefly advanced in his commentary on the *Posterior Analytics*, in which he said that the rising of the Nile at the end of the month was due to the rising of the tide when the moon and sun were in conjunction and their combined power (*vis*) heated, rarefied, and expanded the water.[6] The second was that set out at greater length in *De Prognosticatione* and *De Natura Locorum*,[7] where Grosseteste said that the rising moon drew up from the sea floor mist, which pushed up the tide till the moon's strength increased so much that it drew the mist right through the water, when the tide fell again. The second, smaller monthly tide he explained by lunar rays reflected from the celestial crystalline sphere back to the opposite side of the earth, these being weaker than the direct rays.

The manner in which he held the laws of *lux* to be the generic

---

(*var.* stricta) vel pluribus angulis in modum clavae torosa. Haec, si in transversum solem accipit, colorem talem qualis in arcu videri solet reddit, ut scias non imaginem hic solis esse, sed coloris imitationem ex repercussu.' *Quaest. Nat.* i. 7. Grosseteste cited this work in *De Lib. Arb.* (Baur, 1912, p. 176) and he clearly made use of it in *De Iride* (see below, p. 125).

[1] He explained the variation of the strength of forces acting at a distance by means of his theory of multiplication of species 'according to figures' (cf. below, p. 120, n. 5). After discussing how 'agens multiplicat suam virtutem sphaerice' he went on: 'Alia autem figura . . . scilicet pyramidalis . . . completa est actio quando ab omnibus punctis agentis sive a tota superficie eius veniet virtus agentis ad quemlibet punctum patientis . . . pyramis brevior magis agat, quia conus eius minus distat a fonte suo, et ideo plus virtutis ibi invenitur, quam in pyramide longiori.' *De Luce*, Baur, 1912, pp. 64–65. Cf. Ptolemy, *Optica*, pub. Govi, p. 14.

[2] *De Nat. Loc.* Baur, 1912, pp. 68 sqq.

[3] *Hexaëmeron*, MS Roy. 6. E. v, f. 150vb.

[4] *De Impressionibus Elementorum*, Baur, 1912, pp. 87 sqq.

[5] *De Prognost.* ibid., pp. 41 sqq.

[6] *Comm. Post.* ii. 4, f. 30^r; cf. Aristotle 98^{a}31. The primitive character of this theory as compared with the second one is further evidence for the earlier composition of this commentary.

[7] Baur, 1912, pp. 48 sqq., 69 sqq.; cf. *Hexaëmeron*, MS Roy. 6. E. v, f. 58rb, where Grosseteste briefly adverts to this theory. See Duhem, *Théorie physique*, pp. 364–416; Baur in *RBE* and *Philos. Rob. Grosseteste*, pp. 138 sqq.

cause behind apparently different phenomena Grosseteste made clear when he justified his use of the principle of economy by the nature of *lux* itself[1] and in more detail when he explained the echo, the rainbow, and the reflection of light from a mirror as all being really cases of the repercussion of *lux*.[2] He said:

Of the things that are under the same analogous thing, some are symmetrical therein, as in generated nature, and the mutual difference is as it is in opposite species of which none is the cause of the other; and some, on the contrary, are so constituted in themselves that one is the cause of the other and under the other in causal order, as for example the echo, the rainbow, and the appearance of images in a mirror are as opposite species under one analogous genus which is repercussion, and all are as one in the genus in which through one middle term it is possible to demonstrate one analogous effect. And regarding each separately, by means of the proper middle term the same effect is derived, as we said in the first book about the four proportionals. Since they are interchangeable, what is demonstrated in the demonstration in the fifth book of Euclid is demonstrated also in regard to lines, surfaces, numbers and solids separately in their own sciences. But the echo is the repercussion of sound from an obstacle, just as the appearance of images is the repercussion of visual rays from the surface of a mirror and the rainbow is the repercussion or refraction of rays of the sun in a concave aqueous cloud. For, when light diffusing itself in a straight line comes to an obstacle preventing its advance, it is collected in the place of incidence on the obstacle; and because its nature is to diffuse and generate in a straight line, when it cannot generate itself by advancing directly, it can generate itself only by turning back if the obstacle is an opaque body. Or, if the obstacle is a transparent body, it generates itself off the line and is not direct but penetrates the transparent object at an angle, as the ray of the sun falling on transparent water is reflected back from the surface of the water, as from a mirror, and also

---

[1] See above, pp. 86, 96; below, p. 123.

[2] Light produced the elasticity of air like the seventeenth-century ether: cf. Duhem, *Syst. monde*, v. 358; E. T. Whittaker, *Theories of Aether and Electricity*; Baur, in *Festschrift Georg v. Hertling*, pp. 47, 53. For another discussion by Grosseteste of sound as a movement of the medium see *De Generatione Sonorum*, Baur, 1912, pp. 7 sqq. The drawing of an analogy between the cause of repercussion in light and sound might suggest that Grosseteste would have held that in reflection and refraction they behaved according to the same laws, as was suggested in the Aristotelian *Problemata* (901^b, 904): cf. C. B. Boyer, 'Aristotelian references to the law of reflection', *Isis*, xxxvi (1946) 93. The passage quoted below was Grosseteste's commentary on Aristotle's *Post. Anal.* ii. 15, 98^{a}25 sqq. Aristotle had said in *De Anima* ii. 7, 419^{a}25 sqq. that in sound and smell the object perceived set in motion the intervening medium whose movement in turn affected the sense organ. In the same chapter he asserted that light was not something travelling but a state of transparency of a medium. Grosseteste cited Averroës's commentary on *De Anima* in *De Lineis*, Baur, 1912, pp. 62, 64; above, pp. 50, 107.

penetrates the water, making an angle at the surface itself, and this is properly called a refraction of the ray (*fractio radii*). Therefore, as light (*natura luminis*) is reflected or refracted at the obstacle, so the rainbow is the reflexion or refraction of the light of the sun in a watery cloud and the appearance of images the reflexion of the visual ray at the mirror. For the visual ray is light passing out from the luminous visual spirit to the obstacle, because vision is not completed solely in the reception of the sensible form without matter, but is completed in the reception just mentioned and in the radiant energy (*radiositate*) going forth from the eye.[1] But the substance of sound is light (*lux*) incorporated in the most subtle air, and when the sounding body is struck violently parts of it are separated from their natural position in the whole sounding body. But a natural power sends the parts passing away from the natural position back to the natural position, and the strength of its return makes it again progress beyond the natural position, and once again it returns to the natural position, and this may happen several times till the parts are at length quiescent. And so the natural power produces sound by sending back the parts passing out from the natural position when the object has been struck violently and it causes vibrations in them. In the vibrating parts going forth from their natural position there takes place an extension of the longitudinal and compression of the latitudinal diameter, and when they return to the natural position there is in them an alternate constriction and extension of these diameters. And so, when this motion of extension and constriction in the same object, according to the different diameters, reaches the light (*naturam lucis*) incorporated in the most subtle air which is in the sounding body, sound results. For every natural body has in itself a celestial luminous nature and luminous fire, and the first incorporation of it is in the most subtle air. Hence, when the sounding body is struck and vibrating, a similar vibration and similar motion must take place in the surrounding contiguous air, and this generation progresses in every direction in straight lines. When, however, this generation comes to an obstacle in which the air cannot generate a similar motion in the above-mentioned

[1] Grosseteste accepted the extramission theory of vision adopted by Plato, Aristotle, Euclid, and Ptolemy, according to which visual rays went forth from the eye (see below, pp. 117–18), but he seems to have envisaged something being received by the eye as well. Roger Bacon reconciled the extramission and intramission theories by saying that it could be held that an immaterial visual species went forth from the eye and gave rise to sight, while material light rays entered the eye (see below, p. 152). Grosseteste in *De Iride* made the same distinction, which implied that the active psychological process of seeing went forth from the eye, while material light entered it (Baur, 1912, p. 73). He went on to quote Aristotle's *De Gen. Animal.* v. 1, 781^{a}1–2, 2, 781^{a}20 sqq. Plato (*Timaeus*, 45B–D) had in fact also recognized that sight involved something being passively received into the eye; cf. Beare *Greek Theories of Elementary Cognition*; Cornford, *Plato's Cosmology*, pp. 152 sqq. Avicenna, in his *De Anima* (i. 5, iii, *Opera*, Venetiis, 1508, ff. 4^v–6^r, 10–17), argued in favour of the intramission theory of vision; cf. Wiedemann, 'Zur Geschichte der Lehre vom Sehen' (1890) 470 sqq.; Crombie (1967), below pp. 354–5.

way, the expanding parts of the air are beaten or driven back on themselves and the vibration and motion in the air are again cast back and generated in the reverse direction, and the sound returns because of the obstacle, as with the visual rays. For, since it cannot generate itself in rectilinear progression, it regenerates itself by turning back. For the expanding parts of the air colliding with the obstacle must necessarily expand in the reverse direction, and so this repercussion extending to the light which is in the most subtle air is the returning sound, and this is an echo. Therefore, though what in these three cases in substance and truth is the reversal of light, in the rainbow it is the reversal of light because of cloud. An image is the reversal of visual light, that is the reversal of incorporeal light in the way described.[1]

This passage contains what was perhaps the first attempt to explain the rectilinear propagation of light as a succession of waves or pulses analogous to sound and, taken together with Grosseteste's other applications of mathematical aspects of *lux*, it foreshadowed in a striking manner a methodological principle on which much of modern mathematical physics, particularly since the seventeenth century, has been based. This is the principle that, in order to be described in the language of science, 'subjective' sensations should be replaced by concepts amenable to mathematical treatment.[2] In his account of vision Grosseteste distinguished between the sensation produced by 'species' in sentient beings, and the external physical activity which carried the species of light to the eye. This physical activity was independent of 'whatever may meet it, whether something with sense perception or something without it'.[3] It produced

---

[1] '... Substantia autem soni est lux incorporata in subtilissimo aere, et cum percutitur sonativum violenter necesse est partes eius disgredi a situ suo naturali quem habent in toto sonativo, virtus autem naturalis partes egressas a situ naturali reinclinat ad situm naturalem, et fortitudine reinclinationis sue facit eas iterum progredi ultra situm naturalem, et iterum reinclinat eas ad situm naturalem, et sic fit multotiens donec tandem quiescant partes. Itaque virtus naturalis sonat in reinclinando partes egressas a situ naturali occasione violentis percussionis [et] generat in eis tremorem. In partibus autem trementibus cum recedunt a situ naturali consequuntur extensio diametri longitudinalis et constrictio latitudinalis; et cum redeunt ad situm naturalem est in eis constrictio et extensio predictorum diametrorum permutata; hic motus itaque extensionis et constrictionis in eodem secundum diversos diametros cum pervenerit ad naturam lucis incorporate in subtilissimo aere quod est in sonativo, sonatio est. Omne namque corpus naturale habet in se naturam celestem luminosam et ignem luminosum, et eius prima incorporatio est in aere subtilissimo; percusso itaque sonativo et tremente necesse est consimilem tremorem et consimilem et motionem fieri in aere contiguato circumstante, et progreditur hec generatio in partem omnem secundum incessum rectum. . . .' *Comm. Post.* ii. 4, f. 29ᵛ. Cf. above, p. 109, n. 4.

[2] Cf. also below, pp. 145 sqq. Hence the seventeenth-century distinction between 'primary' and 'secondary' qualities; below, pp. 285-7, 335 (Baeumker).

[3] Above, pp. 110-11.

sensation in a sentient being simply because the sentient being was of
such a nature as to be capable of sensation, and in general its 'effect
is diversified according to the nature of the recipient'. The object of
mathematical physics was to relate those diversified effects to the
mathematical aspects of this physically propagated power.

(3)

Though Grosseteste held *lux* to be the basis of *all* natural causation, it was in visible light that its laws were most plainly manifested
and most easily investigated, and so he naturally paid special attention to the study of optics. The laws of optics, he held, were the basis
of all natural explanation.[1] It is in this science, in his attempt to explain the properties of mirrors and lenses and the rainbow, that his
use of mathematics in conjunction with his other methodological
principles is most clearly and fully seen. He was the first medieval
writer to discuss these subjects systematically.[2] For his knowledge
of optics he relied on Aristotle's *Meteorologica*,[3] Euclid's *Optica*
and *Catoptrica*,[4] the *Optica* attributed to Ptolemy,[5] Avicenna's

---

[1] Cf. Baur, in *Festschrift Georg v. Hertling*, pp. 47, 53, *Philos. Rob. Grosseteste*,
pp. 16–17, 93 sqq., 97 sqq.; Baeumker, *Witelo*, p. 606.

[2] For a general account of Grosseteste's work on optics see Baur, *Philos. Rob. Grosseteste*, pp. 93–133. Such earlier writers as Adelard of Bath, Thierry of Chartres, Gundissalinus, William of Conches, and Alexander Neckam had mentioned certain optical
problems but had not attempted to discuss them fully. Cf. Guillelmi de Conchis *De
Philosophia Mundi* in *Opera* Bedae Venerabilis, Basileae, 1563, ii. 341, where he
briefly discussed sight through a depth of water and reflection from a surface, and hearing as due to a percussion in the air. See also Neckam's *De Naturis Rerum*, C. 153,
'De Visu', where he said 'Quanto namque est remotior, tanto sub minore angulo videtur';
C. 154, 'De Speculo', where he mentioned plane, concave, and convex glass mirrors; and
his *De Laud. Divinae Sap.* Dist. 4, ed. T. Wright, p. 421, where he mentioned the rainbow; but he developed none of these themes.

[3] *De Iride*, Baur, 1912, p. 72; below, p. 117. Cf. above, pp. 35–36.

[4] Cited as 'de speculis', *De Nat. Loc.* ibid., p. 70; *De Iride*, p. 74 (below, p. 119); *De
Calore Solis*, pp. 81, 83; also *Comm. Post.* i. 8, f. 8r (above, p. 95). Euclid's *Optica* and
Catoptrica were published by Jean Pena in 1557 and by Heiberg in 1895; see Sarton,
Introduction, i. 156; Haskins, *Mediaeval Science*, p. 179. Also known as 'De Speculis' was
a compilation made by an unknown author from Euclid's optical writings and Hero's
Catoptrica (below, p. 213, n. 6, p. 216, n. 6) and translated from Arabic into Latin at the
end of the twelfth century: see S. Vogl, 'Über die (Pseudo-)Euclidische Schrift, "De
Speculis"', *AGNT*, i (1909) 419 sqq. For other works 'de speculis' see Björnbo und
Vogl, *Alkindi, Tideus und Pseudo-Euklid. Drei optische Werke*; C. Singer, 'Steps leading to the invention of the first optical apparatus', *SHMS*, ed. Singer, ii. 385 sqq.;
E. Wiedemann, 'Zur Geschichte der Brennspiegel', *APC*, Neue (Dritte) Folge, xxxix
(1890) 110 sqq.; Baur, *Philos. Rob. Grosseteste*, pp. 114–17; below, p. 147, n. 2.

[5] Eugenio the Admiral translated an Arabic version of Ptolemy's *Optica* into Latin
c. 1154; A. Favaro, 'L'Ottica di Tolomeo', *Boll. Bibliog. Storia Scienze matem. fisiche*,
xix, 1886, pp. 115 sqq. For its influence on thirteenth-century optics see S. Vogl,
Physik Roger Bacos, p. 26, and C. Singer, op. cit. Grosseteste does not seem to have

Canon,[1] and perhaps Alkindi's *De Aspectibus*[2] and Averroës's commentaries on the *Physics* and probably also on the *Meteorologica*[3] of Aristotle. He made no reference to Alhazen and it seems improbable that he knew of his work.[4]

Grosseteste's approach to the study of optics followed from the methodological principle of subordination which he adopted. 'The consideration of the rainbow belongs both to the student of optics (*perspectivi*) and to the physicist, but the fact ('*quid*') is the province of the physicist and the reason ('*propter quid*') the province of the student of optics'[5], he wrote, and continued:

First, therefore, we will say that optics (*perspectiva*) is a science which is based on visual figures,[6] and this subordinates to itself the science which is based on figures containing radiant lines and surfaces, whether these radiations are emitted from the sun, from the stars, or from any other radiant body. Nor is it to be thought that the emission of visual rays[7] is

cited this work by name but his references to the experimental demonstration of the law of reflection (*De Iride*, Baur, 1912, pp. 74–75) and his treatment of refraction in *De Lineis* and *De Iride*, and of colour in *De Iride* and *De Colore*, point to its use. Cf. below, pp. 119–23, 126; and see Roger Bacon, *De Multiplicatione Specierum*, ii. 2–3, ed. J. H. Bridges, ii. 462, 466.

[1] *De Nat. Loc.* Baur, 1912, p. 66: 'Avicennam . . . primo artis medicinae' is cited, the passage referred to here being *Canon Medicinae*, i. ii. ii. 8, Venetiis, 1608, i. 103^{a}30; cf. Singer, op. cit.

[2] See Baur, *Philos. Rob. Grosseteste*, p. 100, n. 4, p. 110. Cf. Björnbo and Vogl, op. cit.; H. Suter, *Mathematiker und Astronomen der Araber*. Björnbo proved that the Latin text of Alkindi's *De Aspectibus* which he published was by Gerard of Cremona. In the beginning of this work Alkindi said that he would show first how rays affected our perception and then how they followed the laws of geometry, and he went on to discuss the passage of light rays in straight lines, the properties of mirrors, and the influence of distance and the angle of vision on optical appearances. In Para. 10 he said that both vision and hearing were due to a form of motion. Though Grosseteste does not seem to have cited this work it is probable that he knew it. For Alkindi's tract, *De Radiis Stellicis* (*On Stellar Rays*), see Thorndike, *History of Magic*, i. 643 sqq., ii. 443. See also E. Wiedemann, 'Über al Kindi's Schrift über Ebbe und Flut', *APC*, Vierte Folge, lxvii (1922) 374 sqq.

[3] Baur, 1912, pp. 78, 102–4; *Philos. Rob. Grosseteste*, p. 121. See above, pp. 49, 111, n. 5; below, p. 125, n. 2.

[4] Cf. Sharp, *Franciscan Philos. at Oxford*, p. 120. A Latin version of Alhazen's *Optics* was made at the end of the twelfth century, possibly by Gerard of Cremona. See Baeumker, *Witelo*, pp. 226–33; G. Sarton, 'The tradition of the Optics of Ibn al-Haitham', *Isis*, xxix (1938) 403–6, xxxiv (1942–3) 217.

[5] Cf. above, pp. 91–93, 95. Cf. also Ptolemy, *Optica*, pub. Govi, p. 60; below, p. 118, n. 7.

[6] 'Figures' meant three-dimensional figures; see below, p. 120, n. 5; above, p. 112, n. 1.

[7] 'Visual rays' were rays sent out by the eye (cf. above, p. 114, n. 1) as distinct from radiations from the sun and other luminous bodies. The question whether light was a real movement in space or a product of perception was a common subject of discussion in the thirteenth century: cf. Giles of Rome, *De Intentionibus in Medio*, Q. 1, 'Utrum

only an imaginary condition divorced from things, as those people believe
who consider the part and not the whole. It should be realized, on the
contrary, that visible species (*species visibilis*)[1] is a substance similar to the
nature of the sun when shining and radiating, the radiation of which
species, together with the radiation of the exterior shining body, is entirely
responsible for vision.[2]

The first of the three parts[3] into which Grosseteste divided optics
was concerned with vision (*de visu*), and in this subject he distinguished between the passive (intramitted) and active (extramitted)
aspects of vision.[4] He made some brief but intelligent remarks about
certain optical illusions which he explained by means of the theory
that objects were seen on the straight line in which the visual ray left
the eye, no matter what happened to it afterwards.[5] The second and
third parts of Grosseteste's optics were concerned with mirrors (*de
speculis*) and lenses, respectively, and in them he was able to introduce mathematics.

In his *Optica*[6] and *Catoptrica*[7] Euclid had demonstrated his
theorems from a number of primary postulates about vision and
light rays, and the same procedure was followed by Ptolemy in his
Optica.[8] The law of reflection, which is the basis of the explanation
of mirrors, these two classical mathematicians had both treated as
following from their primary assumptions, though Ptolemy had
demonstrated it experimentally as well.[9] Grosseteste held the law to
follow from the nature of light (*lux*) itself, which he said was propagated according to the *lex parsimoniae*,[10] though he also said that the

lux sit realiter in medio vel intentionaliter' (G. Bruni, *Opere di Egidio Romano*, p. 214);
Roger Bacon, *Opus Maius*, iv, ed. Bridges, i. 216, ibid. v. ix. 2-4, ed. Bridges, ii. 66 sqq.
    [1] Cf. above, p. 110.   [2] *De Iride*, Baur, 1912, pp. 72-73.
    [3] *De Iride*, ibid., p. 73. The psychology of vision was much more fully discussed by
the later thirteenth-century writers on optics, Roger Bacon, Witelo, and John Pecham,
who had before them the example of Alhazen's *Optica*, vi. 4 sqq. See below, pp. 151
sqq., 165, 217; Baeumker, *Witelo*, pp. 610 sqq.   [4] See above, p. 114, n. 1.
    [5] *De Iride*, ibid., p. 75. Cf. Euclid, *Optica*, Theorems 2, 55, and Postulates 5, 6, ed.
Pena; Ptolemy, *Optica*, pub. Govi, pp. 22-29.
    [6] Euclid, *Optica*, Prologue, ed. Pena, p. 4.
    [7] Euclid, *Catoptrica*, Prologue, ed. Pena, pp. 45-46.
    [8] 'Cum ergo in omnibus rebus, quarum scientia quaeritur, aliquibus principiis
universalibus indigetur, videlicet ut praeponantur res sive in effectu sive in consistentia
certae et indubitabiles, ex quibus sequentes demonstrationes sumantur.' Ptolemy, *Optica*,
pub. Govi, pp. 60-61. Cf. Brunet et Mieli, *Histoire des sciences*, pp. 817 sqq.; A. Lejeune,
Euclide et Ptolémée; above, p. 7.   [9] See *Optica*, pub. Govi, pp. 62 sqq.
    [10] *Comm. Post.* i. 8, f. 8ʳ; see above, pp. 86 sqq., 96. This amounted to assuming the
principle of minimum path. Hero of Alexandria, whom Grosseteste did not know, had
shown that in reflection at plane surfaces the path taken by a ray was the shortest
possible one; see below, p. 216. Cf. Ptolemy, *Optica*, pub. Govi, pp. 155-6, xxxv.

law was shown 'by experiments'.[1] 'Universally the angle of incidence and of reflection make equal angles',[2] he said. Of this law, however, he made little further use and his discussion of mirrors was confined to a few remarks based on Euclid's *Catoptrica* about concave mirrors, which, he said, if held to the sun would reflect the rays to one point, the *locus combustionis*,[3] where wool or tow placed at that point would be set alight.

The third part of optics, which he said had been 'untouched and unknown among us until the present time',[4] though he thought that Aristotle[5] had completed it, Grosseteste discussed more fully than the other two.

This part of optics, when well understood, shows us how we may make things a very long distance off appear to be placed very close, and large near things appear very small, and how we may make small things placed at a distance appear as large as we want, so that it is possible for us to read the smallest letters at an incredible distance, or to count sand, or grain, or seeds, or any sort of minute objects. But how this wonder happens will be explained as follows. The visual ray penetrating through several transparent media of different natures is refracted where they meet, and the parts of it existing in the different media are joined at an angle at those meeting-points. This is clear from this experiment which is set out in the first place in the book *De Speculis*:[6] if something is put in a vessel and the observer takes up a position so far away that it can no longer be seen, and then water is poured in, whatever was put in will be seen.[7]

This is shown also, he went on, because 'the subject of the continuous is a body of one nature', so that a visual ray at the junction of two different kinds of media is cut by the junction. But, since 'the whole ray is generated from one principle', the discontinuity at the junction of the two media could not be complete, for if it were the generation would be interrupted. So 'the mean between full continuity and complete discontinuity can only be a point of one ray touching the two parts not in a straight line but at an angle'.

[1] *De Iride*, Baur, 1912, pp. 74–75; see below, p. 123. This statement does not, of course, necessarily mean that Grosseteste did the experiments himself, though the prima facie conclusion from his writings is that he did; see below, p. 122, n. 4.

[2] *De Lineis*, Baur, 1912, p. 62.

[3] *De Nat. Loc.* ibid., pp. 70–71; *De Colore*, ibid., p. 78.

[4] *De Iride*, ibid., p. 73.

[5] Cf. Boyer, *Isis*, xxxvi (1946) 93, n. 14.

[6] This experiment is described by Euclid, *Catoptrica*, Postulate 7, ed. Pena, p. 46; see above, p. 116, n. 4; p. 118, n. 7.

[7] *De Iride*, Baur, 1912, p. 74.

The clear suggestion of the possibility of magnifying lenses made in this passage Grosseteste based on the principle which he had learnt from Euclid and Ptolemy, 'that the size, position and arrangement according to which a thing is seen depends on the size of the angle through which it is seen and the position and arrangement of the rays, and that a thing is made invisible not by great distance, except by accident, but by the smallness of the angle of vision'.[1] The use of lenses depended on increasing this angle of vision by the refraction of light-rays, and Grosseteste tried to arrive at the quantitative law of this refraction.

Ptolemy in his *Optica* had tried to formulate the law of refraction of light.[2] He measured the angles of refraction of the extramitted visual rays[3] passing with various angles of incidence from air into water and glass, and vice versa. He discovered that the visual rays passing from a rare into a dense medium were bent towards the perpendicular to the plane surface between the two media, drawn at the point at which the rays passed through this surface; that with a given angle of incidence the amount of refraction was greater, the denser the dense medium; and that, with given media, the greater the angle of incidence, the greater the refraction. He thought that the amount of refraction increased in simple proportion to the angle of incidence, though in fact his observations in no way corresponded to this law.[4] When a visual ray passed from the dense to the rare medium, he found that it was refracted away from the perpendicular to the common surface.

Some of these results Grosseteste summarized as follows:

If the engaging body does not check the passage of the power (*virtutis*), then the ray falling at equal angles, or perpendicularly, keeps to a straight line of motion and is the strongest. But the one that falls at unequal angles deviates from the straight line of passage which it had in the first body and which it would have to maintain if the medium were uniform. This deviation is called the refraction of the ray (*fractio radii*).[5] This occurs in two

[1] *De Iride*, Baur, 1912, p. 75; above, p. 118, nn. 5, 6, 7, 8.

[2] *Optica*, pub. Govi, pp. xxxi sqq., 144 sqq. See below, p. 219, n. 3.

[3] What follows applies equally to the conception of intramitted light. Visual rays and light rays would go along the same path, in opposite directions; cf. below, p. 152.

[4] Cf. below, p. 225, n. 4. Ptolemy's law held only for small angles of incidence.

[5] In *De Lineis*, Grosseteste classified the operations of power as follows: I. 'super lineas et angulos', where there were (1) 'radii principales' which were of three kinds, 'linea recta', 'linea reflexa', and 'fractio radii'; and (2) 'virtus accidentalis', such as diffused light. II. Operations 'secundum figuras' as spheres and pyramids, where the dispersion of rays in three dimensions was considered. Cf. Ptolemy, *Optica*, pub. Govi, p. 14.

ways. If this second body is denser than the first, then the ray is refracted to the right and passes [on a line] between the straight line of passage and the perpendicular drawn from the place of refraction on this second body.

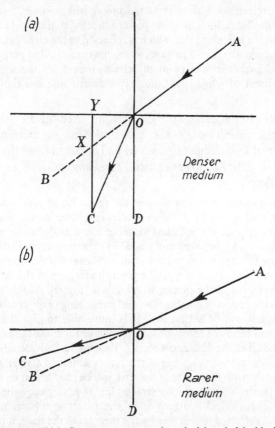

FIG. 1. Diagrams which Grosseteste seems to have had in mind in his discussion of refraction (see pp. 121–4). The source of radiation is at *A*, and the direction of the ray or power (*virtus*) is shown by the arrow. *OD* is the perpendicular to the interface between the two media, *OC* the refracted ray, and *OB* the projection of the incident ray *AO*. Similar diagrams are found in MSS of Roger Bacon's *Opus Maius*, e.g. Roy. 7. F. viii, 13 c., f. 24ʳ. See also Ptolemy, *Optica*, v, pub. Govi, p. 159 and Tab. VIII; éd. Lejeune, pp. 251–3. There are no diagrams in MSS of Grosseteste's own writings. Cf. Fig. 2.

If, however, this [second] body is rarer, then [the ray] is refracted towards the left, away from the perpendicular and on the farther side of the straight line of passage [Fig. 1]. This being so it can be seen that power (*virtus*) coming along the refracted line is stronger than that along the reflected line, because the refracted line does not depart much from the straight line of passage which is the strongest, while the reflected line departs a long way in the opposite direction. Hence reflection weakens the power more than refraction. Of the refracted power it is possible, however, to speak in a double fashion, because power refracted to the right is stronger than that to the left, since that which is refracted to the right passes nearer to the perpendicular line of passage, whether we refer to that perpendicular which is drawn from the point of refraction or from the agent, from the same point of which pass the perpendicular line and the refracted line.[1]

This theory of refraction Grosseteste used in an attempt to explain the operation of the spherical lens or burning-glass,[2] experimental knowledge of which he had obtained from the pseudo-Aristotelian *Liber de Proprietatibus Elementorum*.[3] His explanation was as follows:

In a familiar example we can observe the refraction of rays most beautifully. It is said in the book *De Proprietatibus Elementorum*, and anyone can confirm it,[4] that if a full glass vessel of round body, as for instance a urine flask (*urinale*), be taken and placed in the strong rays of the sun, the rays passing through the rotundity of it, on account of the double refraction mentioned above, run together from the far side of the flask to one point between it and the person who holds it [Fig. 2]. At this point and round it is the region of combustion, and if anything easily combustible is placed there it will be set on fire. It is impossible to give the cause of this except in terms of the double refraction of rays; for the ray passing through the air to the flask encounters in the vessel a body denser than the air. Therefore, according to one of the rules mentioned above,[5] every ray not passing through the centre of the flask will be refracted at its surface to the right, between the imaginary straight line of passage and the similarly imaginary perpendicular drawn from the point of refraction.[6] Then, having been refracted in this way by the medium of the flask, it passes out to the air which receives the rays. There, according to the second rule, it will be refracted again, going away from the perpendicular drawn from

[1] *De Lineis*, Baur, 1912, p. 63.

[2] The spherical lens or 'burning ball' was mentioned in the pseudo-Euclidean *De Speculis* (§ 14) published by Björnbo und Vogl in *Alkindi, Tideus und Pseudo-Euklid*, pp. 105–6. See also Baur, *Philos. Rob. Grosseteste*, pp. 114–15; below, p. 147, n. 2.

[3] M. Grabmann, *Lateinische Aristoteles-Übersetzungen*, pp. 198–204; V. Rose, *Arist. Pseudepig.*, pp. 631 sqq.

[4] 'et quilibet potest probare': this suggests actual experiments.

[5] *De Lineis*, Baur, 1912, p. 63; above, p. 121.

[6] The perpendicular would have to be drawn to the tangent at the point of incidence of a ray on the curved surface.

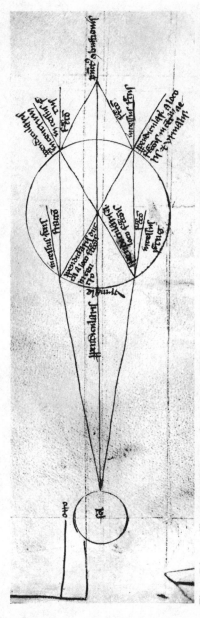

Fig. 2. Diagram illustrating Grosseteste's theory, in *De Nat. Loc.* (see pp. 122, 149), of the focusing of the sun's rays by a spherical lens; from Roger Bacon's *Opus Maius*, iv. ii. 2, MS Roy. 7. F. vii, f. 25ʳ. The same diagram occurs also in MS Roy. 7. F. vii, f. 4ᵛ. See also *De Mult. Spec.* ii. 3.

the point of refraction, on the farther side[1] of the straight line of passage, till it falls on the perpendicular which passes out. From the same point of the sun it is possible to draw one perpendicular ray to the centre of the flask, and this passes through unrefracted because of its strength. All the infinite number of rays, however, which pass out from the same point from which this perpendicular ray passes out, are spread out from the centre and refracted, yet in such a way that through double refraction they can run together on the perpendicular beyond the vessel; and at the point of meeting combustion occurs because of the congregation of rays.[2]

The quantitative law of refraction which Grosseteste put forward for rays (*radii*) passing from a rare into a dense medium was that the refracted ray bisected the angle between the projection of the incident ray and the perpendicular to the common surface[3] at the point of entry of the incident ray into the dense medium.

Now as to the amount of the deflection from a straight line in the ray that is joined at an angle, we shall represent this as follows. Let us suppose that a ray from the eye, passing through the medium of the air, reaches a second transparent medium and is extended in a continuous, straight line,[4] and from the point at which it strikes that medium a line is projected straight down into that medium such that it makes equal angles on all sides with the surface of the medium.[5] I say, then, that the path of the ray in the second medium[6] is along a line that equally divides the angle formed by the imaginary continuation of the ray in a straight line and the line drawn from the point of incidence of the ray straight down into the second medium, such that it makes equal angles with the surface of that medium.[7]

That the size of the angle in the refraction of a ray may be determined in this way, is shown us by experiments similar to those by which we discovered that the reflection[8] of a ray upon a mirror takes place at an angle equal to the angle of incidence.[9] And this same point has been made clear to us by the principle of natural philosophy that 'every operation of

[1] Reading 'ultra' as in Bodleian Lib. MS Laud. Misc. 644, 13c., f. 210ʳ and in *De Lineis*, Baur, 1912, p. 63, l. 19, instead of 'inter' as in Baur's text (p. 71, l. 26) and in other MSS.

[2] *De Nat. Loc.* Baur, 1912, p. 71.

[3] Or to the tangent with curved surfaces.

[4] Fig. 1, *AOB*, with the eye at *A*.

[5] i.e. is perpendicular to the surface: Fig. 1, *OD*.

[6] Fig. 1, *OC*.

[7] In Fig. 1(a), *BOC* = *COD*; see Baur, *Philos. Rob. Grosseteste*, pp. 117–18. Cf. Ptolemy's attempt at the law, *Optica*, v, pub. Govi, pp. 154–5; éd. Lejeune, pp. 243–5, cf. pp. 31*–33*, 262–6; Lejeune, *Recherches sur la catoptrique grecque . . .*, p. 157; above, p. 120, below, p. 225, n. 4.

[8] Called here *refractio*.

[9] Cf. Euclid, *Catoptrica*, Theorem 1, ed. Pena; Ptolemy, *Optica*, pub. Govi, pp. 61, 62–64.

nature takes place in the most perfect, orderly, briefest and best way that is possible'.[1]

He went on to show how to locate the refracted image by means of a construction used by Ptolemy:

Now a thing that is seen through more than one transparent medium does not appear to be as it truly is, but appears to be at the meeting-point of the ray issuing from the eye, extended in a continuous, straight line, and a line drawn from the thing seen which strikes that surface of the second transparent medium that is nearer to the eye, forming equal angles on all sides. [2] This is made clear to us by the same experiment, and similar reasonings, as those from which we learnt that things seen in a mirror appear at the meeting-point of the visual ray extended in a straight line, and the line drawn to the surface of the mirror, forming equal angles on all sides.[3]

Very simple experiments could have shown Grosseteste that his quantitative law of refraction was not correct. He was, in fact, primarily a methodologist rather than an experimentalist, and also, perhaps, he was too much obsessed with the principle of economy, according to which he believed *lux* to behave, and with the alleged similarity between refraction and reflection, to arrive at a correct understanding of the problem. Nevertheless, it was one of the basic principles of his theory of science that theories must be put to the test of experiment and that if they were contradicted by experiment then they had to be abandoned. In the next generation such natural philosophers as Roger Bacon and Petrus Peregrinus and, later, Theodoric of Freiberg were to use this principle as the basis of some really thorough and elegant pieces of experimental research.

To the third part of optics, which was concerned with refraction, Grosseteste said the study of the rainbow (*de iride*) was subordinate, and he tried to use his theory of refraction to explain the form and colours of the rainbow. As usual, he considered theories put forward by earlier writers and submitted them to the tests of 'experience and

---

[1] Cf. above, p. 86.

[2] In Fig. 1(*a*), with the eye at *A*, an object at *C* would be seen at *X*, where *AOB* intersects the cathetus *CY*. See Ptolemy, *Optica*, v, pub. Govi, p. 143; éd. Lejeune, pp. 224–5; Lejeune, *Recherches sur la catoptrique grecque* . . ., pp. 167–9. Cf. Turbayne, 'Grosseteste and an ancient optical principle', *Isis*, l (1959) 467–72; Crombie, 'The mechanistic hypothesis and the scientific study of vision', *Proc. Roy. Microscopical Soc.*, ii (1967) 26; Eastwood, 'Grosseteste's "quantitative" law of refraction', *JHI*, xxviii (1967) 403–14.

[3] *De Iride*, Baur, 1912, pp. 74–5. A diagram illustrating the last sentence is found in MS Roy. 7. F. viii, f. 28ʳ, of Roger Bacon's *Opus Maius*. Cf. Euclid, *Catoptrica*, Theorems 1, 16, ed. Pena, pp. 46, 55; Vogl, *AGNT*, i (1909) 427.

reason' before putting forward his own explanation. The writers on the rainbow to whom Grosseteste was most indebted were Aristotle and Seneca; his immediate Latin predecessors had done no more than mention the phenomenon and at best summarize some earlier explanations of it.[1] Aristotle,[2] who has confused the reflection of colour with refraction,[3] said 'the rainbow is a reflection of sight [i.e. visual rays] to the sun' from drops of water in clouds. He said also that the bow formed part of the circumference the base of a cone of which the apex was at the sun and the axis passed from the sun through the observer's eye to the centre of the bow (Fig. 3). From this it would follow that the higher the altitude of the sun the lower would be the altitude of the rainbow.[4] Seneca had attributed the rainbow definitely to reflection, believing it to be an enlarged re-flected image of the sun.[5] Grosseteste appealed to experience to falsify this explanation by reflection and advanced an original ex-planation of the form of the rainbow in terms of refraction.[6]

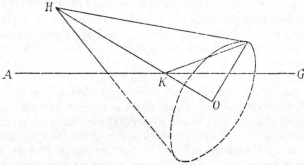

FIG. 3. Diagram illustrating Aristotle's theory of the rainbow (see above). The horizon is at AG and the sun (H), the eye of the observer (K) and the centre (O) of the circle of the rainbow lie on the axis of the cone of which the rainbow forms the visible part of the base above the horizon. See *Meteor.* iii. 5, 376ᵇ–377ᵃ.

[1] Cf. Neckam, *Laud. Divinæ Sap.* Dist. 4, ed. Wright, p. 421. See Baur, *Philos. Rob. Grosseteste*, pp. 119 sqq. Of Grosseteste's other possible optical sources, Euclid, pseudo-Euclid, Ptolemy, Alkindi, and Averroës (cf. below, n. 6) either did not discuss the rainbow or added nothing of importance to Aristotle's treatment. Avicenna mentioned some interesting observations but followed Aristotle in holding that the rainbow was caused by reflection only (see below, p. 157, n. 1, p. 158, nn. 2, 3). For the work of later Arabic writers on the rainbow see below, p. 147, n. 2, p. 196, n. 4, p. 234, n. 1.

[2] *Meteor.* iii. 2–5. For the recovery of Aristotle's diagrams see Theodoricus Teutonicus de Vriberg *De Iride et Radialibus Impressionibus*, hrg. von J. Würschmidt, p. xiv. Cf. A. Sayili, 'The Aristotelian explanation of the rainbow', *Isis*, xxx (1939) 65 sqq.; Boyer, *Isis*, xxxvi (1946) 92 sqq.

[3] *Meteor.* iii. 2, 372ᵃ17–21, ᵃ29–ᵇ9; 4, 373ᵇ33.   [4] *Meteor.* iii. 5, 375ᵇ16–377ᵃ27.

[5] Seneca, *Quaest. Nat.* i. 2–13.

[6] Grosseteste may have been influenced here by *Meteor. cum* Averrois *Expos.* iii. i. 4, Venetiis, 1550, v, f. 209ʳ.

Subordinate to this third part of optics is the science of the rainbow. Now a rainbow cannot be produced by means of solar rays passing in a straight line from the sun and falling into the concavity of a cloud, for they would make a continuous illumination in the cloud not in the shape of a bow, but in the shape of the opening on the side towards the sun through which the rays would enter the concavity of the cloud. Nor can a rainbow be produced by the reflection of the rays of the sun from the convexity of mist descending from the cloud, as from a convex mirror, in such a way that the concavity of the cloud may receive the reflected rays and thus a rainbow appear, because if that were so the shape of all rainbows would not be an arc, and it would happen that in proportion as the sun was higher so would the rainbow be bigger and higher, and in proportion as the sun was lower so would the rainbow be smaller, of which the contrary is manifest to the senses. Therefore the rainbow must be produced by the refraction of rays of the sun in the mist of a convex cloud. For I hold that the exterior of a cloud is convex and the interior of it concave, as is clear from the nature of the light and heavy. That which we see of a cloud must be less than a hemisphere, though it may look like a hemisphere, and when mist descends from the concavity of the cloud this mist must be pyramidally convex at the top, descending to the ground, and therefore more condensed near the earth than in the upper part. There will therefore be altogether four transparent media through which a ray of the sun penetrates, namely, the pure air containing the cloud, secondly the cloud itself, thirdly the highest and rarer part of the mist coming from the cloud, fourthly the lower and denser part of the same mist. It must therefore follow from what has been said above about the refraction of rays and the size of the angle of refraction at the junction of two transparent media, that the rays of the sun are refracted first at the junction of air and cloud, and then at the junction of cloud and mist. Because of these refractions the rays run together in the density of the mist and are refracted there again as from a pyramidal cone and spread out, not into the round pyramid,[1] but into a figure like the curved surface of a round pyramid expanded in the opposite direction to the sun. It is for this reason that its shape is an arc and that with us the rainbow is not[2] seen in the south. And, since the apex of the figure mentioned above is near the earth and its expansion is in the opposite direction to the sun, half of this figure or more than half must fall on the surface of the earth, and the remaining half or less than half must

---

[1] By 'round pyramid' he meant 'cone': cf. above, p. 112, n. 1, p. 120, n. 5. On this Witelo said: 'Conus dicitur pyramis rotunda vel vertex pyramis cuiuscunque rotundae vel laterae.' Vitellonis *Opticae*, iv, Definitio 10, ed. Risner, pp. 117–18. Baur, 1912, p. 76, ll. 30–31, prints 'non in pyramidem secundi rotundam': the word 'secundi' does not appear in MS Roy. 6. E. v, 14 c., f. 241^v or in Bodleian Lib. MSS Digby 98, *c.* 1400, f. 155^r and Digby 104, 14 c., f. 110vb.

[2] The word 'non' occurs, as the meaning requires, in MSS Digby 98, f. 155^r and Digby 190, f. 199^r: other MSS omit it, as does Baur, 1912, p. 76, l. 33.

fall on the cloud opposite the sun. Therefore, when the sun is near rising or setting the rainbow appears semicircular and is greater, and when the sun is in other positions the rainbow appears as part of a semicircle, and in proportion as the sun is higher, so is the part of the rainbow smaller. Because of this, in many places, when the sun has risen to the zenith, no rainbow can appear at noon. What Aristotle said about the variegated bow at sunrise and sunset being of small measure is not to be understood as referring to smallness of size but to smallness of illumination, which comes about because of the passage of rays through a multitude of vapours at this time more than at other times. This Aristotle himself later suggests, saying this to be because of the diminution of that which shines because of the sun's ray in the clouds.[1]

The colours of the rainbow Grosseteste tried to explain by his general theory of colour,[2] but he said that the variation in colour in one and the same rainbow was caused mainly by the quantity of the rays of light. Where there were more rays appeared the brighter colours towards red, and where there were less rays the darker colours towards blue. The difference in quantity of rays was caused by the transparent medium itself which, because of its shape, concentrated the rays in one place and dispersed them in another. This disposition of rays in the rainbow was not fixed, which was why it was impossible to paint a rainbow.

Grosseteste's insistence on the importance of refraction in the formation of the rainbow was a step towards an adequate explanation of the phenomenon, though his attribution of its shape to refractions through successively denser layers of atmosphere was not altogether happy. Had he been followed in this, the essential part played by refraction in *individual* raindrops might have been overlooked.[3] But the manner in which Grosseteste reached his theory exemplifies a method of procedure that has become an indispensable part of experimental science. When faced with a complicated and intractable phenomenon, such as the rainbow was, Grosseteste proceeded to reduce it to terms of a simpler and more tractable phenomenon, the refraction of light at the junction of two media, which he could describe by mathematics and investigate by experiment. The results of this investigation he then applied to the rainbow, which he attempted to deduce, as a particular example, from some general laws of geometrical optics.

[1] *De Iride*, Baur, 1912, pp. 75–77.
[2] See above, p. 111; *De Iride*, Baur, 1912, p. 77. Cf. Aristotle, *Meteor.* 372ᵃ5–6.
[3] See below, pp. 160, 197, 228, 251, 264–5.

VI

Metaphysics of Light

(1)

THE study of physical light had for Grosseteste, in his search for reality and truth, something more than a merely natural scientific interest. Following St. Augustine,[1] he held physical light to be the analogy of that spiritual light by which the mind received certain knowledge of the unchanging forms which he held, as *principia essendi*, to be, in the order of nature, prior to all, the essence of the real. For that reason, as *principia cognoscendi*, these eternal forms, or species, were the starting-point of the most certain demonstration, that found in metaphysics.[2] They existed *ante rem* as 'ideas in the Divine Mind', like Platonic ideas or exemplars, and *in re* as that 'through which particular things are what they are'.[3] Their existence made it possible for metaphysics to answer the question left by physics, to show how it was possible to have an eternally true demonstrative science, necessarily drawn from universal and necessary premisses, of perishable things.[4]

A thing was known exhaustively, Grosseteste held, when the concept of it corresponded to the eternal form existing in God's mind: 'truth is the privation of defect or the plenitude of being; for a tree

---

[1] Cf. St. Augustine's *De Trinitate*, xii. 9–14, ed. Migne (*PL*, xlii) 1005–11, and *De Lib. Arb.* ii. 13 (*PL*, xxxii) 1260–1, which Grosseteste cited in *De Veritate*, Baur, 1912, pp. 137–8. He cited Augustine extensively throughout his philosophical opuscula: cf. *De Unica Forma Omnium*, ibid., pp. 106 sqq., *De Intelligentiis*, ibid., pp. 112 seq.

[2] Above, pp. 58–60.

[3] 'Si intelligamus universalia per modum Aristotelis formas repertas in quiditatibus particularium, a quibus sunt res particulares id quod sunt, tunc universale esse ubique nihil aliud est, quam universale esse in quolibet suorum particularium vel singularium. . . . Nisi forte dicamus, quod universale ubique est, quia intellectus est locus universalium et . . . per modum spiritualem ibi est, ubi est illud, quod intelligitur. . . . Si autem universalia sint idee in mente divina, tunc universalia ubique sunt per modum quo causa prima ubique est. Si vero universalia sint rationes rerum causales create que sunt virtutes site in corporibus celestibus, tunc etiam ipse ubique sunt, quia virtutes corporum celestium ubique reperiuntur. Quomodo autem causa prima ubique sit et quomodo virtutes corporum celestium ubique sint et quomodo intellectus fit ibi ubi est illud quod intelligatur . . . altioris est negotii et non est nostre possibilitatis explanare; verumtamen quod ita sit, scimus, modum autem comprehendere non sufficimus.' *Comm. Post.* i. 18, f. 19rb.

[4] Cf. above, p. 58, n. 2; below, p. 130.

is a true tree when it has the plenitude of being tree and lacks the deficiency of being tree, and what is this plenitude of being except conformity to the reason of tree in the eternal Word?'[1] But just because these eternal unchanging essences were first in the order of nature, were most abstract and remote from sensible things, it was impossible for the weak and sense-bound human intellect, ascending by abstraction from the changing particulars of sensory experience, to reach certain knowledge of them by its own unaided efforts.[2] Commenting on Aristotle's statement that 'the science is more certain and prior which is knowledge at once of the fact and of the reason for the fact', Grosseteste said:

Entities that are prior are nearer to the spiritual light (*luci spirituali*) by whose pouring out intelligible things are made actually visible to the sight of the mind, and they are more capable of receiving this light and more penetrable by the sight of the mind, and so they are more certain and the science which concerns these is the more certain science. For this reason the science of separate incorporeal substances is more certain than the science of incorporeal substances bound to a body, and this again is more certain than is the science of corporeal substances, just as Aristotle said that the science of the soul is more certain than the other natural sciences which are concerned with changeable natural bodies. Nor does this contradict what was said above, that in mathematics error is rare because mathematical things are plainly visible to the intellect, nor what Ptolemy said,[3] namely that in mathematics knowledge is most certain and more certain than in metaphysics; because we hold that Divine things are more visible to the healthy sight of a mind not obscured by phantasmata, just as the brightest bodies illuminated by the sun are seen better by a healthy bodily eye accustomed to the vision of bright things. But for the infirm mental sight, as our sight is whilst we are weighed down by the weight of a corrupt body and with the appearance of corporeal things, are things wrapped up in phantasmata more visible, just as by the infirm bodily eye dark things casting some shadow are seen better than white things flooded by the full light of the sun. Therefore, for the human intellect as it is now in us, mathematical things are the most certain, because the phantasmata of the imagination received through vision help our understanding; but for the intellect as it should be in its most perfect state, Divine things are the most certain, and to the extent that things are prior and natures more sublime, so are they more certain.[4]

[1] *De Veritate*, Baur, 1912, p. 135.   [2] Above, pp. 59, n. 2, 72–74.
[3] Ptolemy, *Almagestum*, i. 1, 2, said that theology was incomprehensible, physics dealt with changing things, and therefore only mathematics was certain.
[4] *Comm. Post.* i. 17, f. 18rb. See Aristotle, *Post. Anal.* 87a31.

For the embodied human intellect the eternal forms existing as *principia essendi* could in fact be known with certainty only when they were shone into the human mind as *principia cognoscendi* by Divine illumination.[1] This illumination was a 'spiritual light which is shed upon intelligible things and the eye of mind (*oculus mentis*), and which has the same relation to the interior eye (*ad oculum interiorem*) and to intelligible things as the corporeal sun has to the bodily eye (*ad oculum corporalem*) and to visible things'. Moreover, 'the more receptive intelligible things are of this spiritual light, the more visible they are to the interior eye, and those things are more receptive of this light of which the natures are more similar to it'. Things prior in the order of nature were more penetrable by this mental sight, 'and the more perfect this penetration, the greater is the certitude'.[2] So by Divine illumination certain and eternally true science became possible.

Every demonstration proceeds from incorruptible things . . . because every perpetual thing is incorruptible. But here the question arises: how are universals incorruptible when particular things are corruptible? . . . To this it can be said that universals are principles of knowledge and for the pure intellect separate from phantasmata it is possible to contemplate the primary light (*lucem primam*) which is the first cause, and principles of knowledge are the uncreated reasons of things, existing from eternity in the first cause. For the conceptions of things that are to be caused, which have existed eternally in the first cause, are the rational principles of things that are to be caused and formal exemplary causes and originative sources. These are what Plato has called ideas and the archetypal universe, and according to the same author they are genera and species and principles, as of being, so of knowledge. Because the pure intellect can intuitively grasp these, it knows created things in them directly with the greatest accuracy; . . . the human mind, which is not fashioned to the pure so that it might contemplate the primary light immediately, often receives irradiation from the created light which is intelligence; and in the descriptions themselves (*in ipsis descriptionibus*) which are intelligence it knows posterior things of which the exemplary forms are those descriptions. . . . Therefore these created ideas are principles of knowledge for the intellect

---

[1] Note the analogy of 'celestial virtue' above, p. 128, n. 3.

[2] *Comm. Post.* i. 17, f. 16vb. He said that 'universalis demonstratio facit magis scire, quia facit illud scire, quod ab oculo mentis est magis visibile'. (f. 17^v.) In ibid. i. 19, f. 20^v, in a discussion of various forms of opinion, he used the same idea and made a comparison of errors of intellectual vision with errors of external vision in defective eyes. William of Auvergne in *De Universo* (in *Opera Omnia*, Venetiis, 1591) gave a much more precise account of the genetic function of this illumination; cf. the views of Aquinas, Bonaventura, etc.: see de Wulf, *Hist. of Mediaeval Philos.* ii. 47 sqq.

irradiated by them, and with such an intellect they are genera and species, and it is clear that these universals are incorruptible. . . . A thing is known in its formal cause, which is that in itself by reason of which it is what it is. . . . The form itself is not a genus or species, but, in as much as this form belongs to the whole compound and is the principle of knowing the whole compound, so is the genus or species both the principle of being and predicable of what the thing is. . . . But the defective intellect, which cannot ascend to the knowledge of these true genera and species, knows things in accidents alone, which accidents follow genera and species and are principles of knowledge alone and not of being.[1]

Apart from God, the light in which all was seen and known, there was no certainty in metaphysics; but by Divine illumination and by this alone man could have certain knowledge of the essence of the real.[2] 'Since . . . the truth of each thing is the conformity of it to its reason in the eternal Word, it is evident that every created truth is seen only in the light of the supreme truth.'[3] And when it was so seen, 'the intellect and science apprehend a thing in the purity of its essence, as things are in themselves'.[4]

The analogy between the corporeal *lux*, whose mathematical laws he held to underlie the operations of physical things, and this spiritual *lux* gave an additional force and interest to Grosseteste's belief that the study of geometrical optics was the key to knowledge of the natural world, and it must be reckoned among the reasons for the popularity of optics and mathematical science in the Oxford school. Grosseteste himself extended the analogy of light to illustrate the relation between the Persons of the Trinity,[5] the operation of Divine grace through the free-will, like light shining through coloured glass,[6] and the relation of pope to prelates and of bishops to clergy: as a mirror reflects light into dark places, he said in asserting his episcopal rights against the Chapter of Lincoln, so a bishop reflects power to the clergy.[7] With some of his followers in Oxford the physical science of optics became a method of arriving at a sort of analogical knowledge of spiritual reality and truth.[8]

[1] *Comm. Post.* i. 7, f. 7; cf. above, p. 58, n. 2.

[2] This view made for scepticism about the possibilities of purely human knowledge. The attempt to discover the natural grounds of certainty was the main impulse behind the advances in inductive logic made later by Scotus and Ockham.

[3] *De Veritate*, Baur, 1912, p. 137.

[4] 'Intellectus enim et scientia apprehendunt res in puritate essentie sue, sicut in seipsis sunt.' *Comm. Post* i. 19, f. 19ᵛ. Cf. above, p. 59, n. 2, p. 66.

[5] *De Lib. Arb.* C. 8, Baur, 1912, p. 179.   [6] Ibid., C. 10, p. 202.

[7] Rob. Grosseteste *Epistolae*, ed. Luard, pp. 360, 364, 389.

[8] Cf. Roger Bacon's (*Opus Maius*, iv, section on 'Mathematicae in Divinis Utilitas',

(2)

The conclusions reached so far, showing Robert Grosseteste's particular contribution to the theory of experimental science, may be summarized as follows:

1. Through the Latin translations of Aristotle's *Posterior Analytics* and *Physics*, of Euclid's *Elements*, and of certain other Greek and Arabic writings on astronomy, optics, and medicine, a coherent theory of scientific investigation and explanation, on which the ideas of twelfth-century writers had been vague, became known in Oxford early in the thirteenth century. According to this theory, the practice of a science involved a double procedure. The first was the advance by induction from the particulars of sense (*scientia quia*) to general principles or universals; the second was the deduction of particular occurrences from the general principles, which thus became their explanation and revealed their cause (*scientia propter quid*). The second of these procedures, which involved the conception of scientific demonstration or proof through causes, was the aspect of the theory of science on which the Greeks had concentrated, taking geometry as their model. In the twelfth and early thirteenth centuries the recovery of this conception of scientific demonstration, or explanation, was necessary to raise contemporary science above a mere collection of rule-of-thumb empirical techniques.

2. Grosseteste seems to have been the first fully to understand, expound, and use both aspects of this theory of science. In his thought he combined the empiricism of the new Aristotelianism with the conception, deriving from the older Augustinian-Platonism, that rational explanations of the world of experience could be provided only by mathematics. In his search for reality and truth he approached the study of nature, for example in his researches into optics and astronomy, having in mind a definite theory of investigation and a definite conception of the meaning of explanation. Logically this theory of science preceded his detailed researches, and chronologically the composition of his works probably took place in the same order.

3. Grosseteste's chief contribution to the theory of experimental science was to initiate the transformation of the Greek procedures,

ed. Bridges, i. 210 sqq.) discussion of the analogy between the transmission of light and of grace on the grounds that 'regulae, quae dictae sunt de speciei multiplicatione sumptae generaliter, intelliguntur in luce et in qualibet specie determinata' (p. 216). Cf. ibid. iv. ii-iii.

with their concentration on demonstrative proof through causes, into a method of research. First, in his discussion of 'resolution and composition', the method of discovering and defining the 'common nature' and so the cause of a given class of occurrences, he showed how a complex phenomenon could be broken up into its constituent elements, then reconstructed theoretically, and explained. Secondly, he recognized that a more abstract theory, capable of providing new knowledge not included in the empirical generalization of the 'common nature', could not be inferred from this generalization, and could be reached only by an act of intuition by the mind reflecting on the classification of facts made by induction. Moreover, he showed that a given set of occurrences might have more than one possible cause. Consequently, he held that the main part played by experiment in scientific research was to verify or falsify each theory by testing its empirical consequences. Grosseteste's theory of falsification, which he based on the principles of the uniformity of nature and of economy, is a striking feature of his theory of experiment. Thirdly, when faced with an intractable phenomenon like the rainbow, he tried to reduce it to terms of simple phenomena which he could study under controlled, experimental conditions.

4. Distinct from, though often in practice scarcely to be separated from, the use of experiment was the use of mathematics in natural science. Of particular significance was Grosseteste's conception of the nature of physical reality, as seen in his Neoplatonic metaphysics or cosmology of light, which led him to the belief that nature could be properly understood only through mathematics. The importance of this belief was that in mathematics he had a tool, a ready-made deductive system which could correlate events and suggest lines of experimental investigation and measurement. Grosseteste showed that the behaviour of many natural things could be deduced from mathematical abstractions, and he discussed in some detail how Aristotle's theory of the subordination of more concrete and particular to more abstract and general sciences enabled physical sciences to make use of mathematical theories. He illustrated this method by original work in astronomy and in optics, to the study of which his 'light metaphysics' led him to give a special importance. Of particular interest was the effect of using mathematical abstractions in showing how to control the experimental conditions under which to study a complicated phenomenon, as, for example, the rainbow.

5. Grosseteste's insistence on the necessity of mathematics for

natural science led him to develop Aristotle's fruitful distinction between mathematical and physical or causal theories. He held that the function of mathematics was simply to describe or correlate occurrences. It could give no knowledge of the efficient or other causes producing change, because it was explicitly an abstraction from such causes, though it could contribute to knowledge of the formal cause. The use of this distinction was a step towards the substitution, in science, of the functional logic of mathematics, a logic of relations capable of describing rates of change, for the 'physical' logic of substance and attribute. Grosseteste held that the nearest humanly possible approach to a complete knowledge of the cause of an occurrence could be acquired through the definition of the substance undergoing change as provided by mathematics and physics together.

6. In natural science, however, knowledge of causes was always incomplete and only probable. It was, in fact, impossible to exhaust either all the facts or all the possible theories that might explain them, and consequently the verification of a particular theory did not exclude the possibility that there might be other theories which were true in the same sense. Grosseteste's theory of verification and falsification implied, in fact, that any particular verified scientific hypothesis was 'true' only in the sense that it held over a given range of observations: it was not uniquely or finally 'true'. It was sufficient, not necessary.

7. Absolute metaphysical certainty about necessary truth, or reality, could be obtained, Grosseteste held, only by Divine illumination. He supported this theory by means of Aristotle's idea that things more abstracted from sense were prior in the order of nature, though less knowable to man. It affected his natural science inasmuch as he regarded physical light as the analogy of Divine illumination.

The development of Grosseteste's methodological ideas by the Oxford school, and the influence of these ideas on the history of European science, will be the subjects of the chapters that follow.

VII

Grosseteste and the Oxford School

(1)

GROSSETESTE'S theory of science determined the approach of the
next generations of Oxford natural philosophers to the physical
world, and their work was in many ways simply an elaboration in
concrete detail of his general principles of investigation and explanation. His insistence on the use of experiment or experience and of
mathematics, his analysis of the problem of certainty in his search
for reality and truth among the things of experience, and the particular significance he gave to the study of optics, remained characteristic of the Oxford school during the thirteenth and fourteenth
centuries.

The intellectual interests of Oxford, Grosseteste was particularly
well placed to influence. He had intimate relations with the University over a long period, first as an undergraduate, then as first
Magister scholarum or Chancellor of the University some time after
1214, later as first lecturer to the Franciscans between 1229 or 1230
and 1235, and finally after 1235 as Bishop of Lincoln, in whose
diocese Oxford lay and under whose jurisdiction its schools came.[1]
This influence was greatest among the Franciscans and for them he
retained a special affection; as he said of them in a letter to Pope
Gregory IX, 'habitantibus in regione umbrae mortis lux orta est eis'.[2]
In the Franciscan house in Oxford he established a special tradition
of learning which was so highly regarded that this house became the
training ground for teachers throughout the English province, attracted students from abroad, and provided teachers for continental
friaries.[3] Grosseteste's teaching was characterized by the study of the

---

[1] See above, p. 44. Only his influence on logic and natural science is relevant here
but in fact it extended into theology, university organization and many other fields; see
Sharp, *Franciscan Philos. at Oxford*; d'Irsay, *Archeion*, xv (1933) 225; A. G. Little and
F. Pelster, *Oxford Theology and Theologians*, pp. 32, 43; *Statuta Antiqua Universitatis
Oxoniensis*, ed. Gibson, pp. xi, xliii, 73–76, 105; Rashdall, *Universities*, iii. 239 sqq.;
Callus, *PBA*, xxix (1943) 252 sqq., *Oxoniensia*, x (1945) 42 sqq.; Gilson, *Philos. au
moyen âge*, pp. 469 sqq.

[2] Rob. Grosseteste *Epistolae*, ed. Luard, p. 180. Matthew Paris (*Chronica Majora*,
ed. H. R. Luard, iv. 599) mentioned Grosseteste's love of the Franciscans.

[3] A. G. Little, 'The Franciscan school at Oxford in the thirteenth century', *AFH*, xix

Bible,[1] of languages,[2] and of mathematics and physical science. Each of these he held to be in a different way essential to knowledge of reality and truth. His belief that the Creator was to be known through the study of His creatures,[3] which is seen in the analogy he saw between physical light and the light of the Creative Mind and in the use he made of natural science in his commentaries on the Bible, came in a special way to inspire his followers in Oxford to interest themselves in natural science. Moreover, he balanced these theoretical incentives by encouraging the study of medicine as part of the Franciscan and Christian duty of caring for the sick.[4] To the Franciscans at Oxford, whom he had taught and protected during his life, Grosseteste also bequeathed his manuscripts.[5] Furthermore, though his influence was greatest in this Order, it extended to the Dominicans.[6] Indeed, Oxford writers in general for the next century recognized their debt to him both for his theory of science and for the details of his researches into optics, astronomy, and other physical questions.[7]

(1926) 807 sqq.; reprinted in Little's *Franciscan Letters, Papers and Documents*, pp. 58 sqq. Cf. Easton, *Roger Bacon*, pp. 206–9.

[1] Cf. Thomson, *Writings of Rob. Grosseteste*, pp. 72 sqq.; Callus, *Oxoniensia*, x (1945) 56 sqq. on his biblical commentaries.

[2] Cf. Thomson, 'A note on Grosseteste's work of translation', *J. Theol. Stud.* xxxiv (1933) 48 sqq., and *Writings of Rob. Grosseteste*, p. 67, in which he shows that Grosseteste translated the pseudo-Aristotelian *De Lineis Indivisibilibus* from Greek; Franceschini, *Roberto Grossatesta*; A. Mansion, 'La Version médiévale de l'Éthique à Nicomaque. La "Translatio Lincolniensis" et la controverse autour de la revision attribuée à Guillaume de Moerbeke', *RNP*, xli (1938) 401 sqq.; Callus, 'The date of Grosseteste's translations and commentaries on Pseudo-Dionysius and the Nicomachean Ethics', *RTAM*, xiv (1947) 186 sqq.; and the references in Rashdall, *Universities*, iii. 240, n. 1, to Grosseteste as a translator; above, p. 45, n. 1.

[3] Cf. Duhem, *Syst. monde*, v. 370 sqq.; Sharp, *Franciscan Philos. at Oxford*; Thomson, *Writings of Rob. Grosseteste*, pp. 100, 108. As R. McKeon, *Selections from Medieval Philosophers*, i. 262, has put it: 'Whereas philosophers in the earlier augustinian tradition found philosophy almost entire in the discovery of God at the centre of all things, Grosseteste seeking to develop the consequences of that philosophy hit upon mathematics as the perfect dialectical instrument for its development; the effect of the application of mathematics was to turn the search for God in things to the elucidation of things, that the inquiry for God was to inspire the first systematic experimental investigation of things.'

[4] H. Felder, *Gesch. d. wissensch. Studien im Franziskanerorden*, pp. 393–4. Cf. above, pp. 75–81. Roger Bacon said that experimental science was the basis of medicine. *Opus Minus*, ed. Brewer, p. 324.

[5] A. G. Little, *Grey Friars in Oxford*, pp. 57 sqq. It was Grosseteste's friendship with the Franciscan Adam Marsh that induced him to make this bequest; see Trivet, *Annales*, ed. Hog, p. 243.   [6] Cf. below, p. 163, n. 4.

[7] See Felder, op. cit., pp. 260 sqq.; Little, op. cit., p. 8, *Franciscan Letters*, pp. 58 sqq. On the recognition of Grosseteste as the founder of Oxford Franciscan studies in general

Perhaps the first to share Grosseteste's interests in natural science was the first Franciscan to succeed him as lecturer in the Oxford house,[1] his friend Adam Marsh. Of these two men Roger Bacon said:

There have been found some famous men, such as Robert, Bishop of Lincoln and Brother Adam of Marsh and many others, who have known how by the power of mathematics to unfold the causes of all things and to give a sufficient explanation of human and Divine phenomena; and the assurance of this fact is to be found in the writings of these great men, as for instance in their works on the impression [of the elements], on the rainbow, on comets, on the generation of heat, on the investigation of the places of the world, on celestial things,[2] and on other questions appertaining both to theology and to natural philosophy.[3]

Of the other Franciscans at Oxford who continued Grosseteste's interest in science, Thomas of York[4] (d. c. 1260), the fourth lecturer, is notable more for helping to establish the status of science than for original work in the subject. Thomas Docking,[5] the seventh lecturer, in a commentary on the Bible quoted word for word the passage in Grosseteste's De Iride about magnifying small objects by arrangements of lenses.[6] Both these men had probably been pupils of Adam

see the remarks of Salimbene (Cronica, editit O. Holder-Egger, p. 233) and of Wyclyf's opponent John Tyssington (J. Felten, Robert Grosseteste, p. 89). Wyclyf himself was also influenced by Grosseteste; see Baur, 1912, p. 7*, Thomson, Writings of Rob. Grosseteste, pp. 82, 84.

[1] Little, Franciscan Letters, p. 67. Thomas Eccleston gives a list of these lecturers.

[2] De Impress. Elem., De Iride, De Cometis, De Calore Solis, De Nat. Loc., and De Sphaera. It is to be noted that Bacon attributes these works to both men, but no works of this kind by Adam Marsh have come down to us. The short work De Accessu et Recessu Maris, which makes use of the theory of multiplication of species, has been attributed to Adam Marsh by F. M. Henquinet, 'Un Recueil de questions annoté par S. Bonaventure', AFH, xxv (1932) 553. Cf. F. Pelster, 'Zwei unbekannte Traktate des Robert Grosseteste', Scholastik, i (1926) 572–3, RTAM, v (1933) 388, n. 38; Thomson, op. cit., p. 117.

[3] Opus Maius, iv. i. 3, ed. Bridges, i. 108. Cf. Opus Tertium, C. 24, ed. Brewer, p. 82 and C. 50, p. 187, where Roger Bacon names Grosseteste as Adam Marsh's teacher; Compendium Studii, C. 8, ibid., p. 469; Communia Mathematica, ed. Steele (Opera Hactenus Inedita, xvi), pp. 117–18. On Adam Marsh see also Felder, op. cit., pp. 278 sqq., and Vogl, Physik Roger Bacos, p. 10.

[4] Little, Franciscan Letters, p. 68; Sharp, Franciscan Philos. at Oxford, pp. 49 sqq. Cf. M. Grabmann, 'Die Metaphysik des Thomas von York (†ca. 1260)', in Festgabe zum 60. Geburtstag Clemens Baeumker, pp. 181 sqq.; E. Longpré, 'Thomas d'York et Matthieu d'Aquasparta', AHDLMA, i (1926) 269 sqq., who says that Grosseteste's rejection of the doctrine of the eternity of the world (as in the last section of the Comm. Phys., printed in abbreviated form in Baur, 1912, pp. 101 sqq.) and his treatment of the problem of creation inspired Franciscan writers on the subject from Bonaventura to Scotus.

[5] A. G. Little, 'Thomas Docking and his relations to Roger Bacon', Essays presented to R. L. Poole, pp. 301 sqq.; reprinted in Franciscan Letters, pp. 98 sqq.

[6] Baur, 1912, pp. 73–74; above, p. 119.

Marsh. Another English Franciscan who was influenced by Grosseteste was Bartholomew the Englishman, who was at Oxford but
became a member of the French province. In his *De Proprietatibus
Rerum*, a popular encyclopaedia, completed probably about 1250,[1]
he used Grosseteste's *De Colore* without mentioning its author and
spoke of the multiplication of species, the cone of 'species radiosa',
the lens, reflection, and refraction.[2]

   A philosophical writer of the same period who shows certain
similarities to Grosseteste is the Dominican, Robert Kilwardby (d.
1279). His *De Ortu Scientiarum*, though simply a theoretical classification of science, was an important contribution to Oxford
scientific thought.[3] The chief significance of Kilwardby's work, in
which he made critical use of the earlier classifications of science by
Hugh of St. Victor and Gundissalinus as well as by Aristotle,
Boethius, and Isidore, Miss Sharp[4] points out to be his account of
the theoretical sciences as arising out of particular, concrete problems encountered in attempting to satisfy the physical needs of the
body, and his recognition that the natural and practical sciences were
not inferior to other branches of knowledge. Each branch, theoretical
and practical, he said, had a particular aspect of reality for its object,
and this aspect could not become the object of any other science. Of
particular interest is his view of the role of mathematics which,
following the Greek tradition for which he cited Isidore of Seville,[5]
he held to have originated with the Egyptians as a set of empirical
rules for measuring surfaces and volumes and to have been transformed into a demonstrative science by the Greeks after Pythagoras.
The pure geometry so developed considered abstract lines and
figures alone, but geometry could be used also to explain the physical world, as in astronomy, and in optics where it was used to
explain the different modes of vision, refraction, and reflection.[6] But

   [1] T. Plassman, 'Bartholomaeus Anglicus', *AFH*, xii (1919) 67–109.
   [2] *De Proprietatibus Rerum*, iii. 17, 'De Virtute Visibili', xix. 7, Coloniae, *c.* 1472. See
Baur, 1912, p. 85*; Thomson, *Writings of Rob. Grosseteste*, p. 93.
   [3] See Baur's ed. of Dominicus Gundissalinus, *De Div. Philos.*, pp. 368–80; and
Sharp, work cited in next note.
   [4] D. E. Sharp, 'The *De Ortu Scientiarum* of Robert Kilwardby (d. 1279)', *NS*, viii
(1934) 1 sqq. She dates the work as probably before 1240–5. It seems, however, that
this date must be advanced to later than 1246–7: see D. A. Callus, 'The "Tabulae super
Originalia Patrum" of Robert Kilwardby, O.P.', in *Studia Mediaevalia R. J. Martin*,
pp. 247–8.
   [5] *De Ortu Scientiarum*, C. 11, Merton MS 261, 1294, f. 22vb; Isidorus Hispalensis
Etymologiarum, iii. 10. See F. M. Powicke, *Medieval Books of Merton College*.
   [6] *De Ortu Scient.* C. 13, f. 24^r; C. 17, f. 26^v.

when applied to the physical world geometry abstracted from all aspects of bodies except the formal cause, which it considered alone, leaving the consideration of motive causes to physics.[1] The theoretical sciences, Kilwardby held, all had their practical aspects, and the practical sciences used theory in their endeavour to supply whatever man lacked, ethics supplying his spiritual and mechanics his bodily needs. Of the mechanical sciences, agriculture, victualling, and medicine contributed to the body's intrinsic needs, and cloth-making, armouring, architecture, and commerce to its extrinsic needs.[2]

(2)

The writer who most thoroughly grasped, and who most elaborately developed Grosseteste's attitude to nature and theory of science was Roger Bacon (c. 1219–92) himself. Recent research has shown that in many of the aspects of his science in which he has been thought to have been most original, Bacon was simply taking over the Oxford and Grossetestian tradition,[3] though he was able also to make use of new sources unknown to Grosseteste, as, for example, the *Optics* of Alhazen. Though it is improbable that Bacon heard Grosseteste's lectures at Oxford, he seems to have become a member of Grosseteste's 'circle' by 1249, and when he became a Franciscan friar he would, no doubt, have had access to his manuscripts.[4] Baur[5] has drawn attention to the many striking parallels between the science of Roger Bacon and that of Grosseteste. The

---

[1] Ibid., C. 14, f. 24ᵛ.   [2] Ibid., C. 37, f. 41ᵛ.

[3] For Roger Bacon's science see *RBE*; Little, 'Roger Bacon', *PBA*, xiv (1928) 265 sqq.; Duhem, *Syst. monde*, iii. 411 sqq., 499 sqq., v. 375 sqq.; R. Carton, *Expérience physique chez Roger Bacon*, also *Expérience mystique de l'illumination intérieure chez Roger Bacon* and *Synthèse doctrinale de Roger Bacon*; C. Baeumker, *Roger Bacons Naturphilosophie*; Thorndike, *History of Magic*, ii. 616 sq.; Sarton, *Introduction*, ii. 952–67, which contains a bibliography down to 1931. T. Crowley's *Roger Bacon* contains an account of his life and works and an extensive bibliography. Bridges's *Life and Work of Roger Bacon* is very inaccurate. See also Stewart C. Easton, *Roger Bacon*; below, p. 351.

[4] See Little, in *RBE*, pp. 1 sqq., and Crowley, op. cit., for Bacon's life. Grosseteste in his *De Prognost.*, written in 1249 (above, p. 50, n. 3), used the Arab lunar calendar, found elsewhere only in his *Compotus Correctorius* but commonly used by Roger Bacon. Little (*Studies in English Franciscan History*, p. 197) raises the question whether Bacon was then Grosseteste's assistant. Crowley (op. cit., pp. 18, 22, 30–2, 72, 195–6) puts Bacon's birth c. 1219 and argues that he began his Arts course in Oxford but completed it in Paris, with an M.A. c. 1240, taught there till c. 1246, and returned to Oxford in 1247. After that date his ideas seem to have undergone a radical change owing to the influence of Grosseteste. Crowley puts the date of his becoming a friar c. 1257. As a friar he seems to have spent a considerable time in Paris and to have written his principal works there (Crowley, op. cit., pp. 32 sqq., 59 sqq.). Cf. Easton, op. cit., pp. 80–1, 87–92.

[5] *RBE*, pp. 30 sqq.; *Philos. Rob. Grosseteste*, pp. 52–63, 92–120.

chief point of resemblance to be noted is Bacon's 'grundsätzliche methodische Auffassung der Naturwissenschaft, und die Erklärung des Wirkens und Werdens in der Natur'.[1] It has been suggested above that Grosseteste in his search for reality and truth began with the theory of science which he developed in his commentary on Aristotle's *Posterior Analytics*, and that he then made use of this theory in his detailed scientific studies. Roger Bacon in his major writings on natural science, as in the *Opus Maius*,[2] *Opus Minus* and *Opus Tertium*,[3] the *De Multiplicatione Specierum*,[4] and the *Communia Mathematica*[5] and *Communium Naturalium*,[6] also first postulated a theory of science as a means of discovering reality and truth, and then used this methodological theory in detailed researches undertaken as an illustration of it as well as for their own sakes. In setting out this theory of science Roger Bacon, like Grosseteste, began with Aristotle's *Posterior Analytics*[7] and he developed particularly those points to which Grosseteste had paid attention: the means of arriving at universals or causes by induction and experiment,[8] and the use of mathematics[9] as the most certain means of demonstrating the connexions between events.

Having laid down the fundamental principles of the wisdom of the

[1] *RBE*, p. 46.

[2] Ed. Bridges. There is a complete English translation based on this edition by R. B. Burke and a partial translation in McKeon's *Selections from Medieval Philosophers*, ii. I have made use of both. For early editions of Roger Bacon's scientific writings see Sarton, *Introduction*, ii. 963; below, p. 278. For the dedicatory letter of the *Opus Maius* see F. A. Gasquet, 'An unpublished fragment of Roger Bacon', *EHR*, xii (1897) 494 sqq.

[3] Ed. Brewer. Missing sections of the *Opus Tertium* were published by P. Duhem, *Fragment inédit de l'Opus Tertium*, and by A. G. Little, *Part of the Opus Tertium of Roger Bacon*. The three *Opera* date from 1266-7.

[4] Published by Bridges in his edition of the *Opus Maius*, ii and iii; it dates from the same period as the *Opera*.   [5] Ed. Steele; above, p. 137, n. 3.

[6] In *Opera Hactenus Inedita*, ed. Steele, ii-iv. This edition, in sixteen fasciculi, contains most of Roger Bacon's scientific writings apart from those edited by Brewer and Bridges. See also Fr. Rogeri Baconi *Compendium Studii Theologiae*, ed. H. Rashdall (Appendix by A. G. Little, *De Operibus* Rogeri Baconi); A. Pelzer, 'Une Source inconnue de Roger Bacon, Alfred de Sareshel, commentateur des Météorologiques d'Aristote', *AFH*, xii (1919) 44 sqq.; S. H. Thomson, 'An unnoticed treatise of Roger Bacon on time and motion', *Isis*, xxvii (1937) 219 sqq.; E. Longpré, 'La Summa Dialectica de Roger Bacon', *AFH*, xiii (1938) 204 sqq.; F. Delorme, 'Le Prologue de Roger Bacon à son traité De Influentiis Agentium', *Antonianum*, xviii (1943) 89 sqq.; below, p. 150, n. 2.

[7] Cf. *Opus Maius*, iv. i. 2-3, vi. 1.

[8] See *Opus Maius*, vi, 'De Scientia Experimentali'; cf. Carton, *Expérience physique chez Roger Bacon*.

[9] See *Opus Maius*, iv, 'Potestas Mathematicae'; cf. D. E. Smith, 'The place of Roger Bacon in the history of mathematics', in *RBE*, pp. 160 sqq.

Latins so far as they are found in language,[1] mathematics and optics, [he said in Part VI of the *Opus Maius*, 'De Scientia Experimentali'] I now wish to unfold the principles of experimental science, since without experience nothing can be sufficiently known. For there are two modes of acquiring knowledge, namely, by reasoning and by experience. Reasoning draws a conclusion and makes us grant the conclusion, but does not make the conclusion certain, nor does it remove doubt so that the mind may rest on the intuition of truth, unless the mind discovers it by the method of experience (*via experientiae*); for many have the arguments relating to what can be known, but because they lack experience they neglect the arguments, and neither avoid what is harmful, nor follow what is good. For if a man who has never seen a fire should prove by adequate reasoning that fire burns and injures things and destroys them, his mind would not be satisfied thereby, nor would he avoid fire, until he placed his hand or some combustible substance in the fire, so that he might prove by experience that which reasoning taught. But when he has actual experience of combustion his mind is made certain and rests in the full light of truth. Therefore, reasoning does not suffice, but experience does. . . . What Aristotle says therefore to the effect that the demonstration is a syllogism that makes us know, is to be understood if the experience of it accompanies the demonstration, and is not to be understood of the bare demonstration.[2]

This experimental science [he went on] has three great prerogatives with respect to the other sciences. The first is that it investigates by experiment the noble conclusions of all the sciences. For the other sciences know how to discover their principles by experiments, but their conclusions are reached by arguments based on the discovered principles. But if they must have particular and complete experience of their conclusions, then it is necessary that they should have it by the aid of this noble science. It is true, indeed, that mathematics has universal experiences concerning its conclusions in figuring and numbering, which are applied likewise to all the sciences and to this experimental science, because no science can be known without mathematics. But if we turn our attention to the experiences that are particular and complete and certified wholly in their own discipline, it is necessary to go by way of the principles of this science which is called experimental.[3]

[1] Cf. S. A. Hirsh, 'Roger Bacon and philology', in *RBE*, pp. 101 sqq.; C. B. Vandewalle, *Roger Bacon dans l'histoire de la philologie*.

[2] *Opus Maius*, vi. 1, ed. Bridges, ii. 167–8. Roger Bacon maintained in this chapter that there were two kinds of experience, namely, through the exterior senses and through interior illuminations, and so he held like Grosseteste that absolute certainty about causes was reached only when the human intellect was aided and its conclusions transformed by the Divine light. In ii. 5, ed. Bridges, i. 39, he said 'philosophy exists through the influence of Divine illumination'.

[3] Ibid., C. 2, ed. Bridges, ii. 172–3; cf. *De Mult. Spec.* Prologue, ed. Bridges,

The other prerogatives of experimental science, besides this first one of confirming the conclusions of deductive reasoning in existing sciences, as, for example, in optics, were, secondly, to add to existing sciences new knowledge at which they could not arrive by deduction, and thirdly, to create entirely new departments of science. By virtue of these two prerogatives the experimenter was able to make a purely empirical discovery of the nature of things. Of the second prerogative Bacon said:

> This mistress of the speculative sciences alone is able to give us important truths within the confines of the other sciences, which those sciences can learn in no other way. Hence these truths are not connected with the discussion of principles but are wholly outside of these, although they are within the confines of these sciences, since they are neither conclusions nor principles. . . . The man without experience must not seek a reason in order that he may first understand, for he will never have this reason except after experiment. . . . For if a man is without experience that a magnet attracts iron, and has not heard from others that it attracts, he will never discover this fact before an experiment. . . . Mathematical science can easily produce the spherical astrolabe, on which all astronomical phenomena necessary for man may be described, according to precise longitudes and latitudes [as in the device described by Ptolemy in the *Almagest*, viii]. But that this body, so made, should move naturally with the daily motion is not within the power of mathematical science. But the trained experimenter can consider the ways of this motion.[1]

Other examples of the exercise of the second prerogative were seen in medicine and in alchemy. The third prerogative was exercised outside the bounds of existing sciences, as in the investigation of natural wonders and prognostications of the future.[2]

The inductive process of the discovery, as well as the verification and falsification of principles or theories, Roger Bacon explained fully and clearly in the example he gave to illustrate the first prerogative, though he did not include discovery in the special meaning he gave to the phrase 'scientia experimentalis' in the passage concerning this prerogative quoted above. But, before discussing this

iii. 185. He resumed the same ideas in the *Opus Tertium*: '. . . Oporteret vero omnia que scripsi verificari per instrumenta et per opera.' *Fragment inédit. . .* , ed. Duhem, p. 138.

[1] *Opus Maius*, vi, 'Capitulum de secunda praerogativa scientiae experimentalis', ed. Bridges, ii. 202–3.

[2] Cf. ibid., iv, 'Astrologia', ed. Bridges, ii. 388–9, where he said that the claims of astrologers should be examined by a historical study of the correlation between the conjunctions of heavenly bodies and events on earth.

'example of the rainbow and of the phenomena connected with it',[1] it would be well to turn briefly to his ideas about the use of mathematics and of optics.

Mathematics, Roger Bacon said, was the 'door and key' 'of the sciences and things of this world'[2] and gave certain knowledge of them. In the first place 'all categories depend on a knowledge of quantity, concerning which mathematics treats, and therefore the whole excellence of logic depends on mathematics'.[3] For 'the categories of *when* and *where* are related to quantity, for *when* pertains to time and *where* arises from place; the category of *condition* (*habitus*) cannot be known without the category of *where*, as Averroës teaches in the fifth book of the *Metaphysics*; the greater part, moreover, of the category of *quality* contains affections and properties of quantities, because all things that are in the fourth class of quality are called qualities in quantities . . .;[4] whatever, moreover, is worthy of consideration in the category of *relation* is the property of quantity, such as proportions and proportionalities, and geometrical, arithmetical, and musical means and the kinds of greater and lesser[5] inequality.'[6] This being the case it was plain that 'mathematics is prior to the other sciences',[7] and since 'in mathematics only, as Averroës says in the first book of the *Physics* . . ., things known to us and in nature or absolutely are the same',[8] the greatest certainty was possible in mathematics. 'In mathematics only are there the most convincing demonstrations through a necessary cause.'[9] 'Wherefore it is evident that if, in the other sciences, we want to come to certitude without doubt and to truth without error, we must place the foundations of knowledge in mathematics.'[10] 'Robert, Bishop of Lincoln and Brother Adam of Marsh' had followed this method and 'if anyone should descend to the particular by applying the power of mathematics to the separate sciences, he would see that nothing magnificent in them can be known without mathematics.'[11]

As an example of the use of mathematics in making known 'the things of this world' Roger Bacon gave astronomy, which 'considers

---

[1] *Opus Maius*, vi. 2, ed. Bridges, ii. 173.   [2] Ibid. iv. i. 1, ed. Bridges, i. 97–98.
[3] Ibid., C. 2, ed. Bridges, i. 103. Cf. Grosseteste, above, p. 60, n. 2.
[4] His examples were straightness or curvature in lines, and the prime and unfactorable in numbers.
[5] For the scholastics a proportion of equality meant $a/b = 1$, a proportion of greater inequality $a/b > 1$, and a proportion of lesser inequality $a/b < 1$.
[6] Ibid., C. 2, pp. 102–3.   [7] *Opus Maius*, iv. i. 3, ed. Bridges, i. 107.
[8] Ibid., p. 105; see above, p. 56, n. 1.   [9] Ibid., p. 106.   [10] Ibid., p. 106.
[11] Ibid., p. 108; above, p. 137.

the quantities of all things that are included among the celestial and all things which are reduced to quantity'. He said that 'by instruments suitable to them and by tables and canons'[1] the movements of the celestial bodies and other phenomena in the heavens and in the air might be measured and reduced to rules on which predictions might be based. In fact he carried on the work of Grosseteste towards the reform of the calendar, making use of Grosseteste's *Compotus* and also sharing his hesitation between the Aristotelian and Ptolemaic astronomical systems.[2]

The special reason why Bacon held that 'in the things of this world, as regards their efficient and generating causes, nothing can be known without the power of geometry', and that 'it is necessary to verify the matter of the world by demonstrations set forth in geometrical lines',[3] was that he accepted Grosseteste's theory of the 'multiplication of species' or power as the basis of all natural operations and the Neoplatonic theory of a 'common corporeity' as the first form giving dimensions to all material substances.[4] Like Grosseteste, he held that the 'multiplication of species' was the efficient cause of every occurrence in the universe, whether in the celestial or terrestrial region, whether in matter or in sense, and whether originating from inanimate things or from the soul.[5] And, he said, 'the force of the efficient cause and of the matter cannot be known without the great power of mathematics',[6] for 'Every multiplication is either with respect to lines, or angles, or figures'.[7]

[1] *Opus Maius*, iv. ii. 1, pp. 109–10.

[2] Ibid., iv, pp. 187 sqq.; ibid., 'Correctio Calendarii', pp. 270 sqq. See Baur, in *RBE*, p. 42; *Compotus* Fratris Rogeri, ed. Steele (*Opera Hactenus Inedita*, vi), p. 40; Duhem, *Syst. monde*, iii. 397–8, 411–42; cf. above, pp. 96 sqq., below, pp. 201 sqq.

[3] *Opus Maius*, iv. iv. 8, ed. Bridges, i. 143–4.

[4] See above, pp. 104 sqq. Duhem ('Roger Bacon et l'horreur du vide', in *RBE*, pp. 241 sqq.) has given an example of Bacon's use of the theory of 'common corporeity' to explain certain facts which were subsequently attributed by science to the effects of atmospheric pressure.

[5] *Opus Maius*, iv. ii. 1, ed. Bridges, i. 111; cf. pp. 210, 216; *De Mult. Spec.* i. 1, ed. Bridges, ii. 408–9 and 417. These passages are clearly derived, sometimes verbally, from *De Lineis*, Baur, 1912, pp. 59–60; above, p. 110. See also *Opus Maius*, ed. Bridges, iii. 183 sqq.; *De Mult. Spec.* i. 1–3, ed. Bridges, ii. 407 sqq., ii. 1, pp. 457 sqq. Cf. S. Vogl, 'Roger Bacons Lehre von der sinnlichen Spezies und vom Sehvorgange', in *RBE*, pp. 205 sqq.

[6] Bacon held that within animate bodies rays passed tortuously along the nerves in response to the operations of the soul. Such 'tortuous species' were impossible in inanimate bodies, where 'species' went in straight lines. See below, p. 155; cf. above, pp. 105, 109, n. 3.

[7] *Opus Maius*, iv. ii. 2, ed. Bridges, i. 112. The rest of this chapter, which is concerned with refraction ('refractio radii et speciei'), the spherical burning lens and

In discussing the 'multiplication of species' Roger Bacon based conclusions on the same basic metaphysical principles that Grosseteste had used. The principle of the uniformity of nature he expressed as follows: 'the effects . . . will be similar to those in the past, since if we assume a cause the effect is taken for granted',[1] and 'those which are of similar essence have similar operations'.[2] The principle of economy he expressed in Grosseteste's own words: 'Aristotle says in the fifth book of the *Metaphysics* that nature works in the shortest way possible, and the straight line is the shortest way of all.'[3] The type of such 'species' was visible light and therefore, like Grosseteste, he made a particular study of geometrical optics, through which he held that it was possible to obtain experimental knowledge of the laws of the operation of these species, which laws were the basis of all natural explanation.[4]

Of the mode of propagation of 'species' Roger Bacon gave an account which resumed and extended some of the essential features of Grosseteste's 'wave' theory.[5] He asserted first that for propagation between two points to occur at all the intervening medium must be a *plenum*: no propagation could pass through an absolute void.

Democritus thought that an eye on the earth could see an ant in the heavens. . . . But we must here state that we should not see anything if there were a vacuum. But this would not be due to some nature hindering species, and resisting it, but because of the lack of a nature suitable for the multiplication of species; for species is a natural thing, and therefore needs a natural medium; but in a vacuum nature does not exist. For vacuum rightly conceived of is merely a mathematical quantity extended in the three dimensions, existing *per se* without heat and cold, soft and hard, rare and dense, and without any natural quality, merely occupying space, as

reflection, is clearly based on Grosseteste's discussion of the same subjects in *De Lineis* (Baur, 1912, pp. 62 sqq.; above, pp. 119, 120–2) and *De Nat. Loc.* (ibid., p. 71; above, p. 122).

[1] 'posita causa ponitur effectus', *Opus Maius*, iv, 'Astrologia', ed. Bridges, i. 389. Cf. above, p. 85.

[2] 'illa quae sunt similis essentiae habent similes operationes', *De Mult. Spec.* i. 1, ed. Bridges, ii. 409. The remainder of this chapter resumes the essentials of Grosseteste's theory of species (cf. above, p. 110) concluding: 'Agens naturale non habet voluntatem nec deliberationem, et ideo uniformiter agit.' (p. 417.)

[3] *Opus Maius*, iv. ii. 2, ed. Bridges, i. 112. Cf. v. i. ii. 1, ed. Bridges, ii. 14. See above, p. 86.

[4] See *Opus Maius*, iv and v; *De Mult. Spec.*, ed. Bridges, ii. 407 sqq., iii. 183 sqq. See below, p. 150, n. 2, for his other writings on optics.

[5] Above, pp. 99, 113–15.

the philosophers maintained before Aristotle, not only within the heavens, but beyond.[1]

He then went on to argue that the propagation was not instanta-neous[2] but took time. Alhazen[3] had brought various arguments against Alkindi's attempt in *De Aspectibus*[4] to prove that 'the ray passes through in a wholly indivisible instant'.[5] After a long discus-sion based on such considerations as that 'a finite force cannot pro-duce any result in an instant, wherefore it must require time', and that since 'the species of a corporeal thing has a really corporeal existence in a medium, and is a real corporeal thing, as was pre-viously shown,[6] it must of necessity be dimensional, and therefore fitted to the dimensions of the medium', Bacon concluded: 'It remains, then, that light is multiplied in time, and likewise all species of a visible thing and of vision. But nevertheless the multi-plication does not occupy a sensible time and one perceptible by vision, but an imperceptible one, since anyone has experience that he himself does not perceive the time in which light travels from east to west.'[7]

This multiplication of species through a medium, he continued, was not a flow of body like water but a kind of pulse propagated from part to part. In this, light was analogous to sound.

For sound is produced because parts of the object struck go out of their natural position, where there follows a trembling of the parts in every direction along with some rarefaction, because the motion of rarefaction is from the centre to the circumference, and just as there is generated the first sound with the first tremor, so is there a second sound with the second tremor in a second portion of the air, and a third sound with the third tremor in a third portion of the air, and so on.[8]

---

[1] *Opus Maius*, v. i. ix. 2, ed. Bridges, ii. 67. Cf. *De Mult. Spec.* iv. 2, ibid., pp. 521 sqq. The reference to Aristotle is to *De Anima*, ii. 7, 419ᵃ15 sqq. Cf. p. 91, n. 1.

[2] Cf. Grosseteste, above, pp. 104, 106.

[3] Alhazeni *Opticae*, ii. 21, ed. Risner, pp. 37-38.

[4] *De Aspectibus*, Section 15, ed. Björnbo and Vogl, in *Alkindi, Tideus und Pseudo-Euklid*, pp. 25-27.

[5] *Opus Maius*, v. i. ix. 3, ed. Bridges, ii. 68.

[6] He showed this in *Opus Maius*, v. i. vi. 4, ed. Bridges, ii. 43-46, in which he dis-cussed also the problem whether intersecting lines of propagated species (e.g. two beams of light) would interfere with each other. See also *De Mult. Spec.* iii. 1-2, ibid., pp. 502-16.

[7] *Opus Maius*, v. i. ix. 3, ed. Bridges, ii. 69-71. He discussed the same subject in *De Mult. Spec.* iv. 3, ibid., pp. 525 sqq.

[8] *Opus Maius*, v. i. viii. 2, ed. Bridges, ii. 57. Cf. Grosseteste, above, pp. 113 sqq.; Aristotle, *De Anima*, ii. 7, 419ᵃ25 sqq.

[With light the species] forms a likeness to itself in the second position of the air, and so on. Therefore it is not a motion as regards place, but is a propagation multiplied through the different parts of the medium; nor is it a body which is there generated, but a corporeal form, without, however, dimensions *per se*, but it is produced subject to the dimensions of the air; and it is not produced by a flow from a luminous body, but by a renewing from the potency of the matter of the air.... As regards Aristotle's statement that there is a difference between the transmission of light and that of the other sensory impressions, ... sound has the motion of the displacement of the parts of the body struck from its natural position, and the motion of the following tremor, and the motion of rarefaction in every direction, as was stated before, and as is evident from the second book of *De Anima*; and ... in the multiplication of sound a threefold temporal succession takes place, no one of which is present in the multiplication of light.... However, the multiplication of both as regards itself is successive and requires time. Likewise, in the case of odour the transmission is quite different from that of light, and yet the species of both will require time for transmission, for in odour there is a minute evaporation of vapour, which is, in fact, a body diffused in the air to the sense besides the species, which is similarly produced.... But in vision nothing is found except a succession of the multiplication. The fact that there is a difference in the transmission of light, sound, and odour can be set forth in another way, for light travels far more quickly in the air than the other two. We note in the case of one at a distance striking with a hammer or a staff that we see the stroke delivered before we hear the sound produced. For we perceive with our vision a second stroke, before the sound of the first stroke reaches the hearing. The same is true of a flash of lightning, which we see before we hear the sound of the thunder, although the sound is produced in the cloud before the flash, because the flash is produced in the cloud from the bursting of the cloud by the kindled vapour.[1]

In the details of his researches into optics and cognate sciences Roger Bacon made use of a number of Grosseteste's ideas, though his work was more mature because of the new sources[2] available

---

[1] *Opus Maius*, v. i. ix. 4, ed. Bridges, ii. 72–73. See also *De Mult. Spec.* i. 3, ii. 1, iii. 1, ed. Bridges, ii. 431 sqq., 457 sqq., 502 sqq. Cf. Aristotle, *De Anima*, ii. 7, 418ᵇ20 sqq.; cf. also *De Sensu et Sensibili*, vi.

[2] e.g. he understood, as in fact Ptolemy and Alhazen had shown, that the angle of refraction varied with different media: 'Et variatur recessus fractionis et anguli quantitas, secundum quod corpus subtilius est minus et magis subtile.' (*De Mult. Spec.* ii. 3, ed. Bridges, ii. 466–7.) Some of Alhazen's optical writings were translated by an unknown hand at the end of the twelfth or beginning of the thirteenth century and were published in 1542, and again in the *editio princeps* of F. Risner in 1572. This included the tract *De Crepusculis*, which was translated by Gerard of Cremona (Baeumker, *Witelo*, pp. 229–32). But many of Alhazen's writings were never translated into Latin and became known

to him and he usually added something original of his own. Besides Grosseteste, his chief sources in optics were Aristotle, Euclid, and pseudo-Euclid, Ptolemy, Diocles (Tideus), Alhazen, Alkindi, Avicenna, and Averroës.[1] He took over and extended Grosseteste's explanation of the variation in the strength of rays according to direction, and according to the distance from the radiating source; examples, respectively, of the multiplication of species 'according to lines and angles' and 'according to figures'.[2] The results he used in an interesting discussion of which the object was to

verify the fact that on the surface of the lens of the eye,[3] although it be small, the distinction of any visible object whatsoever can be made by means of the arrangement of the species coming from such objects, since the species of a thing, whatever be its size, can be arranged in order in a very small space, because there are as many parts in a very small body as there are in a very large one, since every body and every quantity is infinitely divisible, as all philosophy proclaims. Aristotle proves in the sixth book of the *Physics* that there is no division of a quantity into indivisibles, nor is a quantity composed of indivisibles,[4] and therefore

in the West only in the sixteenth century or, in most cases, only with the work of recent scholars. For an account of Alhazen's optics see E. Wiedemann, 'Eine Beobachtung aus der physiologischen Optik', *SPMSE*, xxxvi (1904) 333 sqq., 'Kleinere Arbeiten von Ibn al Haiṭam', ibid. xli (1909) 1 sqq., 'Über die Brechung des Lichtes in Kugeln nach Ibn al Haiṭam und Kamâl al Dîn al Fârisî', ibid. xlii (1910) 15 sqq., 'Theorie des Regenbogens', ibid. xlvi (1914) 39 sqq., 'Ibn al Haiṭam', in *Festschrift J. Rosenthal*, pp. 147 sqq., 'Ibn al Haiṭams Schrift über die sphärischen Hohlspiegel', *BM*, x (1910) 293 sqq., 'Zu Ibn al Haiṭams Optik', *AGNT*, iii (1910–11) 1 sqq.; J. L. Heiberg und E. Wiedemann, 'Ibn al Haiṭams Schrift über parabolische Hohlspiegel', *BM*, x (1910) 201 sqq., 'Eine arabische Schrift über die Parabol und parabolische Hohlspiegel', ibid. xi (1911) 193 sqq.; H. Bauer, *Die Psychologie Alhazens*; H. Suter, 'Die Abhandlung über die Ausmessung des Paraboloides von Ibn al Haitham', *BM*, xii (1912) 289 sqq.; Mustafa Nazif bey, *Al-Hasan ibn al-Haitham. His optical studies and discoveries* (in Arabic); H. J. J. Winter, 'The Arabic achievement in physics', *Endeavour*, ix (1950) 76 sqq.; H. J. J. Winter and W. 'Arafat, 'Ibn Al-Haitham on the paraboloidal focussing mirror', *J. Roy. Asiatic Soc. of Bengal*, xv (1949) 25 sqq. See also Sarton, *Introduction*, i. 721–3, ii. 342; and below, p. 217.   [1] *De Mult. Spec.*, ed. Bridges, iii. 184.

[2] 'multiplicatio secundum figuras'. *Opus Maius*, iv. ii. 2–3, ed. Bridges, i. 111–19; iii. 2, ed. Bridges, i. 123–4; *Comm. Nat.* i. iv. 2, ed. Steele, ii. 48 sqq. Cf. *De Lineis*, Baur, 1912, pp. 64–65; above, p. 112.

[3] He accepted the common view that the lens was the sensitive part of the eye. Cf. *Opus Maius*, v. i. ii. 3, ed. Bridges, ii. 17–18.

[4] Bacon tried to show that the theory that material substance was composed of atoms contradicted the conclusions of geometry about the incommensurability of the side and diagonal of a square. For if these were composed of a discrete number of atoms, the proportion of one to the other would be a rational number (*Opus Maius*, iv. iv. 9, ed. Bridges, i. 151–2). Cf. Grosseteste's ideas on the *continuum*; above, pp. 100–2, 119. For an account of scholastic ideas on the infinitely small and the infinitely large see Duhem, *Léonard de Vinci*, ii. 4 sqq., 368 sqq.

there are as many parts in a grain of millet as in the diameter of the world.[1]

He showed then that it was possible to draw an infinite number of lines from the base of a triangle to the point at its apex.

Roger Bacon made use also of Grosseteste's explanation of the tides.[2] He incorporated a section of *De Natura Locorum* in the section of the *Opus Maius* dealing with the effects of rays on climate,[3] and he seems to be referring to *De Iride* in the remark in the *Opus Tertium* that 'homines habentes oculos profundos longius vident'.[4] He took over Grosseteste's theory of heat and expanded his remarks about the internal strain between the parts of a body, which produced an intrinsic resistance to movement in falling bodies because each part prevented those lateral to it from going straight to the centre of the earth. 'This conclusion, that a heavy body receives a strain in its own natural motion, is proved by cause and effect', he said,[5] and motion under strain generated heat. He made use of Grosseteste's theory of double refraction to explain the operation of a spherical (and hemispherical) lens or burning-glass, adding: 'instruments can be made so that we may sensibly see propagations of this kind; but until we have instruments we can prove this by natural effect without contradiction. . . . Let us take a hemisphere of crystal or a glass vessel, the lower part of which is round and full of water.'[6] This, he said, should be held in the rays of the sun, as Grosseteste described in *De Natura Locorum*.[7] He took up also

---

[1] *Opus Maius*, v. i. vi. 1, ed. Bridges, ii. 35–36. In iv. iv. 13, ed. Bridges, i. 165, Bacon used an ingenious argument to demonstrate the finite magnitude of the universe by a *reductio ad impossibile* leading to the conclusion: 'the part must be equal to the whole, which is impossible; aequabitur . . . pars suo toti, quod est impossibile.' He was discussing two lines extending to infinity, so his conclusion seems to contradict the statement in the last part of the passage quoted on this page. Cf. above, pp. 101–2, 108; below, p. 174, n. 3.

[2] *Opus Maius*, iv. iv. 6, ed. Bridges, ii. 139–42; see above, p. 112.

[3] *Opus Maius*, iv. iv. 3–4, ed. Bridges, i. 133–37; cf. Baur, 1912, pp. 66–69.

[4] *Opus Tertium*, ed. Little, p. 29. Cf. Baur, 1912, p. 73.

[5] *Opus Maius*, iv. ii. 2, iv. iv. 15, ed. Bridges, i. 113, 168. Cf. above, p. 87, n. 1. Duhem (*Léonard de Vinci*, i. 9) has drawn attention to the significance, in the development of the idea of *mass*, of this notion of an intrinsic resistance to free fall in heavy bodies, but he evidently did not realize that Bacon got it from Grosseteste. In *Opus Maius*, iv. iv. 16, Bacon went on to discuss 'Jordanus in libro de ponderibus'. On Jordanus Nemorarius's important contribution to mechanics see Duhem, op. cit. i. 259 sqq. and *Orig. statique*, i. 98 sqq., 354 sqq. Cf. Levi ben Gerson (1288–1344) on the propagation of heat: Sarton, *Introduction*, iii. 602.

[6] *Opus Maius*, iv. ii. 2, ed. Bridges, i. 113; *Comm. Nat.* i. ii. 5, ed. Steele, ii. 30 sqq.; *De Mult. Spec.* ii. 3, ed. Bridges, ii. 471; cf. above, p. 144, n. 5.

[7] See above, p. 122, and Fig. 2.

Grosseteste's suggestion[1] as to the possibilities of using lenses for magnifying small objects, and he made experiments with plano-convex lenses while trying to use the laws of refraction to improve vision,[2] a practical object such as he held to be the final justification of all theoretical science.[3]

If anyone examine letters or other small objects through the medium of a crystal or glass or some other transparent body placed above the letters, and if it be shaped like the lesser segment of a sphere with the convex side towards the eye, and the eye is in the air, he will see the letters much better and they will appear larger to him. For in accordance with the truth of the fifth rule[4] regarding a spherical medium beneath which the object is placed, the centre being beyond the object and the convexity towards the eye, all conditions are favourable for magnification, for the angle in which it is

---

[1] *De Iride*, Baur, 1912, p. 74; above, p. 119. Cf. Little, *Franciscan Papers*, p. 79; Baur, in *RBE*, p. 49.

[2] *Opus Maius*, v. iii. ii; see also *Opus Tertium*, ed. Brewer, p. 111, and *Fragment inédit de l'Opus Tertium*, ed. Duhem. Another example of his method is his experimental and theoretical investigation of the production of a 'burning-point' by a concave mirror illuminated by the sun; see *De Speculis Comburentibus* published in Rogerii Baconis, *Specula Mathematica*, Francofurti, 1614. Bacon said in *Opus Maius*, v. ii. iii. 6, ed. Bridges, ii. 118-19, that the rays coming from the sun 'seem to be parallel', but he treated them as radiating out from a point when he was discussing lenses and mirrors (J. Würschmidt, 'Roger Bacons Art des wissenschaftlichen Arbeitens, dargestellt nach seiner Schrift *De Speculis*', in *RBE*, pp. 229 sqq.; but cf. below, p. 161). In *De Mult. Spec.* ii. 7, ed. Bridges, ii. 486-91, he shows a knowledge of parabolic mirrors, with which the work of Alhazen that had been translated into Latin showed no acquaintance, though Alhazen did write on the subject (above, p. 147, n. 2). Bacon's chief source of knowledge of concave mirrors seems to have been the pseudo-Euclidean *De Speculis* (above, p. 116, n. 4; Heiberg und Wiedemann, *BM*, x (1910) 201 sqq.; Wiedemann, ibid., pp. 293 sqq.). Roger Bacon discussed the properties of surfaces produced by the rotation on their axes of various conic sections. 'Et haec reflexio probatur per experientiam et effectum' (*De Mult. Spec.*, p. 490). He then went on to discuss a section 'ut fiat congregatio omnium radiorum cadentium in superficie speculi ad punctum unum in axe, et non solum fiat ad aliquam determinatam distantiam, sed ad omnem quantum voluerit experimentator perfectus'. A general account of his work in optics has been given by E. Wiedemann, 'Roger Bacon und seine Verdienste um die Optik', in *RBE*, pp. 185 sqq.; see also R. Steele 'Roger Bacon and the state of science in the thirteenth century', in *SHMS*, ii. 133.

[3] See *Opus Maius*, iv, v, vi; *De Mult. Spec.*, ed. Bridges, iii. 183-5. Roger Bacon made the same division of sciences into theoretical and practical as had long been traditional among Latin writers (cf. above, pp. 22, 37). See e.g. for astronomy *Opus Maius*, iv. ii. 1, and for alchemy *Opus Tertium*, C. 12, ed. Brewer, pp. 39-40. On mathematics see *De Mult. Spec.* Prologue, ed. Bridges, iii. 185. In speaking of Bacon's utilitarianism it should be remembered that his presuppositions led him to construe all human activity in terms of the ultimate purpose of contemplating God in eternity: see *Opus Maius*, ii, 'Philosophiae cum Theologia Affinitas', CC. 5-6, and vii, 'Moralis Philosophia'.

[4] Rules regarding the properties of lenses had already been given earlier in this section of the treatise; *Opus Maius*, v. iii. ii. 3. Fig. 4 illustrates Bacon's Rule 4.

seen is greater, the image is greater, and the position of the image is nearer, because the object is between the eye and the centre. For this reason this instrument is useful to old people and people with weak eyes, for they can see any letter however small if magnified enough.[1]

To the eye and its functioning in vision Roger Bacon paid particular attention because, as he said, 'by means of it we search out certain experimental knowledge of all things that are in the heavens and in the earth'.[2] His account of vision was one of the most important written during the Middle Ages and it became a point of departure for seventeenth-century work.[3] Bacon's chief contribution was to try to explain the operation of the eye, of which his account was based largely on the writings of Alhazen and Avicenna,[4] by means

---

[1] *Opus Maius*, v, 'Perspectiva', iii. ii. 4, ed. Bridges, ii. 157. He also discussed concave lenses, ibid., C. 3, p. 151. That weak sight, and particularly the difficulty of reading in the evening, was felt as a serious affliction, and would provide a motive for the invention of spectacles, is shown by the prescriptions of doctors like Petrus Hispanus (d. 1277) who, in his *Liber de oculo* (ed. A. M. Berger as *Die Ophthalmologie des Petrus Hispanus*), recommended an 'Aqua mirabilis ad visum conservandum et contra maculam et defectum visus per vesperas' (§ 42); also drops for anyone who 'post vesperas sole occidente videre non potest' (§ 59). The use of convex lenses of small curvature and long focus to compensate for hypermetropia or 'long sight', a condition common in older people, seems to have begun before the end of the thirteenth century, possibly in association with the Venetian glass industry. In the chapter, *De Cristaleriis* (1300), of the by-laws of Venetian guilds there is mention of *roidi da ogli* and *lapides ad legendum* (G. Albertotti, 'Lettera intorno alla invenzione degli occhiali', *Annal. Ottalmol. e Clin. Oculistica*, l, 1922; E. Rosen, 'The invention of eyeglasses', *J. Hist. Medicine*, xi, 1956, pp. 13 sqq., 183 sqq.—the best account; cf. E. Turrière, *Isis*, vii, 1925, pp. 77–104). Spectacles were probably invented by someone unknown soon after 1286, and were made public by a Dominican friar, Alessandro della Spina. Putting aside Bernard de Gordon (1303), the earliest known medical prescription of spectacles is that by Guy de Chauliac, who in his *Chirurgia Magna* (1363) gives lotions and spectacles as alternative remedies. References by other late fourteenth-century doctors such as Thomas of Sarepta and Valescus de Taranta show that by this time spectacles were in fairly common use. The use of concave lenses to compensate for myopia or 'short sight' apparently did not begin until the sixteenth century. For the history of spectacles cf. E. Bock, *Brille und ihre Geschichte;* G. H. Oliver, *Invention and Discovery of Spectacles;* M. von Rohr, 'Gedanken zur Geschichte der Brillenherstellung', *Forsch. Gesch. Optik*, ii (1937) 121 sqq., 'Aus der Geschichte der Brille', *Beitr. Gesch. Technik*, xvii (1927) 30–50, xviii (1928) 95–117; N. Scalinci, 'A proposito di Alessandro della Spina e di storia della invenzione degli occhiali', *Rivista di Storia crit. Scienze med. nat.* xv (1933) 139–43; C. Singer, 'Steps leading to the invention of the first optical apparatus', in *SHMS*, ii; and the references in Sarton, *Introduction*, ii. 1024 sqq., 1040, iii. 873 sqq., 1199, 1235, 1708. An account of glassmaking and of spectacles, along with other technical inventions, was given by the Italian Dominican, Giovanni de San Gimignano, in his encyclopaedia *Summa de Exemplis et Rerum Similitudinibus*, Lib. ix (*c.* 1313); Sarton, ibid. iii. 921. Cf. also K. Chiu, 'The introduction of spectacles into China', *Harvard J. Asiatic Studies*, i (1936) 186 sqq.

[2] *Opus Maius*, v. i. i. 1, ed. Bridges, ii. 2.   [3] Below, pp. 280–2 sqq.; also p. 217.

[4] Avicennae, *Canon Medicinae*, iii. iii. iii. 1, Venetiis, 1608, i. 530 sqq.; P. de Konig,

of the theory of 'multiplication of species'. Distinguishing like Grosseteste[1] between the psychological act of vision which went forth from the eye, and the physical light which went from the visible object to the eye, he asserted that both the extramitted species of vision and the intramitted[2] species of light from the visible object were necessary.

The reason for this assertion is that everything in nature completes its action through its own force and species alone . . . as, for example, fire by its own force dries and consumes and does many things. Therefore vision must perform the act of seeing by its own force. But the act of seeing is the perception of a visible object at a distance, and therefore vision perceives what is visible by its own force multiplied to the object. Moreover, the species of the things of the world are not fitted by nature to effect the complete act of vision at once, because of its nobleness. Hence these must be aided and excited by the species of the eye, which travels in the locality of the visual pyramid,[3] and changes the medium and ennobles it, and renders it analogous to vision, and so prepares the passage of the species itself of the visible object. . . . Concerning the multiplication of this species, moreover, we are to understand that it lies in the same place as the species of the thing seen, between the sight and the thing seen, and takes place along the pyramid whose vertex is in the eye and base in the thing seen. And as the species of an object in the same medium travels in a straight path and is refracted in different ways when it meets a medium of another transparency, and is reflected when it meets the obstacle of a dense body; so is it also true of the species of vision that it travels altogether along the path of the species itself of the visible object.[4]

To show how the eye focused the species of light entering it he described first the anatomical arrangement of its parts (Fig. 5). Following Avicenna he said that the eye had three coats and three humours. The inner coat consisted of two parts, the *rete* or *retina*, an expansion of the nerve forming a concave net 'supplied with veins, arteries and slender nerves'[5] and acting as a conveyor of

Trois traités d'anatomie arabe, p. 660; Wiedemann, 'Ibn Sînâs Anschauung von Sehvorgang', *AGNT*, iv (1912–13) 239 sqq.; above, p. 114, n. 1, p. 147, n. 2; below, p. 153, n. 3.

[1] Above, pp. 115, 118.

[2] He discussed the views of Plato, Aristotle, Euclid, Ptolemy, the Stoics, Alhazen, Alkindi, Avicenna, and Averroës on extramission and intramission, in *Opus Maius*, v. i. vii. 2–3, ed. Bridges, ii. 49–51.

[3] The notion of 'visual pyramids' (that is, cones) came from Greek sources (Lejeune, *Euclide et Ptolémée*, pp. 51 sqq.), and was developed in Alhazeni *Opticae*, i. 19, p. 10; cf. above, p. 126, n. 1; below, p. 216, n. 3, p. 217, n. 3.

[4] *Opus Maius*, v. i. vii. 4, ed. Bridges, ii. 52–53.

[5] *Opus Maius*, v. i. ii. 2, ed. Bridges, ii. 15.

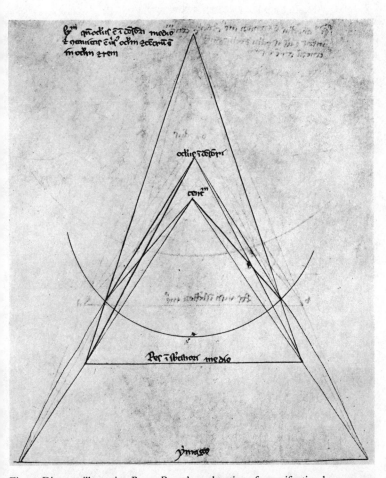

Fig. 4. Diagram illustrating Roger Bacon's explanation of magnification by a convex section of a sphere (*Opus Maius*, v. iii. ii. 3ʳ). The object seen is represented by the line marked 'Res in subtiliori medio', and the rays which reach the eye, marked 'Oculus in densiori', are those which are refracted towards it on crossing the interface. Each end of the magnified image ('ymago') is seen on the projection (badly drawn) of the refracted ray entering the eye. From MS Roy. 7. F. viii, f. 92ᵛ. This MS contains diagrams illustrating Bacon's eight rules for magnification and diminution by spherical surfaces, according to the relative positions of the eye, the centre of the sphere ('centrum'), and the surface. The above diagram illustrates Rule 4. See p. 150, n. 4.

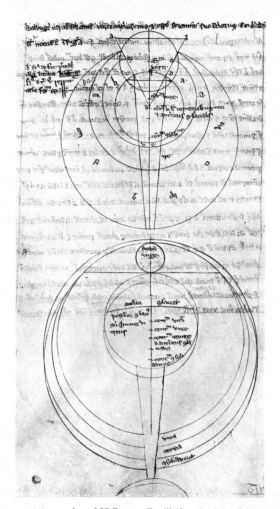

Fig. 5. Diagram of the eye from MS Roy. 7. F. viii (f. 54ᵛ) of the *Opus Maius*: 'I shall draw, therefore, a figure in (which all these matters are made clear as far as is possible on a surface, but the full demonstration would require a body fashioned like the eye in all the particulars aforesaid. The eye of a cow, pig, and other animals can be used for illustration, if anyone wishes to experiment' (v. i. iii. 3, ed. Bridges, ii. 23). Bacon's intention was to draw simply a geometrical diagram showing the various curvatures of the ocular media. By 'centrum' he meant 'centre of curvature'. 'Let *al* be the base of the pyramid, which is the visible object, whose species penetrates the cornea under the pyramidal form and (enters the opening, and which tends naturally to the centre of the eye, and would go there if it were not met first by a denser body by which it is bent, namely, the vitreous humour, *chd*.' (See pp. 153–5.) The 'centre of the eye' is the centre (*b*) of curvature of the anterior convex surface of the lens, which Bacon, follow- ing Avicenna (*Canon*, iii. iii. i. 1), correctly held to be flattened. In the top diagram the refraction should be shown, not as drawn, but at the interface between the convex *posterior* surface of the lens and the concave anterior surface of the vitreous humour (*chd*; *h* is missing). The centre of curvature of this interface (*centrum viitre*) is in front of *b*.

nourishment; and outside this a second thicker part called the *uvea*.[1] Outside the *uvea* were the *cornea*, which was transparent where it covered the opening of the pupil, and the *consolidativa* or *conjunctiva*. Inside the inner coat were the three humours, and so, for light entering the pupil: 'There will then be the *cornea*, the *humor albigineus*, the *humor glacialis* [lens], and the *humor vitreus*, and the extremity of the nerve, so that the species of things will pass through the medium of them all to the brain. . . . The crystalline humour [lens] is called the pupil, and in it is the visual power.'[2]

The theory of vision Bacon described was essentially that of Alhazen[3] and in fact misunderstanding of the functions of the lens and retina remained the chief stumbling block to the formulation of an adequate theory of vision until the end of the sixteenth century.[4] Of the theory that the lens was the only sensitive part of the eye Bacon wrote, using what became known as the method of agreement and difference[5], as Alhazen had done: 'For if it is injured,

---

[1] In modern terminology the *uvea* corresponds to the choroid (including the iris: Vesalius used the same term) and, generally speaking, the *consolidativa* to the sclerotic coat. *Humor albigineus* is the aqueous humour. *Humor glacialis* is generally the lens, but sometimes Bacon used the term to include both the lens (then distinguished as *anterior glacialis* or *humor crystallinus*) and the *humor vitreus*. For the history of the anatomy of the eye in the West see H. Magnus, *Anatomie des Auges bei den Griechen und Römern*, *Augenheilkunde der Alten*, *Anatomie des Auges in ihrer geschichtlichen Entwicklung*; M. Meyerhof und C. Prüfer, 'Die Augenanatomie des Hunain b. Ishāq', *AGM*, iv (1910) 163–90; H. Bauer, op. cit. above, p. 147, n. 2; C. Singer, op. cit. above, p. 151, n. 1; A. Bednarski, 'Das anatomische Augenbild von J. Peckham', *AGM*, xxii (1929) 352 sqq., 'Die anatomischen Augenbilder in den Handschriften des Roger Bacon, Johann Peckham und Witelo', ibid. xxiv (1931) 60 sqq. For a twentieth-century account of the structure and functioning of the eye see M. H. Pirenne, *Vision and the Eye*.

[2] *Opus Maius*, v. i. ii. 3, ed. Bridges, ii. 17–18. See Fig. 5.

[3] Alhazeni *Opticae* i. 16, 25, pp. 8, 15; and see above, p. 147, n. 2. See also D. Kaufmann, *Die Sinne*. Confusion has arisen from the thirteenth-century Latin version of Averroës, *Colliget*, ii. 15, Venetiis, 1553, f. 15ᵛ: 'Sed iuvamentum telae retinae primum est ut det spiritum visibilem per nervos, qui sunt in ipsa, hoc est calorem naturalem, cuius complexio adaptata est in cerebro, et per duos nervos, qui vadunt ad oculos; et etiam nutrit crystallinam humiditatem per viam rorationis, et dat iuvamentum caloris naturalis per arterias, quae sunt in ea. Sed Galenus confitetur quod aranea est ultimitate pervietatis et luciditatis, quia colores et formae imprimuntur in ipsam; ergo ista tela est proprium instrumentum visus, vel per se, vel per adiutorium crystallinae.' Cf. i. 17, iii. 38. V. Fukala ('Der arabische Artz Averrhoës war der erste, welche die Netzhaut als lichtempfindlichen Theil des Auges erkannte', *Archiv für Augenheilkunde*, xlii, 1900, pp. 203–14; cf. Sarton, *Introduction*, ii. 361) argued that Averroës recognized the retina as the light-sensitive organ, but he said only that the retina (1) conveyed the visual spirit and (2) nourished the lens: see Crombie, 'The mechanistic hypothesis and the scientific study of vision', *Proc. Roy. Microscopical Soc.*, ii (1967) 49, n. 81.

[4] Below, pp. 280–2.

[5] This method was formulated by William of Ockham; below, p. 173.

even though the other parts are whole, vision is destroyed, and if it is unharmed and injury happens to the others, provided they retain their transparent quality, vision is not destroyed.'[1] But, in another passage inspired by one of Alhazen's chapters,[2] he stressed the qualification

that vision is not completed in the eye, but in the nerve . . . for two different species come to the eyes and . . . in two eyes there are different judgements. . . . Therefore there must be something sentient besides the eyes, in which vision is completed and of which the eyes are the instruments that give it the visible species. This is the common nerve in the surface of the brain, where the two nerves coming from the two parts of the anterior brain meet, and after meeting are divided and extend to the eyes. . . . But it is necessary that the two species coming from the eyes should meet at one place in the common nerve, and that one of these should be more intense and fuller than the other. For naturally the two forms of the same species mingle in the same matter and in the same place, and therefore are not distinguished, but become one form after they come to one place, and then, since the judging faculty is single and the species single, a single judgement is made regarding the object. A proof of this is the fact that when the species do not come from the two eyes to one place in the common nerve, one object is seen as two. This is evident when the natural position of the eyes is changed, as happens if the finger is placed below one of the eyes or if the eye is twisted somewhat from its place; both species do not then come to one place in the common nerve, and one object is seen as two.[3]

In another passage Roger Bacon tried to show how the 'visible species' were focused on the end of the optic nerve without producing an inverted image. In common with all optical writers before Kepler[4] he failed to understand that such an image was compatible with normal vision.

If the rays of the visual pyramid [Fig. 5] meet at the centre of the *anterior glacialis* [lens], they must be mutually divided and what was right

---

[1] *Opus Maius*, v. i. iv. 2, ed. Bridges, ii. 27. Cf. Alhazeni *Opticae*, i. 16.

[2] Alhazeni *Opticae*, i. 27, p. 16.

[3] *Opus Maius*, v. i. v. 2, ed. Bridges, ii. 32–33. In a later section of the *Opus Maius* Roger Bacon described another experiment to demonstrate the same point, that when 'the two species come to different places on the common nerve' then 'one object appears to be two' (v. ii. ii. 2, ed. Bridges, ii. 94). Three small pyramidal objects were arranged in a row and the midpoint between the two eyes placed on the projection of the line joining them. 'The eyes must then fix their axes on the middle object, which will be seen as one, and both of the other two will appear double' (p. 95). See the diagram in MS Roy. F. viii, f. 74ʳ; cf. Lejeune, *Euclide et Ptolémée*, p. 134. On binocular vision in modern physiology see Pirenne, *Vision and the Eye*, pp. 174 sqq.

[4] Below, p. 282.

would become left and the reverse, and what was above would be below.
. . . In order, therefore, that this error may be avoided and the species of
the right part may pass on its own side, and the left to its side, and so too
of other positions, there must be something else between the anterior of
the *glacialis* and its centre to prevent a meeting of this kind. Therefore
Nature has contrived to place the vitrous humour before the centre[1] of the
glacialis, which has a different transparency and a different centre, so that
refraction takes place in it, in order that the rays of the pyramid may be
diverted from meeting in the centre of the *anterior glacialis*. Since, therefore, all rays of the radiant pyramid except the axis . . . are falling at
oblique angles on the vitreous humour . . . all those rays must be refracted
on its surface. . . . Since, moreover, the vitreous humour is denser than the
anterior glacialis, it follows, therefore, that refraction takes place between
the straight path and the perpendicular drawn at the point of refraction,
as has been shown in the multiplication of species. . . . Thus the right
species will always go according to its own direction until it comes to a
point of the common nerve . . . and will not go to the left. . . . The same is
true of the species coming from all other parts.[2]

Roger Bacon was mistaken in thinking that the vitreous humour
had a higher refractive index than the lens, and in other respects his
theory of vision was far from correct. Nevertheless, his attempt to
solve the problem of how the image was formed behind the lens
was a step in the right direction. He thought that the nerve was
'filled with a similar vitreous humour as far as the common nerve' so
that the 'species' travelled along it without refraction, though caused
by 'the power of the soul's force (*virtutis*) . . . to follow the tortuosity
of the nerve, so that it flows along a tortuous line, not along a
straight one, as it does in the inanimate bodies of the world'.[3] In the
common nerve the judgements of the 'visual faculty' (*virtus visiva*)
were completed, so that it was the seat of 'ultimate perception' in
vision. The other special senses were analogously accommodated.
Where more than one special sense was involved the 'ultimate
perception' occurred at a deeper level, in 'the common sense (*sensus
communis*) in the anterior part of the brain'.[4]

His knowledge of optics Roger Bacon used in the experimental-
mathematical investigation of the cause of the rainbow which he
gave in Part VI of the *Opus Maius* as an example of his method. His
procedure, in fact, followed the essential principles of Grosseteste's

[1] By 'centre' he meant centre of curvature; see Fig. 5.
[2] *Opus Maius*, v. i. vii. 1, ed. Bridges, ii. 47–48.
[3] Ibid., pp. 48–49; cf. *De Mult. Spec.* ii. 2, pp. 463–4; above, p. 144.
[4] *Opus Maius*, v. i. v. 3, pp. 33–34.

methods of combined resolution and composition and of falsification, and it represents the first major advance made in the experimental method after Grosseteste. He began by collecting instances of phenomena similar to the rainbow, both as to the colours and the bow-like shape. He said:

The experimenter, then, should first examine visible objects in order that he may find colours arranged as in the phenomenon mentioned above and also the same figure. For let him take hexagonal stones from Ireland and from India, which are called iris stones in Solinus on the *Wonders of the World*, and let him hold these in a solar ray falling through the window, so that he may find in the shadow near the ray all the colours of the rainbow, arranged as in it.[1] And further let the same experimenter turn to a somewhat dark place and apply the stone to one of his eyes which is almost closed, and he will see the colours of the rainbow clearly arranged just as in the bow. And since many employing these stones think that the phenomenon is due to the special virtue of those stones and to their hexagonal shape, therefore let the experimenter proceed farther, and he will find this same peculiarity in crystalline stones correctly shaped, and in other transparent stones. Moreover, he will find this not only in white stones like the Irish crystals, but also in black ones, as is evident in the dark crystal and in all stones of similar transparency. He will find it besides in crystals of a shape differing from the hexagonal, provided they have a roughened surface, like the Irish crystals, neither altogether smooth, nor rougher than they are. Nature produces some that have surfaces like the Irish crystals. For a difference in the corrugations causes a difference in the colours. And further let him observe rowers,[2] and in the drops falling from the raised oars he finds the same colours when the solar rays penetrate drops of this kind. The same phenomenon is seen in water falling from the wheels of a mill;[3] and likewise when one sees on a summer's morning the drops of dew on the grass in a meadow or field, he will observe the colours. Likewise when it is raining, if he stands in a dark place, and the rays beyond it pass through the falling rain, the colours will appear in the shadow nearby; and frequently at night colours appear round a candle. Moreover, if a man in summer, when he rises from sleep and has his eyes only partly open, suddenly looks at a hole through which a ray of the sun enters, he will see colours. Moreover, if seated out of the sun he holds his cap beyond his eyes, he will see colours; and similarly if he closes an eye the same thing

---

[1] Cf. Seneca, *Quaest. Nat.* i. 7; above, p. 111, n. 6.

[2] See next note.

[3] Avicenna mentioned the rainbows seen in spray from mill-wheels, baths, and oars, and round lamps; see M. Horten, 'Avicennas Lehre vom Regenbogen, nach seinem Werk al Schifâ' (mit Bemerkungen von E. Wiedemann), *Meteorol. Zeitschrift*, xxx (1913) 533 sqq.

happens in the shade of his eyebrows; and again the same phenomenon appears through a glass vessel filled with water and placed in the sun's rays. Or similarly if someone having water in his mouth sprinkles it vigorously into the rays and stands at the side of the rays.[1] So, too, if rays in the required position pass through an oil lamp hanging in the air so that the light falls on the surface of the oil, colours will be produced. Thus in an infinite number of ways colours of this kind appear, which the diligent experimenter knows how to discover.

In a similar way also he will be able to test the shape in which the colours are disposed. For by means of the crystalline stone and substances of this kind he will find the shape straight. By means of the eyelids and eyebrows and by many other means, and also by means of holes in rags, he will discover whole circles coloured. Similarly, in a place where the dew-fall is plentiful and sufficient to take the whole circle, and if the place where the circle of the rainbow should be is dark proportionately, because the bow does not appear in the light part, then the circle will be complete. Similarly, whole circles appear frequently around candles, as Aristotle[1] states and we ourselves experience.

Since, moreover, we find colours and various figures similar to the phenomena in the air, namely, of the iris, halo, and mock-suns, we are encouraged and greatly stimulated to grasp the truth in those phenomena that occur in the heavens.[2]

From an examination of these instances Bacon tried to reach a 'common nature' uniting the rainbow and similar phenomena, and in the course of his argument he considered several different theories and eliminated those contradicted by observation. To explain the variation in the altitude of rainbows he took over Aristotle's[3] theory that the rainbow formed part of the circumference of the base of a cone of which the apex was at the sun and the axis passed through the observer's eye to the centre of the bow, and he confirmed this by showing by measurements with the astrolabe that the sun, the observer's eye, and the centre of the bow were always in a straight line. This explained why the altitude of the bow varied at different latitudes and different times of year, and why a complete circle could be seen only when the base of the cone was elevated above the surface of the earth, as with rainbows in sprays.

[1] Cf. Aristotle, *Meteor.* iii. 4, 374^{a}26 sqq., where similar observations are mentioned.

[2] See *Opus Maius*, vi. 2-12, ed. Bridges, ii. 173 sqq.

[3] *Meteor.* iii. 5, 375^{b}16 sqq. Cf. above, p. 124. In *Opus Maius*, iv, ed. Bridges, i. 212, Bacon ungraciously said: 'Aristotle more than all other philosophical writers has involved us in obscurities in dealing with the rainbow', though he attributed most of the alleged mistakes to the 'many false statements in the translations of the Latins'. Cf. vi. 10, ed. Bridges, ii. 193-4. On Bacon as a philological critic see above, p. 141, n. 1.

The experimenter, therefore, taking the altitude of the sun and of the rainbow above the horizon will find that the final altitude at which the rainbow can appear above the horizon is 42 degrees, and this is the maximum elevation of the rainbow. . . . And the rainbow reaches this maximum elevation when the sun is on the horizon, namely, at sunrise and sunset.[1]

In the latitude of Paris, he said, 'the altitude of the sun at noon of the equinox is 41 degrees and 12 minutes', and therefore in the summer, when the altitude of the sun is greater than 42 degrees, no rainbow can appear at noon. He discussed in some detail the times of year when rainbows could not appear in Scotland, Jerusalem, and other places.

Going on to discuss 'whether the bow is caused by incident rays or by reflection or by refraction, and whether it is an image of the sun . . . and whether there are real colours in the cloud itself', he said: 'to understand these matters we must employ definite experiments'.[2] He pointed out that each observer saw a different bow which moved[3] when he did in relation to trees and other fixed objects, whether he moved parallel to, towards, or away from the bow. There were, he said, as many bows as observers, for each observer saw his bow follow his own movement, his shadow bisecting its arc. Therefore the rainbow could not be seen by 'incident' (i.e. direct) rays, for if it were it would appear fixed in one place like the white and black patches on clouds.

Similarly, when a colour is produced by incident rays through a crystalline stone, refraction takes place in it, but the same colour in the same position is seen by different observers. . . . Moreover, the image of an object seen by refraction does not follow the observer if he recedes, nor does it recede if he approaches, nor does it move in a direction parallel to him; which is evident when we look at a fish at rest in water, or a stick fixed in it, or the sun or moon through the medium of vapours, or letters through a crystal or glass.[4]

---

[1] *Opus Maius*, vi. 4, ed. Bridges, ii. 176–7; cf. CC. 5–6, pp. 178–85. Cf. below, p. 228.

[2] Ibid., C. 7, p. 185. Avicenna had said that the colours of the rainbow were not real but imaginary. He thought that the rainbow was produced by the reflection of sunlight from a dark cloud on to fine water drops in front of the cloud, where the rainbow was seen. He held that there were only three 'simple' colours in the rainbow (Horten, op. cit., pp. 535, 539–41). Averroës also thought that the rainbow was caused by the reflection of sunlight, without refraction, but he held that there were four 'simple' colours and that they were real. See above, p. 111, n. 5, p. 124, n. 2, p. 147, n. 2; below, p. 197.

[3] This observation was described by Alexander of Aphrodisias (below, p. 227, n. 2). Avicenna also mentioned it (Horten, op. cit., p. 542).

[4] *Opus Maius*, vi. 7, p. 188. Cf. Witelo, below, p. 227.

Therefore, since there were only three kinds of 'principal rays' (direct, refracted and reflected),[1] and since 'accidental rays . . . do not change their position unless caused by reflection',[2] the rainbow must be seen by reflected rays. 'All the raindrops have the nature of a mirror',[3] and things seen in a mirror moved when the observer moved, just as the rainbow did. 'There are, then, raindrops of small size in infinite number, and reflection takes place in every direction as from a spherical mirror.'[4] Yet the rainbow could not be an image of the sun produced by such reflection, as Seneca had suggested, because spherical mirrors distorted the shape and changed the size and colour of objects seen in them.

Of the colours seen in the rainbow and in crystals, Roger Bacon said:

If it be said that solar rays passing through a crystal produce real and fixed colours, which produce a species and have objective reality, we must reply that the phenomena are different. The observer alone produces the bow, nor is there anything present except reflection. In the case of the crystal, however, there is a natural cause, namely, the ray and the corrugated stone, which has great diversity of surface, so that according to the angle at which the light falls a diversity of colours result. And viewing them does [not] cause the colours to be present here, for there is colour before it is seen here, and it is seen by different people in the same place. But in the case of the bow the phenomenon is the result of vision, and therefore can have no reality but merely appearance.[5]

The theory that Albertus Magnus had advanced, that the colours of the rainbow were due to differences in density of cloud,[6] Roger Bacon rejected on the grounds that there were no such differences in crystals, or in sprays or dew on the grass, where, nevertheless, similar colours were seen. Real colours such as those seen in hexagonal crystals he attributed to mixtures of white and black, as explained by Aristotle in *De Sensu et Sensibili*.[7] Of the colours of the rainbow he said: 'We need give only the cause of the appearance.'[8] 'It is thought by scientists that these colours are caused by the humours and colours of the eye, for these colours exist merely in appearance.'[9]

Concerning the shape of the rainbow, Bacon considered and rejected two earlier theories. First, he said that it could not be

[1] See above, p. 120, n. 5.   [2] Ibid., p. 188.
[3] Ibid., p. 189.   [4] Ibid., C. 9, p. 192.
[5] Ibid., C. 8, pp. 191–2.   [6] Below, pp. 199–200.
[7] See above, p. 111, n. 5.   [8] Ibid., C. 10, p. 193.
[9] Ibid., C. 12, p. 197. Cf. above, p. 158, n. 2.

produced by the raindrops themselves falling in a cone, for the circular shape appeared in irregular sprays. Secondly, he attacked Grosseteste's theory that the bow was produced by three separate refractions through successively denser layers of moist atmosphere.[1] He said that only one refraction could take place in sprays, yet the same shape was formed as seen in the sky. Moreover, Grosseteste's statement that the refracted rays would spread out, 'not into a round pyramid [i.e. cone], but into a figure like the curved surface of a round pyramid',[2] seemed to Bacon to contradict the law of refraction, according to which the rays would form a regular cone. Nor could the curvature be produced by the moisture, for according to Grosseteste this was not of such a form but was 'a rounded mass of conical form'.

'Another explanation must therefore be sought; and it can be stated that the bow must be in the form of a circular arc.' For the colours of the rainbow did not shift with varying incidence of light like those on the dove's neck,[3] but 'the same colour in one circle of the bow appears from one end to the other, and therefore all parts must have the same position with respect to the solar ray and the eye'.[4] This condition and the appearance of the rainbow would be satisfied if the rainbow were a circle with its centre on the line joining the sun and the eye. He concluded:

everywhere [where there are raindrops] there are conditions suitable for the appearance of the bow, but as an actual fact the bow appears only in raindrops from which there is reflection to the eye; because there is merely the appearance of colours arising from the imagination and deception of the vision. . . . A reflection comes from every drop at the same time, while the eye is in one position, because of the equality of the angles of incidence and reflection.[5]

Bacon's understanding of the part played by individual raindrops in the formation of the rainbow was a real advance,[6] in spite of his rejection of refraction. He extended his knowledge of optics to try to explain halos, mock-suns, and other similar phenomena. His

[1] See above, pp. 124–7. Bacon did not mention Grosseteste by name but referred to 'illi, qui dicunt. . . .' (C. 11, p. 194.) As he quoted *De Iride* literally it is certain that he was referring to Grosseteste and probably to Albertus Magnus (below, pp. 198–9) who adopted Grosseteste's theory.   [2] *Opus Maius*, vi. 11, p. 195.

[3] These colours are mentioned in Alhazeni *Opticae*, i. 3, p. 3.

[4] *Opus Maius*, vi. 11, pp. 195–6.   [5] Ibid., vi. 12, pp. 196–7; cf. below, p. 227, n. 1.

[6] He might have got some of his ideas on this from Albertus Magnus; see below, pp. 197–8.

explanation of the halo is interesting because it was based on the explicit assumption that the sun's rays were parallel. He said in the *Opus Maius* that the halo was caused by rays going out from the sun 'like a cylinder in shape' and becoming refracted on passing through a spherical mass of vapour in the atmosphere between the sun and the eye, so as to go to the eye in a cone. The reason for the shape of the halo was that 'All the rays falling on one circular path round that axis [joining the sun and the eye] are refracted at equal angles, because all the angles of incidence are equal'. But, he continued, 'just as many experiments are needed to determine the nature of the rainbow both in regard to its colour and its shape, so too are they required in this investigation'.[1]

Taking up the same subject in the *Opus Tertium*, he said that each eye saw a different halo, which moved as it did.[2] In this work he attributed the refraction of the sunlight to individual water-drops.[3] He pointed out also that colours seen in a halo were in the reverse order to those seen in the primary rainbow, and that measurements with an astrolabe showed that the diameter of the halo subtended at the eye of the observer an angle of 42 degrees, the same angle as that subtended by the radius of the rainbow.[4] The sentiments with which he concluded his account in the *Opus Maius* of the first prerogative of experimental science are a worthy expression of the ideals of the experimental method by one of its founders:

Hence reasoning does not attest these matters, but experiments on a large scale made with instruments and by various necessary means are required. Therefore no discussion can give an adequate explanation in these matters, for the whole subject is dependent on experiment. For this reason I do not think that in this matter I have grasped the whole truth, because I have not yet made all the experiments that are necessary, and because in this work I am proceeding by the method of persuasion and of demonstration of what is required in the study of science, and not by the method of

---

[1] Ibid., pp. 199–200. The modern theory that the halo is produced by the refraction of light through ice crystals was first put forward by E. Mariotte in his *Traité de la nature des couleurs* in 1686. Previous attempts at an explanation were made by Descartes and Huygens. See J. M. Pernter und F. M. Exner, *Meteorologische Optik*, 2. Aufl., pp. 312 sqq.; A. Wolf, *History of Science, Technology and Philosophy in the 16th and 17th Centuries*, pp. 271 sqq.

[2] *Fragment inédit de l'Opus Tertium*, ed. Duhem, p. 145.

[3] 'in stillicidiis . . . vaporis.' Ibid., p. 147.

[4] Ibid., pp. 140–1, 144. The value 42° for the radius of the rainbow is approximately correct (cf. above, p. 158). The commonest form of halo has a diameter of approximately 44°. See Pernter–Exner, op. cit., pp. 256 sqq., 367, 531; below, pp. 228, 275, n. 2.

compiling what has been written on this subject. Therefore it does not devolve on me to give at this time an attestation impossible for me, but to treat the subject in the form of a plea for the study of science.[1]

(3)

Roger Bacon was by far the most important of Grosseteste's immediate scientific disciples and propagators of his theory of science, and a philosophical work which shows deep marks of the influence of both men is the *Summa Philosophiae* formerly attributed to Grosseteste himself, but now believed by scholars to have been written by a member of the English school probably between 1265–75.[2] The *Summa* was a work not of experimental science but of philosophy, and it followed the rationalist order of beginning with general and abstract principles by which truth might be known, and then using those principles to discuss subjects ever more particular and concrete, of which the problems of 'natural science' occupied about half the total length. It is in the general principles held to be behind the operations of nature that the influence of Grosseteste is most plain. Beginning with the rationalist doctrine that what was certain was true of reality,[3] the Christian Platonist author of the *Summa* was led to find in mathematics the means of acquiring certain knowledge of nature.[4] This use of mathematics he also justified by his metaphysical belief that a natural corporeal point, as distinct from a mathematical point, would generate a *plenum* of space if the rest of the universe were destroyed. Similarly, he said, a single unit of light would generate an indefinite number of points of light, making radiant lines radiating in three dimensions, and produce the spatial *continuum*.[5] Though he did not state explicitly that light was

---

[1] *Opus Maius*, vi, p. 201. The plea was, of course, addressed to Pope Clement IV; see Crowley, *Roger Bacon*, pp. 37 sqq. A work which adds to the evidence for the interest shown by English writers in optics is the *De Visu et Speculis* in a thirteenth-century MS which follows Roger Bacon's *Opus Maius* in MS Roy. 7. F. vii, ff. 64rb–67vb. Little (*RBE*, p. 382, n. 1) attributes this work to Henry of Southwark (?). It consists of an account of theories of vision, mirrors, eye diseases, the rainbow, and the topaz, but has nothing original.

[2] For an account of the evidence of authorship and of the contents of this work see C. K. McKeon, *Summa Philos. Pseudo-Grosseteste*. See also Duhem, *Syst. monde*, iii. 460 sqq.   [3] *Summa*, Tractatus ii, Baur, 1912, pp. 290 sqq.

[4] The same idea has nearly always inspired Platonists in natural science, as, for instance, Grosseteste, Roger Bacon, and the *Summa* in the thirteenth century, Nicholas of Cusa in the fifteenth, Kepler and Descartes in the seventeenth.

[5] Ibid. ix, pp. 412 sqq. In the course of the argument he cited *Pneumatica* by Hero of

the 'form of corporeity', this is what in various statements he seems to imply.[1] Light was the agent through which the operative principle, *natura universalis*, produced its effects;[2] and so the concrete context in which the principles behind the operations of nature could be studied was optics. In the course of a discussion of the intramission and extramission theories of visual perception, in which he took up Roger Bacon's position,[3] he maintained that to every configuration of rays as 'natural lines' through which vision took place there corresponded a configuration of abstract mathematical lines, so that the explanation of the relations between these rays could be found in the laws of geometry.[4]

Though he was no experimentalist himself he was aware of experimental science and he made a very intelligent survey of many of the principal problems that interested his contemporaries. His account of the physiology of the special sense organs and the psychology of sensation, in the section on 'the unity and quiddity of the sensitive

Alexandria: 'Hero egregius philosophus per clepsedras et siphones aliaque instrumenta vanitatem vacui nititur declarare. . . .' (p. 417.) Cf. Heronis Alexandrini *Pneumatica et Automata*, hrg. von W. Schmidt. Hermann Diels has shown that most of the *Pneumatica* is the work of Strato: H. Diels, 'Über das physikalische System des Straton', *SPAWB*, 1893, pp. 101 sqq.

[1] *Summa*, ix. 1, p. 412; xiv. 10, p. 541. In C. 9, p. 540, he said of 'lux, flamma, carbo', and emanations from various heavenly bodies: 'essentia lucis his omnibus sit univoce communis. . . .' In C. 8, pp. 538–9 he distinguished between *lux* and *lumen*. In C. 6, p. 536 he cited Avicebron's *Fons Vitae*.

[2] 'Universaliter itaque virtus corporea operatur per contactum. . . . Cum ergo inter cetera omnia corporea lux, quae vere corporea vel corpus . . . ipsa erit convenientissimum instrumentum immediatius movens corporeas virtutes sua virtute.' (*Summa*, xvi. 6, pp. 595–6.) He referred to the 'spiritus in musculis et nervis' moving animals. See C. K. McKeon, op. cit., p. 182. The *natura universalis* and *forma corporeitatis* came, of course, from Avicebron and were not peculiar to Grosseteste or Roger Bacon; above, p. 105.   [3] See above, p. 114, n. 1, pp. 152–5.

[4] *Summa*, xii. 14, pp. 499 sqq.; C. K. McKeon, op. cit., pp. 206–9. He discussed other forms of multiplication of species or power besides light, e.g. of the power of the moon and sun in causing the tides (xviii. 6, pp. 622 sqq.). He also resembled Grosseteste in using the analogy of light to describe the generation of the persons of the Trinity (vii. 10, pp. 385 sqq.), though he put forward no epistemological theory of illumination. Two other contemporary English philosophers also show Grosseteste's influence. The Dominican Richard Fishacre (d. 1248) said that *lux* was the first body and that it united body and soul in man; he also believed in Divine illumination, though this theory was typically held by many philosophers influenced by Augustine and Avicenna and acceptance of it does not necessarily indicate Grosseteste's influence (F. Pelster, 'Das Leben und die Schriften des Oxforder Dominikanerlehrers Richard Fishacre', *Zeits. kath. Theol.* liv, 1930, p. 544; D. E. Sharp, 'The philosophy of Richard Fishacre', *NS*, vii, 1933, p. 286). The Franciscan Roger Marston said there was a distinct *forma corporeitas* in man and also believed in Divine illumination: F. Pelster, 'Roger Marston O.F.M. (†1303), ein englischer Vertreter des Augustinismus', *Scholastik*, iii (1928) 526 sqq.

soul', is particularly neat.[1] He referred repeatedly to statements being proved or falsified by experiment.[2] Later sections dealt with the generation and growth of plants and animals,[3] with cosmology and astronomy,[4] with the elements and chemical change and combination,[5] with the magnet and the problem of action at a distance,[6] with 'impressions' in the air and other meteorological phenomena,[7] and with minerals[8] and the fossilization of plants and animals.[9] Of particular interest in his treatment of 'impressions' in the air is his account of the rainbow. He held that in the rainbow there were four colours, which were produced by the incorporation of the medium in different degrees into the substance of light refracted through different amounts.[10] The shape of the bow he attributed partly to the concave shape of the cloud in which it appeared, partly to the 'rotundity' of the incident rays, and partly to the refraction of the rays in single drops.[11]

[1] *Summa*, xii, pp. 483 sqq., especially pp. 494 sqq.; ibid. xii. 12, p. 498. He said that the diffusion of *lux* occurred 'subito' (C. 19, p. 510; xiv. 8, p. 538). Attention may be drawn to a passage on lenses apparently used in reading: 'Signum huius est, quod apices litterarum per exiles et alia quaeque minima per medium vitri vel crystalli vel berylli et similium conspecta iuxta spissitudinem corporis perspicui interpositi maiora apparent, quam sunt.' (C. 15, p. 502.) His account of sound and hearing is also interesting for its distinction between the 'subjective' sensation and the external movement of the air in successive percussions, and its reference to *lux*: 'Nervus namque audibilis expansus in tympano auris tangitur quasi ab aëre percusso. . . . Sensus enim recipit species sensibilium teste Aristotele [De Anima, iii. 8] sine materia. Ideo cum materia soni sit aër percussus, auditus accipit sonum, non aërem percussum. . . .' (Ibid., C. 19, pp. 508-9.) He went on, using some of Grosseteste's own phrases: 'Lux enim praedicto modo incorporata subtilissimo aëris effectiva est sensibilitatis soni iuxta Augustinum. . . . Multiplicatur itaque species soni circulariter per naturam lucis.' Ibid., pp. 510-11. Cf. above, pp. 106, 115.

[2] e.g. 'Hoc ipsum Euclides quam pluribus experimentis probare conatus est' (ibid. xii. 16, p. 503); 'Sed et nostri oculi iuxta hoc retibus oculorum aequaliter melius viderent, ac hoc falsum' (C. 17, p. 504); 'sicut philosophi experimentaque multa testantur' (C. 19, p. 511). On pp. 505, 510-11 he referred to 'Albertus etiam Coloniensis'.

[3] *Summa*, xiii, pp. 516 sqq.   [4] Ibid. xv, pp. 543 sqq.

[5] Ibid. xvii, pp. 596 sqq. 'Expertum est . . .' (p. 609), 'alii variis experimentis probant' (p. 613).

[6] Ibid. xvii. 14, pp. 613-14. He held with Averroës that the magnet exerted its attraction by means of 'species magnetis'. Cf. above, p. 163, n. 2; below, p. 211.

[7] Ibid. xviii, pp. 614 sqq.   [8] Ibid. xix, pp. 625 sqq.

[9] Ibid. xix. 2-5, pp. 626-33. His views on this came largely from Avicenna and Albertus Magnus (C. 6, p. 633). See Duhem, *Léonard de Vinci*, ii. 283 sqq.

[10] 'Color autem ipsius fit ex coniunctione et concursu lucis et diaphani minus et minus puri vel perspicui et ita lucem magis et minus frangentis et varie incorporantis, cuius est apparitio apud opacum vel lucis obstaculum.' (*Summa*, xviii. 3, p. 618.) The same explanation of colour was advanced by Witelo; below, p. 230, n. 3, p. 231.

[11] *Summa*, xviii. 3, p. 619.

Another Oxford writer who appreciated experimental science was John Pecham (d. 1292), Kilwardby's successor as Archbishop of Canterbury. In his *Perspectiva Communis* Pecham gave a very clear and concise summary of contemporary optics, based largely on Alhazen, Witelo, and pseudo-Euclid's *De Speculis*.[1] His book contained nothing original but it remained a popular textbook until the seventeenth century.[2] It shows many marks of the influence of Grosseteste[3] and Roger Bacon,[4] though this influence may have been exercised largely through the medium of Witelo.[5] Like these writers Pecham regarded the study of light as a means of introducing mathematical certainty into physics,[6] and he conceived of light as a form of 'multiplication of species'.[7] In the study of light, he said, the argument proceeded both from effect to cause and from cause to effect, and he prayed God the light of all to help him. He arranged his work as a structure of theory built up from a set of empirical facts and the rules of geometry,[8] with the argument sometimes ascending inductively to a 'common nature' and the grasping of a universal, and sometimes descending deductively by

---

[1] 'Alhacen et Vitellio docent peculiaria instrumenta fabricare, quibus anguli reflexionis observari possint. Simplex tamen quadrans, etiam cotidie huius rei nos potest certiores reddere. . . . Quod et angulo incidentie angulus reflexionis sit aequalis, suis comprobatur rationibus. Euclides de speculis habet suas demonstrationes.' (*Perspectiva Communis*, ii. 6, Coloniae, 1592.) See also ibid. ii. 1, 33, 50–52, iii. 13. Cf. below, pp. 213 sqq. Other sources were 'Alkindus de aspectibus . . . Platonici . . . et D. Augustinus' (i. 44). For Pecham see Duhem, *Syst. monde*, iii. 515–17, 525; H. Spettmann, *Psychol. des Johannes Pecham*; Sharp, *Franciscan Philos. at Oxford*, pp. 175 sqq.; A. Bednarski, 'Das anatomische Augenbild von J. Peckham', *AGM*, xxii (1929) 352 sqq., ibid. xxiv (1931) 50 sqq.

[2] *Persp. Comm.* was printed in several early editions, the last being as late as 1627 (Sarton, *Introduction*, ii. 1028–30, iii. 1433, 1565). See below, pp. 277 sqq. V. Doucet regards Pecham as probably also the author of a *Tractatus de Perspectiva et Iride*, of which he printed parts in his 'Notulae bibliographicae de quibusdam operibus fratris Iohannis Pecham', *Antonianum*, viii (1933) 307–28, 425–59.

[3] See below and his explanations of the decrease in the strength of action of rays with distance by means of 'pyramides breviores' and 'longiores' (*Persp. Comm.* i. 19; above, p. 112) and of the spherical burning-lens by double refraction (ibid. iii. 16; above, p. 122). Also: 'si punctus lucis in diaphano ponatur, orbiculariter se diffundit.' Ibid. i, 6; above, pp. 106–9.

[4] See below and his account of the image produced by convex and concave lenses with the eye, lens, and object in different positions: ibid. iii. 9–11; above, p. 150.

[5] Below, pp. 213–32.

[6] 'naturales et mathematicas demonstrationes adiiciam, et partim effectus ex causis, partim vero causas ex effectibus deducam'. *Persp. Comm.* i, Prologue. He also believed in Divine illumination; Spettmann, op. cit.

[7] 'multiplicationi formarum'. *Persp. Comm.* i. 51; cf. ibid. ii. 1, 45. Cf. below, p. 215.

[8] e.g. see his use of 'Elementorum Euclidis'. Ibid. i. 22, ii. 20, 23, 27, 42, 44, 45.

'composition'[1] to consequences by means of which a theory could be verified[2] or falsified[3] by experiment. Like Grosseteste, Roger Bacon, and Witelo he used also the principles of uniformity[4] and of economy.[5] Most of the experiments he described are to be found in his sources, though this does not necessarily mean that he did not carry some of them out himself.[6]

The contents of *Perspectiva Communis* Pecham divided into the same three sections, *de luce et visu*, *de radio reflexo* and *de radio refracto*, as used by Grosseteste.[7] In the first section, besides the use of the theory of 'multiplication of species', his account of certain experiments illustrating the properties of light,[8] of the cause of refraction,[9] and of the anatomy of the eye and the physiology of vision[10] are of particular interest. The second section contains a good summary of the theory of concave mirrors.[11] The last section contains a summary of the theory of convex and concave lenses[12] and

[1] '. . . collatione unius ad alterum' (ibid. i. 56); '. . . arguit per compositionem et ordinationem propositionum.' Ibid. i. 57.

[2] e.g. after a discussion of the perception of size, he said: 'Quod etiam virtus apprehensiva quantitatis, non solum ad angulum, sed et ad longitudinem distantiae respiciat, experimento probatur. Si enim unus oculus respiciat aliquem magnum parietem, et eius quantitatem certificet, manifestum est, si oculo opponatur manus, manum videri sub eodem angulo, vel etiam maiori quam paries visus sit; nec tamen tantae quantitatis apparebit, quantae paries apparuit, quia minus distat, et tamen sub eadem latitudine radiorum et basis apparet.' (Ibid. i. 74; cf. i. 67.) Speaking of the properties of reflected rays, he said: 'Atque huius rei argumenta nobis diversa experimenta praebent'. (Ibid. ii. 1.) And again: 'In speculis sphaericis extra politis, apparet imago in concursu radii cum catheto, id est, linea ducta in centrum spherae. Hoc probari potest experientia, et ex causis naturalibus, ut supra in speculis planis patet.' Ibid. ii. 30.

[3] e.g. he said of the statement that an image seen in a mirror was imprinted on its surface: 'Hoc multipliciter falsum ostenditur. . . . Item si res imprimeretur speculo, diffunderet se undique a speculo, neque requireretur determinatus situs oculi ad videndum rem in speculo, sed posset videri in omni parte respectu speculi, quod falsum est. . . . Item quantitas idoli nunquam excederet quantitatem speculi, quod falsum. . . .' (Ibid. ii. 19.) He also cited an argument from agreement and difference which Alhazen had used: ibid. i. 36; cf. above, p. 153.   [4] Below, p. 167, n. 3.

[5] Rejecting the theory that there was an extramission of visual rays in addition to the reception of light into the eye he said: 'Visio enim sufficienter fit per modum praescriptum, per quem salvari possunt omnia, quae sunt circa visum apparentia. Ergo superfluum est sic radios ponere.' (Ibid. i. 44; cf. above, pp. 114, n. 1, 152.) Also: 'Rectitudo . . . processui lucis, et natura in omni operatione . . . agit secundum lineas brevissimas.' Ibid. ii. 3; above, p. 86.

[6] Cf. ibid. i. 7, ii. 24, iii. 7.   [7] Above, p. 118.

[8] Some interesting experiments dealt with the relative brightness of lights (ibid. i. 7-11).

[9] Ibid. i. 15. The theory came from Alhazen; below, p. 219, n. 5. *Persp. Comm.* iii. 17 contains an interesting discussion of variations in the effects of rays 'vel ex motu obiecti vel ex motu luminosi'.   [10] Ibid. i. 29 sqq. Cf. Roger Bacon, above, pp. 151-5.

[11] Ibid. ii. 17, 39 sqq.   [12] Ibid. iii. 9-10, 16.

concludes with a discussion of current theories of the rainbow, which he considered in the light of the knowledge of optics previously described. Following Witelo, he said that direct, reflected, and re-fracted sunlight were all involved in producing the rainbow.[1] One of the theories of the shape of the rainbow seems to be that advanced by Grosseteste and Albertus Magnus, for he refers to 'certain people' who suggested that the bow was formed by rays from the sun becoming refracted through a cloud as through a spherical lens, and dilating on the farther side 'in a pyramid'.[2] These authors, he said, sought the cause of the shape in the rays themselves, but by an interesting use of the principle of uniformity he showed that it de-pended also on the shape of the refracting medium, because colours produced by hexagonal crystals were not semicircular.[3] He himself held that the shape of the bow was principally due to the cloud. Going on to discuss the cause of the colours he criticized a theory which appears to be Witelo's,[4] but came to no definite conclusions of his own.

(4)

In the field of pure methodology John Duns Scotus[5] (c. 1265–1308) and William of Ockham[6] (before 1300–1349), who in investigat-ing the natural grounds of certainty in knowledge of the things of experience made some important contributions to the theory of induction, both made use of Grosseteste's commentary on the *Posterior Analytics*. Their main points of similarity to Grosseteste are in the use they made of the idea of collecting instances of cor-related events, of the principles of uniformity and economy[7] and, in

---

[1] Ibid. iii. 18; below, pp. 226 sqq.

[2] Ibid. iii. 19; cf. above, p. 126; below, pp. 196 sqq.

[3] 'Si ergo consimilis passio consimilem habet causam, oportet ut causa figurae arcus iridis quaerenda sit in nube et non in radio.' Ibid. iii. 19.

[4] Ibid. iii. 20; below, pp. 229–32.

[5] e.g. 'Scire dicitur quatuor modis, secundum Linconiensem', *Post. Anal. Quaestiones*, i, Prol. ed. Luke Wadding (Ioannis Duns Scoti *Opera Omnia*, i) 342ᵇ; ibid. i, Q. 1, p. 343ᵇ; Q. 10, p. 356ᵇ.

[6] Ockham referred frequently to Grosseteste's *Comm. Post.* in the parts of his *Summa Totius Logicae* dealing with demonstration, the subordination of some sciences to others, the distinction between *demonstratio quia* and *propter quid*, and the *artem diffi-niendi*. See *Summa Tot. Log.* iii. ii. 7, 8, 21, 23, 27, 31, Venetiis, 1508.

[7] The principle of economy or the so-called Ockham's Razor was in fact used by several Franciscan writers before and during this period. Scotus used the form 'Frustra fit per plura quod potest fieri per pauciora' and Ockham used this and also the form 'Pluralitas non est ponenda sine necessitate'. (*Quotlibeta* Guillermi Hokan, v. 5, Parisiis, 1487.) The form 'entia non sunt multiplicanda praeter necessitatem' was first introduced

Ockham's case, of the elimination of false hypotheses by an appeal to experience, and of the distinction between empirical generalizations and causal laws.

Scotus[1] in particular had a special love for Grosseteste and referred frequently to other works besides this commentary, principally to the *Hexaëmeron* and the commentary on the *Physics*,[2] and to *De Iride*.[3] His main contribution to the logic of science was to carry further Grosseteste's examination of the possibility of reaching certain knowledge of the world through induction. Disagreeing with Grosseteste in absolutely rejecting the theory that man could know nothing certain about the world without Divine illumination, a view which he held led to scepticism, he adhered entirely to the Aristotelian theory that knowledge of universals was reached only by abstraction from experienced particulars.[4] He asserted first that although it was impossible to reach necessary and evident knowledge of universals without complete enumeration, which was usually unobtainable,[5] nevertheless probable knowledge could be reached by induction from a sample and, moreover, that the number of instances observed of particular events being correlated increased the probability of the connexion between them being a truly universal and causal one.[6] In general he held that certain knowledge was

in the seventeenth century by a certain John Ponce of Cork, a Scotist: see W. M. Thornburn, 'The myth of Occam's Razor', *Mind*, N.S. xxvii (1918) 345 sqq.; cf. ibid. xxiv (1915) 287–8.

[1] For Scotus see A. G. Little, 'Chronological notes on the life of Duns Scotus', *EHR*, xlvii (1932) 568–82; E. Longpré, *Philos. du B. Duns Scot*; P. Minges, *Joannis Duns Scoti Philos. et Theol.*; Gilson, *Philos. au moyen âge*, 2ᵉ éd., pp. 591 sqq.; C. R. S. Harris's *Duns Scotus* is somewhat inaccurate. Cf. Grajewski, *Franciscan Studies*, N.S., 1941–2.

[2] See P. Minges, 'Robert Grosseteste Übersetzer der Ethica Nicomachea', *PJ*, xxxii (1919) 230 sqq.

[3] Thomson, *Writings of Rob. Grosseteste*, p. 105.

[4] I. Duns Scoti, *Quaest. Sententiarum*, i, Dist. iii, Q. 4, ed. Wadding (*Opera Omnia*, v) 479 sqq. There is a more recent edition of this so-called *Commentaria Oxoniensia* by Marianus Fernandez Garcia (i. 357 sqq.).

[5] Cf. above, p. 71, n. 3.

[6] '*Utrum ad bonum inductionem oporteat inducere in omnibus singularibus*. Arguitur quod non: singularia sunt infinita, ut dicit Porphyrius. . . . Prima est, quod inductio non valet ad concludendum de necessitate, nisi inducatur in omnibus singularibus. . . . Secunda conclusio, quod inductio non valet ad concludendum evidenter, supposito quod inducatur in omnibus singularibus, nisi coassumatur propositio universalis, mediante qua ex singularibus fit syllogismus. . . . Tertia conclusio est quod ad habendum opinionem probabilem, fidem, vel persuasionem, de conclusione universali, sufficit inducere in aliquibus singularibus, licet non inducatur in omnibus, et ideo multae inductiones sunt bonae, arguendo absolute absque hoc, quod in omnibus singularibus inducatur . . . quia multa principia naturalia fiunt nobis evidentia propter sensum, memoriam, et experientiam, ut ista: *Omnis ignis est calidus; omne grave existens sursum*

possible of three types of 'knowable things': first, self-evident first principles such as the laws of identity, contradiction, and excluded middle or the statement that the (finite)[1] whole is greater than the part; secondly, sensory experience, which he held could not be deceived, though judgements about sensed things might be false, as when a stick appeared bent when seen with its lower end dipping into water; and thirdly, consciousness of personal actions and states of mind.[2] The object of natural science, then, was to pass from knowledge of effects gained through the senses to knowledge of causes, and ideally to knowledge of some self-evident proposition,[3] from which the effects could be deduced. He realized that it was often impossible to get beyond mere empirical generalizations, but he held that a well-established empirical generalization could be held with certainty because of the principle of the uniformity of nature, which he regarded as a self-evident assumption of inductive science. He gave a clear summary of his whole theory of science in the following passage from the so-called *Oxford Commentary*:

Concerning the second type of knowable things, that is, concerning things known through experience, I say that though it is not possible to have experience always of all particulars but only of a large number, still one who knows by experience knows infallibly that things are thus, always thus, and thus in all. He knows this by the following proposition reposing

non impeditum naturaliter descendit deorsum, et consimilia, quae facta sunt evidentia per inductionem et non in omnibus singularibus, ut notum est. . . . Et si quaeratur in quot singularibus oportet inducere, respondetur quod de illis non potest assignari certus numerus, sed quandoque oportet inducere in pluribus, quandoque in paucioribus, secundum diversitatem materiae, et secundum diversitatem intellectionis intellectus, qui debet assentire universali. Quarta conclusio, quod in aliquibus, ut respectu praedicatorum per accidens, non sufficit inducere in aliquibus singularibus, sed oportet inducere in omnibus . . . quia in aliquibus est materia talis. . . . Ex praedictis sequitur, quod intellectus quodammodo magis libere assentit quibusdam, quam sensus faciat, sicut in naturalibus, propter evidentiam quam habet de aliquibus singularibus statim assentit, ita est de omnibus, et hoc est, quia in illa materia non potest melius, quam in aliquibus, ut in mathematicis non sufficeret intellectus.' He added: 'in inductione non committitur petitio principii, quia ex quo aliquae singulares sunt notae, et non apparet instantia in aliis, ut dicitur, quare non debet ita esse de aliis, concludenda est universalis. . . . Ideo . . . *Inductio est progressio ab aliquibus singularibus, vel ab omnibus sufficienter enumeratis ad conclusionem universalem.'* I. Duns Scoti *Priorum Anal. Quaest.* ii, Q. 8, ed. Wadding (*Opera Omnia*, i) 340–1. Cf. Mansion, *RNP*, xiii (1906) 260 sqq.; also S. Thomae Aquinatis, *Post. Anal. Expos.* ii. xv, Lect. xx (*Opera Omnia*, i) 400–3.

[1] Cf. above, p. 108, n. 3; p. 148; below, p. 174, n. 3.
[2] *Quaest. Sent.* i. iii, Q. 4, ed. Wadding (*Opera Omnia*, v) 484 sqq.
[3] He was in effect searching for synthetic necessary propositions on which to base certainty about the world. Since Descartes these are what have usually been meant by 'ultimate' explanations; cf. below, p. 312, n. 9.

in the soul: 'whatever occurs as in a great many cases from some cause which is not free [i.e. not free will] is the natural effect of that cause'. This proposition is known to the understanding, even though it had accepted the terms of it from the erring senses, for a cause which is not free cannot produce, as in a great many cases, an effect to the opposite of which it is ordered, or to which it is not ordered by its form. (But a casual cause is ordered to the producing of the opposite of the casual effect, or to not producing it. Therefore, nothing is the casual cause in respect to an effect produced frequently by it and, if it is not free, it is a natural cause.) That, however, this effect occurs by such a cause producing as in a great many cases must be learned through experience, for in discovering such a nature at one time with one such accident and at another with another, it is discovered that however great the diversity of such accidents, such an effect always follows from that nature. Therefore, such an effect follows not accidentally through some accidents of that nature, but through the very nature in itself.

But it must be noted further that sometimes experience is had of a conclusion, as for example that the moon is frequently eclipsed, and then having accepted the conclusion as given, the cause of such a conclusion is inquired by the method of division. Sometimes one proceeds from the conclusion experienced to principles known from the terms, and then from such a principle known from the terms, the conclusion, previously known only by experience, can be known more certainly, namely, by the first kind of knowledge; for it can be known as deduced from a principle known in itself (*ex principio per se noto*), just as the following is known through itself, that an opaque object interposed between a luminous and an illuminated object impedes the multiplication of light to such an illuminated object. And if it were found by division that the earth is such a body interposed between the sun and the moon, it will be known most certainly by demonstration through causes (*propter quid*), and not only through experience as that conclusion was known before the discovery of the principle.

Sometimes, however, there is experience of the principle in such a manner that it is not possible to discover further by division (*per viam divisionis*) the principle known through the terms, but one must stop at some truth which holds as in many cases, of which the extremes are frequently experienced united, as for example, that a herb of such a species is hot. Nor is any other middle term discovered prior by means of which the effect (*passio*) is demonstrated of the subject through causes (*propter quid*), but one must stop at this as at the first thing known by experience. Then, although incertitude and fallibility may be removed by the following proposition, 'the effect, as in a great many cases, of any cause which is not free is the natural effect of it', nevertheless, this is the last grade of scientific knowledge; and perhaps necessary knowledge is not had there of the actual union of extremes, but only of an aptitudinal union. For if the effect is another thing separated from the subject, it could without contradiction be separated from the subject, and the person who knows by experience would not have knowledge that it is so, but that it is formed apt to be so.[1]

William of Ockham also developed inductive logic along lines on which Grosseteste had begun, though he reacted even more violently against contemporary Augustinian-Platonism, strongly attacking Scotus himself, and attempted to return to Aristotle.[2] His main

[1] '*Ostendit qualis certitudo habetur per experientiam, et quod quandoque ex veritate experta, devenitur ad principium notum, ex quo eadem veritas propter quid rursus demonstratur, quandoque vero de ipso principio immediate experientia capitur.* De secundis cognoscibilibus, scilicet de cognitis per experientiam, dico, quod licet experientia non habeatur de omnibus singularibus, sed de pluribus, nec quod semper, sed quod plures, tamen expertus infallibiliter novit, quod ita est, et quod semper et in omnibus; et hoc per istam propositionem quiescentem in anima, "quidquid evenit ut in pluribus ab aliqua causa non libera, est effectus naturalis illius causae". Quae propositio nota est intellectui, licet accepisset terminos eius a sensu errante, quia causa non libera non potest producere ut in pluribus effectum ad cuius oppositum ordinatur, vel ad quem ex forma sua non ordinatur. . . .' *Quaest. Sent.* i. iii, Q. 4, ed. Wadding (*Opera Omnia*, v) 482–3. For a radical criticism of this passage of Scotus cf. Nicholas of Autrecourt in his *Exigit Ordo*: 'concerning things known by experience in the manner in which it is said to be known that the magnet attracts iron or that rhubarb cures cholera we have only a conjecturative habit but not certitude. When it is said that we have certitude concerning such things in virtue of a proposition reposing in the soul which is that *that which occurs as in many cases from an unfree cause is the natural effect of it,* I ask what you call a natural cause; i.e. do you say, that which produced in the past as in many cases, and up to the present, will produce in the future if it remains and is applied? Then the minor is not known, for allowing that something was produced as in many cases, it is nevertheless not known that it ought to be thus produced in the future.' (J. R. Weinberg, *Nicolaus of Autrecourt,* p. 69; J. R. O'Donnell, 'Nicholas of Autrecourt', *MS*, i, 1939, p. 237.) Cf. Grosseteste, above, pp. 70–71. For Nicholas see also H. Rashdall, 'Nicholas de Ultricuria, a medieval Hume', *Proc. Arist. Soc.* N.S. vii (1907) 1 sqq.; J. Lappe, *Nicolaus von Autrecourt;* O'Donnell, 'The philosophy of Nicholas of Autrecourt and his appraisal of Aristotle', *MS*, iv (1942) 97 sqq.; E. Moody, 'Ockham, Buridan and Nicholas of Autrecourt', *Franciscan Studies*, N.S. vii (1947) 113 sqq.; M. H. Carré, 'A medieval attack on metaphysics', *Hibbert J.* xlvii (1949) 226 sqq.; M. Clagett, review of Weinberg's book, *Isis*, xl (1949) 265 sqq.; other references are given by Weinberg on p. 239.

[2] For Ockham's logic and scientific methodology see N. Abbagnano, *Guglielmo di Ockham;* S. Moser, *Naturphilos. Wilhelm von Occam;* E. A. Moody, *Logic of William of Ockham; Tractatus de Praedestinatione . . .* of William of Ockham, ed. P. Boehner; Boehner, 'The notitia intuitiva of non-existents according to William Ockham', *Traditio,* i (1943) 223 sqq., 'The realistic conceptualism of William Ockham', ibid. iv (1946) 307 sqq.; A. C. Pegis, 'Concerning William of Ockham', ibid. ii (1944) 465 sqq.; Gilson, *Philos. au moyen âge,* 2e éd. pp. 638 sqq.; R. Guelluy, *Philos. et théol. chez Guillaume d'Ockham.* For a use to which he put his distinction between real and nominal definitions in science see Maier, *Vorläufer Galileis,* pp. 17 sqq. See also *Tractatus de Successivis* attrib. Ockham, ed. Boehner; Duhem, *Léonard de Vinci,* ii. 85 sqq.; K. Hammerle, *Von*

contribution to the logic of science was to formulate clearly, for the purpose of making a radical attack on the excesses of contemporary metaphysics, methodological principles some of which Grosseteste had introduced. As a basis for his method he accepted the three certitudes of Scotus, but he made radical use of two further principles. The first was the principle of evidence, by means of which he made a distinction between the science of real entities (*scientia realis*),[1] which was concerned with what was known by experience to exist and in which names stood for things existing in nature, and the science of logical entities (*scientia rationalis*), which was concerned with logical constructions and in which names stood merely for concepts. Only 'intuitive knowledge' (*notitia intuitiva*) through experience of individual things, he held, could give certain knowledge of the real.[2] Ockham's second principle was that of economy. By means of these two principles he convinced himself that there could be no certain knowledge of actual substances or causal relations in any particular case (though he did not deny the existence of substance or causation), because experience could be had only of particular objects and not of their causal relations.[3] But he held that it

---

Ockham zu Milton; Hochstetter, *Studien zur . . . Ockham*; Baudry, *ADHLMA*, ix (1934) 155–73; E. Moody, *Franciscan Studies*, N.S. vii (1947) 113 sqq., ibid. ix (1949) 417–42; articles by Boehner, ibid. 1945–6, 1948; Mohan, ibid. v (1945) 235 sqq.; Pegis, *Speculum*, xxiii (1948) 452 sqq.

[1] 'scientia quelibet sive sit realis sive rationalis est tantum de propositionibus tanquam de illis, que sciuntur, quia sole propositiones sciuntur. . . . omnes termini illarum propositionum sunt tantum conceptus et non sunt ipse substantie extra. Quia tamen termini aliquarum propositionum stant et supponunt personaliter, scilicet pro ipsis rebus extra . . . ideo talium propositionum dicitur esse scientia realis.' (*Super Quattuor Libros Sententiarum*, i. ii, Q. 4, M, N, in *Tabule ad Diversas huius Operis magistri Guilhelmi de Ockam. . . .* Lugduni, 1495.) A distinction between *scientia realis* and *scientia rationalis* was also made by St. Thomas Aquinas and other thirteenth-century writers; see Baur's ed. of Dominicus Gundissalinus, *De Div. Philos.*, pp. 377, 392.

[2] Cf. Boehner, *Traditio*, i (1943) 223.

[3] 'Inter causam et effectum est ordo et dependentia maxime essentialis, et tamen ibi notitia incomplexa unius rei non continet notitiam incomplexam alterius rei. Et hoc etiam quilibet in se experitur, quia quantumcumque perfecte cognoscat aliquam rem, nunquam cogitabit cogitatione simplici et propria de alia re, quam nunquam prius apprehendit nec per sensum nec per intellectum.' (*Lib. Sent.* Prologi, Q. 9, F.) For a radical development of this idea see Weinberg, *Nicolaus of Autrecourt*, pp. 31 sqq.; Moody, *Franciscan Studies*, N.S. vii (1947) 113 sqq.; Lappe, *Nicolaus von Autrecourt*, p. 9*; above, p. 171, n. 1. Moody (op. cit., pp. 134 sqq.) has shown that Jean Buridan argued against this conclusion; see Johannis Buridani *Quest. Super Physic.* i. 4, ff. 4ᵛ sqq. Also: 'Aliter enim tu non posses probare quod omnis ignis est calidus, quod omne reubarbarus est purgativus colore, quod omnis magnes vel adamas est attractivus ferri; et tales inductiones non sunt demonstrationes quia non concludunt gratia forme cum non sit possibile inducere in omnibus suppositio . . . intellectus non videns instantiam

was possible to arrive at an empirical knowledge of causal connexions and that such connexions might acquire a universal validity in virtue of the self-evident principle of the uniformity of nature, that 'all individuals of the same kind are so made as to have effects of the same kind in an object of the same kind in the same circumstances'.[1]

The grasping of the universal, he said, might theoretically be possible after experience of only a single instance,[2] but

in most cases a singular contingent proposition cannot be known evidently (*evidenter*) without many apprehensions of single instances, whence it is not easy to know that this herb cured a certain invalid and that it was not the doctor who cured him. And so with many other cases, for it is not easy to grasp that which is experienced, because the same species of effect can exist through many specifically different causes.[3]

It was, however, possible to define logical rules for establishing causal connexions. In fact he formulated what became known as the method of agreement and difference.[4]

This is sufficient for anything being an immediate cause, namely, that when it is present the effect follows and when not present, all other conditions being the same, the effect does not follow. . . . That this is sufficient for anything to be an immediate cause of anything else is clear because if not there is no way of knowing that something is an immediate cause of something else. . . . All causes properly so-called are immediate causes.[5]

nec rationem instandi cogitur ex eius naturali inclinatione ad veritatem concedere propositionem universalem, et qui non vult tales declarationes concedere in scientia naturali et morali non est dignus habere in eis magnam partem.' (Ibid. i. 15, ff. 18vb–19^r.) Cf. David Hume, *An Enquiry Concerning the Human Understanding*, vi. 1, 'Of Probability', ed. L. A. Selby-Bigge, pp. 57–58; and 'In a word, then, every effect is a distinct event from its cause. It could not, therefore, be discovered in the cause, and the first invention or conception of it, *a priori*, must be entirely arbitrary.' Ibid. iv. 1, p. 30.

[1] See next note. Cf. *Lib. Sent.* Prol. Q. 2, M.

[2] '. . . sicut si virtute notitie intuitive accipiatur notitia evidens istius veritatis contingentis: ista herba sanat talem infirmitatem, illa est causa mediata partialis notitie istius conclusionis demonstrabilis: omnis talia herba sanat. Est autem ista notitia intuitiva causa partialis tantum; quia ista notitia non sufficit nisi evidenter sciatur quod omnia individua eiusdem rationis sunt nata habere effectus eiusdem rationis in passo eiusdem rationis et equaliter disposito.' Ibid., Prol. Q. 2, K; cf. Boehner, *Traditio*, iv (1946) 308–10.

[3] *Summa Tot. Log.* iii. ii. 10, f. 66^r. Cf. his discussion of the possibility of reaching complete definitions of things: 'Diffinitiones enim complete nate sunt reddere causam omnium accidentium existentium in re . . . quando aliquid cognoscitur distincte et diffinitive potest cognosci virtute illius notitie omne accidens illius, et per consequens multo fortius omnes passiones.' *Lib. Sent.* Prol. Q. 9, K.

[4] J. S. Mill, *System of Logic*, ii, Ch. 8.

[5] 'istud sufficit ad hoc quod aliquid sit causa immediata, scilicet, quod illa re absoluta posita, ponatur effectus et ipsa non posita, aliis omnibus concurrentibus quantum ad omnes conditiones et dispositiones consimiles, non ponitur effectus. Unde omne quod

Because the same effect might have different causes, it was necessary to eliminate false hypotheses in order to arrive at as certain as possible a knowledge of principles from which demonstration could follow.

So [he said] let this be posited as a first principle: all herbs of such and such a species cure a fevered person. This cannot be demonstrated by syllogism from better known propositions, but it is known only by intuitive knowledge and perhaps of many instances. For since he observed that after eating such herbs the fevered person was cured and he removed all other causes of his recovery, he knew evidently that this herb was the cause of recovery, and then he has experimental knowledge of a particular connection.[1]

'All causes properly so-called', Ockham said, 'are immediate causes.' He denied that it could be proved either from first principles or from experience that any effect had a final cause. 'This is the special characteristic of a final cause, that it is able to cause when it does not exist.'[2] He concluded: 'this movement towards an end is not real but metaphorical'.[3]

est tale respectu alicuius est causa immediata illius, quamvis forte non econverso. Quod autem hoc sufficiat ad hoc, quod aliquid sit causa immediata alterius, videtur esse manifestum, quia, si non, perit omnis via ad cognoscendum aliquid esse causam alterius immediatam. Nam si ex hoc quod hoc posito sequitur effectus et hoc non posito non ponitur effectus, non sequitur illud esse causam illius effectus, nullo modo potest cognosci quod ignis est causa immediata caloris in ligno, quia patet dici quod est aliqua alia causa illius caloris que tamen non agit nisi in presentia ignis. Ex illo sequuntur aliqua. Unum est quod causa universalis amota non fiunt effectus, est causa ita immediata sicut causa particularis, et ideo quia sole absente non producuntur ista generabilia et corruptibilia, que tamen producuntur mediantibus causis particularibus, et ideo sol est causa immediata eorum, nisi forte fingas quod sol est causa alicuius quid est causa immediata eorum, sed semper quod sol alicuius est causa immediata, scilicet vel effectus vel causae ipsius effectus, et hoc sufficit ad propositum. Aliud sequitur quod quando amota causa universali vel particulari non ponitur effectus, quod tunc neutra illarum est causa totalis sed tamen partialis, quia neutra illarum ex quo si sola non potest producere effectum est causa efficiens, et per consequens neutra est causa totalis. Aliud sequitur quod omnis causa proprie dicta est causa immediata, quia illa causa qua amota vel posita nihilominus ex natura rei sequitur effectus, et qua posita aliis circumscriptis non sequitur effectus, non potest convinci esse causa, sed huiusmodi est omnis alia causa a causa immediata, sicut patet inductive.' *Lib. Sent.* i. xlv, Q. 1, D.

[1] Ibid. Prol. Q. 2, G. Cf. Grosseteste on scammony, above, p. 74.
[2] *Quotlibeta*, iv. Cf. *Summule in Lib. Phys.* ii. 6, Venetiis, 1506.
[3] *Lib. Sent.* ii, Q. 3, G. See Abbagnano, op. cit., pp. 189 sqq. For a similar remark by Albertus Magnus, see below, p. 194, n. 2. In the *Centiloquum Theologicum* (Conclusio 1, E, F) attributed (probably wrongly) to Ockham, there is a discussion of the assertion, 'quod non sit processus in infinitum in moventibus', concluding that this, though unproved, was '. . . probabilius quam suum oppositum . . . quia omnes apparentiae aeque evidenti vel evidentius possunt salvari ponendo finitatem in moventibus et unum primum quam infinitatem ponendo, et ideo potius debet poni.' See Boehner's

Ockham himself was no experimentalist. In fact, in his own system of thought, the *scientia experimentalis* of Roger Bacon, a science of instruments and manual operations, had become the *scientia intuitiva* of epistemology.[1] But, in spite of that, the effect of his logical and epistemological doctrines was to predispose natural philosophers to seek knowledge of nature by experiment.[2] Ockham held that the regular sequences of events were simply sequences of fact, and that the attempt to discover substances and causes that would display the rational connexion between them was an impossible enterprise. Therefore, the only reliable knowledge of contingent, natural events was that acquired by observation. Moreover, 'physical' explanations in Aristotle's sense nearly all failed because of the unknowability of substance. The practical programme for natural science was simply to correlate observed facts, or 'save the appearances', by means of logic and mathematics.[3]

A striking example of Ockham's own use of these methodological principles is his treatment of the problem of motion, of which he formed a conception that was to be used in the seventeenth-century theory of inertia. Aristotle had said that since every effect required

---

ed. in *Franciscan Studies*, N.S. i (1941), March, pp. 58 sqq., 69–70; ibid. June and Sept., and 1942; and Boehner's articles in ibid. iv (1944) 151–70, x (1950) 191 sqq. Cf. Delisle Burns, 'William of Ockham on continuity', *Mind*, N.S. xxv (1916) 508 sqq.; T. B. Birch, 'The theory of continuity of William of Ockham', *Philos. of Science*, iii (1936) 501; and the edition of Ockham's *De Sacramento Altaris*, by T. B. Birch. On the subject of infinity itself the *Centiloquium* develops a point discussed by Grosseteste and Roger Bacon (cf. above, p. 108, n. 3, pp. 148–9). In Conclusio 17, C, it is said: 'nullum est inconveniens partem esse aequalem suo toti vel non esse minorem, quia hoc invenitur non tantum intensive sed etiam extensive. Intensive sicut in proposito vel ubicumque una pars est infinitae virtutis intensive . . . quia in toto universo non sunt plures partes quam in una faba, ex quo in una faba sunt infinitae partes.' Cf. *Quotlibeta*, i, Q. 9; Abbagnano, op. cit., pp. 207–13; Duhem, *Léonard de Vinci*, ii. 15 sqq., 40 sqq.

[1] Cf. Michalski, 'Les Courants philosophiques à Oxford et à Paris pendant le xive siècle', *BIAPSL*, 1920, pp. 59 sqq.

[2] As R. McKeon has put it in a vivid passage, 'the spirit and the enterprise' of early medieval philosophy was 'of faith engaged in understanding itself'. Then, between Augustine and Aquinas (and Grosseteste): 'From the consideration of truth as the reflection of divine things, philosophy passed to the consideration of the truth of things situated between God and man, deriving their truth from God, but causing truth in the human mind. . . . In that step philosophy had become somewhat other than faith knowing itself, and thereafter it can play another role than that set by the inspiration of the theology: theology can concern itself with the domain of things as they are related to God, and there remains for philosophy the domain of things in their relations to things and to man. The next step, that taken by the scotists and ockhamites, is in the enlarging and exploring of the subjects so revealed, of logic, physics, and metaphysics.' *Selections from Medieval Philosophers*, ii, pp. ix–x, xiv–xv.

[3] Cf. Abbagnano, op. cit., pp. 193–233; Moser, *Naturphilos. Wilhelm von Occham*.

a cause and the effect ceased with the cessation of the cause, therefore motion, for example that of a projectile, required for its
maintenance the operation of continuous efficient causation. This
principle was interpreted by all known writers on the subject down
to Ockham as implying that a projectile, on leaving the hand or
mechanism of projection, was kept in motion either by some extrinsic cause such as the air, or by an intrinsic cause, a *fluxus formae* or a
forma fluens, such as the *impetus impressus* postulated by the French
physicist, Jean Buridan (*fl. c.* 1328–42).[1] Ockham altogether rejected
this implication. He defined motion as a concept, having no reality
apart from moving bodies, that was used to describe the fact that
from instant to instant a moving body changed its spatial relationships with some other body without intermediate rest. There was
no need to postulate any external or internal efficient cause to explain such a sequence of events.

Motion is not such a thing wholly distinct in itself from the permanent
body, because it is futile to use more entities when it is possible to use
fewer. But without any such thing we can save the motion and everything
that is said about motion. Therefore it is futile to postulate such other
things. That without such an additional thing we can save motion and
everything that is said about it is made clear by considering the separate
parts of motion. For it is clear that local motion is to be conceived of as
follows: positing that the body is in one place and later in another place,
thus proceeding without any rest or any intermediate thing other than the
body itself and the agent itself which moves, we have local motion truly.
Therefore it is futile to postulate such other things.[2]

---

[1] See Duhem, *Mouvement abs. et rel.*, *Léonard de Vinci*, iii. 40 sqq.; E. J. Dijkster-
huis, *Val en Worp*; B. Jansen, 'Olivi, der älteste scholastische Vertreter des heutigen
Bewegungsbegriffs', *PJ*, xxxiii (1920) 137 sqq.; Michalski, 'La Physique nouvelle et les
différents courants philosophiques au xiv⁰ siècle', *BIAPSL*, 1927, pp. 93 sqq.; S. Pines,
'Les Précurseurs musulmans de la théorie de l'impetus', *Archeion*, xxi (1938) 298 sqq.;
M. D. Chenu, 'Aux origines de la "Science Moderne"', *RSPT*, xxix (1940) 206 sqq.;
M. Clagett, *Giovanni Marliani and the Late Medieval Physics*; Maier, *Impetustheorie*,
Vorläufer Galileis, pp. 132 sqq.; Sarton, *Introduction*, iii. 540–6; E. Faral, 'Jean Buridan.
Notes sur les manuscrits, les éditions et le contenu de ses ouvrages', *AHDLMA*, xv (1946)
1 sqq.; above, p. 171, n. 2; below, pp. 201–3. In an article contributed to *Isis* (xxxix,
1948, p. 41) Clagett has pointed out that Bacon discussed an early form of 'impetus'
theory. He discussed whether the projectile continued its motion 'secundum virtutis
influentiam' and rejected this theory because he held that the moving power must be
substantially joined with the body moved; see *Quaest. Phys.* vii, ed. F. M. Delorme and
R. Steele (*Opera Hactenus Inedita*, xiii) 338. Cf. Grosseteste, above, p. 84, n. 6.

[2] *Tract. Successivis*, i, 'Tractatus de Motu', ed. Boehner, p. 45. He went on: 'Idem
etiam patet de motu alterationis, quod non oportet ponere ibi aliam rem a rebus permanentibus' (p. 46); 'Patet etiam de motu augmentationis et diminutionis, quod nulla alia

I say therefore that the moving thing in such a motion [i.e. projectile motion], after the separation of the moving body from the first projector, is the moved thing itself, not by reason of any power in it; for this moving thing and the moved thing cannot be distinguished. If you say that a new effect has some cause and local motion is a new effect, I say that local motion is not a new effect . . . because it is nothing else but the fact that the moving body is in different parts of space in such a manner that it is not in any one part, since two contradictories are not both true.[1]

It is clear how 'now before' and 'now after' are to be assigned, treating 'now' first: this part of the moving body is now in this position, and later it is true to say that now it is in another position, and so on. And so it is clear that 'now' does not signify anything distinct but always signifies the moving body itself which remains the same in itself, so that it neither acquires anything new nor loses anything existing in it. But the moving body does not remain always the same with respect to its surroundings, and so it is possible to assign 'before and after', that is, to say: 'this body is now at A and not at B', and later it will be true to say: 'this body is now at B and not at A', so that contradictories are successively made true.[2]

Moreover, Ockham said, the conception of immobility could apply only to an ideal point, and only when it was considered as such a point could the centre of the universe be said to be immobile. The actual earth as well as the heavens could be considered as being in motion relative to that point.[3]

(5)

Some contemporaries of William of Ockham, who were also directly influenced by Grosseteste's theory of science, went beyond a purely philosophical approach to scientific problems and made some original contributions to practical methods of correlating observations by means of mathematics. Ockham's conceptualism

res est ibi a rebus permanentibus' (p. 47). Cf. Maier, *Vorläufer Galileis*, pp. 17–18. The same problem arose over action at a distance, e.g. in the case of light: 'Quando medium illuminatur primo a sole, quaero utrum in medio sint aliquae res distinctae ab ipso lumine et caeteris rebus permanentibus, quae per illuminationem fiunt in medio, aut non.' *Tract. Successivis*, i, ed. Boehner, pp. 33 sqq.; cf. below, p. 212, n. 2.

[1] *Lib. Sent.* ii, Q. 26, M; at the end of a discussion of action at a distance, below, p. 212, n. 2; Latin text in Maier, *Zwei Grundprobleme*, pp. 157–8. On 'ubi' in the fourteenth century see Duhem, *Mouvement abs. et rel.* See Moody, *JHI*, xii (1951) 395–403.

[2] *Tract. Successivis*, iii, 'Tractatus de Tempore', ed. Boehner, pp. 121–2. Cf. O'Donnell, *MS*, i (1939) 223–4; Weinberg, *Nicolaus of Autrecourt*, pp. 168 sqq.

[3] *Summule in Lib. Phys.* iv. 19–21. Ockham developed these ideas in the course of a discussion of 'immobility by equivalence', which Scotus had defined. See Duhem, *Mouvement abs. et rel.*, pp. 66, 76 sqq. Maier *Vorläufer Galileis*, pp. 9 sqq.; below, pp. 201–4.

had done away with the possibility of discovering the causal form; science must concern itself simply with correlating the sequences of fact in individual things. Somewhat earlier, Roger Bacon had said that 'all categories depend on a knowledge of quantity'.[1] During the first half of the fourteenth century two methods of expressing functional relationships were used both in Oxford and in Paris.[2] The first was the 'word-algebra' used in mechanics by Thomas Bradwardine in Oxford. In this, generality was achieved by the use of letters of the alphabet instead of numbers for the variable quantities, but the operations of addition, division, &c., performed on those quantities were described in words instead of being represented by symbols as in modern algebra. The second method of expressing functional relationships was by the use of graphs in connexion with what was known as 'latitude of forms'.[3] This geometrical method was used in optics by John of Dumbleton in Oxford and afterwards in dynamics by Nicole Oresme[4] in France. These fourteenth-century writers were still primarily concerned with the question how, in principle, to express change of any kind, whether in quantity or quality, in terms of mathematics, and any treatment they gave of particular optical or dynamical problems was in most cases simply to illustrate a point of method. Yet they succeeded in taking the first steps towards the creation, out of the statically conceived Greek mathematics, of the algebra and geometry of change that were to transform science in the seventeenth century.

Thomas Bradwardine (c. 1290–1349) was the real founder of the school of scientific thought associated with Merton College, and he stood in the same relationship to Oxford thought in the fourteenth century as Grosseteste did to that in the thirteenth.[5] Of Grosseteste's writings he cited the commentary on the *Posterior Analytics* and

---

[1] See above, p. 143.

[2] See Maier's chapter on 'Der Funktionsbegriff in der Physik des 14. Jahrhundert', in *Vorläufer Galileis*, pp. 81 sqq., and also pp. 111 sqq.   [3] See below, pp. 181–6.

[4] On the establishing of the connexion between algebraic functions and graphical representations and the invention of analytic geometry thereby, and on Oresme's contribution to this, see Maier, *An der Grenze . . .*, pp. 288 sqq., 'La doctrine de Nicolas d'Oresme sur les "configurationes intensionum" ', *RSPT*, xxxii (1948) 52 sqq.; see also Boyer, *Concepts of the Calculus*, pp. 60–95, 'The invention of analytic geometry', *Scient. American*, 1949, Jan., pp. 40 sqq.; Duhem, *Léonard de Vinci*, iii. 375 sqq.; H. Wieleitner, 'Der "Tractatus de Latitudinibus Formarum" des Oresme', *BM*, xiii (1913) 115 sqq., ibid. xiv (1914) 193 sqq.; Dugas, *Histoire de la mécanique*, pp. 58 sqq.

[5] For Bradwardine see the bibliography given by Sarton, *Introduction*, iii. 668–71 and particularly Duhem, *Léonard de Vinci*, iii. 294–305, 500; Clagett, *Giovanni Marliani*, pp. 129 sqq.; Maier, *Vorläufer Galileis*, pp. 3, 81–110, 160 sqq.

some of his other philosophical works,[1] and he quoted Grosseteste's ideas on the *continuum* in his own *Tractatus de Continuo*.[2] This work, with that of Ockham, Richard Swineshead or Suiseth (called 'Calculator'), Dumbleton, Oresme, and other fourteenth-century writers, helped to lay the logical foundations of the calculus.[3] Bradwardine's principal contribution to the idea of mathematical functions was made in his *Tractatus Proportionum*[4], completed in 1328.

The problem that Bradwardine attempted to solve in the *Tractatus Proportionum* was to find an adequate mathematical function to express the fundamental dynamical law then accepted, the so-called Peripatetic law of motion.[5] This law derived from Aristotle's *Physics* (vii. 5, 249[b]26–250[b]10) and it stated that velocity was proportional to the power of the mover divided by the resistance of the medium.[6] Bradwardine accepted Aristotle's theory of the physical factors involved, but he questioned the accuracy of his precise mathematical expression of the relationship between them. It had been pointed out by earlier writers that according to Aristotle's law of motion there should be a finite velocity with *any* finite values of power and resistance, yet in fact if the power was smaller than the resistance it might fail to move the body at all. To escape this difficulty they assumed that velocity was proportional to the *excess* of power over resistance, and that motion took place only when the proportion of power to resistance was greater than 1. Bradwardine tried to show how *change* in velocity was related to power and resistance. First, he considered some other equations that had been put forward to express the relationship between the dependent variable (velocity) and the two independent variables (power and resistance), and he

---

[1] Thomson, *Writings of Rob. Grosseteste*, pp. 84, 91, 120; Baur, 1912, pp. 107* sqq.

[2] He referred to 'adinvicem mediatis Lincof.' which probably meant Grosseteste's discussion of continuity in *De Luce* and *De Iride*; see above, pp. 106–7, 119. See E. Stamm, 'Tractatus de Continuo von Thomas Bradwardina', *Isis*, xxvi (1936–7) 16–17; cf. M. Curtze, 'Über die Handschrift R. 4º. 2, Problematum Euclidis explicatio der Königl. Gymnasialbibliothek zu Thorn', *Zeits. f. Math. u. Phys.*, Suppl. xiii (1868) 85 sqq.

[3] For a brief, clear discussion of the contributions of these fourteenth-century writers to the foundations of analytical geometry and infinitesimal calculus see Boyer, op. cit.

[4] *Tract. Proport.* Thome Bradwardini, Parisiis, 1512 (?).

[5] Maier writes: 'Man möchte beinahe sagen: Bradwardine wollte die Principia mathematica philosophiae naturalis seines Jahrhunderts schreiben.' *Vorläufer Galileis*, p. 86, n. 10. Maier has made an analysis of Bradwardine's treatise.

[6] The importance of this rule of Aristotle's in the development of statics, particularly by Jordanus Nemorarius and his school, has been shown in detail by Duhem in his *Orig. statique*. Cf. B. Ginzburg, 'Duhem and Jordanus Nemorarius', *Isis*, xxv (1936) 341 sqq.; Dugas, *Histoire de la mécanique*, pp. 19 sqq., 38 sqq.

rejected them because they did not satisfy certain physical assertions or did not hold for all values. The equation that he asserted held for all proportions greater than 1 of power (m) to resistance (r) can be expressed in modern terminology, where v is velocity, as follows: $v = \log (m/r)$.[1]

The defect of Bradwardine's treatment of dynamics was that he made no measurements, and it must be admitted also that his conception of the problem of motion, quite apart from his attempt to solve it, leaves much to be desired. Yet his formulation of the problem in terms of an equation, and one in which the complexity of the relationships involved was fully recognized, was an original and important contribution to mathematical physics in general and to dynamics in particular. Through him fourteenth-century natural philosophers, both in Oxford and Paris, got the beginnings of a conception of the use of mathematical functions in physics, and fifteenth-century Italy saw the beginnings of an experimental investigation not only of his dynamical function but also of the Peripatetic law of motion itself.[2] In Oxford, the numerous writers of tracts on 'proportions', and the 'Calculatores', among whom Richard Swineshead (Calculator), William of Heytesbury and John of Dumbleton were outstanding, all wrote under the direct inspiration of Bradwardine. In Paris he had a direct influence on the most important members of the school, Jean Buridan, Nicole Oresme, Albert of Saxony, and Marsilius of Inghen, all of whom used his function. In Italy at the end of the fourteenth century Blasius of Parma criticized this function. In the fifteenth century Giovanni Marliani made even severer criticisms and carried out some striking though unsuccessful experiments with pendulums and balls rolling down inclined planes in an investigation of the whole basis of the Peripatetic law of motion.[3] This law, and Bradwardine's function with it, survived,

---

[1] Maier, *Vorläufer Galileis*, p. 92; see pp. 86 sqq.; Moody, *JHI*, xii (1951) 399–403.

[2] See Maier, *Vorläufer Galileis*, pp. 95–110; Duhem, *Léonard de Vinci*, iii. 296 sqq., 405 sqq., 481 sqq. (on the influence of Oxford logic on Italian science). It is perhaps surprising that at Merton, where astronomical observations received due attention, no experiments seem to have been made in mechanics, though further examination of MSS may possibly reveal some. See R. T. Gunther, *Early Science in Oxford*, ii; Sarton, *Introduction*, iii. 660–76, 1499–1502.

[3] Clagett (*Giovanni Marliani*, pp. 139–40) points out that the arguments against the Peripatetic law and against Bradwardine's law which Marliani based on these experiments were for the most part erroneous, and that Marliani himself partly recognized this. His main arguments against the laws were, in fact, directed to pointing out their internal inconsistency. Yet the existence of such experiments is an historical fact of great interest. See Joannis Marliani Mediolanensis *Questio de Proportione Motuum in*

however, until the seventeenth century. Galileo swept away both by a better use than Bradwardine of mathematical functions, and a better use than Marliani of experiments with pendulums and balls rolling down inclined planes.[1]

John of Dumbleton (fl. 1331–49) made a more direct use than Bradwardine of Grosseteste's theory of science. Dumbleton was at different times a fellow of Merton and of Queen's Colleges, and his *Summa Logice et Philosophie Naturalis* was widely read both in Oxford and Paris.[2] In the first part of this *Summa*[3] he was concerned with the signification of terms, the method of definition, and other logical questions, and he referred frequently to Plato, Aristotle, Porphyry, Avicenna, and Averroës. In his discussion of definition in Chapters 22–28 he took the usual view that the first process of knowing in physics passed from effect to cause, from the particulars of sense more knowable to us to the universals more knowable 'in nature', before it could be succeeded by the second process of demonstration from cause to effect, from universal to particular. For his discussion of this first process he made use of Grosseteste's treatment of the methods of resolution and composition[4] and of his distinction between material and formal definitions.[5]

In the second part of the *Summa* Dumbleton dealt with the important question of the 'latitude' or 'intension and remission' of qualities, and in the third part he discussed the measurement of rate of change (whether in local motion, change of quality or growth) in relation to some fixed scale, as of distance or time, which was known as 'extension' (*extensio*). These subjects were very popular both in Oxford and Paris in the fourteenth century.[6] A change was

Velocitate, MS Vat. Lat. 2225, 1444, ff. 11ʳ–37ʳ; Brit. Mus. MS Harley 3833, 1470, ff. 1 sqq. (Printed version, Pavia, 1482.)   [1] See below, pp. 307–8.

[2] For Dumbleton see Duhem, *Léonard de Vinci*, iii. 410–12, 424–41, 460–8, and in *RBE*, pp. 281–3; Maier, *An der Grenze*. . . . pp. 48 sqq.

[3] Joannis de Dumbleton, *Summa Logice et Philosophie Naturalis*, Prologue, Cambridge MS Peterhouse 272, f. 1ʳ. This is a fourteenth-century MS: see M. R. James, *Manuscripts in the Library of Peterhouse*. I have used also Oxford MS Merton 306, 14c., ff. 7ʳ sqq.

[4] '. . . ut patet per Lincolniensem primo posteriorum'. *Summa*, i. 27, MS Peterhouse 272, f. 8ᵛᵇ.

[5] '. . . ut ponit Lincolniensis diffinitionem materialem esse universaliorem diffinitione formali licet convertantur in significatione.' (Ibid., f. 9ʳ.) He referred again to 'iuxta Lincolniensem primo posteriorum capitulo secundo dixit quod scientia principiorum . . .' in ibid., C. 28, f. 9ʳᵇ.

[6] On the 'latitude of forms' see Duhem, *Léonard de Vinci*, iii. 314 sqq.; Boyer, *Concepts of the Calculus*, pp. 73 sqq., 81 sqq.; Maier, *Intensiven Grösse . . ., An der Grenze . . .* pp. 257 sqq., *Vorläufer Galileis*, pp. 81–131; above, p. 178, n. 4. For the connexion of

said to be 'uniform' when, in uniform local motion, equal distances were covered in equal intervals of time, and 'difform' when, in accelerated or retarded motion, increments of distance were added or subtracted in successive intervals of time. Such a 'difform' change was said to be 'uniformly difform' when equal increments were added or subtracted in successive intervals of time, and 'difformly difform' when unequal increments were so added or subtracted. Sometimes the relationship between intensity and extension was expressed graphically, the 'latitude' of intensity being put on the vertical axis and the extension (sometimes called *longitudo*[1]) on the horizontal axis.[2]

Dumbleton drew a distinction between real latitude or real change in quality and nominal latitude or the quantitative equivalent of such qualitative change.[3] He maintained that in reality no species of quality suffered change. Each degree of intensity of a given genus of quality, for example heat, represented a different species of the genus, and when a body in which the quality inhered suffered change it lost one real species of quality and acquired another. So in reality when a quality changed there was no addition or subtraction of parts such as there was when an increase or decrease of quantity took place.[4] But for purposes of description a change of quality could be considered as involving the addition or subtraction of different amounts of intensity of the quality for each unit of 'extension' of the subject in which it inhered.[5]

He went on in the third part of the *Summa* to give a logical demonstration for a nominal latitude, or as he called it *latitudo improprie dicta*, of the important rule that 'the latitude of a uniformly difform movement corresponds to the degree of the mid-point'.[6]

this method with Roger Bacon's notion of 'linea intensionis' see Maier, *Impetustheorie*, 2. Aufl., p. 97, n. 8; cf. p. 101 for Oresmes's reference to Grosseteste. Cf. Clagett, *Osiris*, ix (1950) 131–61.   [1] Cf. *Summa*, iii. 11–12; MS Peterhouse 272, f. 14ʳ.

[2] If velocity (i.e. 'intensity of motion') or latitude were plotted against time (i.e. 'extension of time'), uniform velocity would then be represented by a straight line drawn from the point on the vertical axis corresponding to the velocity or 'degree of latitude' and running parallel to the horizontal time-axis; uniformly difform velocity by a straight line drawn from the same point and receding from or approaching the horizontal axis according to whether the motion were accelerated or retarded; and difformly difform velocity by a curved line behaving in the same way.

[3] He said in the Prologue of the *Summa* that he was going to speak in the second part 'de intentione qualitatis uniformis et difformis latitudinis secundum rem seu secundum nomen'. MS Peterhouse 272, f. 1ʳ.

[4] *Summa*, ii. 14–26; MS Peterhouse 272, ff. 14ᵛᵇ–18ʳ; Maier, *An der Grenze . . .*, pp. 48–51, 286.   [5] Cf. Roger Bacon, above, p. 143.

[6] *Summa*, iii. 9–11; MS Peterhouse 272, f. 25; Merton 306, f. 33ʳᵇ sqq. See Duhem, op. cit., pp. 464–8; Maier, op. cit., pp. 280, 286.

This meant that, for example in local motion, the space traversed in a given time by a body moving with uniform acceleration was equal to that traversed in the same time by a body moving uniformly with the velocity reached at the mid-point of time. Nicole Oresme was to prove this rule geometrically, and in the seventeenth century it was to become the basis of the kinematic law of freely falling bodies.[1] As Duhem[2] has shown, Oresme knew of its enunciation in Oxford.

This 'method of latitudes' Dumbleton used in the fifth part of the *Summa*, in a discussion which may owe something to Grosseteste though he did not mention him by name, to examine the problem of the variation in the strength of action of light with distance. This subject he had already touched briefly in the course of the second part of the *Summa*.[3] Having devoted the fourth part to a discussion of the elements, Dumbleton said that in the fifth part he would inquire into 'spiritual action' and first into 'the form of light through which spiritual action is chiefly made known to us'.[4] 'The fifth part', he said, 'treats of spiritual action, and whether light belongs to any element and how it exists simply or subsequent to anything else is discussed. In this part the questions of the differences of superior and inferior forms which act by light and of uniform and difform action in regard to the agent and patient are also discussed.'[5]

---

[1] Cf. Maier, *Vorläufer Galileis*, pp. 111–31. Duhem (op. cit., pp. 481 sqq., 493 sqq.) has shown how these Parisian and Oxonian ideas spread in Italy in the fifteenth century and how they influenced Galileo and Descartes in their analysis of free fall (pp. 562 sqq.). Cf. Maier, *Impetustheorie*, p. 376, *An der Grenze* . . ., pp. 337–8, *Vorläufer Galileis*, pp. 125–6; A. Koyré, *Études galiléennes*, i–iii; Dugas, *Histoire de la mécanique*, pp. 57 sqq., 68 sqq., 128 sqq., 152 sqq.; Moody, *JHI*, xii (1951) 399–403.

[2] Duhem, op. cit., p. 405; cf. Maier, *An der Grenze* . . ., pp. 279–82, 331. In the third part of the *Summa*, as Duhem (pp. 424–7) has pointed out, Dumbleton also expounded the work of Jordanus Nemorarius and his school on mechanics; and in the sixth part, on powers, he went on to discuss the problem of the persistence of movement in projectiles and in the heavenly bodies. He explained the former, as Duhem (op. cit., pp. 434–8; *RBE*, pp. 281–3) has shown, by Roger Bacon's theory that the body would behave in such a way as to preserve the *continuum* of 'universal nature' and prevent a void caused by the recession of the air in front of it.   [3] *Summa*, ii. 32–33; MS Peterhouse 272, f. 19.

[4] 'Completa determinatione de actione reali inter formas et qualitates sensibiles communiter, de actione spirituali inquiramus duobus requisitis in omni actione pura forma agente et subiecto nato pati sub eadem. Primo de forma lucis per quam nobis maxime apparet actio spiritualis determinemus utrum illa singulariter alicui elemento vel alicui mixto naturaliter competat vel indifferenter omni elemento et corpori supra coelesti eadem forma specifica lucis conveniat. Secundo discutiendum quid disponit medium ad hoc quod ipsum sit capax ut actionem spiritualem recipiat.' *Summa*, v. 1; MS Peterhouse 272, f. 44ʳ.

[5] 'Quinta pars agit de actione spirituali, si lux alicui elemento competat, qualiter

Concerning the form of light Dumbleton said, after a brief discussion in which he pointed out that the flame of a candle was produced by the consuming of the substance of the candle: 'From which experiences and reasons it is clear that the form of light results from the proportion of the primary qualities[1] to the density or rarity of matter, and not that light itself is some element naturally, as the primary qualities are produced.'[2]

Going on to discuss the question of the variation in strength of illumination[3] with distance, he showed first how to get a quantitative expression for the degrees of intensity of a quality. He said:

It remains to inquire whether spiritual agents act uniformly as to latitude. Latitude that is effected uniformly according to proportion I understand as follows: take the points of the medium distant from the points which terminate such action, then the more remitted degrees correspond to the same points. Not that any quantitative part of the medium has as much latitude as the part of the medium which is equal to it, because from this it would follow that there would be no latitude in quality except in terms of quantity, and the more the latitude was extended in terms of quantity the greater would be the intensity. The consequence is impossible and therefore so is that from which it follows. But one must imagine it as follows: the whole latitude of intensity corresponds to the point that is immediate to the agent, as in a pyramidal body the base corresponds to its whole depth; and as in a pyramidal body, according as points terminate lines which are like the diameters of the bases of proportional parts and according as they are smaller proportionately, so are the points in an illuminated medium. In a latitude uniformly extended, the degrees correspond to the points according as they have proportionately less of the whole latitude, that is of the highest degree; and so it must be understood of every uniformly extended latitude that when in some subject the highest degree (which is the whole latitude of that quality) is extended so that the

simplex vel resultans existat enarrat. Item eadem pars de differentia formarum superiorum et inferiorum lumine agentium et de actione uniformi et difformi respectu agentis et passi dubia edisserit.' *Summa*, Prologue; MS Peterhouse 272, f. 1ʳ.

  [1] i.e., hot, cold, dry, wet.

  [2] 'Ex quibus experimentis et rationibus apparet formam lucis ex proportione primarum qualitatum una cum densitate vel raritate materie resultare et non quod ipsa lux aliquod elementum naturaliter sicut qualitates prime consequuntur.' *Summa*, v. 1; MS Peterhouse 272, f. 44ʳᵇ. Here he differed from Grosseteste.

  [3] This subject was discussed also by Richard Swineshead (Calculator) in his *Liber Calculationum* (Padua, 1477): see Thorndike, *History of Magic*, iii. 382–3. In an anonymous fourteenth-century work, *A est unum calidum*, the technique of 'latitudes' was applied also to the variation in intensity of heat: see Duhem, *Léonard de Vinci*, iii. 474–7.

degree half as intense corresponds to the midpoint rather than to the extreme, and so on, then such a latitude is uniformly extended.[1]

He went on to postulate a direct relationship between the strength of the luminous body and the distance through which it acted at a given intensity, and an inverse relationship between the density of the medium and the distance of action,[2] sometimes using the sun[3] or a candle[4] as examples of luminous sources. With a medium of uniform density or rarity he said, in the course of an involved argument in which it is not always easy to see which view he is supporting, that a luminous body A 'acts difformly and more weakly (remissius) at remote points than at near points, because of the distance'.[5]

---

[1] 'Restat inquirere utrum agentia spiritualia agunt uniformiter quantum ad latitudinem. Sic de latitudine intendo acta uniformiter quod proportionaliter, sicut puncta medii distant a puncto terminante talem actionem, ita eisdem punctis gradus remissiores correspondent. Non quod quelibet pars quantitativa medii tantam latitudinem continet sicut pars medii sibi equalis, nam ex hoc sequitur quod nulla esset latitudo in qualitate nisi secundum quantitatem, et tunc quanto per maiorem quantitatem latitudo extenderetur tanto maior esset latitudo intensione. Consequens impossibile, et ideo illud ex quo sequitur. Sed oportet imaginari sic, quod puncto immediato agenti correspondet tota latitudo intensive sicut in corpore pyramidali basi sue correspondet tota sua profunditas, et sicut in corpore pyramidali puncta secundum quod terminant lineas que sunt quasi diametri basium partium proportionalium et secundum quod sunt minores proportionaliter, ita puncti in medio illuminato. [In] aliqua latitudine uniformiter extensa punctis correspondent gradus secundum quod proportionaliter habent minus de latitudine tota, id est de gradu summo. Et ita intelligendum est de omni latitudine uniformiter extensa quod cum in aliquo subiecto gradus summus (qui est tota latitudo illius qualitatis) ita extenditur ut in duplo remissior gradus correspondet medio puncto quam extremo et ita deinceps tunc talis uniformiter extenditur.' *Summa*, v. 7; MS Peterhouse 272, f. 47^r; Merton 306, f. 61^r. For this version of this passage I have used both MSS, which vary in some details.

[2] 'ponitur quod sint duo media uniformiter rara C D et sint duo luminosa A B sub eodem gradu potentie et luminis. . . . Et maioratur A in potentia solum ita quod sufficiat agere per maiorem distantiam quam prius. . . . Ponitur tunc quod C medium condensatur continue ita quod A non agat ad maiorem distantiam quam prius propter condensationem factam in C, et ad omnem punctum C medii conservatur idem gradus luminis sicut iam est.' Loc. cit.

[3] 'debilitatur lux distans a sole.' *Summa*, v. 8, MS Peterhouse 272, f. 47rb. See also ii. 32, f. 19^r.

[4] '. . . ut si ymaginemus quod candela agat iam per bipedalem quantitatem lumen remissum sub medio; si igitur illa candela sic disposita quanto sua actione concrescat in unam pedalem quantitatem, illud lumen in primo pedali est duplum intensive ad illud quod prius fuit actum vel multo intensius, et causa est quia candela iam agit duo lumina nunc coextensa in primo pedali que prius egit in duabus et totum aggregatum est intensius lumen, et per hoc experimentum probatur dicta propositio, id est qualitates simul coextendi.' *Summa*, ii. 33; MS Peterhouse 272, f. 19rb. See also *Summa*, v. 10; MS Peterhouse 272, f. 47vb.

[5] 'A aget difformiter et remissius ad puncta remota quam ad propinqua propter distantiam.' *Summa*, v. 7; MS Peterhouse 272, f. 47$^{ra, \, b}$.

He concluded: 'If, therefore, *A* acts weakly only because of the distance, then, according as they are proportionately distant, so *A* proportionately brings about degrees in them of the same degree which it has itself.'[1] But 'a luminous body does not act uniformly difformly in a uniformly dense medium'.[2] Thus Dumbleton appreciated the fact that the decrease in intensity of illumination was not simply proportional to the distance from the luminous body, though he did not succeed in formulating the exact quantitative relationship between latitude of intensity and extension in distance.[3]

Other Oxford writers of the first half of the fourteenth century continued to make use of Grosseteste's scientific ideas. In methodology, Walter Burley (d. after 1337), a fellow of Merton College, based his ideas on definition[4] and on the discovery of causal principles from their effects,[5] respectively, on Grosseteste's commentaries on the *Posterior Analytics* and on the *Physics*. William of Collingham also cited these commentaries by Grosseteste in his commentary on the first book of the *Physics*, the only other authors cited being Aristotle himself and Averroës.[6] Henry of Harclay, William of Alnwick, and Robert Holkot (d. 1349) quoted Grosseteste's views on infinite aggregates and measurement from his commentary on the *Physics*.[7] In optics, Walter of Odington (*fl.* 1301–30),

---

[1] 'Si igitur solum aget A remisse propter distantiam igitur secundum quod proportionaliter distant ita proportionaliter agit gradus sub gradu quem iam habet.' Loc. cit.

[2] 'luminosum non agit unum uniformiter difformiter in medio uniformiter denso.' *Summa*, v. 8; MS Peterhouse 272, f. 47^v. In his *Quaest. super Euclidis Elementa*, Oresme may possibly have been referring to Dumbleton: Question 15 reads: 'Utrum diffusio vel multiplicatio virtutis corporum circa se sit uniformiter difformis, v. gr. sicut illuminatio medii vel influentia aliqua vel multiplicatio specierum in medio.' Vatican MSS Vat. Lat. 2225, 1444, ff. 90ra–98vb; Chisianus F. iv. 66, 15 c., ff. 22vb–40rb. His answer was in the affirmative; see Maier, *An der Grenze . . .*, pp. 340–1. For Oresme's treatment of sound, see Maier, ibid., p. 322.

[3] This was done for the first time by Kepler, who first formulated what was in effect the inverse square law; see *Ad Vitellionem Paralipomena*, i. 9, Francofurti, 1604, p. 10; Wolf, *Science, Technology, and Philosophy in the 16th & 17th Centuries*, p. 245; below, p. 284, n. 3.

[4] *Scriptum* Gualteri Burlei *super Lib. Post. Arist.* i. 2, Venetiis, 1514, f. 4vb; ii. 1, f. 44^r; ii. 3, f. 44vb.

[5] Gualteri Burlei *in Physicam Expos. et Quest.* i, Venetiis, 1501, ff. 6^v, 24vb, 25^r, 31^v; ii, f. 56vb; cf. above, pp. 56, 103. Wyclyf also quoted Grosseteste's *Comm. Phys.* in his *De Ente Primo*, ed. S. H. Thomson, p. 104; cf. Thomson, *Writings of Rob. Grosseteste*, pp. 82, 84. On Burley see Michalski, 'La Physique nouvelle et les différents courants philosophiques au xive siècle', *BIAPSL*, 1927, pp. 95–102, 120–5, 142–4.

[6] See Duhem, *Léonard de Vinci*, iii. 423–4.

[7] Above, p. 100, n. 3; Roberti Holkot *Super Lib. Sent. Quest.* ii, Q. 2, Art 5, 'An Deus potuit producere mundum ab aeterno?' Lugduni, 1497. Cf. Duhem, *Léonard de Vinci*,

a Benedictine monk of Evesham who made astronomical observations in Oxford and was also connected with Merton, made use of the theory of multiplication of species in a discussion of vision, concave mirrors, and the spherical burning-glass, which he explained by double refraction.[1] Simon Tunsted (d. 1369), another Oxford Franciscan, when discussing the cause of the tides, gave a long exposition of 'Lincolniensis Tractatu suo de Refractionibus Radiorum'.[2]

These strands of evidence show that Grosseteste's name was still remembered[3] in Oxford a century after his death, but perhaps of even greater importance in showing the strength of his influence are the natural philosophers in whose writings his methodology appears anonymously and simply as part of their approach to science. As his ideas were elaborated by his successors it would be natural for Grosseteste's own name to drop out, but it is possible to see the continuation of his experimental and mathematical methods in English science in the fourteenth century, as, for example, in the measuring instruments and trigonometrical techniques developed by Richard of Wallingford (c. 1292–1335)[4] for use in astronomy, or

ii. 401–2; Duhem does not seem to have been aware of the existence of Grosseteste's *Comm. Phys.* Cf. also above, p. 179.

[1] *Tract. de Mult. Specierum in Visu* ... per Walterum de Evesham, Cambridge Univ. Lib. MS I i. I. 13, 14 c., ff. 44ᵛ–51. Walter of Odington was also the author of the *Icocedron* (ibid., ff. 51ᵛ–55ᵛ) in which he tried to measure the four qualities quantitatively in degrees and to express their 'intensions' and 'remissions' graphically; see Thorndike, *History of Magic*, iii. 128–40, 682–4; Sarton, *Introduction*, iii. 661–2.

[2] Tunsted's *Quaest. Meteor.* was printed in I. Duns Scoti *Opera Omnia*, ed. Wadding, iii; see pp. 65–66. On Simon Tunsted see Sarton, *Introduction*, iii. 1568. Tunsted's account of the rainbow seems to have been based largely on that of Albertus Magnus, whose explanation was based on that of Grosseteste (below, pp. 196 sqq.): see *Quaest. Meteor.* iii. 8–9, in I. Duns Scoti *Opera*, iii. 96 sqq.

[3] The figure he cut in the popular imagination as one who had found the means of gaining power over natural forces is seen by the reference in the fourteenth-century poet John Gower's *Confessio Amantis*, iv, ll. 234 sqq., to 'the grete Clerc Grosseteste' who was able 'an Hed of bras To forge, and make it for to telle Of such thinges as befelle'. Stevenson in his *Robert Grosseteste*, p. 57, has drawn attention to the similarity between this legend relating to Grosseteste and the sixteenth-century legends relating to Roger Bacon and Dr. Faustus. Cf. Sir J. E. Sandys, 'Roger Bacon in English literature', in *RBE*, pp. 359 sqq. Similar and even more spectacular legends were told also of Albertus Magnus.

[4] See J. D. Bond, 'Richard Wallingford', *Isis*, iv (1922) 458 sqq., 'Quadripartitum Richardi Walynforde de Sinibus Demonstratis', *Isis*, v (1923) 99 sqq.; R. T. Gunther, *Early Science in Oxford*, ii. 337 sqq.; Sarton, *Introduction*, iii. 662–8. Western trigonometry was founded by John Maudith (*fl.* 1310), a fellow of Merton College, Richard of Wallingford, and the Provençal Jew, Levi ben Gerson (1288–1344), whose work on the subject was translated into Latin in 1342 for Pope Clement VI. In spite of the earlier work of the Merton school, it seems to have been Levi whom Regiomontanus used as his source. See Sarton, op. cit. iii. 598, 661, 667–8.

in the diary of weather records kept at Oxford during 1337–44 by William Merlee, with a view to making predictions for farmers.[1] In the development of these methods English science expressed its characteristic genius.[2] That it was able to do so was due to the initiative of Robert Grosseteste, who provided the Oxford school with a theory of science just such as was needed at that point of history. He was the 'true teacher' described in his own words, quoted in the fourteenth century:

Unde ad hanc intentionem illustris vir Linconiensis primo Posteriorum ait: Non solum doctor exterius in aure sonans docet nec solum littera visa docet, sed ille verus doctor qui interius mentem illuminat et veritatem demonstrat.[3]

[1] See Thorndike, *History of Magic*, iii. 141 sqq. Merlee wrote a separate treatise on weather prediction, *De Future Aëris Intemperie*. A contemporary English meteorologist, John of Eschenden, does refer to 'Linconiensis' in connexion with weather prediction and also on the question of the beginning of the world (Thorndike, ibid., pp. 120, 325 sqq., 330). At the end of the fourteenth century another English writer, Thomas Werkwoth, also cited Grosseteste in connexion with astronomical observations at Oxford: L. Thorndike, 'Thomas Werkwoth on the motion of the eighth sphere', *Isis*, xxxix (1948) 212 sqq. On medieval weather records and weather prediction, see Sarton, *Introduction*, iii. 117, 675–6, 1743; Thorndike, op. cit. iii. 119–27, iv. 256, 612; G. Hellmann, *Wetterprognosen und Wetterberichte des xv. und xvi. Jahrhundert, Meteorologische Beobachtungen vom xiv. bis xvii. Jahrhundert* (for William Merlee), *Denkmäler mittelalterlicher Meteorologie, Wettervorhersage im ausgehenden Mittelalter*; L. Thorndike, 'A weather record for 1399–1406 A.D.', *Isis*, xxxii (1939) 304 sqq.

[2] Cf. Maier's remarks on this point: 'Die Stärke der Oxforder liegt weniger auf spekulativ-theoretischem als auf methodisch-rechnerischem Gebiet. Neue physikalische Erklärungsversuche finden sich kaum bei ihnen, dafür haben sie nicht nur in methodologischer Beziehung eine grosse Leistung vollbracht, sondern haben auch in mancher Einzelfrage tiefer und richtiger gesehen als die Pariser und haben es vor allem besser verstanden, die Probleme rechnerisch in Angriff zu nehmen.' *Vorläufer Galileis*, p. 4. On the prominence of mathematics, optics, and astronomy in the Oxford curriculum in the later Middle Ages see Rashdall, *Universities*, ed. Powicke and Emden, iii. 152 sqq.; for comparison with Bologna, Paris, and some German universities see i. 248 sqq., 449 sqq.

[3] Quoted by Thorndike, *University Records*, p. 416 (see also pp. 211–12) from the mid-fourteenth-century *De Commendatione Cleri*, MS Vat. Pal. Lat. 1252, 15 c., f. 102ᵛ; cf. *Comm. Post.* i. 1.

VIII

Grosseteste, Oxford and European Science

(1)

THOUGH outside England Grosseteste did not found a school of scientific thought as he did in Oxford, his own direct influence, as well as the influence of the Oxford school on the beginnings of the modern Western scientific tradition as a whole, was considerable and even decisive. It would be forcing the evidence to suggest that the theory of experimental science which, from the thirteenth century, came to direct the scientific activity of the West, was the unique creation of Oxford. The truth seems to be that Oxford took the lead in a general movement in Western Christendom. The advances made in thirteenth- and fourteenth-century Paris, Italy, and the Germanies were to a large extent the result of an independent use of the Greek and Arabic sources as they became available in Latin. Yet Oxford's lead in methodology enabled her to a considerable degree to dominate the conceptions of natural science forming in other, contemporary centres. In fact, the chief scientific personality in thirteenth-century Paris and the Germanies, Albertus Magnus himself (*c.* 1206–80), formed his theory of science under the direct guidance of Grosseteste's own works. Moreover, a theory of experimental science essentially the same as that developed by Oxford logic may be traced through the principal writings of later scientists down into the seventeenth century.

The foundation of Grosseteste's influence abroad might have been laid by his personal acquaintance with Continental scholars. Though there is no contemporary evidence that he continued his studies at Paris, it seems likely that he went there to go on with theology after the dispersion of Oxford scholars in 1209.[1] It has been suggested that he remained there till as late as 1225.[2] In any case he was friendly with some of the principal philosophers and

[1] See above, p. 44; and especially Callus, *Oxoniensia*, x (1945) 49 sqq. Further circumstantial evidence that Grosseteste studied in Paris has been brought forward by D. A. Callus, 'The *Summa Theologiae* of Robert Grosseteste', in *Studies in Mediaeval History presented to F. M. Powicke*, p. 194.

[2] J. C. Russell, 'Phases of Grosseteste's intellectual life', *Harvard Theol. Rev.* xliii (1950) 100, 105–7.

teachers at Paris, for example, William of Auvergne[1] and the English Franciscan Alexander of Hales,[2] and was well known among the French clergy.[3] His 'light metaphysics' seems to have exerted a strong influence on the French poet and bibliophile, Richard de Fournival.[4] The great Italian Franciscan theologian, Bonaventura, might perhaps also have derived some of his ideas on the role played by light in the universe from Grosseteste.[5] It was, however, the Dominican leader, Albertus Magnus, who owed most to Grosseteste's direct influence. Grosseteste met the second Master-General of the Order of Preachers, the mathematician Jordanus of Saxony (Jordanus Nemorarius), when the latter visited Oxford in 1229–30,[6] shortly after his preaching had led to Albertus becoming a Dominican in Padua.[7] Jordanus could have formed a link between the two

[1] Rob. Grosseteste *Epistolae*, ed. Luard, p. 250. Cf. Baeumker, *Witelo*, pp. 392 sqq.; Baur, *Philos. Rob. Grosseteste*, p. 6.

[2] Rob. Grosseteste *Epistolae*, p. 335. Cf. Baeumker, *Witelo*, p. 682, n. 414; Sharp, *Franciscan Philos. at Oxford*, p. 22, n. 2; above, p. 42, n. 7, p. 105.

[3] Stevenson, *Robert Grosseteste*, pp. 16, 55. Grosseteste's friend, the English logician William of Shyreswood or Sherwood (d. after 1267), may possibly have helped to extend Grosseteste's influence at Paris. After studying at Oxford and becoming treasurer of Lincoln Cathedral, William taught at Paris where Petrus Hispanus (who became Pope John XXI) heard him (Stevenson, pp. 42, 248; Pegge, *Life of Robert Grosseteste*, p. 247; *Die Introductiones in Logicam des* Wilhelm von Shyreswood, ed. by M. Grabmann, p. 12; J. C. Russell, *Dict. of Writers of Thirteenth Cent. England*, p. 200). Roger Bacon (*Opus Tertium*, C. 2, ed. Brewer, p. 14) commended William for his knowledge and said he was far wiser than Albertus Magnus: 'Nam in philosophia communi nullus major est eo.' William and Petrus Hispanus were leading figures in the development of the analysis of the relation between things, thought, and language which was the characteristic interest of the *logica moderna* of the late thirteenth and fourteenth centuries. Petrus Hispanus was also a distinguished eye doctor (see above, p. 151, n. 1) and he made some contributions to the logic of experiment (see above, p. 81, n. 2). See *Syncategoremata* of William of Sherwood, ed. J. R. O'Donnell; *Summulae Logicales* of Peter of Spain, ed. J. P. Mullally (there is also a more complete edition by I. M. Bocheński). This kind of logic has been revived in the 'calculus of propositions' of the twentieth century; see J. Łukasiewicz, 'Zur Geschichte der Aussagenlogik', *Erkenntnis*, v (1935-6) 111 sqq. Grosseteste was well known in France also for his translation of the *Nicomachean Ethics*. His version was used by Albertus Magnus whom, according to A. Pelzer ('Le Cours inédit d'Albert le Grand sur la Morale à Nicomaque', *RNP*, xxiv, 1922, pp. 348-52, 361), it initiated into Greek studies, and also by Thomas Aquinas, Albert of Saxony, and Nicole Oresme, who translated it into French (Sarton, *Introduction*, ii. 584, iii. 1431, 1493). It was in fact the standard medieval version. Cf. above, p. 45, n. 1, p. 136, n. 2.

[4] A. Birkenmajer, 'Robert Grosseteste and Richard Fournival', *MH*, v (1948) 36 sqq.

[5] Sharp, loc. cit.; Baur, in *Festschrift Georg v. Hertling*, p. 45.

[6] Callus, *Oxoniensia*, x (1945) 53. Grosseteste later corresponded with Jordanus; see Roberti Grosseteste *Epistolae*, pp. 131-3. The date of this letter is given as 1237. See also above, p. 96, n. 3, p. 149, n. 5. On Jordanus as a mathematician see Duhem, *Orig. statique*, i. 98 sqq.; Sarton, *Introduction*, ii. 613-16; Trivet, *Annales*, ed. Hog, p. 211.

[7] H. C. Scheeben, *Albert der Grosse*, pp. 12-13; Mandonnet, below, p. 191, n. 4.

men. Another possible link was Grosseteste's English Dominican friend, John of St. Giles, who might have been a lecturer in the house opened by the Order in Oxford and who later became personal physician to Grosseteste at Lincoln.[1] Stevenson has suggested that John might have met Albertus when he visited Cologne in 1235–6. Roger Bacon certainly knew Albertus Magnus, whom he could have met when both were teaching in Paris *c.* 1243–6.[2] But whatever the manner in which Albertus became aware of Grosseteste's ideas, the effect on his scientific thought is evident in his writings.[3]

Albertus Magnus resembled Grosseteste in setting out a theory of experimental science in a commentary on the *Posterior Analytics* and, in fact, he used Grosseteste's commentary for this purpose. This theory of science he put into practice in a series of studies written in the form of commentaries on Aristotle and other authors. The bulk of his scientific writing seems to have been done between *c.* 1245 and 1260, during two periods as lecturer at the Dominican house at Cologne,[4] though some of it probably dates from the last decades of his life. His object, as he said, was 'to make all parts of philosophy intelligible to the Latins'.[5] Inevitably much of what he

---

[1] Rob. Grosseteste *Epistolae*, pp. 60–62 (1235), 132–3 (1237); Matthaei Parisiensis *Chronica Majora*, ed. R. H. Luard, v. 400, 705; Pegge, op. cit., p. 222; Stevenson, op. cit., pp. 55, 67, 120, 182–3. Cf. Scheeben, op. cit., pp. 18–22. On John, see Sarton, *Introduction*, ii. 546.

[2] Crowley, op. cit., pp. 31, 196, above, p. 139, n. 4; Little, in *RBE*, pp. 4 sqq., *PBA*, xiv (1928) 269; Scheeben, op. cit., pp. 16 sqq.; d'Irsay, *Archeion*, xv (1933) 225. Cf. below, pp. 200–7.

[3] This has been indicated by the seventeenth-century editor of Albertus's works, Pierre Jammy. In the *Posteriorum*, ed. Jammy (*Opera*, i), there are marginal references to Grosseteste on pp. 526 (see below), 536 (on the *continuum*, see below), 547, 551 (see below), 566–7 (where Albertus is discussing Ptolemy's views on the relative certitude of physics, mathematics, and metaphysics, as in *Comm. Post.* i. 17, f. 18rb; above, pp. 129–30), 578, 580, 589, 601 (i. v. 7 where Albertus is discussing 'Universale autem quod est in omnibus' and the gloss reads: 'Vide Linco. quomodo universale est ubique'; cf. *Comm. Post.* i. 18, f. 19rb; above, p. 128, n. 3), 607 (on true and false opinions), and 629 (on lightning and thunder).

[4] For Albertus's life, see Scheeben, op. cit.; P. Mandonnet, 'La Date de naissance . . .', *Rev. thomiste*, N.S. xiv (1931) 233 sqq; F. Pelster, 'Um die Datierung . . .', *PJ*, xlviii (1935) 443 sqq. For his work see G. von Hertling, *Albertus Magnus*; Thorndike, *History of Magic*, ii. 517 sqq., 720 sqq.; H. C. Scheeben, 'Les Écrits d'Albert le Grand d'après les catalogues', *Rev. thomiste*, N.S. xiv (1931) 260 sqq.; and 'Serta Albertina', ed. P. A. Walz, *Angelicum*, xxi (1944). For a preliminary account of his theory of science see A. Mansion, 'L'Induction chez Albert le Grand', *RNP*, xiii (1906) 115 sqq., 246 sqq. See also below, p. 192, n. 4; and Sarton, *Introduction*, i. 934–44; M. H. Laurent et M. J. Congar, 'Essai de bibliographie albertinienne', *Rev. thomiste*, N.S. xiv (1931) 422 sqq.; F. Van Steenberghen, 'La Littérature albertino-thomiste (1930–7)', *RNP*, xli (1938), 126 sqq.   [5] *Physicorum*, i. i. 1, ed. Jammy, ii. 1.

wrote was copied from earlier sources. But in the course of his commentaries, inserted either as phrases or sentences in the original text itself, or as special books or chapters of 'digressions', he described a large number of highly intelligent personal observations and used them to test the different theories advanced as explanations. His best-known scientific work was done in zoology,[1] botany,[2] geology,[3] and chemistry.[4] He has an honourable place also in the history of meteorological optics, and among the particular sciences it is in this that Grosseteste's influence is most obvious.

Natural science, according to Albertus, was not simply a description of facts but an inquiry into causes.[5] The first stage in this inquiry was the observation that certain events were frequently correlated, and science could be built only upon events that always or frequently happened in the same way.[6] To have science properly speaking events must always happen in the same way and then it was possible to know causal essences and necessary laws. *Principia*

---

[1] Albertus Magnus, *De Animalibus Libri XXVI*, hrg. von H. Stadler. In this edition Stadler has distinguished between Albertus's insertions and Michael Scot's translation of the text of Aristotle and Avicenna. Cf. *De Motibus Animalium*, i. ii. 1–3, ed. Jammy, v.

[2] *De Vegetabilibus Libri VII*, ed. E. Meyer and C. Jessen.

[3] *De Mineralibus*, ed. Jammy, ii; *De Causis Proprietatum Elementorum*, ed. Jammy, v.

[4] *De Alchimia Libellus*, ed. Jammy, xxi. For accounts of the various aspects of Albertus's scientific work see P. Aiken, 'The animal history of Albertus Magnus and Thomas of Cantimpré', *Speculum*, xxii (1941) 205 sqq.; A. Arber, *Natural Philosophy of Plant Form*; H. Balss, *Albertus Magnus als Zoologer*; A. Delorme, 'La Morphogenèse d'Albert le Grand dans l'embryologie scolastique', *Rev. thomiste*, N.S. xiv (1931) 352 sqq.; Duhem, *Études sur Léonard de Vinci*, ii. 309 sqq. (geology); A. Fellner, *Albertus Magnus als Botaniker*; H. W. K. Fischer, *Mittelalterliche Pflanzenkunde*; S. Killermann, *Die Vogelkunde des Albertus Magnus*; R. Liertz, *Der selige Albert der Grosse als Naturforscher und Lehrer*; E. H. F. Meyer, *Geschichte der Botanik*, iv; J. R. Partington, 'Albertus Magnus on alchemy', *Ambix*, i (1937) 3 sqq.; F. A. Pouchet, *Sciences naturelles au moyen âge*; F. Strunz, *Albertus Magnus*; J. Wimmer, *Deutsches Pflanzenleben nach Albertus Magnus*. See also *Studia Albertina*, pp. 112, 234; below, p. 352.

[5] 'Scientia enim naturalis non est simpliciter narrata accipere, sed in rebus naturalibus inquirere causas.' (*De Mineral*. ii. ii. 1, ed. Jammy, ii. 227.) Albertus said also that Providence acted through natural laws and intermediate agencies, which were open to human investigation. 'Deus sublimis naturas regit et administrat per naturales causas, et illas hic quaerimus postquam divinas, quia non sunt proximae, non de facili possumus eas investigare.' (*Meteor*. iii. iii. 20, ed. Jammy, ii. 118.) 'Voluntas [Dei] causa prima est omnium, licet et alia sint causae essentiales et proximae rebus secundum omne genus causae, quas licuit quaerere philosophis, quando quaerunt de naturis et scientiis rerum.' *Summa Theol*. i. xx. lxxix. ii. i. 1, ed. Jammy, xvii. 461.

[6] *Posteriorum*, i. ii. 1, ed. Jammy, i. 526a. A marginal gloss by the editor reads: 'Tangit divisionem quadrimembrem ipsius scire quam ponit Linconiensis.' The passage is in fact a paraphrase of Grosseteste's *Comm. Post*. i. 2, f.2vb, translated above, pp. 58–59.

cognoscendi were identical with *principia essendi*, as in metaphysics.[1]
In the study of the contingent events of the natural world, however,
correlations were frequent rather than invariable, and it was possible
to reach only probable connexions. Moreover, a given effect might
have more than one possible cause.[2] Therefore in the natural
sciences or 'arts' it was necessary to test theories by experiment.[3]
Thus the inquiry into causes in the world of experience fell into the
two stages distinguished by Grosseteste.[4] First, by the *via resolutionis* the investigator argued inductively from the composite objects
of sense perception to knowledge of their elements and principles,
of the 'common nature' which defined the cause.[5] Then by the
deductive *via compositionis* he showed that the universal principle

[1] *Posteriorum*, ii. v. 1, p. 657a.

[2] '. . . utrum in demonstrativis contingat eiusdem effectus et unius non eandem esse
causam cum effectu convertibilem, sed alteram, aut hoc non contingat? . . . non potest
esse, quod idem habeat plures causas et quod causa diffinite et determinate non sequatur
ad effectum determinatum . . . posito causato non diffinite ponitur causa.' (Ibid. ii. iv. 8,
p. 652.) Cf. Grosseteste, above, p. 81.

[3] 'Earum autem, quae ponemus, quasdam quidem ipsi nos experimento probavimus,
quasdam autem referimus ex dictis eorum, quas comperimus non de facili aliqua dicere
nisi probata per experimentum. Experimentum enim solum certificat in talibus, eo
quod de tam particularibus naturis syllogismus haberi non potest.' *De Veget.* vi. i. 1,
Section 1, ed. Meyer and Jessen, pp. 339–40.

[4] 'Et haec vocatur via compositionis secundum quam universale (secundum id quod
est) principium formale est particularis; et particulare se habet ad singulare sicut subiectum et suppositum in ipso: et hoc modo prius secundum naturam est universale, et
posterius secundum naturam est particulare, et postremum est singulare, super quod
immediate cadit sensus. In via autem resolutionis ultimum efficitur primum, et e converso primum fit ultimum. Resolutio enim est compositi in simplicia, et posterioris in
prius, et causati in causam. Et incipit ab ultimo secundum naturam quod immediatum
sensibile est sensuum, non quidem per se vel commune sensatum, sed per accidens . . .
quia via resolutionis est via intellectus abstrahentis, quae vadit ad primam naturam
formaliter naturantem quae est etiam principium intelligendi id quod naturat.' (*Posteriorum*, i. ii. 3, ed. Jammy, i. 528^b.) See also ibid. i. i. 1, pp. 513–14, ii. i. 1, pp. 610 sqq.,
i. iii. 6–7, pp. 563–6; *Physicorum*, i. i. 6, ed. Jammy, ii. 8–10; and Régis, in *Studia
Mediaevalia R. J. Martin*, pp. 309 sqq. and 313 sqq. (on Aquinas); S. E. Dolan, 'Resolution and composition in speculative and practical discourse', *Laval théol. et philos.* vi
(1950) 9 sqq.

[5] 'Quia quaecunque participant aliquod genus commune, participant omnia consequentia illius generis per illam communem naturam generis, et illa communis natura
generis erit causa participandi consequentia ad illam naturam.' (*Posteriorum*, ii. iv. 6,
p. 649.) He went on to show how 'in hac arte inveniendi causam dicemus communia
nomina generum. . . . Quia in illis hoc commune et naturale accidens erit causa quare
insit passio, quae sub illo communi sunt accepta. Unde considerare etiam oportet si aliud
aliquod commune accipiatur secundum accidens commune pluribus. Tunc enim oportet
considerare in suis partibus, scilicet specialibus sub illo communi proximo acceptis.'
(Ibid., pp. 649–50.) He concluded a discussion of the property 'having horns':
'Sic igitur per commune accidens particularibus demonstrantur inesse passiones illius
communis.'

gave the observed facts a rational explanation (*propter quid*).[1] In natural science, he added, only material, efficient, and formal causes could be used for demonstration; final causes could be used only metaphorically.[2]

In his conception of the material universe Albertus resembled Grosseteste in accepting the Neoplatonic theory that *materia prima* was actual extension underlying all other accidents, especially sensible qualities.[3] He discussed but rejected Grosseteste's theory that light (*lumen vel lux*) was the first form that gave dimensions to matter and acted also as the first principle of movement and as the intermediary between mind and body.[4] He disagreed with Grosseteste's views on the *continuum*[5] and on infinity.[6] Nevertheless, Albertus's Neoplatonism predisposed him to value mathematics as a means of explaining the world of experience,[7] though he was not himself of a mathematical cast of mind. He excelled rather in the observational and experimental sciences, and also as a logician.[8] This experimental

---

[1] Cf. Grosseteste, above, pp. 54, 64–66. Albertus also distinguished between formal and material definitions in a manner and in phrases which suggest that he had Grosseteste's *Comm. Post.* ii. 2, f. 25^{rv} (above, p. 68, n. 3) before him: 'Dicunt . . . quidam modernorum. . . .' (*Posteriorum*, i. ii. 17, ed. Jammy, i. 551–2.) The editor's gloss reads: 'Ista est sententia Linco. et est secunda expositio.' Cf. also ibid. ii. ii. 10, pp. 630–1.

[2] 'In naturalibus passionibus non fit demonstratio per causam finalem . . . et si movet efficientem, hoc est metaphorice dictum; actum enim et opus moventis non facit, nisi efficiens.' (*Posteriorum*, ii. ii. 11, p. 632.) He added, however: 'natura non facit frustra' (p. 633). Cf. Ockham, above, p. 174.

[3] *Metaph.* xi. i. 7, ed. Jammy, iii. 133. In contrast, St. Thomas Aquinas held the purer Aristotelian doctrine that *materia prima* was pure potentiality: *Summa Theol.* iii, Q. 77, Art. 2.

[4] See *Posteriorum*, ii. iii. 4, ed. Jammy, i. 638: 'Quidam autem dicunt quod lumen vel lux est substantia, cuius natura formalis est se multiplicare per emissionem partis a parte'; also *De Anima*, ii. iii. 6, ed. Jammy, iii. 76. This chapter of Albertus's *De Anima* was quoted in pseudo-Grosseteste's *Summa*, iii. 20, Baur, 1912, p. 511. See also *De Gen. et Corrupt.* ii. i. 5, ed. Jammy, ii. 48^a; *De Causis et Processu Universitatis*, i. ii. 1, ed. Jammy, v. 541 (the analogy between the intellectual light from the Divine Intellect and the physical light from the sun).

[5] *Posteriorum*, i. ii. 8, p. 536. The marginal gloss reads: 'Nota opinionem quae videtur esse Linconien. hic', and on a later passage: 'Impugnatio opinionis Linco.' Cf. above, pp. 106–8, 119.

[6] In an infinite magnitude, 'nullum habeat proportionem ad totum'. *Physicorum*, iii. ii. 5, ed. Jammy, ii. 129. Cf. above, p. 100, n. 3, pp. 108–9, 148, 174, n. 3, p. 186.

[7] 'naturalis considerat et demonstrat per omnes causas, et mathematicus per duas tantum [formam et materiam]. Et tamen nobilior et certior est cognitio mathematica quam naturalis, et hoc est propter puritatem et certitudinem cognitorum, quae in abstractione a motu et materia considerat. Naturalis autem considerat ea permixta ad materiam, et ut accipiunt incertitudinem et contingentiam et mutabilitatem.' *Posteriorum*, ii. ii. 11, p. 633.

[8] Cf. Albertus's discussions of truth, falsehood, impossibility, and probability in *De*

bias is plain in his extension of Grosseteste's work on comets, the tides, heat, and, above all, the rainbow, in which he made good use of experimental verification and falsification.

In his discussion of comets Albertus made use of simple observations to verify or falsify the various theories that had been put forward to explain them.[1] For the tides he accepted Grosseteste's theory of the manner in which the moon acted, and showed how the occurrence of tides was correlated with the movements of the moon round its deferent.[2]

His treatment of heat was an attempt to understand the nature of the heat of the sun.[3] This involved some simple experiments and the use of the method of agreement and difference. He pointed out that some substances generated univocally products of the same species as themselves, whereas other substances generated equivocally products of a different species.[4] He maintained, as Grosseteste had, that all heat was caused by local motion, which agitated and separated the parts of bodies.[5] How, then, was heat generated by motion by the light of the sun? Heat could not be caused by the sun's motion, because all the heavenly bodies moved, yet they did not all produce heat.[6] Nor could heat be caused by the movement of the light itself, because light was not a body and did not move. On the other hand, it could not be denied that heat did accompany the light, because the senses showed that a place in bright sunlight was hot, and in shadow cold, and a burning-mirror which concentrated

Sophisticis Elenchis (i. ii. 6 sqq., ed. Jammy, i. 853 sqq., where he distinguishes between propositions sensu diviso and sensu composito), and in De Caelo et Mundo (i. iv. 6, ed. Jammy, ii. 66). Cf. above, p. 190, n. 3.

[1] 'per inductionem probant quod non competit eis impressio nisi stellae cometae.' (Meteor. i. iii. 4, ed. Jammy, ii. 16b.) Of each of three other theories whose consequences contradicted observations he said 'falsum est'. (Ibid. i. iii. 8, p. 19.) Cf. Grosseteste's De Cometis, above, pp. 88–90.

[2] Causis Prop. Elem. i. ii. 5, ed. Jammy, v. 306. Cf. Grosseteste's De Nat. Loc., De Prognost., above, p. 112.

[3] De Caelo et Mundo, ii. iii. 3, ed. Jammy, ii. 108a.

[4] 'quaedam substantiarum habent generans univocum, sicut cum homo ex homine generatur, et tunc generatio fit a sibi simili secundum speciem; quaedam autem habent genera aequivoca, sicut cum virtute stellarum ex putrefactis producuntur animalia.' Ibid. ii. iii. 1, p. 105b.

[5] 'per confricationem partis ad partem' (ibid., p. 106). Cf. Grosseteste's De Calore Solis, above, p. 87, n. 1. For similar theories of heat in the thirteenth century see R. S. Marx, 'A xiiith century theory of heat as a form of motion', Isis, xxii (1934) 19–20; A. Mitterer, 'Der Wärmebegriff des hl. Thomas nach seinem physikalischen Weltbild und dem der Gegenwart', Studien und Texte Martin Grabmann gewidmet, pp. 720 sqq.

[6] 'Cum omnes simul moveantur, si esset calor ex motu tantum, omnes operarentur calorem.' De Caelo et Mundo, ii. iii. 3, ed. Jammy, ii. 108a. Cf. above, p. 88.

the rays to a point produced fire. This heat could not have been produced by the light *per se*, for then, he said, arguing by agreement
and difference,[1] wherever there was light there would be heat, which
was not the case. In fact, he said, light caused heat in two ways:
by the proximity of the radiant source, and by the reflection and
refraction (*reflexio*) of rays. Grosseteste had made the same distinction in *De Natura Locorum* and Albertus's discussion seems to be
based on his. Albertus habitually used the word *reflexio* to cover
both reflection and refraction, and his precise intention can be discovered only from the context. That he had both meanings in mind
here is shown by the fact that he used the word when discussing
both a burning-mirror and a burning-lens.[2] He concluded his discussion by asserting that the reason why light, though it had no
body, caused heat, was that light was the proper form of the heavenly
bodies which universally caused change in the matter of the world.
So light did not cause heat *ex se* by its own motion, but because it
caused change and motion in matter.[3]

Albertus's investigation of the form and colours of the rainbow
was the first of the four studies of this phenomenon that followed
Grosseteste's and were to culminate in Theodoric of Freiberg's
successful explanation.[4] Albertus wrote his treatise, *De Coronis et
Iride quae Apparent in Nubibus*, which forms Tractatus IV of Book
III of the *Meteororum*, some years before Bacon's *Opus Maius* and
Witelo's *Perspectiva*. His treatment of the problem was based directly
on Grosseteste's *De Iride* and consisted largely of an elaboration and
modification of Grosseteste's theory by means of simple experiments.

---

[1] 'quod semper operatur aliquem effectum, videtur esse causa illis essentialis. Lumen
igitur semper operatur calorem, videtur esse per se causa caloris, et videtur sic, quod
lumen per se opponatur frigori. Et hoc est falsum. Videtur ergo quod lumen non sit
causa caloris per se. . . . Lumen autem dupliciter est causa caloris, et hoc est per vicinita-
tem et per reflexionem radiorum.' Loc. cit. Cf. Grosseteste's *De Nat. Loc.* and *De
Colore*, above, p. 119. Albertus seems to have been following Alkindi and Avicenna in
holding that light was different from heat: E. Krebs, *Meister Dietrich*, p. 42; below,
p. 243.

[2] '. . . in reflexione multi radii diriguntur ad punctum unum . . . sicut apparet in
berillo vel crystallo vel forte vitro bene rotundo et impleto aqua frigida, quae opposita
sibi fortissima illuminatione. . . .' *De Caelo et Mundo*, ii. iii. 3, p. 109a. Cf. above, p. 122.

[3] Ibid., p. 109.

[4] For parallel Arabic writings on the rainbow, and knowledge of them in the West,
see above, p. 124, n. 1, p. 125, n. 2 (Averroës), p. 147, n. 2 (Alhazen), p. 156, n. 3,
158, nn. 2, 3 (Avicenna); below, p. 234, n. 1 (Qutb al-din al-Shirazi and Kamal al-din
al-Farisi). See also E. Wiedemann, 'Arabische Studien über den Regenbogen', *AGNT*,
iv (1912–13) 453 sqq.; A. M. Sayili, 'Al-Qarafi and his explanation of the rainbow',
Isis, xxxii (1940) 16 sqq.; Sarton, *Introduction*, ii. 23, 1018, iii. 708–9.

He began by giving a brief account of Greek,[1] Roman, and Arabic[2] work on the rainbow and other 'appearances' in the clouds, and concluded these introductory chapters with a 'digression showing what was true and what false in the statements of the ancients'.[3] He considered in particular two theories advanced in Classical Antiquity to explain the rainbow: that of Seneca, who said that the rainbow was a compound image of the sun formed from a multitude of reflections from individual raindrops;[4] and that of Posidonius, who said that the reflection was produced by the whole cloud acting as a single concave mirror. Albertus said that it was undoubtedly light coming from *individual* raindrops and not from the cloud as a whole that produced the rainbow, and he tried to show that the actual appearance of the rainbow was different from that which would be produced by a large concave mirror. For example, if the concavity of the mirror faced the sun, the image would be reversed; if it faced the earth, either nothing would be seen at all or the reversed image would be seen by a second reflection from mist under the cloud.[5] The outer surface of the cloud acting as a convex mirror could not produce the observed appearances either, for then the image of the sun would be seen as a complete circle whereas the rainbow was a semicircle.[6]

The efficient cause of the rainbow, Albertus said, was 'the returning rays of the sun repercussed and reflected in many refractions'[7] by raindrops (the material cause) falling from a cloud, so that the rays formed an image on vapour standing opposite the cloud; 'and this reflection of rays is in part similar to the reflection of rays coming through a window into a vessel of water and refracted on to the opposite wall'. An even better result could be produced, he said, by sprinkling many small drops of water into the rays coming through a window; in that case each drop reflected the rays to

---

[1] A reference 'in Timaeo Platonis' (*Meteor.* iii. iv. 6, ed. Jammy, ii. 124) shows the continued interest in this work.

[2] He gave a fuller account of 'sententiam Avicennae et Algazelis et Nicolai Peripatetici de iride' in ibid., C. 26, pp. 138–9. Cf. Horten, *Meteorol. Zeitschrift*, xxx (1913) 533 sqq.

[3] *Meteor.* iii. iv. 9, p. 126.

[4] 'quot sunt guttae in aëre, tot sunt specula.' Ibid., C. 8, p. 125.

[5] 'quod nunquam videtur', he said of these conclusions; 'quod iterum est falsum.' He concluded: 'Manifestum est ergo, quam iris non figuratur in concavo nubis. Suppone-bant tamen hoc pro certo omnes antiqui, et multi modernorum supponunt hoc, ne-scientes virtutem speculorum.' Ibid., C. 9, p. 126.

[6] Ibid., p. 127.

[7] On Albertus's use of 'reflexio' see above, p. 196. Here he also uses 'refractio' to mean refraction.

others and to the opposite wall, on which an image with the colours of the rainbow was formed.[1] It was in fact the nature of transparent bodies such as mist or glass that, even when they themselves had no colour, rays passing through them produced colours on an opaque body on which they fell. This is what happened when the sun's rays passing through raindrops fell on an opaque screen of mist and appeared as a rainbow.[2] The colours so produced were real colours existing in the external world and not simply products of the imagination, even though the transparent bodies producing them had no colour themselves.[3]

To explain the shape of the arc in which the colours of the rainbow were formed, Albertus adopted Grosseteste's theory that the sun's rays were refracted through four successively denser layers of moisture descending as rain in a 'pyramid' (i.e. cone) from a cloud.[4] The rainbow could be formed only when the sun illuminated this 'aqueous cone' from below the cloud, for otherwise the cloud itself would prevent the rays from reaching it. The efficient cause of the semicircular shape of the bow was that the rays refracted through this cone[5] of moisture themselves went in a cone, of which the upper semicircle of the base fell on the clouds and was seen as a rainbow, and the lower semicircle fell on the earth.[6] The colours appeared only in a bow formed by the rim of the base because the sun's rays were unable to pass through the density of matter in the centre of the cone of moisture, which therefore appeared dark. This could be shown by an experiment, for if a hemispherical crystal vessel were filled with black ink, and placed in the sun's rays, only the semi-

---

[1] *Meteor.*, C. 10, p. 128. Albertus began this passage by saying that having considered the other ancients 'redeamus ad sententiam Aristotelis'. But he went much beyond Aristotle. Cf. Grosseteste, above, p. 126; below, p. 199, n. 4.

[2] 'haec est natura omnis pervii, sicut aëris humidi et vitri, quod quando radius venit in ipsum, et non in ipso coloratur aliquo colore, quod radius transiens per ipsa defert illum colorem super corpora terminata, quae sunt post pervia illa.' Ibid., C. 12, pp. 128-9.

[3] Ibid., C. 13, p. 130. Posidonius had said the colours seen in the rainbow and in light that passed through a prism were imaginary: 'cum tamen isti colores non sint in lapide, nec in pariete, nec in sole.' Ibid., C. 8, p. 125[b]. Cf. Avicenna, above, p. 158, n. 2.

[4] 'Ex parte autem solis intelligendum est, quod non in omni situ potest facere iridem in nube, quia non ab omni situ et irradatione solis ad nubem fiet reflexio ad oculos intuentium et ad solem. Oportet enim, quod sol irradiet nubem inferius ubi sunt illa quatuor perspicua quae diximus. . . . Radii ergo in extremo illius multiplicati, propter multam eorum refractionem generant colores iridis . . . in profundo . . . colorem viridem clarum . . . in superiori . . . ruborem ad modum coloris vini rubei . . . in medio . . . citrinus . . .' Ibid., C. 14, p. 131. Cf. above, pp. 125-7.

[5] 'globosa pyramidaliter'. Ibid., C. 14, p. 131[b]. Cf. C. 23, pp. 136-7.

[6] Cf. above, pp. 124, 157, 160, n. 1.

circular edge appeared bright, owing to the opacity of the ink in the centre.[1]

Of the colours produced by the refraction of rays in the raindrops making up this cone of moisture falling from the cloud, green appeared at the bottom in the denser drops, yellow above that, and red at the top in the most tenuous part of the moisture.[2] That the colours of the rainbow were produced in this way by the variation in the density of moisture could be shown, he said, by several experiments. First, when a rainbow was produced by the sun shining on the spray made by the oars of a rowing-boat, green appeared in the denser spray at the ends of the oars which struck deeply into the water, and red in the rarer spray near the sides of the boat. Similarly, when small drops of water were sprinkled where the sun's rays formed a boundary with a shadow, the colours of the rainbow were produced on the floor or opposite wall because of the darkness mixed with brightness in the drops of the mist. Albertus adopted the normal Aristotelian explanation and attributed the colours formed by spray of different densities to the variation in brightness and darkness caused thereby, for he said that the cause of the colours in both these experiments was the same. Also, when a long angular crystal was placed at the boundary of sunlight and shadow, the colours of the rainbow could be seen very clearly on the opposite wall. The same colours could be produced with iris stones found in Germany and the Red Sea, and Seneca had said that the same colours could be produced by a prism of clear glass.[3] In all these experiments green appeared in the rays passing through the thicker part of the stone or glass at the base, and red in the rays passing through the thinner part at the apex. Therefore, he concluded, the colours of the rainbow were produced by the diversity of the moisture falling from the cloud.[4] These colours, he said, were present in

[1] Ibid., C. 15, p. 132[b].

[2] See above, p. 198, n. 4. Ibid., C. 21, p. 135. Sometimes the middle colour separated into two, making four in all. Aristotle held that there were only three primary colours in the rainbow, red, green, and violet (*Meteor.* 374[b]30–35); cf. above, p. 111, n. 5.

[3] See above, p. 111, especially n. 6; and p. 127.

[4] 'Colores autem iridis ex causis supra dictis generari, multis astruitur exemplis, quorum unum est . . . quando . . . radius solis resplendet in aqua per remum percussa . . . Aliud exemplum est, quod si accipiatur aqua pura et aspergatur minutissimis guttis leniter et tenuiter, ita quod non cito cadat, quae aspersio Arabice vocatur hallebe, et opponatur solis radio tali artificio, ita quod pars eius sit in umbra, et pars in radio, videbuntur post aspersionem illam in terra vel in pariete colores similes coloribus iridis, propter obscurum permixtum cum claro in speculis guttularum rorationis illius. Unde causa in omnibus his exemplis est una, quia in una aqua quae percutitur per remos, est

all clouds illuminated by the sun, though they could not be seen in all because of the brightness of the sunlight. But he said that they could be seen confusedly in the reflection of a cloud in standing water or in a black flask filled with clear water or oil, because then the brightness of the sunlight was reduced by the blackness of the water or flask and colours could appear.[1] He concluded his study of the rainbow with some observations on lunar rainbows[2] and an account of the times and places at which both lunar and solar rainbows could appear.[3] And, he added at the end of his explanations, 'haec est causa quod Aristoteles dicit quod in iride naturalis debet scire quia et geometer debet dicere propter quid'.[4]

(2)

Light can be thrown on the influence of the Oxford school in the thirteenth century by an examination of the relations of Roger Bacon with continental scientists.[5] In two different branches of science, astronomy and optics, his influence and Grosseteste's definitely stimulated original work abroad. In a third branch, magnetics, Roger Bacon was somehow concerned with the investigations of Petrus Peregrinus, though the precise relationship between the two men is difficult to discover.

sicut in roratione, scilicet quod solis radii diversimode colorantur in aqua, et postea transeuntes per aquam illam, ponunt colorem istum super corpora super quae cadunt ex sole. Alia etiam exempla nos probavimus saepe in crystallo angulosa longa, cuius si pars teneatur in umbra et pars in radio solis, resultabunt clarissimi colores iridis in terra vel in pariete oppositis. Et similiter fit in lapide qui ... iris vocatur ... Seneca etiam dicit si vitrum ... angulosum ... in sole et umbra ... teneatur, eodem modo colores generabit. Et in omnibus his, ubi radius percutit super profundius et spissius lapidis vel vitri, ibi fit color viridis, et in sublimi et in uno angulo ubi tenuis est lapis, generatur color rubeus multum clarus, et in medio caeruleus [citrinus?] generatur, qui diversificatur secundum quantitatem spissitudinis mediae inter angulum et maximum lapidis spissitudinem. Isti ergo colores in iride sunt ex diversitate humidi aquei quod descendit a nube.' (*Meteor.* iii. iv. 19, pp. 134–5). 'Caeruleus seu citrinus' were used as synonyms for yellow by more than one author of the period (cf. below, p. 237, n. 5; above, p. 198, n. 4). On this subject the following is of interest: 'citrinus, qui albore virorem admixtum habet, qualis est color auri, leonum aut maturescentium segetum. Hunc Aristoteles xanton, Albrechtus magnus ceruleum vocat. Sunt et qui glaucum et fulvum appelitent.' Jodocus Eysennacensis *Tocius Philosophie Naturalis Summa*, iv. 2, Erffordie, 1517, f. 58ʳ. Cf. below, p. 269.   [1] *Meteor.* iii. iv. 20, p. 135. Cf. Aristotle, *Meteor.* 374ᵇ25–30.
    [2] *Meteor.* iii. iv. 22, p. 136. He could see no reason for Aristotle's statement that these were seen only twice in fifty years: ibid., C. 11, p. 128ᵇ; Thorndike, *History of Magic*, ii. 548.   [3] *Meteor.* iii. iv. 24–25, pp. 137–8.   [4] Ibid., C. 24, p. 137.
    [5] For a general account of Roger Bacon's influence see Little, in *RBE*, pp. 24–31, *PBA*, xiv (1928) 265 sqq.; Sarton, *Introduction*, ii. 952–67; Thorndike, *History of Magic*, ii. 616 sqq. His work on many subjects, mathematics and optics, geography, calendar reform, alchemy, medicine, biblical criticism, and the study of languages, was known and used down into the seventeenth century.

The influence of Grosseteste and Roger Bacon in astronomy took place mainly through the movement which they initiated to reform the calendar.[1] This influence occurred mainly in Paris. The Italian astronomer and mathematician, John Campanus of Novara (*fl. c.* 1261-92), who worked in Paris, wrote his *Compotus Major* in direct imitation of Grosseteste,[2] and this and Campanus's other writings on astronomy and astronomical instruments stimulated further work in the Paris school. One of those influenced by Campanus was Guillaume de St. Cloud,[3] and to his *Kalendarium* (1296) Guillaume wrote an introduction, on the practical value of scientific research, which he borrowed from Roger Bacon's *De Secretis Operibus*. Guillaume de St. Cloud was himself an excellent observer, and from his time a remarkable school of astronomical observation grew up in Paris,[4] matching the one at Merton College, Oxford. The Paris school numbered among its most prominent members Jean de Linières, Geoffroi de Meaux, Jean de Meurs, and Firmin de Beauval, the last two of whom in 1345 made a report on the reform of the calendar for Pope Clement IV. No practical steps were taken, however, and Cardinal Pierre d'Ailly drew up a further report, for which he made direct use of the *Compoti* of Grosseteste and Roger Bacon, for the Council of Constance in 1414-18.[5] No practical measures followed this report either, and several further attempts were made during the next century and a half to bring the calendar up to date. When the Gregorian reform finally came in 1582, the remedies adopted were very much the same as those suggested in the fourteenth century.[6]

While this practical work was being done, a decisive step in theoretical astronomy was taken by a contemporary of Guillaume de St. Cloud, the Franciscan astronomer Bernard de Verdun, who was

---

[1] See above, pp. 97, 144. Cf. Thorndike, *Latin Treatises on Comets*, pp. 91-92, 108-9, 117-19, 156, 161-2, 231; above, pp. 89, n. 1, 195, for Grosseteste and comets.

[2] Duhem, *Syst. monde*, iii. 281, 317-26; iv. 49, 119-24; Sarton, *Introduction*, ii. 583-6, 985-7.   [3] Duhem, op. cit. iv. 10-19, 580; Sarton, op. cit. ii. 990-1.

[4] Duhem, op. cit. iv. 30-74; Sarton, op. cit. iii. 649-60; Thorndike, op. cit. iii. 268-324. As at Merton these Parisian astronomers were also mathematicians, and their work in both fields was used by such later writers as Regiomontanus and Luca Pacioli; see the references in Sarton, loc. cit. and also ibid., pp. 638 sqq. on Italian work; Thorndike, *Science and Thought in the Fifteenth Century*, pp. 147 sqq., 157 sqq.; above, p. 187, n. 4.

[5] Sarton, op. cit. iii. 1108-9. On Roger Bacon's influence, through Pierre d'Ailly's *Imago Mundi*, on Christopher Columbus see Little, in *RBE*, p. 30; Sarton, op. cit. iii. 1148, 1859. See Baur, *Philos. Rob. Grosseteste*, pp. 53, 63.

[6] Thorndike, op. cit. iv. 102-3, 388, 453, 561; v. 251, 265, 281, 340-2 (on Regiomontanus), 408, 427; Kaltenbrunner, *Vorgeschichte der Gregorianischen Kalenderreform*.

also influenced by Roger Bacon. Bernard seems to have been the first medieval astronomer to decide firmly for the Ptolemaic as against the Aristotelian astronomical system.[1] The controversy between the Aristotelians and the Ptolemists could be decided, he said, only by an appeal to observation, and of the two only the Ptolemaic system 'saved the appearances' and made it possible to construct tables. A contemporary of Bernard, Giles of Rome (c. 1247–1316), added to Bernard's appeal to observation the further principle that, of two hypotheses which equally well saved the appearances, the simpler was to be used.[2] The application of these two principles led immediately to some remarkable theoretical innovations. In his *Lucidator Astronomiae*, composed about 1310, Pietro d'Abano went so far as to suggest that the heavenly bodies were not borne on spheres but moved freely in space,[3] and by the beginning of the fourteenth century the theory had been broached that the 'appearances' could be 'saved' by considering the earth instead of the heavens to be in motion.[4] This latter theory was put forward in a more cogent form later in the fourteenth century by Nicole Oresme (c. 1323–82), after fundamental criticism of Aristotelian physics both in Paris and Oxford had begun to make possible the conception of relative motion in an infinite, geometrical space.[5] Oresme said:

> touz philosophes dient que pour nient est fait par pluseurs ou par

[1] Duhem, 'De l'influence exercée par Bacon sur Bernard de Verdun', in *Fragment inédit de l'Opus Tertium*, pp. 64–69; *Syst. monde*, iii. 398, 442–60; *Annal. philos. chrétienne*, vi (1908) 291 sqq.; Sarton, *Introduction*, ii. 990. Cf. above, pp. 5–6, 96–98, 144.

[2] Cf. above, p. 6; Duhem, *Syst. monde*, iv. 5 sqq., 93–94, 106–19; Sarton, op. cit. ii. 922–6. Giles wrote a commentary on the *Post. Anal.* which contains some interesting discussions on forming definitions by the 'via collectiva', on probability, mathematics, and physics, and on other methodological subjects (Venetiis, 1495).

[3] Duhem, *Syst. monde*, iv. 241 sqq. For Pietro see Sarton, *Introduction*, iii. 439 sqq.; Thorndike, *History of Magic*, ii. 874 sqq.

[4] Duhem, 'François de Meyronnes et la question de la rotation de la terre', *AFH*, vi (1913) 23–25; *Syst. monde*, iv. 124–7, v. 231; Sarton, op. cit. iii. 530. Speculation on this subject seems to have been stimulated by the condemnation in 1277 by the Archbishop of Paris, Étienne Tempier, of a number of Averroist propositions, among which was the assertion that the earth, at the centre of the universe, was necessarily at rest; Duhem, *Léonard de Vinci*, ii. 411–14.

[5] See Duhem, *Mouvement abs. et rel.*; E. Borchert, *Lehre von der Bewegung bei Nicolaus Oresme*; Maier, *Vorläufer Galileis*, pp. 9–25; Sarton, op. cit. iii. 1486–97; D. B. Durand, 'Nicole Oresme and the mediaeval origins of modern science', *Speculum*, xvi (1941) 167 sqq.; A. Koyré, 'Le Vide et l'espace infini au xive siècle', *AHDLMA*, xxiv (1949) 45 sqq. Cf. above, pp. 175–7; Ockham was well known in the fourteenth-century Paris school, e.g. Albert of Saxony wrote *Quaestiones in Occami Logicam* (Bologna, 1496).

grandes operacions ce qui peu(s)t estre fait par moins d'operacions ou par plus petites. Et Aristote di(s)t en le viii^e chapitre du premier [*De Caelo*]¹ que Dieu et nature ne font rien pour nient. Or est il ainsi que se le ciel est meü de mouvement journal, il convient mettre es principalz corps du monde et ou ciel ii manieres de mouvemens aussi comme contraires : un d'orient en occident et les autres *e converso*, comme souvent dit est. Et avecques ce, il convient mettre une isneleté² excessivement grande, car qui bien pense et considere la hautesce ou distance du ciel et la grandeur de lui et de son circuite, se tel circuite est fait en un jour, honme ne pourroit ymaginer ne penser comment l'isneleté du ciel est merveill[eus]ement et excessivement grande et aussi comme inopinable et inestimable. Et donques puisque touz les effetz que nous voions peuent estre faiz et toutes apparences salveez pour mettre en lieu de ce une petite operacion, ce est a savoir le mouvement journal de la terre qui est tres petite ou resgart du ciel, sans multeplier tant de operations si diverses et si outrageusement grandes, il s'ensuit que Dieu et nature les avroient pour nient faites et ordenees; et ce est inconvenient, comme dit est.³

Thus Oresme used the principles of economy and 'saving the appearances' to take the first steps towards the 'Copernican revolution' in astronomy, just as Ockham had done in his preparation for the 'Galilean revolution' in dynamics.⁴ The same principles, as well as some of Oresme's more detailed arguments against Aristotelian

¹ See *Livre du ciel*, f. 16^b, p. 209 (ed. cit. below, n. 3).   ² Velocity.
³ Maistre Nicole Oresme, *Le Livre du ciel et du monde*, ii. 25, f. 143^cd, ed. A. D. Menut and A. J. Denomy, p. 278. Oresme quoted '*La Perspective* de Witelo' in support of his contention that motion as seen was simply a change in the relative position of three or more points, the observer being at one of them (ibid. f. 139^a, p. 272). See Duhem, 'Un Précurseur français de Copernic: Nicole Oresme, 1377', *Rev. gén. des sciences pures et app.* xx (1909) 866 sqq. Cf. Galileo, above, p. 85, n. 4, below, p. 309.
⁴ See above, p. 17?. It is interesting that Oresme should so completely have accepted these two methodological principles, as well as the principle of relative motion, as to have made the following suggestion for interpreting a passage of the Bible over which Galileo came to grief: 'quant Dieu fait aucun miracle, l'en doit supposer et tenir que ce fait Il sanz muer le commun cors de nature fors au moins que se peüst estre. Et donques se l'en peu(s)t salver que Dieu aloingna le jour ou temps de Josué par arrester le mouve-ment de la terre ou de la region de cibas seulement laquelle est si tres petite et aussi comme un point ou resgart du ciel, sans mettre que tout le monde ensemble fors ce petit point eüst esté mis hors de son commun cours et de son ordenance et meïsmement tielz corps comme sont les corps du ciel, ce est moult plus raisonable.' (*Livre du ciel*, f. 144^a, p. 279.) He concluded: 'Mais considéré tout ce que dit est, l'en pourroit par ce croire que la terre est ainsi meüe et le ciel non, et n'est pas evident du contraire; et toutevoies, ce semble de prime face autant ou plus contre raison naturelle comme sont les articles de nostre foy ou touz ou pluseurs. Et ainsi ce que je ay dit par esbatement en ceste maniere peut aler valoir a confuter et reprendre ceulz qui voudroient nostre foy par raysons impugner.' (f. 144^bc, p. 279.) Cf. A. C. Crombie, 'Galileo's "Dialogues Concerning the Two Principal Systems of the World" ', *Dominican Studies*, iii (1950) 105 sqq.; and below, pp. 309–10.

physics, were to be used by Copernicus when he came to put forward a yet more cogent mathematical theory as an alternative to
Ptolemy's.[1]

(3)

Of Roger Bacon's relations with Petrus Peregrinus[2] the only
definite evidence exists in parallel passages in the writings of the
two men and in marginal glosses in some manuscripts of Roger
Bacon's *Opus Tertium*. The parallels are sufficiently striking in
themselves to make some kind of dependence of one upon the other
extremely probable. For example, their discussions of magnetism
have much in common, and Roger Bacon seems to be referring to
Petrus Peregrinus when writing of an instrument using a spherical
magnet to follow the movements of the heavens, of the construction
of burning-mirrors, and perhaps of the perpetuum mobile.[3] Both
writers also took the same haughty attitude to their contemporaries.[4]
Moreover, Roger Bacon in Cap. 13 of the *Opus Tertium* wrote: 'et
ideo pono radices experientiarum circa ista, quas nullus Latinorum
potest intelligere nisi unus scilicet magister Petrus.'[5] There is no
direct proof that this 'magister Petrus' was in fact the 'Petrus de
Maharne Curia', that is Petrus Peregrinus, mentioned in several

---

[1] On the history of astronomical hypotheses from the fourteenth century through
Nicholas of Cusa and others to Copernicus and Galileo see Duhem, *Annal. philos.
chrétienne*, vi (1908) 300–2, 352–77, 482–514, 561–92; *Mouvement abs. et rel.*, pp. 109
sqq.; Koyré, *Études galiléennes*, iii.

[2] For Petrus Peregrinus see in particular E. Schlund, 'Petrus Peregrinus von Maricourt: sein Leben und seine Schriften', *AFH*, iv (1911) 436–55, 633–43; v (1912) 22–40.
This excellent study contains practically everything that is known about its subject. See
also S. P. Thompson, 'Petrus Peregrinus de Maricourt and his Epistola de Magnete',
PBA, ii (1905–6) 377 sqq.; P. Picavet, 'Le Maître des expériences, Pierre de Maricourt',
in *Hist. générale et comp. philos. médiévales*, pp. 233 sqq.; P. F. Mottelay, *Bibliog.
Hist. of Elect. and Magnetism*, pp. 45 sqq.; Sarton, *Introduction*, ii. 1030–2; E. O. von
Lippmann, *Gesch. der Magnetnadel*, pp. 27 sqq.; A. C. Mitchell, 'Chapters in the history
of terrestrial magnetism', *Terrest. Magnetism and Atmosph. Elect.* xxxvii (1932) 125 sqq.,
xlii (1937) 244; F. Daujat, 'Note sur un fondateur de la physique du magnétisme au
xiiie siècle: Pierre de Maricourt', *Thalès*, ii (1935), 58–61.

[3] *Opus Maius*, iv. ii. 2, ed. Bridges, i. 116; ibid. vi, ed. Bridges, ii. 202–3 (see above,
p. 142), 218; *Opus Minus*, ed. Brewer, pp. 383–4, 385; *Opus Tertium*, C. 13, ed. Brewer,
pp. 46 sqq., C. 33, p. 113, C. 36, pp. 116–17; *Secretis Operibus*, C. 3, ed. Brewer, p. 532,
C. 6, pp. 537–8. Cf. Petri Peregrini Maricurtensis *De Magnete*, i. 10, ii. 2, 3, hrg. von
G. Hellmann.

[4] 'Vulgus philosophantium nescit causam experientiae...', *Opus Minus*, ed. Brewer,
p. 384; 'vulgus inexpertum', *Secretis Operibus*, C. 6, p. 537; 'vulgus studentium', *De
Magnete*, i. 1.

[5] *Opus Minus*, C. 13, ed. Brewer, p. 43; cf. pp. 46–47.

later glosses on other passages in this chapter. But after a careful consideration of all the evidence Schlund has left little doubt that he was.[1]

Roger Bacon's relationship to Petrus Peregrinus seems to have been that of pupil to master. Bacon wrote of this 'dominus experimentorum' much as he wrote of Grosseteste, and it is possible that he studied under him in Paris. In a passage written in 1267 on the value of experiment he gave the following account of him:

And this science certifies all natural and artificial things in the particular and in the proper discipline by perfect experience; not by argument, like the purely theoretical sciences, nor by weak and imperfect experiences, like the practical sciences. And therefore this science is the master of all the preceding sciences, and the end of all theoretical argument. . . . One man I know, and only one, who can be praised for his achievements in this science. Of discourses and battles of words he takes no heed: he follows the works of wisdom, and in these finds rest. What others strive to see dimly and blindly, like bats in twilight, he gazes at in the full light of day, because he is a master of experiment. Through experiment he gains knowledge of natural things, medical, chemical, and indeed of everything in the heavens or earth. He is ashamed that things should be known to laymen, old women, soldiers, ploughmen, of which he is ignorant. Therefore he has looked closely into the doings of those who work in metals and minerals of all kinds; he knows everything relating to the art of war, the making of weapons, and the chase; he has looked closely into agriculture, mensuration, and farming work; he has even taken note of the remedies, lot-casting, and charms used by old women and by wizards and magicians, and of the deceptions and devices of conjurors, so that nothing which deserves inquiry should escape him, and that he may be able to expose the falsehoods of magicians. If philosophy is to be carried to its perfection and is to be handled with utility and certainty, his aid is indispensable. As for reward, he neither receives nor seeks it. If he frequented kings and princes, he would easily find those who would bestow on him honours and wealth. Or, if in Paris he would display the results of his researches, the whole world would follow him. But since either of these courses would hinder him from pursuing the great experiments in which he delights, he puts honour and wealth aside, knowing well that his wisdom would secure him wealth whenever he chose. For the past three years he has been working at the production of a mirror that shall produce combustion at a fixed distance;

[1] Schlund, *AFH*, iv. 448–9. Another gloss naming Petrus de Maricourt occurs in C. 11, p. 35; Schlund, pp. 445–6, has shown that the words 'Petrus de Maharn-Curia Picardus' which are printed in the text by Brewer occur only in later MSS; in earlier MSS they are a marginal gloss. A further anonymous reference in the text to an experimental expert ('unus solus . . .') occurs in C. 12, p. 41.

a problem which the Latins have neither solved nor attempted, though books have been written upon the subject.[1]

In this passage and in the passages referring to Petrus Peregrinus in the other works written during 1266–7 Roger Bacon mentions experiments that were either in progress or planned for the future.[2] Petrus did not write his De Magnete until 1269. The conclusion of his tract, written as a letter to his Picard countryman, Sygerus de Foncaucourt, in fact provides the only certain date in the meagre records of his life: 'Finished in camp at the siege of Lucera in the year of our Lord 1269 on the 8th day of August.'[3] Roger Bacon must therefore have known Petrus while this 'master of experiments' was actively engaged in his work. Moreover, Roger Bacon in the Opus Minus described one set of experiments, with a lodestone held above or below a floating magnet, which do not appear in De Magnete.[4]

And this is a miracle of nature in part known, namely, that iron follows the part of a magnet that touches it, and flies from the other part of the same magnet. And the iron turns itself after moving to the part of the heavens conformed to the part of the magnet which it touched. Now four parts of the world are surely distinguished in the magnet, namely, east, west, north and south, and they can be recognized by an experiment in which it is well shown to what part of the heavens a given part turns. And then if the iron is touched by the northern part of the magnet, it will follow that part however it is moved about, namely, upwards or downwards, to the

---

[1] Opus Tertium, C. 13, ed. Brewer, pp. 46–47. In Opus Tertium, C. 33, p. 113 Bacon speaks as if the mirror had already been made: 'Et jam per Dei gratiam factum est hoc speculum per sapientissimum Latinorum.' Cf. C. 36, p. 116. In Opus Maius (iv. ii. 2, ed. Bridges, i. 116) written earlier in 1266–7 Bacon says, in discussing parabolic mirrors: 'Moreover, the most skillful of the Latins is busily engaged on the construction of this mirror.' No work on burning-mirrors by Petrus Peregrinus is known, though in De Magnete, ii. 2, he says: 'Qualiter autem ferrum stet in aere per virtutem lapidis in libro de operibus speculorum narrabimus'; cf. Schlund, AFH, iv. 639. On Roger Bacon's own understanding of the properties of a surface produced by rotating a conic section on its axis see above, p. 150, n. 3. See also Witelo on the same subject, below, pp. 218–19.

[2] See above, p. 140, n. 3, p. 204, n. 3. In Opus Minus, ed. Brewer, p. 385 he refers to an experiment that was yet to be done in which a magnet was used in the construction of an instrument to follow the movements of the heavens. Petrus Peregrinus described this instrument in De Magnete, i. 10 (see below, p. 210). Bacon wrote: 'de corpore vel instrumento quod moveretur ad motum coeli, quod omnia instrumenta astronomiae transcenderet; hoc quidem fieri debet de magnete.' Cf. Opus Maius, vi, ed. Bridges, ii. 202–3 (above, p. 142) and Secretis Operibus, C. 6, ed. Brewer, p. 537; Schlund, AFH, iv. 638–9. Secretis Operibus was probably written a few years before 1266 (Little, in RBE, p. 9; cf. Easton, Roger Bacon, pp. 111–13; below, p. 207, n. 3).

[3] Schlund, op. cit. iv. 450–5. The siege was being conducted by Charles of Anjou.

[4] Cf. i. 8. It is possible, of course, that Bacon got this from Petrus in conversation.

right or left, and in all different positions. And so much is it captivated that if the iron is put [to float] in a vessel full of water and the hand [with the magnet] is placed under the vessel, the part touched dives into the water in the direction of the magnet. And if the magnet is brought beyond us anywhere above the iron, the part touched flies up towards whatever place the magnet is brought. And if the other end of the magnet is presented to the same part of the iron, this part flies from it as from an enemy, as a lamb from a wolf. And when the magnet is removed the touched part turns itself towards the place of the heavens similar to the part of the magnet.

Ordinary philosophers do not know the cause of the common observations concerning this part, and believe that the Nautical Star [Pole Star] brings it about. But it is not the star that effects it but the part of the heavens; and the three other parts of the heavens, namely, south, east and west, operate as well as the north. Similarly they do not take note of the fact that these four parts of the world may be distinguished in the magnet. But many attribute [the effects observed] to one part, which agrees with the Nautical Star in natural property.[1]

In 1266 Roger Bacon was already about fifty and had already maturely grasped the Grossetestian theory of experimental science expounded in the *Opus Maius*. Therefore the possibility cannot be excluded that Petrus Peregrinus learnt something of his method from Roger Bacon[2] and so, indirectly, from Grosseteste himself.[3] Certainly Petrus's statements about method and his utilitarian attitude are entirely in agreement with those of the Oxford school. In the well-known second chapter of *De Magnete*, Book I, he wrote:

You must realize, dearest friend, that while the investigator in this subject must understand nature and not be ignorant of the celestial motions,

---

[1] *Opus Minus*, ed. Brewer, pp. 383–4. Mitchell in his 'Chapters in the history of terrestrial magnetism', *Terrest. Magnetism and Atmosph. Elect.* xlii (1937) 243, 271, 272, sees in the last paragraph an allusion by Roger Bacon to the fact that the direction of the magnetic needle does not coincide with the geographical meridian. But what Bacon is saying is that it is not the Pole Star that causes the magnet's behaviour but the part of the heavens, and he asserts that 'influences' may come from any part of the heavens ('continuas et perpetuas recipiant influentias a partibus coeli'). Magnetic declination seems to have been recognized by the early fifteenth century, and German makers were fixing compasses marked with the amount of declination to sun-dials by 1450. For the later history of this subject see Mitchell, op. cit., pp. 246 sqq., and ibid. xliv (1939) 77 sqq.

[2] Some sixteenth-century writers thought that Petrus Peregrinus had plagiarized Roger Bacon or even that Roger Bacon had written *De Magnete* himself; Schlund, op. cit. iv. 444, 448, v. 22 sqq.

[3] It is to be presumed that Bacon did not meet Petrus Peregrinus till after he had met Grosseteste (probably by 1249; above, p. 139). His earliest reference to Petrus appears to be in *Secretis Operibus*; above, p. 206, n. 2; cf. Eastoñ, *Roger Bacon*, pp. 88–89.

he must also be very diligent in the use of his own hands, so that through the operation of this stone he may show wonderful effects. For by his industry he will then in a short time be able to correct an error which he would never do in eternity by his knowledge of natural philosophy and mathematics alone, if he lacked carefulness with his hands. For in investigating the unknown (*In occultis enim operibus*) we greatly need manual industry, without which we can usually accomplish nothing perfectly. Yet there are many things subject to the rule of reason which we cannot completely investigate by the hand.[1]

The work described in *De Magnete* is the best known example of the use of the experimental method in the thirteenth century. The treatise is divided into two parts, of which the first is a description of a series of experiments which laid the foundation of the scientific study of magnetism, and the second is an account of the construction of certain instruments based on these results. 'We shall not', Petrus Peregrinus wrote in the first chapter of Book I, after summarizing the contents of his treatise, 'communicate in this epistle any information save about the manifest properties of the stone, on the ground that this teaching will form part of a tract in which we shall show how to construct physical instruments.'

The account of the experiments on magnetism begins in Cap. 3 of the first book with a description of how to recognize a lodestone, in particular by its attracting of iron. In Cap. 4 the author described two methods of finding the poles[2] of a rounded lodestone. The first was to place a magnetized needle at various points on its surface and to mark off the meridian lines along which the needle lay. The two points where the lines met would be the poles. The result could be confirmed by the second method, which was to observe the points at which the needle stood upright. In Cap. 5 he showed how to distinguish the north and south poles of the magnet. The lodestone was put in a vessel which was floated in water in a larger vessel, and

---

[1] That Petrus Peregrinus was a mathematician is indicated by Roger Bacon's remarks in *Opus Tertium*, C. 11. That he might have known medicine also is indicated by Bacon's statement in ibid., C. 13: 'scit naturalia per experientiam et medicinalia et alkimistica et omnia tam coelestia quam inferiora' (see above, p. 205). This knowledge is supported by Petrus Peregrinus's own statement in *De Magnete*, i. 6: 'Et hoc evacuatur quorundam fatuitas dicentium quod si scamonea choleram ratione similitudinis attrahat, ergo magnes magnetem magis quam ferrum attrahet, quod falsum supponunt, cum sit verum quod patet experimento.' Cf. Schlund, *AFH*, iv. 637, 643; above, pp. 74, 80. There are English translations of *De Magnete* by S. P. Thompson and H. D. Harradon.

[2] Schlund, *AFH*, iv. 636, n. 5 said that Petrus was the first writer known to him to use the word 'polus'. Roger Bacon used 'pars'. Petrus said in i. 4: 'hic lapis in se gerit similitudinem celi'.

however it was turned it would aline itself so that 'each part of the stone will be in the direction of its own part of the heavens'.[1] In Cap. 6 he described how the southern part of a floating magnet would always follow the northern part of another magnet brought near it, and vice versa, whereas the poles of the floating magnet were repelled by like poles of the other magnet. When an oblong piece of iron was touched by a magnet and floated on a piece of wood or straw in water, he said in Cap. 7, the part which had been touched by the south pole of the lodestone would point towards the north pole of the heavens, and vice versa. But, he said in Cap. 8, the poles of the iron could be reversed by 'violence' by a lodestone: 'And the cause of this is the impression of that which acted last, confounding and altering the virtue of the first.' The reason for the attraction between unlike poles, he went on in Cap. 9, was that 'in its attraction the stone of stronger virtue is active whilst that of weaker is passive. . . . The agent strives not only to join its patient to itself but to unite with it.' This could be shown by breaking a lodestone into two or more pieces, when it would be found that the pieces formed separate magnets each with a north and south pole. These pieces could be cemented together again, with each arranged in the same relative directions as they were before they were broken, and a single magnet reformed, but not in any other relative directions. 'For nature tends towards being or acts in the better way in which it can. It chooses first the first order of action or of method in which the identity is better preserved than in the second.' Cap. 10 is devoted to 'the inquiry whence the magnet receives the natural virtue which it has'. This was certainly not from deposits of lodestone at the North Pole of the earth, he said, because lodestone was mined in many parts of the globe.[2] Moreover, since the magnet pointed south as well as north, 'we are right in supposing that the virtue in the poles of the stone flows in not only from the northern part but also from the southern part'. Further, the north pole of the magnet did not point exactly at the Nautical Star but to the meeting point of the meridian circles. 'From these facts therefore it is manifest that it is from the poles of the heavens that the poles of the magnet

[1] Cf. Alexander Neckam in *De Naturis Rerum*, C. 98, ed. Wright, p. 183. See G. Hellmann, 'Die Anfänge der magnetischen Beobachtungen', *Zeitschr. Gesells. Erdkunde zu Berlin*, xxxii (1897) 126-7.

[2] He said also that the pole was uninhabitable because it was day for one half of the year and night for the other half. Roger Bacon had discussed this at length in *Opus Maius*, iv. iv. 3, ed. Bridges, i. 132 sqq.

receive their virtue.' But in fact not only the poles but the whole stone receives virtue, from the whole heavens. This could be shown, he said, by fixing a spherical lodestone between two sharp pivots so that it could move like an armillary sphere, when it should follow the movements of the heavens. It is plain, however, from his account of this apparatus that Petrus had not yet succeeded in getting the results expected.

'The natural operations of the magnet having been viewed,' Petrus began the second book of his treatise, 'let us pass on to the ingenious contrivances which depend on a knowledge of its natural workings.' In Caps. 1 and 2 he described and drew two neat instruments, combining a magnet with an astrolabe, for determining the azimuths of heavenly bodies. In one a floating magnet was used, and in the other a magnet on a brass or silver pivot.[1] With these instruments, he said, time could be told from the azimuth and, when longitudes and latitudes were known, it was possible to navigate on land or sea. Petrus concluded his treatise with a description and drawing in Cap. 3 of a wheel which, he said, 'will move continually and perpetually' by the action of a fixed lodestone upon small iron magnets attached to the rim of the wheel.

No further experimental study of magnetism on the scale of Petrus Peregrinus's *De Magnete* is known before 1600, when William Gilbert published his work of the same title.[2] Gilbert acknowledged his debt to Petrus and, in fact, he incorporated all Petrus's experiments in his own book.[3] In the late thirteenth and early fourteenth centuries, however, there were some interesting theoretical discussions,

[1] This seems to be the first mention of a pivoted magnet.

[2] This does not mean that no work was done in the subject. For the history of magnetics between Petrus Peregrinus and Gilbert see G. Hellmann, *Rara Magnetica*, in which the texts of Petrus's *De Magnete* and other treatises on magnetism are printed; Mottelay, op. cit.; Mitchell, op. cit.; von Lippmann, op. cit.; Sarton, *Introduction*, i. 764, ii. 629, 1031, iii. 143, 538.

[3] In his *De Magnete*, p. 5, Gilbert wrote: 'Ante Fracastorium opusculum extat nomine Petri cuiusdam Peregrini ducentis amplius annis satis pro tempore eruditum quod nonnulli ex Rogerii Baconi Angli Oxoniensis opinionibus dimanasse existimant.' Cf. ibid. i. 3, p. 13 (*terrella*); ii. 35, p. 107; iii. 1, p. 116; iv. 1, p. 153; vi. 4, p. 223. Gilbert names a large number of predecessors, ancient, medieval, and sixteenth century, though allowance has to be made for an arrogance resembling that of Roger Bacon in his opinions of some of them. These references may be discovered in the index of P. F. Mottelay's translation of Gilbert's book (London, 1893). Mottelay (p. 332) has pointed out that Nicolao Cabeo also used Petrus Peregrinus's *De Magnete* for his *Philosophia Magnetica*, iii. 4 (1629). A large number of MSS and printed editions of *De Magnete* exist, so it must have been well known from the time it was written down into the seventeenth century; for these see Schlund, *AFH*, v. 22–40.

in which Oxford methodology played a prominent part, about the precise nature of magnetic attraction. These centred round the philosophical problem of action at a distance, and were usually associated with attempts to explain the related phenomenon of gravity.

In his commentary on the *Physics* Averroës had put forward a theory of magnetism in keeping with the Aristotelian principle that the mover must be substantially united with the body moved.[1] According to this theory a magnet did not really attract a piece of iron, but induced in it a 'magnetic quality', a 'virtue', or power to move itself. The iron was thus moved towards the magnet by a moving power which was substantially part of itself. Roger Bacon gave an account of this theory in one of his early works, the *Questions on the Physics*,[2] which he wrote probably when he was teaching in Paris, and the theory was popular with French writers of the late thirteenth and early fourteenth century. Of particular interest is the version of the theory put forward by the French medical writer, Jean de St. Amand (*fl. c.* 1261–98). In a passage from his *Antidotarium Nicolai* recently published by Thorndike,[3] he said:

Take a magnet of which one part has the property of the south and the other of the north and put a needle above that stone so that it lies on the stone. Then one end of the needle touches one end of the magnet and the other the other, and there flows into the end of the needle the virtue of that part which it touches, so that, if it touches the southern, the southern virtue flows in. Then let the needle be raised higher. Then, since there is a current from the magnet through the entire needle placed directly above it, that part of the needle in which at first there was southern virtue will become northern, as the current from the magnet flows through the whole needle. So that if we should suppose a dish full of water to be placed directly underneath the needle, the current would flow into the bottom of the dish. Similarly that part of the needle which first touched the southern part when it was rubbed against or lay on it, when that part is rubbed on that part directly, that part which at first possessed the southern property now has northern property. And then that which at first was southern, since it is now northern, is attracted by the southern part of the magnet, since it does not attract the southern, as has been said. And by the fact that one is attracted the other seems to be repelled. And so in this sort of

---

[1] Averroës, *In Libros. Phys.* vii. iii. 1, Venetiis, 1552, iv, f. 143vb.

[2] *Quest. Phys.* vii, ed. Delorme and Steele (*Opera Hactenus Inedita*, xiii) 338–9.

[3] L. Thorndike, 'John of St. Amand on the magnet', *Isis*, xxxvi (1946) 157; Joannes de Sancto Amando *Super Antidotarium Nicolai*, Venetiis, 1508, f. 351^r.

phenomena like is not actually attracted by like, but because it is possible that parts possessing the same form and species should have diverse properties, one being complete, the other incomplete, from which attraction results.

A somewhat similar theory, which made of magnetic attraction a particular case of 'multiplication of species', was put forward by the early fourteenth-century French Averroist, Jean de Jandun (d. 1328), in his commentary *In Libros Aristotelis de Caelo et Mundo* (iv, Q. 19).[1] He held that the power or 'virtue' that moved the iron to the magnet was induced in it by *species magnetica* that were propagated from the magnet through the medium by successive modifications of parts in contact, until they reached and modified the iron itself.

To all these theories William of Ockham applied the pruning-hook of his methodological principles. He could see no reason to object to action at a distance, and he cut out from his explanation the intermediate 'species' which were postulated simply to avoid having to postulate such action and were not necessary to 'save the appearances'. He rejected the Aristotelian theory that the moving power must be in immediate contact with the body moved. It could act at a distance. Similarly, he said, the sun in producing light on the earth acted at a distance, and so did the magnet in attracting a piece of iron.[2] Ockham's arguments prepared the way for Newton to 'save the appearances' by his theory of universal gravitation, and it is interesting that in the seventeenth century Leibniz brought the same philosophical objection to action at a distance against this theory. In the study of magnetism precisely the same philosophical problem led Faraday to postulate his lines or tubes of force; Michell and Coulomb, inspired by Newton, had shown how to 'save the appearances' with the law that the strength of magnetic attraction was inversely proportional to the square of the distance.

---

[1] See Duhem, *Léonard de Vinci*, ii. 84-85; Sarton, op. cit. iii. 538.

[2] 'probo quod non semper movens immediatum est simul cum moto, sed quod potest distare probo, quia sol causat lumen hic inferius iuxta terram, et non medium illumina-tur . . . ergo sol potest agere per medium distans immediate. . . . Tertia experientia est de magnete. . . . Trahit, dico, immediate, et non virtute aliqua existente in medio vel ferro, ergo lapis ille immediate agit in distans non agendo in medium. Consequentia patet ad sensum: . . . ubi agens est unum, et idem est passum semper sequitur idem effectus, ceteris paribus. Si ergo virtus in ferro moveat ferrum et non magnes, ergo, destructo magnete per potentiam divinam, adhuc ferrum ibi moveretur per potentiam sibi impressam: et tunc quaero ad quam partem mundi, aut superius aut secundum lineam rectam etc. . . .' *Lib. Sent.* ii, Q. 18, D, E. Cf. Q. 26, G-M, above, p. 177, n. 1. See Duhem, op. cit., pp. 85-86; Whittaker, *Aether and Electricity*, 1951, pp. 56-59, 171-2.

(4)

That both Grosseteste and Roger Bacon almost certainly influenced the Silesian optical writer Witelo[1] (b. *c.* 1230) in his metaphysical conception of light has been pointed out by Birkenmajer,[2] and evidence of the same influence is found also in the details of his treatment of special optical problems and in the associated theory of science. Witelo's *Perspectiva* (or *Optica*) was in effect a textbook of optics, based largely on Alhazen's *Optica* but also on other sources, to which he made original additions. It was completed probably in 1270 at Viterbo[3] and dedicated to William of Moerbeke,[4] and it remained the best and most popular textbook of optics in the West until the seventeenth century.[5] Though Witelo did not refer by name, among his sources,[6] to Grosseteste or Roger Bacon, or

[1] For Witelo see C. Baeumker, *Witelo*, 'Zur Biographie des Witelo', *HJ*, xxxiii (1912) 359-61, 'Zur Frage nach Abfassungszeit und Verfasser des irrtümlich Witelo zugeschriebenen Liber de Intelligentiis', in *Miscellanea Ehrle*, i. 87 sqq.; Duhem, *Syst. monde*, v. 358-74; A. Birkenmajer, 'Études sur Witelo, i-iv', *BIAPSL*, 1918, pp. 4 sqq., 1920, pp. 354 sqq., 1922, pp. 6 sqq. (these studies are in Polish with French summaries; there is an Italian translation of iv, 'Witelo e lo Studio di Padova', in *Omaggio dell' Accad. Polacca all' Univ. di Padova*, pp. 147-68); Thorndike, *History of Magic*, ii. 454-6; Ueberweg-Geyer, *Gesch. der Philos*. ii. 474-7, 761; A. Bednarski, 'Die anatomischen Augenbilder in den Handschriften des Roger Bacon, Johan Peckham, und Witelo', *AGM*, xxiv (1931) 60 sqq.; Sarton, *Introduction*, ii. 1027-8; de Wulf, *Hist. Mediaeval Philos*. ii. 234-5.

[2] Birkenmajer, op. cit. ii (1920), and in *MH*, v (1948) 36. Cf. Thorndike, op. cit.

[3] Baeumker, *Witelo*, pp. 201-24. Witelo referred in his *Perspectiva* to observations on rainbows made near Viterbo. See Vitellonis *Opticae*, x. 67, ed. Risner, p. 462; below, p. 230, n. 2. (All references made below are to this edition of the *Perspectiva* or *Optica*.) Witelo appears to have studied at Padua before going to Viterbo, and he referred to observations made at or near there in *Optica*, x. 42, p. 440 (see below, p. 226, n. 4) and x. 70, p. 464. See Birkenmajer, op. cit. iv (1922).

[4] Vitellonis *Opticae*, Prol., p. 1; Baeumker, *Witelo*, p. 127. Witelo appears to have had a Thuringian father and a Polish mother, and to have been born in Silesia, then a fief of Poland. He said in *Optica*, x. 74, p. 467: 'in nostra terra, scilicet Poloniae'. William of Moerbeke was with the Papal Court at Viterbo, with breaks, from 1268 to at least 1277. Witelo himself possibly had some connexion with the Papal Court. See Baeumker, *Witelo*, pp. 201-24.

[5] Below, pp. 273, 278 sqq.; Baeumker, *Witelo*, pp. 185 sqq., 237-8.

[6] Witelo wrote of 'taedium verbositatis Arabicae, implicationis Graecae, paucitas quoque exarationis Latinae' (*Opticae*, Prol., p. 1; Baeumker, *Witelo*, p. 128). He mentioned among his sources, besides Alhazen's *Optica* and *De Crepusculis*, principally Euclid's *Elementa* (in Campanus of Novara's version), *Optica* and *Catoptrica*, and the *Conica* of Apollonius of Perga (ibid., pp. 2 and 129), though he cited also several other Greek mathematicians, including Theon, Archimedes, Proclus, Ptolemy, Theodosius, Menelaus, and Pappus (Baeumker, op. cit., pp. 226-35). The first book of the *Perspectiva* was in fact devoted to giving a full account, which had no counterpart in Alhazen's *Optica*, of geometrical theorems which were to be used for the optical problems discussed in the later books. Of new optical sources the chief was Hero of Alexandria's

indeed to any other medieval Latin writer on optics, the resemblances between his *Perspectiva* and certain of the writings of these two authors are so close that there can be little doubt that he knew them. Some of the parallel passages could have come from no other source. Certainly Witelo's effective combination, for purposes of research, of experiment with geometry, of manual skill with rational analysis and synthesis, is completely in the spirit of the Oxford school. The principal source of inspiration of many of his experiments was undoubtedly Alhazen, whose work he often simply repeated. But scarcely less important was the influence, not only in 'light metaphysics' but also in the theory of science and in his treatment of such problems as the rainbow,[1] of the ideas that seem to have come from Grosseteste and Roger Bacon.

The fundamental importance of 'light metaphysics' in directing Witelo's scientific thought is shown by the prologue to the *Perspectiva*, which was addressed to William of Moerbeke; and this has so much similarity of content and phrase with Grosseteste's *De Luce*, *De Motu Corporali*, and *De Lineis*, and with Roger Bacon's *Opus Maius* and *De Multiplicatione Specierum*, that it seems more than probable that it was directly inspired by some or all of those works.[2] Beginning with the Neoplatonic theory of the emanation of power from God, Witelo distinguished between the intellectual and corporeal modes of this power. He went on to say: 'Of corporeal influences sensible light is the medium' which connects the superior with the inferior world and bears the forms which generate in matter.[3] This light travelled in straight lines in rays and varied its action according to the angle at which it impinged on a surface,[4] for the action of

Catoptrica, which William of Moerbeke had translated under the title *Ptolemaei de Speculis* (Thorndike, *History of Magic*, ii. 455; Sarton, *Introduction*, ii. 830). Witelo cited this as a work by Ptolemy in *Opticae*, v. 5, p. 192 and C. 18, p. 198; below, p. 216, n. 6.

[1] Some of his account of work on the rainbow suggests a knowledge of Albertus Magnus, e.g. in *Opticae*, x. 70, p. 464, he said: 'Unde viderunt lunae iridem observatores nocturni in Alemania bis in uno anno' (cf. above, p. 200). Witelo could scarcely not have known the work of so well-known a writer as Albertus Magnus, especially since he received part of his early education in Paris (Baeumker, in *Miscellanea Ehrle*, i. 95), and through him he would have gained indirect knowledge of some of Grosseteste's scientific ideas.

[2] Of Witelo's debt to *De Mult. Spec.* Birkenmajer (*MH*, v, 1948, p. 36) goes so far as to say: 'the frequently quoted introduction to his *Perspectiva* can hardly be understood at all unless this influence is taken into account'.

[3] *Vitellonis Opticae*, Prol., p. 1; Baeumker, *Witelo*, pp. 127-8.

[4] Ibid., pp. 1 and 128.

things varied not only according to the things themselves but also according to their modes of action.[1]

And considering [he continued in his introductory remarks to William of Moerbeke] that the power of the form is sent in the same manner into the contrary and into the senses, that light is the first of all sensible forms,[2] and that we intend to investigate the efficient causes of all sensible things, in which vision (*visus*[3]) shows us very many differences; it seems desirable to study these causes by means of visible entities, just as this form of investigation appealed also to the men, of whom there were many before our time, known as students of optics (*perspectivorum*), and who have treated of this problem. And this seems to me a suitable name for them, though, in order that the present work may correspond to your tastes, the intention of writing will be more to show forth the most hidden mode of action of natural forms. For because in the senses the visual power acts in such a way as to be seen (*visus*[3] plus *perceptibiliter agitur*), in natural things where there are no senses this power is by no means absent; for the presence of the senses adds nothing to the actions of natural forms. And so, since every mode of vision can be treated by mathematical or natural-scientific demonstration, I will deal, according to the small measure of my ability, with that relating to the natural actions of forms through visible effects [which can be studied] according to the three modes of vision. In all these modes of vision the natural forms go to the eye and visual rays do not go out to seize the forms of things. Therefore, if vision does not result from the presence of forms radiating to natural bodies exposed to them, this is not because no natural action is taking place, but because the forms affect dissimilar bodies according to the possibility present.[4]

In fact Witelo meant by 'form' the same as Grosseteste and Roger Bacon meant by 'species', and, like them, he studied optics because he held visible light to be simply an example of the propagation of power which was the basis of all natural efficient causation.[5] The three modes of vision to which he referred were those which took place, respectively, through direct, reflected and refracted rays, and invisible forms of power were propagated in the same manner. The

---

[1] Loc. cit.

[2] 'quod lumen sit primum omnium formarum sensibilium.' Ibid., pp. 2 and 129.

[3] On the meaning of this word cf. Thimonis *Quaest. Metheor.* iii. 1, Venetiis, 1522, f. 106[vb]: 'Aristoteles . . . intendit per visum radium visuale et non potentiam visivam nec organum, et ille erat modus loquendi perspectivorum, scilicet, Ptholomei et aliorum.' See below, p. 261.

[4] Vitellonis *Opticae*, Prol., p. 1; Baeumker, *Witelo*, p. 129. The last two sentences contain an assertion of the intramission theory of vision. Cf. Grosseteste, above, pp. 110, 114, 118; Roger Bacon, above, p. 152.

[5] Vitellonis *Opticae*, iii. 6, pp. 87–88. Cf. Baeumker, *Witelo*, pp. 606–9.

direct rays were the most powerful because they went in straight lines. Power decreased with distance.[1] In reflected or refracted rays power was increased by concentration (*aggregatio*) at a point, as could be shown by the increase in light or heat that could be produced by a concave mirror[2] or a lens.[3] Moreover, all rays, however propagated, Witelo held, went according to the metaphysical principle that nature acts in the shortest way and does nothing unnecessary.[4] Of the operation of this principle he gave several examples,[5] among which was a demonstration, derived from Hero's *Catoptrica*, that the multiplication of forms during reflection took place by the shortest route. This corresponds to the principle of minimum path, which Witelo justified by a metaphysical form of the principle of economy: 'It would be futile (*frustra fieret*) for anything to take place by longer lines, when it could better and more certainly take place by shorter lines.'[6]

The methods by which the various modes of operation of these forms were to be investigated were, according to Witelo, by observation and experiment[7] and by mathematics.[8] The inductive process of collecting instances[9] in order to discover the 'common nature' he used, like Roger Bacon, in his study of the rainbow,[10] but the most valuable results achieved by purely observational methods were, perhaps, in the psychology of vision, which he tried to relate to the

[1] Vitellonis *Opticae*, Prol., p. 3; Baeumker, *Witelo*, p. 131; *Opticae*, ii, Petitiones, p. 61; ii. 47, p. 81. Cf. Grosseteste's *De Lineis*, Baur, 1912, p. 61; above, p. 86.

[2] See below, pp. 218–19.

[3] Vitellonis *Opticae*, x, Prol., p. 403, x. 57, p. 450; cf. Grosseteste, above, p. 111 and p. 87, n. 1. Witelo's use of 'pyramis radialis' and 'pyramis illuminationis' (see Lib. ii, Definitiones 9 and 10, p. 61) resembles Grosseteste's account of variation of action 'according to figures', and similar discussions by Roger Bacon (cf. above, p. 112, p. 120, n. 5). For Greek notions of 'visual cones' see Lejeune, *Euclide et Ptolémée*, pp. 51 sqq.

[4] 'Item quod natura nihil frustra agit, sicut nec deficit in necessariis.' Vitellonis *Opticae*, ii, Petitiones 8, p. 61.

[5] These included the path of a falling body and the trajectory of an arrow, the composition of a spider's web, and the path followed by a dog. (Vitellonis *Opticae*, v. 5, p. 192.) Cf. Grosseteste, above, pp. 85–86, p. 118, n. 10.

[6] Vitellonis *Opticae*, v. 18, p. 198. He proved geometrically in i. 17–18, pp. 9–10 that the path taken by the ray reflected at an angle equal to the incident angle was shorter than any other possible path. Cf. [Claudii Ptolemei] *De Speculis*, ii, hrg. von W. Schmidt (Heronis Alexandrini *Opera Omnia*, ii. 1) 320: 'utique patet velocitatem conatus brevissima fieri', from which it followed that the angles of incidence and reflection were equal. Cf. above, p. 213, n. 6; Grosseteste, above, pp. 96, 123.

[7] Cf. below, p. 218, n. 2; p. 220, n. 1; p. 232.

[8] Vitellonis *Opticae*, Prol., p. 2; Baeumker, *Witelo*, p. 129.

[9] Vitellonis *Opticae*, iii. 72, p. 116. Cf. Baeumker, *Witelo*, pp. 623–31.

[10] See below, pp. 226–32.

anatomy[1] and physiology of the optical nervous system. Many of his ideas came from Alhazen,[2] as, for example, his use of 'visual pyramids',[3] his adherence to the intramission theory of vision,[4] and most of his discussion of how a single object was seen with two eyes. But, for his attempts to account for vision by the multiplication of 'visual forms', not only from the object seen to the eye, but also along the optic tract, and to show how single vision with two eyes was achieved by the union of the two 'forms' in the optic chiasma,[5] he was probably indebted to Roger Bacon.[6] Also like Roger Bacon was his stressing of the point that, while he thought that the lens was the sensitive organ,[7] vision was not *completed* until the visible forms had passed through the body of the lens to the nerve.[8] 'For', he said, 'the form received on the surface of the lens passes through the body of the lens and then is spread out over the sensitive body which is in the optic nerve, and comes to the anterior part of the brain, in which is the ultimate perception.'[9] Towards understanding how the image was formed behind the lens Witelo contributed

[1] His account of the anatomy of the eye came mainly from Alhazen (*Opticae*, i. 4 sqq.), but he believed that his sources had based their descriptions on dissection: 'Sic ergo patet quoniam humores et tunicae oculi sphaerice se intersecant; et patet declaratio definitionis propositae oculi secundum omnium eorum experientiam qui de ipsius anatomia hactenus scripserunt. . . .' Vitellonis *Opticae*, iii. 4, p. 87. Like Roger Bacon he knew that the lens was flattened; above, Fig. 5. Cf. Bednarski, *AGM*, xxiv (1931) 60 sqq.

[2] Cf. H. Bauer, *Die Psychologie Alhazens*; above, p. 153, nn. 1, 3; p. 147, n. 2.

[3] Vitellonis *Opticae*, iii. 18, p. 93. See above, p. 126, n. 1; p. 152, n. 3. Cf. Grosseteste, above, p. 117. Witelo used this conception of 'visual pyramids' or cones in his account of the perception of size and distance; see iii. 52, p. 109, C. 73, pp. 116–17, iv. 20, pp. 126–7, C. 27, pp. 130–1.

[4] Vitellonis *Opticae*, iii. 5–6, pp. 87–88 (cf. above, p. 114, n. 1; below, n. 6). Witelo thought that direct vision (*aspectus simplex*) took place instantaneously, i.e. that the *formae visibiles* multiplied or propagated themselves instantaneously (iii. 55, p. 110; ii. 2, p. 63). He thus adhered to the opinion of Aristotle and Grosseteste against that of Alhazen and Roger Bacon (cf. Alhazeni *Opticae*, ii. 21, pp. 37–38). See above, pp. 106, 146.

[5] Vitellonis *Opticae*, iii. 28, pp. 98–99. Cf. iii. 69, p. 115, iv. 103–4, p. 162; Alhazeni *Opticae*, i. 27, pp. 16–17, iii. 9, pp. 79–80; Baeumker, *Witelo*, pp. 613–16. On this point in modern physiology cf. Pirenne, *Vision and the Eye*, pp. 174 sqq.

[6] Cf. above, pp. 153–5. Witelo resembled Roger Bacon also in his grouping and treatment of Alhazen's twenty-two *visibilia*, of which two, light and colour, were *per se visibilia* (Vitellonis *Opticae*, iii. 59, p. 111; cf. Alhazeni *Opticae*, ii. 18, p. 35; *Opus Maius*, v. i. i. 3, ed. Bridges, ii. 5–7) and in his notion of *intentio formarum*, by which vision took place. This being a spiritual activity it occurred instantaneously. Vitellonis *Opticae*, iii. 69, p. 115. Cf. ibid. iii. 6, p. 88 (above, p. 215, n. 5); above, n. 4, p. 114, n. 1, pp. 151–5; Baeumker, *Witelo*, pp. 615–20, 625.

[7] Vitellonis *Opticae*, iii. 4, pp. 85–87; Baeumker, *Witelo*, pp. 132–6.

[8] Vitellonis *Opticae*, iii. 20, p. 94.

[9] Above, n. 5.

little, but he made some admirably original observations on the more purely psychological aspects of vision. These related chiefly to direct perception and the effects of association and reasoning on vision, and such problems as illusions, visual beauty, and the perception of distance and size and of the third dimension of space.[1]

The most outstanding feature of Witelo's method was his combination of manual and technical skill with mathematics for quantitative experiments with instruments. An excellent example of the use of this combination in the construction of an instrument is his work on the parabolic mirror, with which Alhazen's writings as known in Latin showed no acquaintance, though Roger Bacon had understood its essential properties.[2] The problem was to construct a burning-mirror that would concentrate the sun's rays at a single focal point.[3] After discussing the properties of a set of plane mirrors arranged to form the sides of a polygon, and of a hemispherical concave mirror which, he said, focused the sun's rays not to a point but on a line,[4] he went on to describe the construction of three types of mirror that would focus to a single point. In each case he gave an account of the geometrical construction of the curve which, when rotated about an axis, would produce the reflecting surface. The first produced a surface corresponding to that produced by the intersection of the concave surfaces of eccentric hollow spheres,[5] and the second a surface corresponding to that produced by the intersection of the concave surfaces of hollow cones. The latter he claimed to have invented himself.[6] The last and best was the surface

---

[1] These subjects were discussed in Lib. iii and iv. For an account of Witelo's psychology see Baeumker, *Witelo*, pp. 609–40, and pp. 132–79 where some of the most interesting sections of these books are printed.

[2] See above, p. 150, n. 3; p. 206, n. 1. Witelo devoted Lib. v–ix of his *Perspectiva* to an account of mirrors, for which Alhazen, Euclid, and Hero were the principal sources. His experimental attitude appears frequently, as, for example, when he described how to construct out of iron a double convex-concave mirror that would produce a variety of images. He said: 'et plus experientia quam scriptura docebit imaginum diversitates', and he concluded: 'Ingenium vero modernorum et futurorum addat quod libuerit, quia sufficienter dedimus cogitantibus principia multorum talium adiuventionum.' (Vitellonis *Opticae*, ix. 35, pp. 391–2.) He gave an interesting account in x. 62, p. 454, of an illusion produced by the reflection of the subject's own image from mist, which he said could be reproduced by mirrors.

[3] Vitellonis *Opticae*, Prol., p. 3; Baeumker, *Witelo*, pp. 130–1; *Opticae*, v. 65, p. 223.

[4] Vitellonis *Opticae*, viii. 68, pp. 365–6.

[5] In this case he described also a mechanical method of construction: 'Huius autem rei mechanicum artificium tradendum cogitavimus illis qui per manualem fabricam intendere voluerint praemissis, cuius forma talis est. . . .' Ibid. ix. 37, pp. 393–4.

[6] Ibid. ix. 38, pp. 394–5.

produced by the rotation about its axis of a parabola and, after a discussion, based on Apollonius's *Conica*,[1] of the properties of parabolas, Witelo went on to describe the actual manufacture of a parabolic mirror out of a concave piece of iron. Two equal parabolic sections were drawn on a rectangular sheet of good iron or steel, and cut out. The parabolic edge of one was sharpened for cutting and that of the other made like a file for polishing. These sections were then used, with some mechanism to rotate them about their axes, to cut and polish the concave surface of the piece of iron so that it formed a parabolic mirror. The same method could be used, he said, for rotating the other two curves which produced surfaces that reflected all incident rays to a single focal point.[2]

Another important example of Witelo's method is his work on the measurement of the angles of refraction at the surfaces between air and water, air and glass, and glass and water, respectively. He made most of these measurements by repeating, with certain innovations, experiments described by Alhazen, whose own work was based on similar experiments by Ptolemy.[3] Alhazen gave no results, though he corrected Ptolemy by pointing out that the amount of refraction was not simply proportional to the angle of incidence, and he seems to have been the first to appreciate the 'reciprocal law', that is that a ray crossing the interface between two media would, when reversed, retrace its original path.[4] Witelo's results are almost identical with those obtained by Ptolemy but contain, in addition, figures for the 'reciprocal law'.

'Proof of this proposition', Witelo said of a statement about the behaviour of light at the junction of two transparent media, 'depends on experiments with instruments rather than on other kinds of demonstration. Therefore when someone wants to find out the manner in which rays of light are refracted in a second transparent medium denser than the first, as in water, which is denser than air',[5] let him use the instrument described by Alhazen.

---

[1] Ibid. ix. 39–43, pp. 398–402. Cf. Lib. i.

[2] Ibid. ix. 44, pp. 402–3. Possibly the mechanism for rotating the sections was a simple form of lathe (see below, p. 220, n. 2). Winter (*Endeavour*, ix, 1950, pp. 76 sqq.) has reproduced some diagrams from a manuscript of a work by Alhazen showing the use of such an instrument.

[3] See Ptolemy, *Optica*, pub. Govi, pp. xxiv sqq., 144–55; above, pp. 118, 120.

[4] Alhazeni *Opticae*, vii. 11–12, pp. 244–7; below, p. 225, n. 4.

[5] Vitellonis *Opticae*, ii. 42, p. 76. Witelo gave an interesting explanation of refraction based on the theory that when light passed through a dense medium its propagation was inhibited (cf. above, p. 217, n. 4): 'Impulsiones proiectationum factarum perpendiculariter

Of the construction of this instrument for measuring the angle between incident and emergent rays Witelo gave a very detailed and practical description.[1] It consisted of a cylindrical brass vessel which had fixed to the under side at the centre of its base a pivot, which was placed in the corresponding circular hole in a metal bar by which the cylinder was borne.[2] The cylindrical vessel could thus be

sunt fortiores eis quae fiunt oblique. . . . Quia itaque omnis corporis densitas impedit transitum luminis. . . . Omnis itaque lux pertransiens corpus diaphanum motu velocissimo et insensibili pertransit, sic tamen quod per magis diaphana velocior fit motus quam per minus diaphana. . . . Cum ergo lux pertransiverit corpus aliquod diaphanum oblique, et occurrerit corporali alii diaphano grossiori, tunc corpus grossius resistit luci vehementius quam prius corpus rarius resistebat, necesse est ergo quod propter resistentiam illius corporis densioris motus lucis transmutetur, et si resistentia fuerit fortis tunc motus ille ad partem contrariam refringetur.' For rays passing from a rare to a dense medium: '. . . . Accidit ergo ut declinet ad partem aliquam per quam facilior sit transitus quam per illam partem ad quam per lineam incidentiae movebatur; facilior autem motuum et plus adiutus coelesti influentia est super lineam perpendicularem; quod enim vicinius est perpendiculari facilioris est transitus quam remotius ab illa.' (Ibid. ii. 47, pp. 81–82.) He used the results of his experiments on refraction to support this theory: 'secundum rationem praemissam fortitudinis perpendicularium et per experientias instrumentales per 42 et 44 huius.' In one case he also eliminated a false possibility by the principle: 'frustra ergo incidebat: natura autem frustra nihil agit, sicut in principio suppositum est', and he adverted to the true possibility: 'ut etiam ostensum est experimentaliter per 43 huius.' For rays passing from a dense to a rare medium: 'Motus itaque radii incidentis oblique secundum lineam a c in corpore secundi diaphani densioris, quod est b e f, componitur ex motu in partem perpendicularis a b, transeuntis per corpus b e f in quo est motus, et ex motu facto lineam c b, quae est perpendicularis super lineam c g. Quoniam enim transitus perpendicularis est fortissimus et facillimus motuum et densitas corporis resistit termino motus ad quem intendebat, linea a c necessario movebitur ad perpendicularem c g. . . .' (Cf. x. 13, p. 415.) The last part of this explanation, according to which the motion of light was composed of two motions at right angles which were differently affected when light struck the surface between two media obliquely, came from Alhazen Opticae, vii. 8, pp. 240–2. Cf. F. M. Shuja, Cause of Refraction as Explained by the Moslem Scientists; Sarton, Introduction, iii. 707; below, pp. 265–6, 283–4, 288.

[1] 'Radii quorumcunque luminum et multiplicationes formarum, secundum rectas lineas protenduntur. Alhazen 2, n. 7. Hoc quod proponitur non demonstratione sed instrumentaliter potest declarari. Diversitas tamen antiquorum ad hoc probandum pluribus et diversis usa est instrumentiis, nos vero utimur isto quod hic subscribimus, quod regularius hinc proposito credimus convenire. Assumatur itaque vas aeneum rotundum convenienter spissum, ad modum matris astrolabii. . . .' (Vitellonis Opticae, ii. 1, p. 61.) He went on to describe the instrument, following Alhazeni Opticae, vii. 2, pp. 231–3. The same emphasis on the need for experiment rather than argument is seen in his other chapters on the use of this instrument, e.g. 'Experimentaliter etiam et hoc propositum theorema potest declarari' (Vitellonis Opticae, ii. 43, p. 77; 44, p. 78; 45, p. 80; 46, p. 81); 'Illud quod particularibus experientiis hactenus instrumentaliter probatum est, naturali demonstratione intendimus adiuvare' (ii. 47, p. 81; x. 12, p. 415). See also especially x. 3–8, pp. 406–13; below, pp. 221 sqq. Besides his measurements of refractive angles he gave in these chapters an account of experiments to show the main qualitative facts about the behaviour of light at the junction between two transparent media (cf. above, pp. 120–2; Alhazeni Opticae, vii. 3–8, pp. 233–42).

[2] In describing the making of this instrument he said: 'et ponatur hoc vas secundum

made to rotate on this pivot, and the instrument was used by resting the bar across the sides of a rectangular glass container in such a manner that the axis of the cylinder was horizontal, the bar being cut away so that this axis could lie below the top of the container.

A little way above the base, a circle was drawn round the inside wall of the cylindrical vessel at a constant distance from the circular base. The wall was perforated with a small round hole at each end of a diameter of this circle. A little way from one of these holes a small strip of metal, with an identical hole with its centre on the same diameter, was fixed to the base inside the vessel. This arrangement could act as a sight. The circle itself was marked off into 360 degrees and into minutes.[1] Light from the sun or a candle[2] shining through the 'sight' (i.e. through the hole in the wall inside which the small metal strip was fixed, and through the hole in that strip) would then travel along the diameter of the graduated circle and out through the hole in the opposite wall. Moreover, when the cylinder was rotated this diameter rotated about its own centre. For experiments with refraction the instrument was therefore so arranged that this centre lay on the interface between the two transparent substances. The angle of incidence at this point could then be altered simply by rotating the cylinder through the required arc as shown on the graduated circle.

Before making his experiments on refraction Witelo used this instrument to show that not only white light, but also colours travelled in straight lines in a single uniform medium. This he did by placing pieces of coloured material in the path of solar rays entering the 'sight' and observing that they passed out through the hole in the opposite wall of the vessel.[3]

To measure the angles of refraction between air and water, the glass container in which the instrument lay was filled with water up to the centre of the latter's circular base (Fig. 6). The instrument was

sui puncta media in tornatorio, et tornetur quousque peripheria eius sit intrinsecus et extrinsecus verae rotunditatis' (Vitellonis *Opticae*, ii. 1, p. 61); and 'Et deinde reducatur vas ad tornatorium, et signentur in ipso tres circuli aequidistantes. . . .' (p. 62.) The same phrases occur in the Latin version of Alhazeni *Opticae*, vii. 2, pp. 231–2.

[1] Vitellonis *Opticae*, ii. 1, p. 62; Alhazeni *Opticae*, vii. 2, p. 232.

[2] 'Cum itaque propositam conclusionem experimentaliter placuerit declarare, opponatur instrumentum praemissum corpori solari vel alteri corpori luminoso cuicunque vel etiam candelae, et applicetur centrum foraminis instrumenti. . . .' Vitellonis *Opticae*, ii. 1, p. 63.

[3] Ibid. ii. 1, p. 63.

rotated until the diameter (kfz)[1] passing through the two holes in
the wall was horizontal to the surface of the water. The 'sight' (k)
was then directed towards the sun at sunrise, and the rays passed
straight along this diameter and out at the opposite hole. The instrument was then rotated so that the 'sight' was a specified number of
degrees above the surface of the water. When the sun had risen
sufficiently its rays again entered the 'sight' and were then refracted,

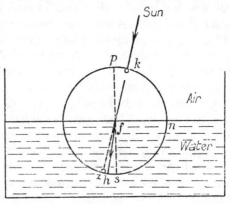

FIG. 6. Witelo's apparatus for measuring angles of refraction. See
pp. 220–4; Vitellonis *Opticae*, ii. 1, x. 5, ed. Risner, pp. 62, 409.
The cylindrical vessel *pns* is perforated at *k* (the 'sight') and *z*.
When *pfk* is 10°, then *zfh* is 2° 5′.

at the centre (f) of the graduated circle, so as to form a point of
light (h) on that circle. This point was marked and the amount of
refraction read off. In this manner the angles of refraction were
measured with different angles of incidence at intervals of 10
degrees.[2]

To measure the angles of refraction at a plane surface between
air and glass, a glass hemisphere was arranged with its plane surface
perpendicular to the base of the instrument, and the centre of this
surface (and so of the sphere of which the glass section formed half)
always at the centre (f) of the graduated circle. Rays entering the
'sight', and being refracted at the plane surface of the glass at this

---

[1] *Quantitates angulorum refractionis ex aere ad aquam experimentaliter declarare. Alhazen, 10, n. 7.* [i.e. vii. 10]. Ibid. x. 5, pp. 408–10.

[2] The angle of incidence is, of course, that which the incident ray makes with the
perpendicular drawn to the refracting surface at the point of refraction, as Witelo stated:
ibid. x, Definition 8, p. 404.

point (*f*), would then always travel within the hemisphere of glass itself along a radius of the sphere. They would, therefore, pass through the curved surface of the hemisphere unrefracted and allow the angles of refraction to be measured at the plane surface only. To measure the angles of refraction of light passing from glass and into water, the container was filled with water as before and the glass hemisphere was arranged with its plane surface on the surface of the water and its curved surface above.[1]

In all cases Witelo gave results for light passing in *both* directions between two media. With air and glass these could be obtained by simply rotating the glass hemisphere,[2] but to measure the refraction of light passing *from* water into air or glass he would have had to adopt a slightly different technique. Alhazen did not discuss such measurements, though he described the same technique for some qualitative experiments on refraction and Witelo simply adapted it. Instead of allowing the sun's rays to shine through the 'sight', he looked through it and observed the point at which a stylus, which he moved round the graduated circle, came into view.[3] With this technique he was observing the angle of incidence necessary for the rays coming from the stylus to pass through the 'sight' when the latter was in a given position. To get measurements with a series of angles of incidence with intervals of 10° he would therefore have had to adjust the 'sight' in accordance with the results obtained when the light was passing in the opposite direction, and then to verify that the point of the stylus in fact appeared at the expected point on the graduated circle. The amount of refraction, as he pointed out, is the same in both directions, with a given angle of incidence.[4] He gave his complete results in the table reproduced on page 224.[5]

On the extreme right of this table are shown the angles of refraction between air and water calculated from the modern refractive

---

[1] Ibid. x. 6, p. 411. Cf. Alhazeni *Opticae*, vii. 11, p. 246.

[2] Vitellonis *Opticae*, x. 6, p. 410. Cf. ibid. ii. 44–45, pp. 78–81; Alhazeni *Opticae*, vii. 11, pp. 244–5.

[3] Vitellonis *Opticae*, x. 4, p. 407. Cf. Alhazeni *Opticae*, vii. 14, pp. 249–51.

[4] Vitellonis *Opticae*, x. 6, p. 411; see also C. 7, p. 412.

[5] Ibid. x. 8, p. 412. The figures for 'anguli refracti' in each case show the angle which Witelo claimed to have measured. This was the angle which the refracted ray (*f h*) made with the perpendicular (*f s*) drawn to the refracting surface at the point of refraction (see Fig. 6). The amount of refraction (the 'anguli refractionis' shown in the adjacent column in each case) was obtained from the difference between the 'angulus refractus' and the angle of incidence. This gave the angle through which the refracted ray was deflected from its original course.

Tabula quantitatis angulorum incidentiae omnibus sequentibus communis	Anguli refracti ab aere ad aquam	Anguli refractionis eiusdem	Anguli refracti ab aere ad vitrum	Anguli refractionis eiusdem	Anguli refracti ab aqua ad vitrum	Anguli refractionis eiusdem	Angles of refraction from air to water calculated from refractive index 1.333
10	7° 45'	2° 5'	7° 0'	3° 0'	9° 30'	0° 30'	7° 29'
20	15° 30'	4° 30'	13° 30'	6° 30'	18° 30'	1° 30'	14° 52'
30	22° 30'	7° 30'	19° 30'	10° 0'	27° 30'	3° 0'	22° 1'
40	29° 0'	11° 0'	25° 0'	15° 0'	35° 0'	5° 0'	28° 49'
50	35° 0'	15° 0'	30° 0'	20° 0'	42° 30'	7° 30'	35° 4'
60	40° 30'	19° 30'	34° 30'	25° 30'	49° 30'	10° 30'	40° 3'
70	45° 30'	24° 30'	38° 30'	31° 30'	56° 0'	14° 0'	44° 49'
80	50° 0'	30° 0'	42° 0'	38° 30'	62° 0'	18° 0'	47° 37'

Tabula quantitatis angulorum incidentiae omnibus sequentibus communis	Anguli refracti ab aqua ad aerem	Anguli refractionis eiusdem	Anguli refracti a vitro ad aerem	Anguli refractionis eiusdem	Anguli refracti a vitro ad aquam	Anguli refractionis eiusdem	Angles of refraction from water to air calculated from refractive index 1.333
10	12° 5'	2° 5'	13° 0'	3° 0'	10° 30'	0° 30'	13° 24'
20	24° 30'	4° 30'	26° 30'	6° 30'	21° 30'	1° 30'	27° 8'
30	37° 30'	7° 30'	40° 30'	10° 30'	33° 0'	3° 0'	41° 49'
40	51° 0'	11° 0'	55° 0'	15° 0'	45° 0'	5° 0'	58° 59'
50	65° 0'	15° 0'	70° 0'	20° 0'	57° 30'	7° 30'	(Total reflection)
60	79° 30'	19° 30'	85° 30'	25° 30'	70° 30'	10° 30'	
70	94° 30'	24° 30'	101° 30'	31° 30'	84° 0'	14° 0'	
80	110° 0'	30° 0'	118° 10'	38° 0'	98° 0'	18° 0'	

index. In the absence of knowledge of the kind of glass which Witelo used it is impossible to give the corresponding figures for the other cases because the refractive indices of different kinds of glass are appreciably different.[1] It will be seen that Witelo's results for the angles of refraction of light passing from air into water are reasonably accurate, but that the figures for light passing in the reverse direction are far from satisfactory. A glance at the figures in the bottom half of the table shows, in fact, that Witelo could not have measured any of these angles of refraction. He seems to have derived them from the angles in the top half of the table by an attempt to apply the reciprocal law, which, however, he did not apply correctly. Moreover, he evidently did not know that at the higher angles of incidence no refraction would occur at all because all the light would be reflected.[2] Thus half the results shown in the bottom half of the table are not only inaccurate but impossible.

Witelo tried to express his results in a number of mathematical generalizations.[3] In modern terminology these may be stated as follows:

Let the angle of incidence be i, and the amount of refraction r (*angulus refractionis*). Then, if $i_1 > i$,

$$r_1 > r;$$

$$r_1 - r < i_1 - i;$$

$$\frac{r_1}{i_1} > \frac{r}{i}.$$

Making r negative when refraction is towards the perpendicular, when the second medium is denser $i + r < i$, and when the second medium is rarer $i + r > i$ (these are the *anguli refracti*).

In all cases $\dfrac{i + r}{i}$ varies according to the densities of the different media.[4]

---

[1] But see Ptolemy, *Optica*, pub. Govi, pp. xxiv sqq.

[2] This fact was discussed by Theodoric of Freiberg; below, pp. 236–7, 249.

[3] '. . . Haec itaque sunt quae accidunt lucibus et coloribus, et universaliter omnibus formis, in diffusione sui in corporibus diaphanis et in refractione quae accidit in illis omnibus tam secundum se quam in respectu ad visus. Patet itaque quod quaerebatur.' Vitellonis *Opticae*, x. 8, pp. 412–13.

[4] Ptolemy had stated in effect that $i/r =$ constant; see his *Optica*, pub. Govi, pp. xxxiv sqq., 155 sqq., above, pp. 120–3. Alhazen had pointed out that the amount of refraction increased with the angle of incidence, but not in simple proportion: Alhazeni *Opticae*, vii. 10, p. 243. For the modern law of refraction see below, p. 274, n. 7.

Having given an account of the refraction of light at different surfaces, Witelo went on to discuss the properties of convex and concave lenses. Of these he seems to have had only a theoretical knowledge,[1] and his account came largely from Alhazen[2] and perhaps from Roger Bacon,[3] though he made some original observations on the magnification of objects under water.[4] He attempted also an explanation of the twinkling of the stars.[5] A more successful application of his knowledge of refraction was his study of the rainbow, and here he followed the method, developed earlier in the century, of trying to reduce a complicated phenomenon to elements that could be studied by controlled experiments. The only source of knowledge of the rainbow which he acknowledged by name was Aristotle's *Meteorology*, but his chapters contain much that is not in this work and which seems, in fact, to have been derived from Roger Bacon and perhaps Grosseteste and Albertus Magnus.[6]

The problem set for Witelo by the rainbow was to explain the concentration of rays of light so that they appeared to sight as a bright, coloured semicircle. A concentration of rays, he said, could be produced by either reflection or refraction, and in a preliminary chapter he tried to show that the rainbow was produced by both.[7] The rays by which the rainbow was seen must have been reflected, he said, because they came to the eye at angles equal to those at

---

[1] See Vitellonis *Opticae*, iii. 52, p. 109, C. 73, pp. 116–17; iv. 20, p. 126, C. 28, p. 131; x. 23–48, pp. 424–44. There is an interesting discussion on the variation of the image in different positions in relation to a spherical lens in x. 40, ending: 'Horum autem situum diversitatem ex praehabitis principiis demonstrandam relinquimus ingenio perquirentis.' (p. 439.) In x. 43 there is an account, taken from Alhazeni *Opticae*, vii. 49, p. 277, of an experiment on focusing a spherical lens, ending: 'Sed et in his multa est diversitas, quam relinquimus studio perquirentis.' (p. 441.)

[2] Alhazeni *Opticae*, vii. 38–50, pp. 270–8.

[3] e.g. the account, in x. 48, of the spherical and hemispherical burning lenses, which he explained by the theory of double refraction (cf. above, pp. 122, 149). He gave an interesting geometrical explanation of the formation of the focal point, saying that all the rays striking the surface at the same angle were refracted at equal angles. He concluded the chapter: 'Sed et in horum experimentatione est maxima latitudo, quam relinquimus ad talia curiosis.' (p. 444.) Cf. Alhazeni *Opticae*, vii. 9, pp. 242–3. Cf. also Roger Bacon's account of the rules regarding the properties of lenses; above, p. 150.

[4] 'Patet ergo propositum per experimentum', he said, and went on to speak of observations in water 'in loco subterraneo in concavitate montis qui est inter civitates Paduam et Vicentiam (qui locus dicitur Cubalus). . . .' Vitellonis *Opticae*, x. 42, p. 440.

[5] Ibid. x. 55, pp. 449–50. He followed Alhazeni *Opticae*, vii. 15–16, pp. 251–2, CC. 51–55, pp. 278–82, in his account (x. 49–54, pp. 444–9) of the effects of atmospheric refraction on the appearance of the stars.

[6] Cf. above, p. 124, n. 1; pp. 155–61; p. 196, n. 4.

[7] Vitellonis *Opticae*, x. 65, pp. 457–8. Cf. above, pp. 125, 158.

which the incident rays from the sun struck the drops.[1] They must also have been refracted because, unlike a simply reflected image, when an observer approached or retreated from the bow,[2] it advanced before or followed after him, respectively. 'Therefore the rainbow is seen not only by reflection but by the refraction of light within the body from which it is reflected.'[3] It was seen, in fact, as part of the circumference of the base of a cone produced by the rays going to the eye, which was on the axis of the cone. As the observer approached or retreated from the rainbow, or moved to the right or left, he placed his eye on the axis of a different cone, of which an infinite number were produced by the multitudinous rays of light reflected from water drops in the atmosphere. This theory he supported by a simple experiment in which a rainbow in an artificial spray was seen to change its position according to whether the observer shut one eye or the other.[4]

To explain the shape of the rainbow Witelo constructed a theory to show that the rays must be concentrated in the required manner by any collection of dispersed drops of water,[5] as, for example, in spray from the oars of a rowing boat.[6] In the atmosphere he held that drops of water would condense as spheres owing to the equality in all directions of the forces acting on each drop. A collection of such drops would form a mist. Rays from the sun would meet the drops on the outside of the mist; and, of the rays falling on each drop, some would be reflected and some would be refracted to a point beyond it on a straight line passing through its centre, as by a spherical lens. These drops would thus concentrate the rays into the depths of the mist, where they would fall on the outer surfaces of other drops.[7] These surfaces would reflect them back again in many directions. The rainbow would be seen in the rays which, after going out from the sun to the mist in one cone, were reflected back to the eye of the observer on a shorter cone with the same base and axis. The sun was at the apex of the incident cone and the eye at the apex of the reflected cone, and the sun, eye, and centre of the

[1] Cf. Aristotle, *Meteor.* 373ᵇ15–34.

[2] This observation, which he attributed to 'Philippus sodalis Platonis', is described in Alexandri Aphrodisiensis *Meteor. Commentatio*, Venetiis, 1540, f. 39ʳ.

[3] Roger Bacon had reached the opposite conclusion: cf. above, pp. 158–9.

[4] Vitellonis *Opticae*, x. 73, pp. 466–7.

[5] Ibid. x. 66, pp. 458–60; cf. C. 69, pp. 463–4.

[6] Cf. above, pp. 156–7, 199; Aristotle, *Meteor.* 374ᵃ15–ᵇ7.

[7] Cf. above, p. 226, n. 7.

rainbow were always in a straight line on the common axis of these cones.[1] Only the returning rays from the circumference of the base were seen because only these were reflected to the eye, and therefore the rainbow appeared as a bright bow and not as a bright circular area.[2] It appeared as a continuous bow because, though each ray was distinct, there was a large number of them very close together.

Witelo's account of how he supposed the rays would be concentrated by refraction through individual drops, and then reflected from the outer surfaces of other drops, was somewhat more precise than the earlier explanations of the rainbow. To show that a rainbow would be seen in mist only if rays with such a history were able to come to the observer's eye, he described an experiment in which an observer saw a rainbow in an artificial spray only when he was in the right position in relation to it. Witelo's model would not, in fact, have produced the results he expected, though almost certainly it was by modifying his model that an adequate one was eventually constructed.[3]

An important point discussed by Witelo was 'the observation by certain people that the altitude of the rainbow and the altitude of the sun together[4] always make 42°, which is shown by the present theorem to be impossible'.[5] He contended that different amounts of refraction produced by variations in the density of the moisture in the atmosphere would produce small variations in the radius of the rainbow. In fact, the radius may vary appreciably according to the size of the raindrops, and with a very fine mist the angle it subtends may be reduced by several degrees from 42°. These variations were not taken into consideration by the fol-

---

[1] See above, p. 125, Fig. 3; cf. Aristotle, *Meteor*. 375^{b}16 sqq. For a geometrical treatment of such cones see Vitellonis *Opticae*, x. 64, pp. 456–7.

[2] Cf. above, pp. 160, 198.   [3] Below, pp. 235–9.

[4] Roger Bacon (above, p. 158) mentioned measurements which showed that the maximum altitude a rainbow could reach was 42°, when the sun would be on the horizon; and that the maximum altitude of the sun at which a rainbow could appear was likewise 42°, when the rainbow would be on the horizon. These results would follow if the rays from the sun to the rainbow always made an angle of 42° with the rays returning from the bow to the eye. Cf. above, p. 161, n. 4.

[5] Vitellonis *Opticae*, x. 78, pp. 470–1. In CC. 73–79, pp. 466–71 he discussed the appearance of the rainbow in different regions (e.g. 'in nostra terra, scilicet Poloniae, habitabili, quae est circa latitudinem 50 graduum': C. 74, p. 467), at different seasons of the year, and with the sun at different altitudes. He repeated Aristotle's statement (*Meteor*. 375^{b}16) that the greatest figure a rainbow could form was a semicircle, and he showed how to find the radius of a given rainbow (C. 77, p. 470). Cf. above, pp. 126, 158.

lowers of Witelo who constructed the first adequate theory of the
rainbow, which indeed depended on their ignoring them.[1]

Of the colours seen in the rainbow Witelo said that there had been
no reasonable treatment by mathematicians and natural philosophers, with the possible exception of the explanation 'in terms of
the difference in the matter of the rainbow according to the nature
of smokiness, disorder and darkness'.[2] But, he added, after much
thought and experiment he was able to give the true explanation.
He achieved his explanation by an intelligent relating of his theory
of the shape of the bow to the theory of colour deriving from Aristotle,[3] according to which the different colours were produced by
the admixture in different degrees of the darkness of the water with
the brightness of the sunlight. His account of the observations and
experiments which he made to support this theory was not only
a good example of inductive reasoning, but a real step towards a
satisfactory explanation of colour.

According to Witelo, each of the concentric circles of colour seen
in the rainbow was produced by a cone of rays reflected to the eye
of the observer from drops in a different region of the mist.[4] The
outer circle was produced by rays reflected from the surface of the
mist, and since these were the shortest and strongest rays this
circle was the brightest colour, red.[5] The inner circles were produced by the rays which had been refracted into the interior of the
mist, before being reflected to the eye on a set of cones of which each
base successively subtended a slightly smaller angle at the eye. The
nearer a cone was to the inside, the longer he thought was its axis,
and therefore the greater the distance the rays had to travel to the
eye. These inside rays, weakened by refraction and by distance and,
moreover, having to pass through denser layers of mist in the lower
regions away from the sun, incorporated successively more darkness
and so produced the darker colours seen in the circles inside the red.[6]

This theory Witelo supported by quoting some other cases of
colours being produced by shadows. For example, the darkness of

---

[1] See below, pp. 251–5, 274, 275, n. 2.   [2] Vitellonis *Opticae* x. 67, pp. 460–1.

[3] *Meteor.* 374ᵃ–375ᵃ. Cf. above, p. 111, n. 5; pp. 199–200.

[4] Vitellonis *Opticae*, x. 67, p. 461; cf. above, pp. 227–8.

[5] White was, of course, brighter than red because it had no darkness mixed with it,
though it was not strictly a colour. On the production of red, cf. Vitellonis *Opticae*,
v. 157, p. 188.

[6] Witelo (ibid. x. 67, p. 462) accepted Aristotle's opinion that there were only three
simple or 'primary' colours in the rainbow (red, green, and violet), any others (e.g.
yellow) being due to mixtures of primaries. See above, p. 111, n. 5, p. 199, n. 2.

the water made the sea look green, and the colours of the rainbow could be seen in the shadows of the eyelashes and in the necks of ducks and peacocks, where the special structure of the feathers projected shadows in all directions.[1] In all these examples, he said, and in natural and artificial rainbows, the production of colours could be attributed to the incorporation of different degrees of darkness with the light. This was a 'univocal and convertible' proximate cause of colour, and no other could be found.[2]

The precise manner in which the different colours were produced by the incorporation of darkness in the rays Witelo then investigated by means of experiments with refraction through crystals and spherical glass vessels filled with water. 'This is the manner', he said, 'in which colours are generated by the weakening of light through refraction towards the perpendicular leading from the centre of the body of the sun to the surface of one of the parallel sides of the crystal', and in the rays that 'are refracted from the perpendicular on account of the nature of the second, rarer medium, namely air.'[3] First he took a piece of crystal of square section and parallel sides

---

[1] For similar observations see Alhazeni Opticae, i. 3, p. 3; Roger Bacon, above, pp. 156–7, 160.

[2] 'Nec enim alias praemissorum caussas nostro potuimus indagare ingenio. Existentibus enim tantum 22 visibilibus nullum aliorum visibilium praeter umbram et lumen horum colorum apparentium visui videtur esse caussa, unde et hanc colorum iridis aestimamus proximam esse caussam. Nullum tamen vidimus quem intellectus suus in hoc modicum intelligibile direxerit, sed huius rei facilis omnes alii difficiles visi sunt dare caussas. Nos tamen hac caussa ut univoca et convertibili erimus contenti.' (Vitellonis Opticae, x. 67, p. 461.) Cf. below, p. 276. At the end of this chapter he mentioned an observation on a rainbow seen in a waterfall near Viterbo (p. 462). In CC. 71–72, pp. 464–6, he discussed the secondary rainbow, which he thought was a reflection of the primary bow: hence the reversal and weakening of the colours; cf. Aristotle, Meteor. 375^{a}30–^{b}15. He added: 'et talem iridem non unam nec duas tantum, sed etiam quatuor simul vidimus Paduae, sole iam ad vesperum declinante.' (C. 69, p. 464.)

[3] 'Ex crystallo hexagona soli opposita colores iridis generantur. Huiusmodi enim colores generantur ex debilitatione luminis propter refractionem ad perpendicularem ductam a centro corporis solis ad superficiem unius parallelogrammi ex lateribus crystalli . . . refringuntur a dicta perpendiculari propter naturam secundi diaphani rarioris, scilicet aeris . . . et est quasi quaedam dispersio radiorum. Apparent autem colores in istis luminibus sic reflexis vel refractis propter mixtionem nigredinis coloris crystallini lumine penetrante. . . . Quoniam ubi radio luminis perpendiculari magis quo ad superficiem incidentiae . . . tunc fit color rubeus. In aliis vero radiis secundum sui debilitatem et coloris corporis et umbrarum plurium commixtionem alii colores medii generantur. . . . Non enim defertur color vel forma visibilis ad visum nisi per naturam lucis, quae est in ipso, poteritque per experientiam his dictis multa addere diligens inquisitor.' (Vitellonis Opticae, x. 83, pp. 473–4.) Cf. above pp. 111, 156, 159, 199. No such experiments are described in Alhazen's known writings, though cf. his Opticae, vii. 38, pp. 270–1.

and held it with one of its sides directly towards the sun. The light passed through unaltered. Then he held it with one of its angles towards the sun, and observed that the rays emerging from the crystal were refracted towards the continuation of the diagonal connecting this angle with the one opposite it. These rays produced, on the earth or other opaque body on which they fell, two coloured patches in which red and a mixed, somewhat green, colour could be distinguished.[1] The amounts of the different colours varied with the position of the crystal.

Next he took a crystal of hexagonal section and parallel opposite sides and held it with one of its sides directly towards the sun. The rays fell perpendicularly upon this side and so passed straight through the crystal unaltered. But on the two adjacent sides the rays fell obliquely and were therefore refracted both as they entered the crystal, and as they left it by one of the other three sides away from the sun. 'And', he said, 'there is a certain dispersion of rays.' In these rays colours appeared, because of the admixture with them of the darkness of the crystal and the shadows of the sides. The colours of the rainbow, of which he held three to be 'simple' or 'primary', appeared in the rays emerging from each of the three lower sides of the crystal. In the light emerging from any particular side red appeared nearest the perpendicular drawn to that side at the point of refraction. These rays contained the least admixture of darkness because, being the least refracted, they were the strongest;[2] moreover, the nearer the rays were to the perpendicular the more were the darkness and shadows of the crystal reflected (presumably back into the crystal). In the weaker rays refracted at greater angles from the perpendicular the other colours were produced by greater admixtures of darkness.

Witelo seems to have been suggesting, as pseudo-Grosseteste had done,[3] that the colours seen in refracted rays were produced by differential refraction: the greater the refraction the weaker the rays, and therefore the greater the admixture of darkness. But he thought that reflection also weakened the rays and so produced colours, as for example in the rainbow itself, though, as he pointed out, the

---

[1] The square crystal would act as two prisms producing two overlapping spectra with red outside and 'mixed' colours in the middle.

[2] The weakening of light by refraction is mentioned also in Alhazeni *Opticae*, vii. 38, pp. 270–1. Grosseteste also said that the more refracted rays were weaker; above, pp. 120–2.

[3] Above, p. 164.

colours produced by crystals were indistinguishable from those seen in the rainbow.

He went on to describe some further experiments on refraction. To produce a better artificial rainbow he covered two sides of a hexagonal crystal with opaque wax, leaving a clear side between them, and placed the crystal with its remaining three sides directed towards solar rays admitted into a darkened room through a small hole. A small rainbow with very clear colours was produced and variations occurred in the effect if the crystal was rotated. After describing some other experiments with hexagonal crystals, he concluded with an account of the production of an artificial rainbow by a spherical glass flask filled with water.[1] The subject was unexplored and experiment was the guide: 'For the colour or visible form is carried to vision only by the nature of light which it contains; and to what has been said the careful inquirer will be able by experiment to add many things.'

[1] Vitellonis *Opticae*, x. 84, p. 474. He pointed out, however, that no colours were seen at the focal point of light refracted through a spherical lens. Ibid., C. 83, p. 473.

IX

Experimental Method and Theodoric of Freiberg's Explanation of the Rainbow

(1)

PERHAPS the most perfect use of the experimental method during the century following Grosseteste's work was that made by Theodoric (or Dietrich) of Freiberg (d. *c.* 1311),[1] a German Dominican, in his work on the rainbow. This is a model example of the thirteenth-century theory of experimental science in practice, and a model of experimental procedure for all time. Independently of some Arabic contemporaries, whose writings did not become known

---

[1] For Theodoric of Freiberg see E. Krebs, *Meister Dietrich*; M. de Wulf, 'Un scolastique inconnu de la fin du xiiie siècle', *RNP*, xiii (1906) 434 sqq.; C. Gauthier, 'Un psychologue de la fin du xiiie siècle, Thierry de Fribourg', *Rev. augustinienne*, xv (1909) 657 sqq., xvi (1910) 178 sqq., 541 sqq.; A. Dyroff, 'Über Heinrich und Dietrich von Freiberg', *PJ*, xxviii (1915) 55 sqq.; Duhem, *Syst. monde*, iii. 383 sqq., 'Physics—History of', in *Catholic Encyc.* xii. 50; A. Birkenmajer, 'Drei neue Handschriften der Werke Meister Dietrichs', in *Vermischte Untersuchungen*, pp. 70 sqq. Further references are given in Ueberweg-Geyer, *Gesch. der Philos.* ii. 554–60, 778; M. de Wulf, *Hist. Mediaeval Philos.* ii. 279 sqq., 294; Sarton, *Introduction*, iii. 704–6. Theodoric was probably a native of Freiberg in Saxony (Krebs, op. cit., pp. 3–13, 26*–27*, 56*). He was a Dominican of the German province, probably entering the Order quite young and completing his studies in Paris. He is, perhaps, the 'Theodoricus' who was prior of the house at Würzburg in 1285. He was provincial of the German province from 1293 to 1296, graduated in theology at Paris in 1297, became prior of Würzburg again until 1303, and was 'vicar' of the German province in 1310, soon after which he seems to have died. In 1304 he went as German 'elector' to the General Chapter of the Order at Toulouse, and there the Master-General, Aymerich, instructed him to write an account of his work on the rainbow; see Theodoricus Teutonicus de Vriberg, *De Iride et Radialibus Impressionibus*, Prol. Epist., hrg. von J. Würschmidt, p. 33. Extracts from *De Iride* were first published by Giambattista Venturi in *Comm. Storia e Theor. Ottica*, 1814, i. 149 sqq.; extracts were published also by G. Hellmann, *Meteorol. Optik, 1000–1836*, and by Krebs, op. cit., pp. 26*–40*. The full text of *De Iride* was published by Würschmidt, op. cit., and all references given below are to this edition. Parts of Theodoric's other scientific and philosophical writings were published by Krebs, op. cit.; see also Krebs, 'Le traité "De esse et essentia" de Thierry de Fribourg', *RNP*, xviii (1911) 516 sqq. Besides the published texts, I have consulted the MSS F.IV.30, 14 c., in the Öffentliche Bibliothek der Universität Basel, and Vat. Lat. 2183, 14–15 c. Only three MSS of *De Iride* are known, the third being the fourteenth-century *Codex Lipsiae* 512 (Würschmidt, op. cit., p. xiii).

in Europe till the twentieth century,[1] Theodoric between 1304 and 1310 gave for the first time a satisfactory solution of a problem which every major thirteenth-century optical writer in the West had tackled.[2] Theodoric's work was the completion of almost a century's steady research, and it is almost certain that it became the basis of Descartes's treatment of the subject.

The main stages in the thirteenth-century West, towards Theodoric's satisfactory explanation of the concentration of sunlight so that it appeared as a bright coloured bow, were as follows. Grosseteste[3] took over Aristotle's theory that the rainbow was seen as part of the circumference of the base of a cone, of which the apex was at the sun and the axis passed through the observer's eye to the centre of the base, a theory which explained the relation observed between the altitude of the sun and of the bow at different times, seasons, and places. He tried to show that the light was concentrated in a bow not by reflection from raindrops, as Aristotle had said, but by the refraction of the sun's rays through successively denser layers of atmospheric mist. The cloud as a whole acted as a large lens and focused the sunlight so that it appeared as an image on a second cloud opposite the sun. Adapting the theory of colour developed by Aristotle and Averroës, according to which the different colours were caused by the combination, in different proportions, of brightness and darkness, Grosseteste said that the brighter colours towards red appeared on the side of the bow where the concentration of rays was greater, and the darker colours towards blue where it was less. He

---

[1] For the work of Qutb al-din al-Shirazi (1236–1311) and Kamal al-din al-Farisi (d. c. 1320), who gave an explanation of the rainbow similar to Theodoric's, see E. Wiedemann, 'Über die Brechung des Lichtes in Kugeln nach Ibn al Haiṭam und Kamâl al Dîn al Fârisî', *SPMSE*, xlii (1910) 15 sqq.; 'Zu den optischen Kenntnissen von Quṭb al Dîn al Shirâzî', *AGNT*, iii (1910–11) 187 sqq.; 'Zu Ibn al-Haiṭams Optik', ibid. iii (1910–11) 1 sqq.; 'Zur Optik von Kamâl al Din', ibid., pp. 161 sqq.; 'Arabische Studien über den Regenbogen', ibid. iv (1913) 453 sqq. See also K. Brockelmann, *Gesch. arab. Literatur*, ii. 211 and Supplement ii. 295; H. Suter, *Mathematiker und Astronomen der Araber*, pp. 158–9, 'Nachträge und Berichtigungen. . . .' *Abh. Ges. math. Wissens.* xiv (1902) 176; Sarton, *Introduction*, ii. 23–24, 1017–20, iii. 707–8. This work of Qutb al-din al-Shirazi and Kamal al-din al-Farisi was never translated into Latin and for this reason alone it cannot have been known to Theodoric of Freiberg. These eastern and western contemporaries also lived far apart. The similarity of their independent work was no doubt the result, as Sarton (*Introduction*, ii. 23–24, iii. 141–2) suggests, of their making use of the same sources. See also *De Iride*, ed. Würschmidt, pp. 2–4. Cf. above, p. 124, n. 1; p. 125, n. 2; p. 147, n. 2; p. 150, n. 3; p. 158, nn. 2, 3; p. 196, n. 4; pp. 226 sqq.

[2] 'Et his annexa est difficultas philosophica valde, sed magis insolubilis quam aliqua praeter iridem', Fr. Rogeri Bacon, *Opus Maius*, v. ii. iii. 7, ed. Bridges, ii. 120.

[3] See above, pp. 111, 125–7.

said that there were seven colours between white and black, though Aristotle had said that only three were 'simple' or 'primary', namely red, blue, and green.

Albertus Magnus[1] accepted the main features of Grosseteste's explanation of the rainbow but emphasized the importance of refraction in *individual* drops of water as well as through the different layers of the cloud as a whole. The different colours, of which he thought with Aristotle only three were 'simple', were produced, he said, by differences in the density of the mist, the darker colours appearing in the light passing through the denser layers. This, he said, was what happened when sunlight was passed through a prism, from which red emerged nearer the apex and the darker colours towards the base, and he showed that his theory agreed with experiments with spherical balls and with other observations.

Against this emphasis on refraction, Roger Bacon[2] returned to Aristotle's view that the rainbow was produced by the reflection of the sun's rays from myriads of raindrops, each observer seeing a different rainbow in the rays reflected to his eyes by a particular set of drops. The rainbow was seen in the rays coming from the cloud directly to his eye; not, as Grosseteste had supposed, as an image formed on a second cloud. Relative to fixed objects on the earth the rainbow seen by any observer moved with him and therefore, Roger Bacon said, its colours had an essentially different cause from those seen in hexagonal crystals, which did not move with the observer. He held, in fact, that they were subjective. Concerning the relation of the position of the rainbow to that of the sun Roger Bacon recorded one observation of fundamental importance, for he said that the maximum altitude of the bow, reached when the sun was on the horizon, was 42°.

Witelo[3] once more asserted that the light producing the rainbow was refracted as well as reflected by spherical drops of water in the atmosphere, and he supported this opinion by a number of experiments. He held that the rainbow was seen in the rays which, after going out from the sun to the mist in one cone, were reflected back to the eye of the observer on a shorter cone with the same base and axis. The part of the circumference of this base above the horizon appeared as a bright coloured bow, he said, because the sun's rays were concentrated, by refraction through individual drops acting as spherical lenses, on to the outer surfaces of other drops behind

[1] See above, pp. 196–200.   [2] See above, pp. 155–61.   [3] See above, pp. 226–32.

them, and from these drops they were reflected to the eye of the observer. Witelo mentioned the measurements showing that the angle between the rays going from the sun to the top of the bow, and the rays going from the top of the bow to the eye, always contained an angle of 42°, but his theory led him to suppose that this angle would vary with the density of moisture. To explain the colours of the rainbow Witelo combined his explanation of the shape with the theory that colours were produced by the admixture, in different degrees, of the darkness of the water with the brightness of the sunlight. Retaining Aristotle's theory of the three 'simple' colours, he showed in effect that in light refracted through hexagonal crystals or spherical flasks filled with water, the least refracted rays appeared red and the most refracted blue; the greater the refraction the greater the weakening of the rays,[1] and therefore the greater the admixture of darkness. He thought that rays could be weakened and colours produced also by reflection, and that both reflection and refraction operated in producing the colours of the rainbow. The different circles of colour, he said, were the circumferences of the bases of a series of cones one inside the other, each, from red to blue, subtending a slightly smaller angle at the eye of the observer.

Theodoric of Freiberg's great contribution was to show that the appearance of the rainbow could be explained by assuming that the rays by which it was seen had been both refracted and reflected *inside* single raindrops. He recognized a fact of which Witelo was ignorant,[2] that when the angle at which light was incident upon the boundary between two transparent media was increased above a critical angle, all the light was reflected.[3] He showed, by means of

---

[1] Grosseteste had said that the more refracted rays were weaker; see above, pp. 120–2.

[2] See above, p. 225.

[3] See *De Iride*, i. 9–11, ii. 8, 18 sqq., pp. 49 sqq., 78, 97 sqq.; below, pp. 246, n. 3, 249, and Figs 7, 8. Cf. 'Possumus tamen de ratione hic dictorum naturaliter aliquid coniicere, dicendo quod, sicut premissum est, natura linee regularis facit planum in superficie, secundum quod planum opponitur aspero, et sic habet naturam speculi. Et natura superficiei sic plane facit dyaphanitatem in corpore, et per consequens inducit in ipsum tale corpus naturam speculi: et signum illius est quod per eandem naturam in genere, ut premissum est, apparet locus ymaginis extra locum ipsius rei, sicut in speculis planis contingit, scilicet in concursu duarum linearum, ut predictum est. Habent igitur huiusmodi corpora perspicua interminata naturam speculi in se, in suo genere et sue proprietatis, ut representent ea que sunt corporum qualitates in sui profundo, non sicut communia specula, que solum recipiunt res secundum suas superficies. Si igitur fiat radiatio ex magis spisso corpore dyaphano, puta de aqua in aerem, et incidat radiatio oblique, sicut dictum est supra, sparguntur radii in latum. Et haec sparsio in tenui corpore, puta in aere, proportionaliter collectioni radiorum in spisso corpore, puta in aqua, et eam speculariter representat, non iam ratione superficei, quia superficies eodem

experiments with hexagonal crystals and with model 'raindrops' in the shape of spherical crystal balls and glass flasks filled with water, that the rays were refracted on entering each raindrop, reflected at the inner surface, and refracted on passing out again, so as to go to the eye on a line making a constant angle with the incident rays. These emergent rays were differentiated into the different colours, and Theodoric correctly explained the order of colours seen in the primary bow, and the reversal of this order in the secondary bow.

Of his thirteenth-century Latin predecessors in the study of the rainbow, the only one whom Theodoric cited by name was Albertus Magnus, but the evidence indicates beyond reasonable doubt that he knew also the work of Witelo, probably that of Roger Bacon, and perhaps that of Grosseteste. With the writings of Albertus Magnus, who was one of his predecessors as provincial of the German province of the Order of Preachers, he was certainly familiar.[1] He cited him by name in his writings on astronomy[2] and certain other subjects,[3] and though he did not mention his name in any of his optical writings his statements about the nature of colour,[4] about the names of the colours,[5] and about an erroneous theory of the rainbow due to Posidonius,[6] suggest parallel passages by Albertus Magnus. In another passage he specifically attacked the theory that the different colours of the rainbow were produced by successive layers of cloud with different densities.[7]

The sources Theodoric named in his optical writings were Aristotle's

modo se habent quocumque modo differant corpora secundum spissitudinem et tenuitatem. Si enim aeri apponatur aliud corpus magis tenue, si radiet in aerem, ibi radii colliguntur qui ante spargebantur quando radiabatur ex aqua in aerem. Sic ergo perspicuum profundum habet naturam speculi sui generis et representat qualitates corporum ex quibus fit radiatio quantum ad sui profundum, utrum videlicet sint magis vel minus terminata vel spissa.' Theodorici Teutonici de Vriburgo, De Coloribus, C. 16, MS Vat. Lat. 2183, f. 120ᵛ; cf. Wallace, Theodoric of Freiberg, pp. 170–1, 376, below, pp. 353–4.

[1] It has even been suggested that Theodoric was a pupil of Albertus, though this is improbable: Krebs, Meister Dietrich, pp. 17–19, 47.

[2] 'dominum Albertum illum famosum', De Intelligentiis et Motoribus Caelorum, C. 3, in Krebs, op. cit., p. 57*; cf. Duhem, Syst. monde, iii. 383–96.

[3] 'Avicenna, Averrois, Albertus, Thomas', De Miscibilibus in Mixto, Prooemium, in Krebs, op. cit., p. 45*; De Tribus Difficilibus Articulis, in Krebs, op. cit., p. 84*; cf. also Krebs, op. cit., pp. 50, 216*.

[4] 'auctor in tractatu suo de sensu et sensato' (De Iride, ii. 4, p. 68) may refer to Albertus; see Krebs, op. cit., pp. 23*, 47; below, p. 243, n. 6.

[5] 'caeruleus seu citrinus' (De Iride, ii. 1, p. 60); cf. above, p. 199, n. 4; below, p. 243, n. 7, p. 244, n. 1.

[6] De Iride, ii. 24, pp. 107–13; below, p. 241; see above, p. 160, n. 1, p. 197.

[7] De Iride, ii. 2, pp. 64–5; above, pp. 125–6, 198.

Meteorologica and other writings, Euclid's *Elements,* Theodosius's *Sphaera,* Ptolemy's *Almagest,* and various works by Avicenna and Averroës.[1] In *De Iride,* he referred also frequently to *liber perspectivae, in quarto perspectivae, in septimo perspectivae, perspectivae,*[2] and to *auctor perspectivae.*[3] Krebs has shown that most of these citations correspond to the matter of Alhazen's *Optica* and not to works by Ptolemy, Roger Bacon, Witelo, or Pecham.[4] But some of the references to *auctor perspectivae* could certainly apply as well to Witelo, Alhazen's commentator, as to Alhazen himself.[5] This is particularly true to the citations connected with the production of colours by the weakening of light by refraction through hexagonal crystals or transparent spheres;[6] in fact, no experiments of this kind are mentioned in the known writings of Alhazen in Latin.[7] Another resemblance to Witelo is Theodoric's use of the expression *lumen . . . aggregatur et conculcatur*[8] to explain the greater brightness of the red rays emerging from such bodies. Moreover, in writing of the spherical burning lens Theodoric mentioned 'students of optics' (*perspectivorum*)[9] in the plural, and his account suggests a knowledge of the thirteenth-century Latin writings on this instrument. The use elsewhere of the phrases *multiplicatio seu speciei transmissio*[10] and *impressionum propria forma seu species est lumen*[11] suggests that Theo-

---

[1] See the indices in Krebs's *Meister Dietrich* and Würschmidt's edition of *De Iride.*

[2] *De Iride,* pp. 38, 39, 41, 48–49, 77, 98, 115, 128.

[3] Ibid., pp. 43, 77, 100, 117, 119.

[4] Krebs, *Meister Dietrich,* pp. 40–41.

[5] e.g., cf. *De Iride,* pp. 88 (there is no colour without light), 89 (rays have breadth) with Vitellonis *Opticae,* x. 83, p. 474, and ii. 3, pp. 63–64, respectively. Cf. above, pp. 232, 219, n. 5; below, p. 246, nn. 1, 2.

[6] *De Iride,* ii. 8, p. 76, C. 17, p. 96; iii. 6, p. 156. See also i. 8, p. 48. Cf. above, pp. 230 sqq., below, p. 246.

[7] Cf. Wiedemann's papers, above, p. 147, n. 2. The weakening of light by refraction is mentioned in Alhazeni *Opticae,* i. 3, vii. 38.

[8] *De Iride,* ii. 15, p. 90. See also pp. 91, 94; ii. 4, p. 69; and *De Luce et eius Origine,* in Krebs, *Meister Dietrich,* pp. 21*, 22*; below, pp. 243, 248, n. 4. Cf. Vitellonis *Opticae,* x. 83, pp. 473–4; above, p. 230, n. 3; cf. above, p. 216, n. 3, p. 226, n. 7, p. 227, n. 5, p. 229, n. 2; and Grosseteste, above, p. 123.

[9] 'Quod propter probationem perspectivorum patet sensibile experimento in lapide cristallino sphaerico, quem berillum vocant. . . .' *De Iride,* ii. 30, pp. 121–2; cf. above, pp. 119, 122, 226, n. 3. In another passage he wrote of the weakening of light by reflection: 'quod pertractatur apud perspectivos et etiam per experientiam habetur. . . .' Ibid. iii. 9, p. 161; cf. below, p. 242, n. 4; above, pp. 120–2, 199, 229 sqq.

[10] '. . . multiplicat et transmittit speciem suam ad visum, quae multiplicatio seu speciei transmissio vocetur radiatio rei ad visum.' *De Iride,* i. 5, p. 42.

[11] *De Iride,* i. 1, p. 36; below, p. 242, n. 7. Also: 'formae vel speciei sunt formae radiantes.' Ibid. ii. 7, pp. 74–75; see also pp. 100, 128.

doric might in fact have known Roger Bacon or Grosseteste as well as Witelo, who always used the word *forma*[1] where Bacon and Grosseteste used *species*. Theodoric's reference to the fact that the rainbow seen by an observer moved with him, because as he moved his eyes received rays coming from different drops of water in the atmosphere, could have come either from Roger Bacon or Witelo, or from their source, Alexander of Aphrodisias.[2]

There is, then, strong circumstantial evidence, though no direct proof, that Theodoric knew, and was influenced by, the work not only of Albertus Magnus, but also of the other main thirteenth-century Latin writers on optics. It would, indeed, have been difficult for him, with his Parisian training and his prominence in a great teaching Order, not to have become acquainted with writings that were so widely cited by his contemporaries. Moreover, like these other Latin writers, Theodoric was a Neoplatonist and was led to the study of optics by 'light metaphysics'.[3] And as they were all more or less intimately connected with the Oxford school, it is not surprising to find that Theodoric's statements about method, as well as his experimental work, were in the same tradition.

In keeping with the philosophical motive that had inspired the thirteenth-century work or scientific method, Theodoric began his treatise on the rainbow with the statement that the best science was that which either dealt with the most noble subjects or provided the most certain knowledge, and he went on to say that knowledge of the rainbow, itself a subject of admirable beauty, was guaranteed 'by the combination of various infallible experiments with the efficacy of reasoning, as is clear enough from what follows'.[4] Continuing with

[1] For Witelo, see above, p. 215.

[2] *De Iride*, ii. 2, p. 65; C. 24, p. 112; C. 31, pp. 123-4. Cf. Roger Bacon, above, p. 158; Witelo, above, p. 227, n. 2. Another resemblance to Witelo is Theodoric's account (*De Iride*, ii. 40, p. 140, below, p. 255, n. 4) of the rainbow as the common base of two pyramids or cones; cf. Witelo, above, p. 227.

[3] Cf. below, pp. 242 sqq. Theodoric's Neoplatonism was based principally on St. Augustine and on Proclus's *Elementa Theologiae*, which had been translated into Latin by William of Moerbeke, to whom Witelo dedicated his *Perspectiva*. See *De Intelligentiis*, C. 7 in Krebs, *Meister Dietrich*, p. 59* (emanation theory); *De Tribus Difficilibus Articulis*, ibid., pp. 64*, 70*, 76*; *De Intellectu et Intelligibili*, ibid., pp. 119* sqq. See also ibid., pp. 64 sqq.; Baeumker, 'Der Platonismus im Mittelalter', in *Studien und Charakteristiken* . . ., pp. 160 sqq.; de Wulf, *Hist. Mediaeval Philos.* ii. 279-84.

[4] 'Est autem harum rerum notitia certioribus viis et efficacioribus rationibus certificata concurrentibus ad hoc simul variis et infallibilibus experimentis cum efficacia rationum, prout ex sequentibus satis claret.' *De Iride*, Prol. Epist., p. 34.

an account of the method to be used in studying the rainbow,[1] he said:

The first thing to be considered is the statement of the Philosopher [Aristotle] in the *Posterior Analytics*, namely, that in the science of the rainbow it is the function of physics to determine what the rainbow is (*quid est*) and of optics to determine the reason (*propter quid*). The meaning of this statement, as is shown in the same book, is that definition is twofold, whether it be of the subject or of the effect (*sive subiecti sive passionis*). One form of definition tells what the thing is in itself absolutely, and this form, if it be of the subject, can be the origin of a demonstration,[2] just as the subject itself to which this definition belongs is the origin of a demonstration. But if it be the definition of the effect, the definition is the conclusion of a demonstration, just as that effect itself is, according to the Philosopher in the same book. And according to the first mode of defining, it pertains to natural philosophy, in considering the rainbow, to say what it is (*quid est*), as for example they may tell in this or some similar manner that the rainbow is some sort of concentration (*emphasis*) in rainy or cloudy air, qualitatively determined in this manner as to the number, order and position of the colours extended in an arc above the level of the horizon.

There is another form of definition by which is determined what is the being of a thing (*quod est esse rei*), namely by the definition telling both what it is and the reason. This is one and the same definition of the subject and of the effect, telling what the subject is and why the effect happens, because it introduces the cause of the effect happening in the subject and is therefore the middle term of the demonstration,[3] and moreover that definition and the whole demonstration differ only by position,[4] according to the Philosopher. In this way it is the function of optics to determine what the rainbow is, because in so doing it shows the reason for it, in so far as, to the aforesaid description of the rainbow, is added the manner in which this sort of concentration may be produced in the luminous radiation going from any shining heavenly body to a determined place in the cloud, and then by particular refractions and reflections of rays is directed from the determined place to the eye. For this reason, therefore, the science of optics subordinates to itself the science of the rainbow and of the other impressions produced by rays in the sky. And because of what has been said it is convenient, indeed necessary, for optical and philosophical reasoning to be used together in this present matter.[5]

---

[1] 'Quis modus philosophicae considerationis competat scientiae de iride et aliis radialibus impressionibus.' *De Iride*, i. 2, p. 36.

[2] Theodoric was familiar with arguments 'descendentes ex possibilitate talis naturae communis.' Ibid. ii. 12, p. 84. Cf. above, pp. 63–66.

[3] 'dicens quid est subiecti et propter quid passionis, quia importat causam passionis in subiecto, et ideo est medium demonstrationis.'

[4] See above, p. 53, n. 4.   [5] *De Iride*, i. 2, pp. 36–37. Cf. above, pp. 54, 117, 124.

Theodoric's method of investigating the cause of the rainbow involved not only a combination of geometry and experiment, but also two logical devices in common use among his Oxford predecessors, namely, the principles of falsification and of economy. In disposing of an erroneous theory according to which the rainbow was supposed to be produced by sunlight reflected from the surface of one cloud on to the concave surface of another cloud, where the observer saw it, he used two main lines of argument. First, he showed that empirical consequences deduced from the theory were contradicted by experience:[1] e.g. the expected order of the colours on the concave cloud would be the reverse of that seen[2] and the colours would remain stationary instead of moving as the observer moved. A second, subsidiary argument was that to postulate two clouds was superfluous since all the appearances could be saved by assuming that the rainbow was seen in rays coming to the eye directly from one cloud.[3]

His treatise, *De Iride et Radialibus Impressionibus*, on 'impressions' seen in the sky, Theodoric divided into four parts.[4] In the first part he began by dividing these *impressiones* into two classes, *naturales* (comets, *ignes volantes*, clouds, mist, &c.), and *radiales*.[5] He went on to give an account of the three modes of apprehending anything by vision (by direct, reflected, and refracted rays)[6] and an enumeration of fifteen different species of *impressiones radiales* which he

---

[1] 'Quod autem dicunt de generatione iridis ex modo reflexionis radiorum solarium a nube rorida in aliam nubem, nec rationi nec manifesto sensus convenit.' Ibid. ii. 24, p. 108.

[2] 'quod falsum est et secundum manifestum sensum videmus contrarium in iride inferiori, quae est principalis.' (Ibid., p. 111; cf. above, pp. 125, 197, n. 5.) He used the same argument in *De Intelligentiis* when he said of the system of concentric spheres advanced by Aristotle and Averroës to explain the planetary motions: 'the falsity can be demonstrated by the effect (*per efficaciam*)' (Duhem, *Syst. monde*, iii. 393). Theodoric preferred Ptolemy's astronomical system.

[3] 'Est etiam superfluum ponere tales duas nubes, ut dicunt, cum una ipsarum et sola posita . . . possit . . . omnis apparentia salvari, sicut infra ostendetur.' (Ibid., p. 112.) The two-cloud theory discussed by Theodoric is the same as that mentioned by Albertus Magnus in his criticism of Posidonius, and Theodoric's criticisms are similar to those of Albertus (above, pp. 197 sqq.). Theodoric also mentioned two experiments which 'dicunt isti' (i.e. writers on the rainbow): the production, first, of a rainbow by sprinkling water into the sun's rays shining on a wall; and, secondly, of the same colours by 'tribus vel quatuor vitris coloratis' (*De Iride*, ii. 24, pp. 108, 113). The first was mentioned by both Aristotle (*Meteor.* 374ᵃ35 sqq.) and Albertus (above, p. 198, n. 1), and the second by Albertus (above, p. 198, n. 2).

[4] *De Iride*, Prol. Epist., pp. 34–35.

[5] Ibid. i. 1, pp. 35–36.

[6] Ibid. i. 3–5, pp. 38–43; cf. above, pp. 120, n. 5, 158–9.

had observed or read about.[1] These included primary and secondary rainbows and the appearance of the sky in their neighbourhood, white and red rainbows, white and coloured halos round the sun and moon, mock suns, parahelia and colours in stars seen through mist. These, he said, were all the types of *impressiones radiales* known to him and he thought that any others would prove to be reducible in form, appearance, and cause to one of them.[2] In their production five types of radiation were involved.[3] These were a single reflection,[4] a single refraction, two refractions and a single internal reflection in a drop of water or a crystal sphere, two refractions and two internal reflections in the same, and total reflection at the boundary of two transparent media.[5] He concluded the first part of *De Iride* with an account of different types of atmospheric moisture in which *impressiones radiales* were generated.[6] This moisture was either continuous (*vapores, nubes et caligines*) or discontinuous (*nubes, rorida, pluvia, nebula*).

The second, third, and fourth parts of *De Iride* Theodoric devoted to the primary rainbow, the secondary rainbow, and the halo and the remaining types of *impressiones radiales*, respectively.

(2)

Of all these *impressiones radiales* Theodoric said that light was the form and the transparent medium the matter.[7] The nature of light he discussed in *De Luce et eius Origine*, beginning with the question: 'By what way is the light scattered and heat distributed upon the earth? (Job 38.) This difficult question the Lord proposed

---

[1] '*Enumeratio radialium impressionum, quae apparent in alto huius elementaris regionis ...sive per scripturam sive per propriam experiendi diligentiam. ...*' *De Iride,* i. 6, p. 44.

[2] 'Si autem aliqui alii deprehensi sunt per aliorum ampliorem experientiam, aestimo, quod omnes tales ad aliquem praedictorum modorum reducuntur et quantum ad suam formam et apparitionem et quantum ad suas causas.' Ibid., p. 47.

[3] '*De modis radiationum, ex quibus generantur dictae radiales impressiones. ...*' Ibid. i. 7, p. 47.

[4] 'in quantum autem talis radiatio causat apparentiam colorum resultantium ex ipsa tali radiatione, experimur hunc modum impressionis in pennis pavonum et anatum et filis telae aranearum et aliis pluribus.' Ibid. i. 7, p. 48. Cf. Roger Bacon and Witelo on the production of colours by reflection.

[5] On these see ibid. i. 8–11, pp. 48–52. See also Krebs, *Meister Dietrich,* pp. 51–52, 29*. Cf. above, p. 236.

[6] *De Iride,* i. 12, p. 52. See i. 12–17, pp. 52–56.

[7] 'Radiales. ... Quarum impressionum propria forma seu species est lumen secundum tales vel tales incidentias et fractiones irradiationum et talibus vel talibus coloribus tinctum et per consequens sic vel sic figuratum.' Ibid. i. 1, p. 36.

to holy Job.'[1] The problem was to explain why a transparent medium took the 'form' of light in the presence of a luminous body. According to Theodoric, 'Light is a real quality or form of the transparent medium', but nevertheless only an 'accidental form' or disposition of the medium.[2] Light was not itself an active power but the result of the active disposition of the medium to aggregate its parts in the presence of a luminous body, and this disposition was the efficient cause of brightness.[3] Visible light was thus the result of the actualization of a potentiality of the medium. Of the heat that accompanied it light was simply the vehicle.[4] The perception of light was possible because of the relationship established between light and the organs of vision.[5] Moreover, he said that 'formally light is the whole substance of colour'. In a separate treatise, *De Coloribus*, he went on:

That which is light in the depths of a transparent medium, namely, that which is its active principle and form which makes it bright, is colour in a bounded medium, which makes the same thing coloured. Hence, as light is educed from an accidental potential in an unbounded medium by the presence of a luminous body, so that in its depths it becomes bright, so colour is brought into actuality by being educed from an accidental potential by the presence of such a luminous body.[6]

The number of real 'simple' colours intermediate between white and black Theodoric maintained was four.[7] Aristotle had said that

---

[1] *De Luce*, C. 1, MS Vat. Lat. 2183, f. 65vb; Krebs, *Meister Dietrich*, p. 18*. In C. 2, MS Vat. Lat. 2183, f. 66^r, Theodoric discussed the relation between God and physics, and concluded that the natural philosopher investigated not God's direct, omnipotent will but the divinely willed laws of nature. Cf. Albertus Magnus, above, p. 192, n. 5. Krebs, *Meister Dietrich*, p. 75, n. 3.

[2] 'Lumen est realis qualitas seu forma dyaphani . . . sed forma accidentalis; omnis autem forma accidentalis naturalis non est nisi dispositio quedam. . . .' *De Luce*, C. 8, MS Vat. 2183, f. 67^r; cf. Krebs, op. cit., p. 20* and pp. 27-50, for a full discussion of Theodoric's theory of light and colour.

[3] 'Idem patet in speciali ex natura luminosi quod inquantum luminosum non habet virtutem activam in se, quod patet primo in effectu quia lumen formaliter est tota substantia coloris. . . . lumen non est nisi vehiculum "activorum" virtutum, sive agant calefaciendo sive infrigidando; . . . luminosum non importat nisi lumen conculcatum; non est enim luminosum nisi conculcatio partium dyaphani in actu lucidi.' *De Luce*, C. 16, MS Vat. Lat. 2183, f. 68^r. Cf. ibid., C. 17, f. 68^v. Cf. *De Iride*, ii. 4, p. 69; above, p. 238, n. 8.

[4] Cf. Albertus Magnus, above, p. 195.

[5] *De Luce*, C. 7, MS Vat. Lat. 2183, f. 67^r; Krebs, op.cit., pp. 19*-20*.

[6] *De Coloribus*, C. 1, MS Vat. Lat. 2183, f. 118^v; Krebs, op. cit., p. 23*. See also *De Iride*, ii. 4, p. 69, C. 5, p. 70, C. 14, pp. 87-88.

[7] 'Sunt autem hi quatuor colores secundum manifestum sensum, primus rubeus seu purpureus, secundus caeruleus, quem xancton vocant, viridis autem tertius, quartus

only three were real, namely red, green, and blue, and Aristotle's
followers had said that the fourth colour, yellow, seen in the rainbow, was merely the result of some sort of deception of vision,[1] for
example by distance. But, Theodoric asserted, while granting that
the authority of Aristotle was to be respected, 'we know also that
according to that same Philosopher one ought never to renounce
what has been made manifest by the senses'.[2] He continued:

It is manifest in daily experience that in spiders' webs, which are
stretched out and closely covered with many drops of dew in a suitable
position with respect to the sun and the eye, the colour in question, namely
yellow, appears most plainly between the other colours of the rainbow in
its place and order as in the rainbow; and so close to the eye, if one wishes,
that there is scarcely a hand's breadth or less between the eye and the web.
The same thing is seen in the rainbow which is often seen round mill-
wheels and which is produced there because of the ample flow and great
scattering of drops of water dispersed by the fall of water on to the wheels.
The same thing is plainly seen also in drops of dew dispersed on the
grass if one applies the eye very close to them so that the drops have a
determined position with respect to the sun and the eye.[3] Then in a particular position red appears, but when the eye is moved a little from that
position yellow appears plainly and quite distinct from the other colours.
Then with a further change of position the other colours of the rainbow
appear in the usual number and order.
Again the same thing is apparent when things are seen with the colours
of the rainbow through a hexagonal crystal, where, with the eye in one and
the same position with respect to the crystal, all four colours appear, even
when the eye is held very close to the crystal.[4]
Precisely the same may be said of an example which is plain to everyone
and even clearer than those already described. For it can be clearly seen
that walls or other bodies placed in the way are coloured with all four usual

vero lazulius, quem alurgum nominant.' De Iride, ii. 1, p. 60. Cf. above, p. 111, n. 5;
p. 199, n. 2; p. 229, n. 6; Krebs, op. cit., pp. 35, 24*.
    [1] 'caeruleus seu citrinus, quem xancton vocant . . . non est verus color in se secundum
propriam suam naturam, ut dicunt, sed solum secundum apprehensionem visus . . .
citrinus seu glaucus. . . .' (Loc. cit.) The names of the colours suggest that Theodoric
was referring to Albertus Magnus and Witelo. See above, p. 199, nn. 2, 3; p. 229,
n. 4, p. 230, n. 3.
    [2] 'Scimus autem, quod secundum eundem Philosophum a manifestis secundum sen-
sum nequaquam recedendum est. Videmus autem manifeste dictum colorem sive citrinum apparere in iride inter rubeum et viridem. . . . (De Iride, ii. 1, p. 61.) He expressed
the same empirical attitude in his De Elementiis Corporum Naturalium in quantum sunt
Partes Mundi, C. 9, in Krebs, Meister Dietrich, p. 52*: 'Ego etiam per propriam exami-
nationem sensus adverti idem et non solum ego sed etiam plurimi modernorum hoc
idem invenerunt.' Cf. Duhem, Syst. monde, iii. 387–96; above, p. 241, n. 2.
    [3] Cf. Roger Bacon, above, p. 156.   [4] Cf. Witelo's experiment, above, p. 230, n. 3.

colours by the radiation which goes from the sun through the oft-mentioned hexagonal crystal, where next to red (*rubeus*) yellow (*citrinus*) gleams very brightly, then green (*viridis*) and next to that blue (*alurgus*) according to whatever nearness to the eye you please.[1]

The reality of the colour in question, namely yellow, between the other colours of the rainbow, is plainly seen also if a person standing in the shade sprinkles water into the light of the sun, the eye being in, and the sprinkling being done from, a position between the sun and the place in which the water is sprinkled, as the Philosopher [Aristotle] says.[2]

Therefore it can be most certainly asserted that the said colours, which appear in the rainbow, are truly and really four.[3]

These four intermediate colours and the two extremes (white and black) were produced, Theodoric said, by variations of the same cause,[4] and he went on to investigate this cause experimentally. His explanation of colour was in fact a version of the Aristotelian theory of combinations of brightness and darkness. He attributed the production of the colours to the different proportions in combination of the formal principle, the brightness of the light, with the material principle, the transparency of the medium, and he identified the degree of transparency with the degree of unboundedness of the medium.[5] The formal was the active principle and the material the passive, and Theodoric tried to show how the different colours would result from different combinations of the two pairs of opposite qualities, greater and less brightness and greater and less boundedness, in the same way as the four Aristotelian elements were produced by different combinations of the primary qualities, hot, cold, wet, dry.[6]

[1] 'secundum propinquitatem visus ad dictos colores, quem quisque voluerit.' This is what MS Basel F.IV.30, f. 10ᵛ, reads, and what I have translated. The phrase printed in *De Iride*, p. 62, ll. 19–20, is meaningless. Cf. p. 61, l. 30.

[2] *De Iride*, ii. 1, pp. 61–62. He went on to dispose of an absurd argument from analogy which Aristotle advanced for there being only three colours: '. . . et similia ridiculosa.' Ibid., pp. 62–63.   [3] Ibid., p. 63.

[4] 'In generatione autem iridis necessario omnes similiter concurrunt et omnes apparent secundum suas species et loca distincta. Cuius causa est . . . quod omnes hi medii colores secundum suam totalitatem in generatione mediorum ex tota sua causa constant, tam quoad causam efficientem, quam quoad causam materialem seu corpus subiectum cum suis propriis dispositionibus, quantum etiam ad principia sua formalia; de quibus . . . agitur in tractatu nostro de coloribus.' Ibid., pp. 63–64.

[5] 'multa et pauca luminositas. . . multa et pauca diaphanitas.' (Ibid. ii. 4, pp. 68–69.) Cf. *De Coloribus*, CC. 1–5, MS Vat. Lat. 2183, ff. 118ᵛ–119ʳ. The basis of Theodoric's theory of combinations of brightness and transparency was Averroës's *De Sensu et Sensato*; see Krebs, *Meister Dietrich*, pp. 33 sqq., 23* sqq.

[6] *De Iride*, ii. 4–5, 10–13, pp. 67–71, 79–87.

In a transparent body, for example, a hexagonal or spherical crystal or a spherical flask filled with water, he said, the degree of boundedness was greater the nearer a point in the body was to its surface.[1] Moreover, he pointed out that the experimental fact that a light-stream, on emerging from a refracting body, spread out more and more the farther it went from the body, showed that it was not simply a geometrical line but had breadth and depth like a column. Different points on the cross-section of this column would therefore pass through parts of the transparent body with different degrees of boundedness.[2]

These notions Theodoric combined with the contemporary under-standing of refraction.[3] He knew that light falling perpendicularly on to the surface between two transparent media passed through unrefracted, and that light falling obliquely on such a surface was refracted at a determined angle, which depended on the nature of the media.[4] Light passing from a rarer to a denser medium was refracted towards the perpendicular to the common surface, and this perpendicular and the incident and refracted rays were all in the same plane. The light falling perpendicularly, he reasserted, retained its full strength and therefore suffered no 'qualitative affections'. Its brightness remained undiminished and it remained white.[5] The oblique light, however, was refracted and therefore weakened, and so was more affected by the resistance which all bounded bodies offered. According to the degree to which brightness was weakened by different amounts of refraction,[6] and to the degree of bounded-

---

[1] 'Lux autem non radiat sine colore et color sine luce; ideo oportet medium, per quod fit radiatio, partim esse terminatum, partim interminatum.' De Iride, ii. 5, p. 70.

[2] 'de causis diversitatis situs colorum radialium . . . quod omnis radiatio, seu sit radiatio lucis, seu coloris . . . spissitudinem quandam habet in sua substantia . . . sicut longitudinem habet in suo processu, sic et latitudinem et profunditudinem habet in sua substantia per modum cuiusdam columnae . . . ut experimento patet. . . .' (Ibid. ii. 15, pp. 89–90.) See also C. 7, p. 74, where reference is made to Alhazeni Opticae, iv. 16, ed. Risner, p. 112. The same point is made in Vitellonis Opticae, ii. 3, pp. 63–64.

[3] He gave a summary of this in De Iride, ii. 8, pp. 75–78. Figs. 7, 8 belong to this chapter: it contains an account of total internal reflection in hexagonal crystals and spheres (above, p. 236, n. 3, below, p. 249).

[4] What must be one of the earliest references to spectacles occurs in Theodoric's De Intellectu et Intelligibili, iii. 25, in Krebs, op. cit., p. 193*. Speaking of the sense organs he said: 'talia, quae dicta sunt, sunt instrumenta naturae. In usu autem et opera-tione aliquorum sensuum non nunquam etiam arte utuntur, ut patet de illis, qui vident per berillum et similia.' Cf. above, p. 151, n. 1, p. 164, n. 1.

[5] Blackness was the result of the total absence of brightness; De Coloribus, C. 6, MS Vat. Lat. 2183, f. 119ʳ; Krebs, Meister Dietrich, pp. 24*, 37.

[6] Theodoric thought also that the colours of the rainbow were produced partly by

ness of the parts through which the column of light passed, the four colours emerged at determined positions, red being closest to the original line of incidence. 'Sensible experience showing us this', he said:

If radiation from the sun enters obliquely into any body of the kind discussed, such oblique incidence is necessary in this way for the production of these colours: the radiation after its emergence from the opposite side of the [transparent] body is differentiated into the four usual colours; and a solid [opaque] body on which it falls is coloured with the same colours in the same order,[1] namely, so that the brighter colours, red and yellow, keep to the side of the original line of incidence and consequently on the side of the passage of such radiation near the angles and angular sides, then the other less bright colours, green and blue, follow in their place and always, as has been said above, in the same inviolable order by which yellow follows red, and after that comes green, and finally blue.[2]

By an application of the principle of the uniformity of nature Theodoric held that wherever the four intermediate 'simple' colours were seen in the same order, they had the same total cause.[3] These colours were not only quantitatively but also specifically different.[4] All other colours were merely the result of mixtures of 'simple' ones.[5]

The inadequacy of Theodoric's theory of colour is clearly shown by the changes he had to ring on the combinations of opposites to make it agree with the observations; in contrast, his almost unfailing

weak dispersed light falling on the drops of water in the atmosphere, as well as by the direct light; De Iride, ii. 5, p. 70, see Krebs, op. cit., pp. 38, 55.

[1] Reading 'eundem' instead of 'eum' in De Iride, p. 92, l. 8; MS Basel F.IV.30, f. 19ᵛ, reads 'eum situm'.

[2] De Iride, ii. 16, p. 92. For similar experiments see De Coloribus, CC. 8–9, MS Vat. Lat. 2183, f. 119ᵛ; Krebs, Meister Dietrich, pp. 24*–25*.

[3] 'De causa autem ordinis istorum colorum ad invicem, quo semper et infallibiliter ubicunque dicti quatuor colores ex radiatione fulgent, semper iuxta rubeum apparet citrinus, deinde iuxta hunc viridis, consequenter autem iuxta hunc lazulius, hoc considerandum, quod in omni generatione entium, quae secundum totalitatem suae generationis ex tota sua causa constant, quantum ad omnia sua principia causalia essentialia, sicut ex huiusmodi totis principiis causalibus constant in suis specificis formis in una coordinatione suae generationis, ita ratione talium principiorum causalium ab invicem secundum suas species distinguuntur.' De Iride, ii. 12, pp. 83–84. Cf. ii. 1, pp. 63–64 (above, p. 245, n.4), C. 11, pp. 81–82.

[4] 'medii colores a se invicem secundum speciem differunt. Permixtio autem albi et nigri . . . non diversificat speciem; magis enim et minus speciem non variant.' (Ibid. ii. 3, pp. 66–67.) For a longer treatment of the problem of qualitative and quantitative change see Theodoric's De Magis et Minus, MS Vat. Lat. 2183, ff. 127ᵛ–130ᵛ; Krebs, op. cit., pp. 11*–14*. See also De Luce, C. 13, ff. 67ᵛ–68; Krebs, op. cit., pp. 20*–21*.

[5] De Coloribus, C. 6, MS Vat. Lat. 2183, f. 119ʳ; Krebs, op. cit., p. 24*.

adherence to experimental facts is all the more striking. According to theory the four intermediate colours should have arisen as follows: brightness and boundedness produced red, brightness and unboundedness yellow, darkness and unboundedness green, darkness and boundedness blue.[1] But as this contradicted the fact that blue emerged from a transparent body, for example a hexagonal crystal, on the side of the light-stream farthest from the sides of the body, he introduced the surprising notion that 'colour as colour' had an unbounded 'intentional' nature and 'light as light' a bounded nature, though he reasserted the principle that there was no light without colour or colour without light.[2] Hence, he said, the darker colours appeared in the less bounded, and the brighter colours in the more bounded, parts of the medium.[3] The reason for the appearance of the brighter colours in the light passing through the more bounded parts of the transparent body (e.g. hexagonal crystal) was that in this region the rays became more concentrated by reflection from the sides.[4] He correctly observed, however, that when a screen was held at less than a minimum distance 'of one or two digits' from the crystal the emerging light falling on it appeared white, and that when the eye was substituted for the screen the four colours appeared in the emerging rays in the reverse of the usual order.[5] The first of these facts he attributed to the strength of the light itself, which prevented the reduction of the four opposite qualities *ad mediam proportionem* until it had emerged about the width of two fingers from the crystal.[6] The second fact he tried to attribute to the operation of radiation *in quantum coloratum*.[7]

(3)

Having worked out his theory of the colours seen in light refracted through hexagonal crystals and transparent spherical balls, Theodoric used the latter as a model by which to explain the rainbow. This involved three important discoveries which he made by means

[1] *De Iride*, ii. 11, pp. 82–83. These four colours corresponded with the four elements, respectively, fire (hot–dry), air (hot–wet), water (cold–wet), earth (cold–dry).

[2] Ibid. ii. 14, pp. 88–89. See also pp. 14–15, and Krebs, op. cit., p. 38.

[3] *De Iride*, ii. 12–16, pp. 83–94. Cf. Albertus Magnus, above, p. 199.

[4] *De Iride*, ii. 15, p. 90; C. 16, p. 92. Cf. Witelo, above, p. 230.

[5] 'Experimento enim perpendimus . . .' *De Iride*, ii. 17, pp. 94–95.

[6] Ibid., pp. 95–96; cf. ii. 6, p. 72, and p. 11.

[7] Ibid. ii. 17, p. 96. The modern explanation of this is that the reversal of colours is subjective.

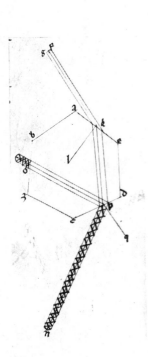

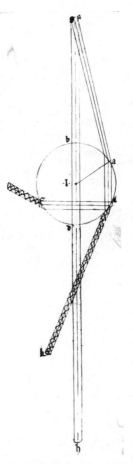

Fig. 7. The passage of light through a hexagonal crystal, showing internal reflection and the formation of colours (cross-hatched). From Theodoric of Freiberg's *De Iride*, ii. 8, MS Basel F. IV. 30, f. 15ʳ. See p. 246, n. 3.

Fig. 8. The passage of light through a spherical ball, showing internal reflection and the formation of colours (cross-hatched). From Theodoric of Freiberg's *De Iride*, ii. 8, MS Basel F. IV. 30, f. 15ᵛ. See p. 246, n. 3, p. 249. In this (diagram the angles of incidence and reflection at the inner surface of the drop are incorrectly drawn unequal.

of a careful experimental study of the paths of the different rays in a light-stream entering a spherical crystal ball or glass flask of water, which he used as a model raindrop. His first discovery was that some of the light was reflected by the inner surface of such a sphere (Figs. 7, 8).[1] He said:

Let the radiation enter the oft-mentioned transparent body and pass through it to the opposite surface and from that be reflected internally back to the first surface by which it originally entered, and then after passing out let it go to the eye; such radiation, I say, in as much as it is produced by a transparent spherical body, serves to explain the production of the rainbow. . . . Moreover, since, as was said above, any incident ray or radiation is not linear and indivisible but has depth and breadth like a column, therefore in any diagrams in the present work a light stream is represented by two lines bounding the light stream on either side.[2]

The light-stream was, he said, refracted on entering the sphere, reflected at the inner surface, and refracted a second time on passing out again. In his account of the passage of the rays through a large sphere he seems to have been deceived by obscure reasoning from his theory of the 'intentional' unboundedness of 'colour as colour' into thinking that the rays passing nearest the centre of the sphere would show the colour red. That is, he supposed that the ray *qms* in Fig. 9 would appear red, and that the ray *hlr*, which emerged from the sphere below the red ray, would appear blue.[3] This is a reversal of what would be the observed order of the colours. Nevertheless, he correctly argued that the rays representing the individual colours would intersect inside the sphere after being reflected once by the inner surface. This implies that he correctly understood, as Witelo had done,[4] that the colours were formed *inside* the sphere after the first refraction, and not merely on the re-emergence of the rays into the air.[5]

In a very small sphere, for example a dewdrop or a raindrop, he argued that the colour red would appear in the rays passing nearest

---

[1] Cf. above, p. 236, n. 3; *De Iride*, i. 8–11, above, pp. 241–2; ii. 8, above, p. 246, n. 3.

[2] *De Iride*, ii. 18, p. 97.

[3] He concluded his account (ibid. ii. 18–20, pp. 97–102) with the remark: 'Istae autem apparitiones colorum manifesto experimento patent, sed ratio eorum patet ex iam dictis. . . .' He could not have observed what he claimed.

[4] Above, p. 231.

[5] 'Sic ergo proportio seu pars *qm* defert ad visum magis claros colores sive rubeum et citrinum, pars autem alia sive *hl* repraesentat alios.' (Ibid. ii. 19, p. 100.) In fact *qm* would be blue and *hl* red.

the outer surface, owing to the concentration of the rays in a small body.[1] That is, in Fig. 10 the red rays would appear on the line *o* at the bottom of the emerging light-stream, and the other colours in order above it. This is the order that would be observed. In a small sphere the rays intersected after the internal reflection, just as in a large sphere, but he said he would not draw in the paths of the individual rays inside the sphere.[2] He showed, by an experiment in which two streams of light were passed, respectively, through the two halves of a hexagonal crystal so that they intersected before falling on to a screen (Fig. 11), that the different colours could intersect without losing their identity.[3] The light-stream which was refracted on entering raindrops, reflected internally once, and refracted a second time on emerging into the air, produced the lower (primary) rainbow.

Theodoric's second discovery was to show that when a sphere was held in a suitable position in relation to the sun and to the eye, and either the eye or the sphere itself was raised and lowered, then, because the light-stream 'has width and depth', different colours were seen according to the position taken.[4] Thus all the colours could not come to the eye simultaneously from the same sphere, and if they were all seen at the same time the different colours must come from different spheres. Therefore the different colours seen in the rainbow must come from different drops in the atmosphere.

Thirdly, Theodoric showed that besides these colours emerging after a single internal reflection, there was a second coloured light-stream which had undergone a second internal reflection before being refracted out of the sphere. In this second stream the colours emerged in the reverse order to those in the first stream that had emerged after being reflected only once, because it had passed round the inside of the sphere in the opposite direction to the first stream; it entered the sphere on the lower side and after the two internal

---

[1] 'quod etiam sensibiliter apparet, si quis intendat visum in huiusmodi guttas sphaerales sparsas in herbis.' Ibid. ii. 21, pp. 102–3.

[2] Ibid. ii. 21, p. 103.

[3] 'Experimento autem sensibili luce clarius videmus. . . .' Ibid. ii. 23, p. 107. Cf. Witelo's experiment, above, p. 231, n. 1, and Roger Bacon, above, p. 146, n. 6.

[4] 'manifestum est, quod sole radiante et sphaerula positis in uno situ intransmutato, sicut visu transmutante se in deorsum vel in sursum alii et alii colores veniant ad visum et . . . sole et visu in eodem situ intransmutatis, si sphaerula mutet situm secundum sursum et deorsum, secundum hoc etiam dicti colores diversi veniunt ad visum.' (*De Iride*, ii. 21, pp. 104–5.) The same experiment was described by Descartes in *Météores*, below, p. 274; see also pp. 266, 273, 277.

reflections emerged from the upper side (Fig. 14). This second stream produced the upper (secondary) rainbow.[1]

After disposing of a false theory held by certain authors,[2] Theodoric went on to apply his model to the rainbow itself, considering first the lower bow. He asserted that the material cause of the rainbow was the spherical drops of mist (*nubes rorida*) or rain (*pluvia*)[3] in the atmosphere, and the efficient cause the sunlight which entered drops that were in a determined position with respect to the sun and the eye, and was internally reflected once.[4] Only in the rays coming from those particular drops was the rainbow seen;[5] in certain other rays which came to the eye after being reflected from the convex outer surfaces of drops only white was seen.[6] The rays in which the lower rainbow was seen entered a particular drop, were reflected internally once, and emerged at points that were determined according to the laws of reflection and refraction (Fig. 12).[7] Therefore the angle which the rays going from the sun to a particular drop made with the rays returning from this drop to the eye was constant for all drops, and this angle determined the altitude (and the distance to the right or left) of the drops in which a rainbow would appear when the sun was in a particular position. Moreover, if an observer moved his position he saw a rainbow in a different set of drops.[8]

In discussing the angle between the sun, the lower rainbow, and eye Theodoric made two mistakes, one of principle and the other,

[1] Continuing the description of the experiment described in the previous footnote, he said: 'Contingit enim secundum transmutationem visus et sphaerulae eo modo, qui dictus est, colores secundum situm contrarium praedicto apparere.' *De Iride*, ii. 21, p. 105; see above, p. 242, n. 5; below, pp. 255-9.

[2] Ibid. ii. 24, 107 sqq.; see above, pp. 237-9, 241.

[3] Ibid. ii. 25, p. 113; cf. i. 15, above, pp. 237, 241-2. Cf. Albertus Magnus, above, p. 198; Witelo, above, p. 227, n. 5.

[4] *De Iride*, ii. 25, p. 114; cf. i. 9 (*De tertio modo radiationis*), above, p. 242. See below, p. 252.

[5] In ibid. ii. 26-29, pp. 114-20, a preliminary account of the rainbow is given. In the diagrams accompanying these chapters the rays coming from the sun are drawn diverging instead of parallel. Cf. above, p. 161, below, p. 274.

[6] Ibid. ii. 28, pp. 117-19. This would dispose of a theory of the rainbow such as Roger Bacon's; above, p. 160.

[7] 'et sic quaelibet tria puncta [*n, d, m*] cuiuslibet dictarum incidentiarum secundum locum et situm determinata sunt a natura secundum proprietatem fractionis, reflexionis et conversionis a speculis concavis secundum angulos determinatos incidentiae et reflexionis, qui semper sunt aequales. . . . Et sola talis et nulla alia incidentia et reflexio a quocunque puncto dicti arcus [*n m*] repraesentat colores iridis. . . .' *De Iride*, ii. 30, pp. 122-3.

[8] Ibid. ii. 31, pp. 123-4.

apparently, a slip. The first arose because he did not realize that, when compared with the distance between the bow and the eye, the sun was virtually infinitely distant and its rays virtually parallel;[1] he supposed in fact that the size of the angle between them was actually determined by the ratio of the lengths, respectively, of the rays going from the sun to the bow and from the bow to the eye.[2] The second mistake was that he said that the size of this angle was not 42°, as Roger Bacon and Witelo[3] had written, but 22°.[4] The same mistake occurs in later sections of De Iride[5] and in more than one manuscript, and Krebs has suggested that Theodoric originally copied a wrong figure and based all his other figures on this.[6] To complete his carelessness Theodoric said that anyone could measure and confirm this figure with an astrolabe![7] It represented the maximum elevation of the bow, when the sun was on the horizon.[8]

The collection of drops in which the colours of the rainbow appeared, he went on to show, did not consist of points but had breadth, and so the colours appeared in four adjacent bands. In the most elevated of these drops appeared the outer band, and in the less elevated the other three bands forming arcs of successively smaller radius.[9] 'The manner in which the colours which appear in the rainbow come to the eye, in the case of the lower rainbow,' he continued, 'may now be considered. For this purpose some knowledge relevant to the subject may be resumed from physics.' A summary followed of the results of his work showing the order of the colours emerging from 'a little aqueous or crystalline sphere [sphaerula]', and showing that the collection of drops in which the rainbow appeared had 'the breadth of the whole rainbow and also of each of its separate colours', and 'that the place of incidence of the radiation into any drop' and the places of internal reflection and of emergence

[1] Cf. above, p. 251, n. 5; cf. Roger Bacon, above, p. 150, n. 3, p. 161.

[2] De Iride, ii. 34, p. 127; C. 32, p. 124; iii. 7, p. 157.

[3] See above, pp. 158, 228.   [4] Ibid. ii. 34, pp. 126-7.

[5] Ibid. ii. 46, p. 148; iii. 14, p. 174; iv. 8, pp. 184-5. In the last passage Theodoric said, as Roger Bacon had done (above, p. 161, n. 4), that the angle subtended by the diameter of the rainbow was twice that of the halo; but whereas Bacon gave the correct values, Theodoric halved them both (below, p. 259, n. 2).

[6] See Krebs, Meister Dietrich, pp. 55-56, 32*-33*; De Iride, pp. 19-20. Theodoric took the division of the semicircle into 180° from Ptolemy's Almagest. Krebs suggests that he wrote down 158° (instead of 138°) for the greater arc between the top of the bow and the horizon, thus leaving 22° (instead of 42°) for the lesser arc. The diagram accompanying ii. 34 is careless also.

[7] De Iride, ii. 34, p. 127.   [8] See below, p. 255.

[9] De Iride, ii. 37, p. 133; cf. CC. 7, 15, 21; above, p. 246, n. 2, p. 250, n. 4.

had 'breadth, according to the different parts of which breadth the different colours of the rainbow shine so that any one of such parts has a breadth corresponding to one of the colours'. Moreover, 'in proportion as the radiation is incident along an oblique line more removed from the perpendicular, so does it go forth to the eye along another oblique line more removed from the same perpendicular.'

[So] all the colours do not come simultaneously to the eye when it is in one and the same position with respect to the drop, but different colours come to the eye according to the different positions in which it is put with respect to a particular drop. And so if all the colours are seen simultaneously, as happens in the rainbow, this must necessarily result from different drops which have different positions with respect to the eye and the eye to them. I will therefore represent the horizon by the straight line ab [Fig. 13], which is also the diameter of the sphere with its centre at c. Let the circle of altitude cutting the horizontal at right angles be adb. Let the place in the circle of altitude to which are elevated the little spherical drops in which the rainbow appears be dh. Since this does not consist of points but has breadth, as has been said, let the separate regions in which the particular colours appear be $defgh$; but let it suffice to represent by a single little sphere the aggregation or collection of elevated drops corresponding to any particular colour. Therefore let the place of incidence (which, as said above, has breadth) in any one of the said drops be indicated by the arc ln. Similarly let the place (which also has breadth) on which the radiation falls inside the little sphere be os; let the place of exit towards the eye be tz[1] and the separate parts of the same breadth be $tvxyz$; let the place where the whole radiation bearing the colours of the rainbow falls on the diameter of the sphere in the horizon be 51 and the separate places in which particular colours fall be 54321. Let the sun be placed at the surface of the horizon, so as to take a very clear example.

With the other things which we are remembering here, let not this also be forgotten, namely, that the arc drawn in the drop between the place of incidence, that is ln, and the place of exit to the eye, that is z, y, x, v, t, is greater or smaller according to whether the drop is more or less elevated in the circle of altitude above the horizon. Therefore, taking the little spherical drops elevated in the circle of altitude to the highest place from which the incident radiation from the sun can be sent to the eye, namely to de, this radiation falls on the surface of the drop in the arc ln and there, on entering the body of the drop, it is refracted towards the perpendicular and falls on the opposite internal surface of the drop in the arc os; thence it is sent back as from a mirror to the original surface, on which it falls in

---

[1] MS Basel F. IV. 30, f. 33^v reads tz (as required by the meaning of the passage), not sz, as in Würschmidt's published text (*De Iride*, p. 136, l. 10).

the arc *tz*, and going forth from there it is refracted away from the perpendicular, and, passing to the eye, it exhibits the colour red in that part of it which in its passage through the body of the drop passes near the angles and sides and narrow limits of the drop; and so the part *vt* of the radiation comes with a red colour to the eye, at the centre of the sphere, at the part of the horizon marked by 21 in the upper set of boundaries.[1] But the other three colours, namely yellow, green and blue, fall on the diameter of the sphere[2] *acb* between the eye and the sun, with yellow at 32 in the upper set of boundaries designated by these numbers, green at 43, and blue at 54, and they do not come to the eye. Only the colour red comes to the eye from the drop and indeed from the whole collection of little spherical drops elevated in the circle of altitude to *de*.

But the radiation entering the drops which are more depressed in the circle of altitude, namely those at *ef*, is sent to the eye in such a manner that, from the part *xv* of the arc *zyxvt*, the colour yellow comes to the eye at the part of the horizon 32 in the second, lower set of boundaries,[3] from whichever of the elevated drops are at the said place *ef* in the circle of altitude. But the colour red falls on the diameter of the sphere[4] in front of the eye, that is between the eye and the place where the rainbow appears; the other two, namely green and blue, fall on the diameter of the sphere behind the eye, that is between the eye and the sun; and none of these comes to the eye except only yellow.

When, however, the drops are depressed to a third position, namely *fg*, lower in the circle of altitude than those already discussed, from certain of them the colour green comes to the eye from the part *yx* of the arc *zyxvt*. Red and yellow then fall on the diameter of the sphere[5] in front of the eye, that is between the eye and the place where the rainbow appears; the fourth colour, blue, falls on the diameter of the sphere behind the eye between the eye and the sun, according to places indicated in the preceding paragraphs.

But from the drops in the lowest of the four positions in the circle of altitude, namely *hg*, the fourth colour, blue, comes to the eye from the part *zy* of the arc *zyx*. The other colours, namely red, yellow and green, fall on the diameter of the sphere in front of the eye or between the eye[6] and the rainbow, and none of all these colours comes to the eye except only blue.

[1] i.e. those shown by the upper row of numbers (54321) at the bottom of Fig. 13.

[2] Here (*De Iride*, p. 137, l. 3) and elsewhere, as indicated below, Würschmidt has misread 'sphaerae' as 'sphaerulae'. In each case reference to MS Basel F. IV. 30 has confirmed the reading demanded by the sense; in this case see f. 33ᵛ.

[3] Reading 'limitis' (p. 137, l. 12) as in MS Basel F. IV. 30, f. 33ᵛ.

[4] 'Sphaerae', ibid.

[5] Ibid. f. 34ᵛ.

[6] Würschmidt (*De Iride*, p. 137, l. 31) omitted the words 'sive inter visum' found in MS Basel F. IV. 30, f. 34ᵛ.

And so all the colours of the rainbow are seen at the same time and the whole rainbow appears in the circle of altitude in different little spherical drops according to whether they are more or less elevated to different parts of the arc *hd*, from which particular parts particular colours come to the eye in the manner described. But from drops elevated in the circle of altitude above the said arc *hd* no incident radiation is sent to the eye. The drops depressed below the said arc send some radiation incident on them to the eye, but not with the colours of the rainbow but with white light unmixed with colour, as is discussed above and more fully below.[1] Therefore, since, for the reasons stated, the colour red shines in the highest part of the circle of altitude, next to this yellow, thirdly green, and finally blue, it follows that the upper and outer circle is red, the next below yellow, then follows green, and the lowest and inner circle is blue.[2]

The reason for the circular form of the rainbow was that the same determined conditions held for all the spherical drops. Therefore all the rays in which a particular colour was seen, that is the rays coming from the drops to the eye, made the same angle with the rays going from the sun to the drops.[3] The rainbow, in fact, formed the circumference of the common base of two cones of rays with the same axis, one cone having its apex at the eye and the other its apex at the sun.[4] When the sun was on the horizon the bow was at its maximum elevation and was seen as a half-circle; as the sun rose, the bow sank.[5]

Of the upper rainbow Theodoric said that the material cause was again the spherical drops of mist or rain in the atmosphere, and that the efficient cause was the sunlight which suffered *two* internal reflections in each drop.[6] The sunlight producing this rainbow entered each drop on its lower side, was refracted, reflected twice internally, and refracted out again at a determined angle to the incident light. The rainbow was seen only in the drops from which this emerging light came to the eye of the observer.

To illustrate these points and the other special points that will be discussed below, let the circle of altitude be represented by *adc* [Fig. 14], its diameter (which is the diameter of the sphere[7]) by *abc*, which represents

---

[1] *De Iride*, ii. 28, pp. 117–19; CC. 45–46, pp. 144–8.

[2] Ibid. ii. 38, pp. 133–8.

[3] Ibid. ii. 39, pp. 138–40; see also C. 31, p. 123. Cf. Witelo, above, p. 227.

[4] 'Est autem iam dictus circulus basis communis duarum pyramidum. . . .' *De Iride*, ii. 40, p. 140; see also C. 44, pp. 143–4. Cf. Witelo, above, p. 227.

[5] Ibid. ii. 42–43, pp. 142–3; see above, p. 252. Cf. Witelo, above, p. 228.

[6] Ibid. iii. 1, p. 149.

[7] 'Sphaerae', MS Basel F. IV. 30, f. 38ᵛ.

also the circle of the horizon, the position of the sun by *a* and of the eye by *b*. Let the little sphere *fghk* represent the whole collection of little spherical drops elevated to the place where the rainbow is produced, and let the centre of this little sphere be *e*. . . . It is plain that none of the radiation which falls on the surfaces of drops standing in relation to the sun and the eye, and is immediately reflected from those surfaces without penetrating into the interior of the drops, goes to the eye. Therefore, it must follow that the sunlight by which the upper rainbow is produced and appears plainly to the senses, penetrates into the interior of the drops and thence is reflected to the eye, and outside these two modes of radiation and reflection by which the rainbow is produced it is impossible to imagine any other.[1]

To speak generally, the mode of radiation by which the upper rainbow is produced is as follows. Just as in the lower rainbow the sunlight enters any particular drop on the side which is uppermost, or more removed from the diameter of the sphere[2] of the world (or the side which is upwards or towards the right or the left, as was the case above), but is reflected to the eye from the lower side of the drop, or the side nearer to the diameter of the sphere[3] of the world; so . . . in the production of the upper rainbow, the sunlight enters the drop on the side which is lower, or nearer the diameter of the sphere[4] of the world, whether the drop be elevated above the horizon in the circle of altitude to the top of the rainbow, or whether it stands to the right or the left of the observer; and so this sunlight, which enters into the body of the drop and penetrates to its opposite concave surface, is reflected thence to the eye from the upper side of the drop,[5] on the side more removed from diameter of the sphere of the world. This mode of radiation can be observed experimentally if one places a transparent crystalline stone, which they call beryl, or any clear spherical little drop, in such a position in relation to the sun and the eye, that the eye is between the sun and the little sphere standing to one side of the straight line of incidence from the sun to the eye.[6]

The place of incidence of the sunlight on the lower side of the little spherical drop is, on the surface of any particular drop, at *f* on the line *af* below the perpendicular *ae* [Fig. 14]. From this place of incidence the sunlight entering and penetrating[7] into the interior of the drop falls on to its concave opposite surface, for example at the point *g*,[8] and from this point the ray is reflected upwards as from a concave mirror, the angles of

---

[1] *De Iride*, iii. 2, pp. 149–50.   [2] 'Sphaerae', MS Basel F. IV. 30, f. 38ᵛ.
[3] *De Iride*, iii. 2, pp. 149–50.   [4] 'Sphaerae', MS Basel F. IV. 30, f. 38ᵛ.
[5] 'Sphaerulae', ibid.
[6] *De Iride*, iii. 3, p. 151; cf. ii. 8, p. 78; above, p. 246, n. 3; see also, above, p. 250.
[7] He pointed out that at this point when the sunlight 'enters obliquely it is refracted'. Ibid. iii. 6, p. 156.
[8] The sense requires, and MS Basel F. IV. 30, f. 39ʳ reads, '*g*', not '*d*' as in *De Iride*, ed. Würschmidt, p. 152, l. 21.

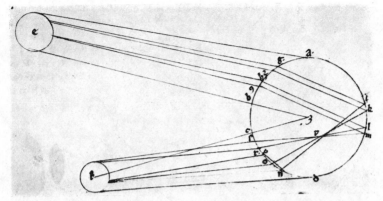

Fig. 9. The paths of rays inside a transparent sphere, from Theodoric of Freiberg's *De Iride*, ii. 18–20, MS Basel F. IV. 30, f. 21ʳ. From the sun *e* one set of rays (incorrectly shown diverging) strikes the sphere on the arc *qh*, is refracted to the opposite surface at *lm*, and thence reflected internally. The reflected rays *lr* and *ms* intersect at *t*, and at *s* and *r* respectively the rays are refracted again and so go (incorrectly shown converging) to the eye at *f*. Theodoric thought that in a sphere 'of some notable quantity' red would appear in the upper ray emerging at *s* and the other colours appear between *s* and *r*. In fact, the red ray would be *hlr*; pp. 249–50, Fig. 10. Another set of rays falling at a more oblique angle strikes the sphere at *zg*, is refracted to *ik* and reflected to *no*, intersecting as before. The ray *in* is reflected once more from *n* to *p* (falsely drawn).

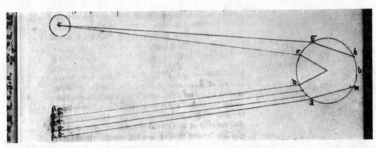

Fig. 10. The production of colours in rays passing through a raindrop, from Theodoric of Freiberg's *De Iride*, ii. 21, MS Basel F. IV. 30, f. 23ʳ. The paths of the individual rays inside the drop and their intersection after reflection are not shown. The four lines of emerging rays represent the four colours, red (*o*, below), yellow (*p*), green (*q*) and blue (*r*, top). See p. 250; cf. Fig. 9.

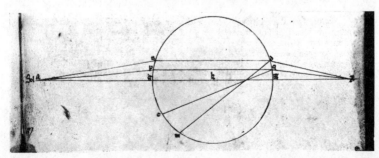

Fig. 12. The determination of the angle between incident and emergent rays producing the primary rainbow, from Theodoric of Freiberg's *De Iride*, ii. 30, MS Basel F. IV. 30, f. 29ʳ. See p. 251, n. 7.

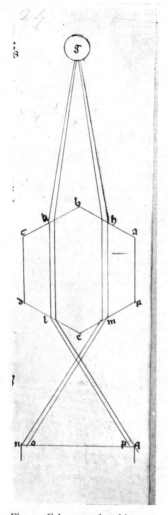

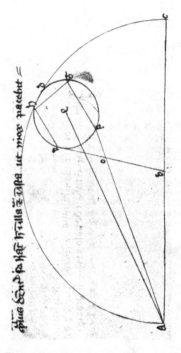

Fig. 14. The determination of the angle between incident and emergent rays producing the upper rainbow, from Theodoric of Freiberg's *De Iride*, iii. 2, 5, MS Basel F. IV. 30, f. 38ʳ. See pp. 255–7.

Fig. 11. Colours produced by rays passing through each half of a hexagonal crystal and intersecting, so that when they fall on a screen red is at *o* and *p*, and blue at *n* and *q* (see p. 250). From Theodoric of Freiberg's *De Iride*, ii. 23, MS Basel F. IV. 30, f. 24ʳ.

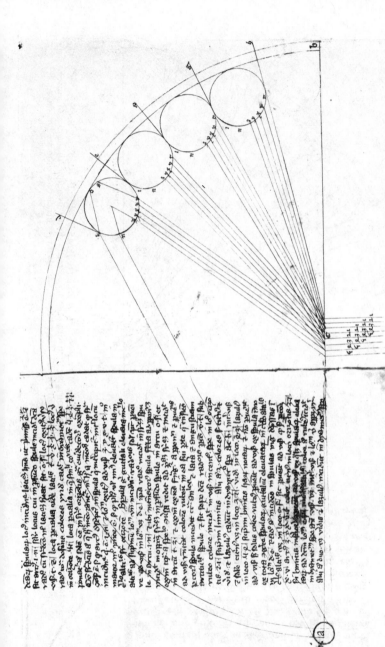

Fig. 13. The formation of the lower rainbow, from Theodoric of Freiberg's *De Iride*, ii. 38, MS Basel F. IV. 30, ff. 33ᵛ–34ʳ. See pp. 252–5. The incident rays going from the sun to the *different* drops should be parallel, which they would not be if they were all shown in the diagram; the coloured rays emerging from each individual drop should be diverging instead of parallel; all the rays of a given colour emerging from the different drops should be drawn parallel. The paths of the individual rays inside each drop are not shown (see Fig. 9).

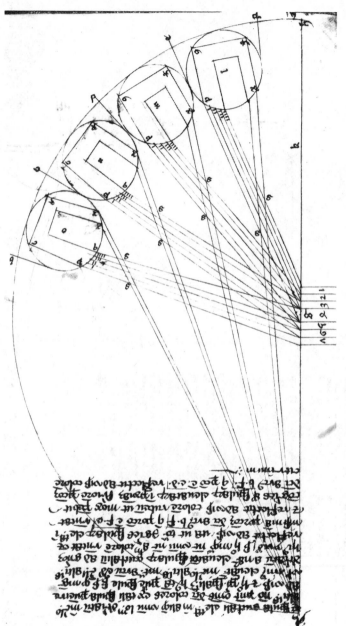

Fig. 15. The formation of the upper rainbow, from Theodoric of Freiberg's *De Iride*, iii. 6–7, MS Basel F. IV. 30, f. 40ʳ. See pp. 257–8. The incident rays should be drawn parallel; the coloured rays emerging from each drop are correctly shown diverging; all the rays of a given colour emerging from the different drops should be drawn parallel. The paths of individual rays inside each drop are not shown.

incidence and of reflection being equal, so that it falls on the point *h* in the upper part of the drop. At this point *h* the ray is again bent as by a concave mirror, the angles of incidence and reflection being equal; it comes to a place near the point of incidence of the perpendicular line coming from the sun, and falls on *k*. Thence, on emerging from the drop, it is refracted away from the perpendicular at its point of incidence and comes to the eye along the line *kb*[1], so that the two lines, namely, the line of incidence of the sunlight falling on the lower side of the little sphere, and the line of reflection to the eye from the upper side of the little sphere (that is *kb*), intersect at the point *o* between the sun and the drop, as is seen in the diagram.[2]

The arc of the upper rainbow had the same centre as that of the lower bow, and Theodoric correctly stated that the angle between the rays incident upon and emerging from the drops in which the upper bow was seen, was about 11° greater than the corresponding angle for the lower bow. Thus the upper bow was always seen at an altitude about 11° higher than the lower bow.[3] His explanation of the upper bow took account of four characteristics, namely, the reversal of the order of the colours as compared with that seen in the lower bow, the circular form, and the darker appearance and rarer occurrence of the upper, as compared with the lower bow.[4] Beginning with the first characteristic, he pointed out that in the upper, as in the lower rainbow, the different colours came to the eye from drops at different altitudes,[5] and that 'we may consider the height or thickness of this radiation to be divided, at its exit from any of the said bodies, into four adjacent parts, in particular ones of which the particular colours shine'.[6] He went on, as he had done for the lower rainbow, to discuss in detail the path of each colour through a drop at each of the four altitudes at which a different colour was seen, showing the order of the colours to be a consequence of his general theory of colour.

Therefore with the little spherical drop, or rather whole collection of drops [*sphaerulae*], elevated in the circle of altitude to the arc *fb*, let us consider the lower part *fe* [Fig. 15]. To take a very clear example, when the

---

[1] The sense requires, and MS Basel F. IV. 30, f. 39ᵛ reads, '*kb*', not '*kl*' as in *De Iride*, ibid., l. 30.

[2] *De Iride*, iii. 5, pp. 152–3.

[3] Ibid. iii. 4, pp. 151–2. On the basis of his incorrect figure for the radius of the primary bow he supposed that that of the secondary bow subtended an angle of 33° at the eye: ibid. iii. 14, p. 174; iv. 8, pp. 184–5. See above, p. 252.

[4] Ibid. iii. 6, pp. 153–4.

[5] Ibid., pp. 154–5.

[6] Ibid., p. 156.

sun is at a point on the horizòn, the sunlight [*radiatio solaris*] falls on to any one of the said drops on a part of its lower side, namely the arc x, and there entering the body of the drop it turns by its incidences and reflections round the opposite concave surface of the drop until it comes to its place of exit, namely the arc pq, on emerging from which it is refracted away from the perpendicular because it encounters a rarer body, namely air; and so by much circumgyration it meets the original line of incidence, ax, and after intersecting it at gg[1] comes to the eye g. Therefore, since that portion or part of the radiation by which it emerges near p goes round nearest to the angles and arcs and angular sides of the drop, it is certain,[2] according to the above, that this same part of the radiation, which is designated in the diagram by one mark [|], will look red. The other three colours, namely yellow, green, and blue, which are designated by the remaining marks [| |, | | |, | | | |], fall on the diameter of the sphere[3] between the eye and the centre of the rainbow k . . . namely at 3, 2, 1.

⸗And so, [he concluded after discussing the drops at ed, dc, and cb] since in the production of this rainbow the colour red comes to the eye from the bottom of the arc fb, which is determined by nature for the production of this rainbow according to the elevation of the little spherical drops in it, and since yellow is reflected to the eye next to red from the next part above it in the said arc, green shines from the third part of the arc two places above red, and finally blue comes from the topmost part, therefore it is plain that the colours of this upper rainbow are in reverse order to that seen in the lower rainbow.[4]

Of the other three characteristics of the upper rainbow, Theodoric attributed the circular form to the same cause as in the lower bow, namely the equality of the angles of incidence and emergence of the rays at all the drops.[5] The maximum size the visible bow could reach was a semicircle.[6] The darker appearance of the upper bow he attributed to the double internal reflection of the light passing through the drops; experience showed that all radiation was weakened by reflection.[7] The rarer occurrence of the upper bow he explained by saying that the drops would seldom be extended sufficiently to produce the upper bow and, moreover, that so much

---

[1] MS Basel F. IV. 30, f. 40ᵛ reads 'f' as in Würschmidt's text (p. 157, l. 7), but the diagram shows that 'gg' is meant.

[2] 'certum est secundum praedicta', MS Basel F. IV. 30, f. 40ᵛ. The reading in *De Iride*, p. 157, l. 10, does not make sense. In a passage below that here translated, Würschmidt's transcription 'cd' (p. 158, l. 4) should read 'ed' (MS cit. f. 41ʳ).

[3] 'Sphaerae', MS Basel F. IV. 30, f. 41ʳ.

[4] *De Iride*, iii. 7, pp. 156–9.

[5] Ibid., p. 159; cf. ii. 39; above, p. 255.   [6] Ibid. iii. 8, p. 160.

[7] Ibid. iii. 9, p. 161; see also C. 10, pp. 162–4; above, p. 231.

light was absorbed by the double reflection that, even with a sufficient extension of drops, the upper bow might sometimes be
invisible.[1]

Of the other 'impressiones radiales' treated in the fourth part of
De Iride Theodoric's explanations were less successful, though they
are of interest in showing how he tried to account for a wide
variety of similar phenomena by means of a single theory of refraction and colour. He incorrectly stated that the angle subtended at
the eye by the radius of the halo (which formed a circle with the sun
at its centre) was, as measured by an astrolabe, $11°$.[2] Of most of the
phenomena considered in this part of Theodoric's treatise no satisfactory explanation was in fact given for centuries after his death.[3]

---

[1] Ibid. iii. 11, p. 164.
[2] Ibid. iv. 8, pp. 183–4. Theodoric has halved the radius of the halo as he did that of
the rainbow; above, p. 252, n. 5. Krebs (*Meister Dietrich*, pp. 33*, 37*) and Würschmidt
(*De Iride*, p. 28, n. 1) have mistaken the correct value for the radius of the halo. Cf.
Roger Bacon, above, p. 161, n. 4.
[3] See Krebs, *Meister Dietrich*, pp. 59–62; Pernter–Exner, *Meteorol. Optik*.

X

Experimental Method and the Transmission of Thirteenth- and Fourteenth-century Writings on the Rainbow, Colour, and Light to the Seventeenth Century

(1)

THEODORIC OF FREIBERG'S explanation of the rainbow affords striking proof of the effectiveness of the medieval theory of experimental science in solving a concrete problem, and it naturally raises the question of continuity with sixteenth- and seventeenth-century work on the same problem, and particularly with the work of Descartes. The evidence, in fact, shows that in spite of the small number of manuscripts[1] of *De Iride* itself, knowledge of Theodoric's theory of the rainbow was never lost. Moreover, the whole Latin medieval tradition of experimental optics begun by Grosseteste was widely known to sixteenth- and seventeenth-century writers and formed a point of departure for their own work.

The first writer to quote Theodoric of Freiberg's ideas was his Dominican pupil,[2] Berthold of Mosburg, who in 1318 wrote a commentary on Aristotle's *Meteorologica*. Berthold was a lector at Cologne and he shared the Neoplatonic ideas of Albertus Magnus and Theodoric, whom he mentioned among his sources in his *Expositio in Elementationem Theologicam Procli*. He was himself quoted by Nicholas of Cusa.[3]

---

[1] See above, p. 233, n. 1.

[2] Another contemporary Dominican, John of Paris (*c.* 1269–1306), wrote a commentary on the *Meteorology* and a treatise *De Yride*, which are both lost, though they may be identical with an anonymous continuation of St. Thomas Aquinas's commentary on the *Meteorology* which includes an account of the rainbow. St. Thomas commented on the first two books only. See M. Grabmann, 'Studien zu Johannes Quidort von Paris, O. Pr.', *SKBAW*, 1922, No. 3; Sarton, *Introduction*, iii. 991–3. The anonymous continuation was made perhaps too early to mention Theodoric's theory of the rainbow.

[3] For Berthold of Mosburg see M. Grabmann, 'Studien über Ulrich von Strassburg', *Zeitsch. kath. Theol.* xxix (1905) 626, 'Der Neuplatonismus in der deutschen Hochscholastik', *PJ*, xxiii (1910) 53–54, *Mittelalterliches Geistesleben*, ii. 312, 366, 384, 390,

Another fourteenth-century writer who may have had some knowledge of Theodoric's theory of the rainbow was Themon Judaei (or Judaeus), a Westphalian who was a prominent teacher in the University of Paris.[1] He was thrice elected proctor of the English nation, in 1353, 1355, and 1356, and was treasurer of it from 1357 to 1361, when he was succeeded by Albert of Saxony. The form of his *Questiones super Quatuor Libros Metheororum*,[2] in which he gave an explanation of the rainbow which included part of Theodoric's theory, was in fact inspired by Albert of Saxony's commentaries on Aristotle's *Physica*, *De Caelo*, and *De Generatione et Corruptione*. The contents of the *Questiones* shows that Themon was, at least in intention, a true follower of the school of experimental science begun by Grosseteste. He cited by name the principal thirteenth-century writers on optics from Grosseteste to Witelo, adopted their theory of 'multiplication of species',[3] and put into practice the theory of experimental verification and falsification they had worked out. The sources he mentioned are Grosseteste,[4] Albertus Magnus,[5] Thomas Aquinas,[6] Roger Bacon,[7] Witelo,[8] Robertus Anglicus,[9] and

421–2; Krebs, *Meister Dietrich*, p. 50, n. 2; Würschmidt, *De Iride*, p. xiv, n. 1; Ueber-weg-Geyer, *Gesch. der Philosophie*, ii. 560, 578–9; Sarton, *Introduction*, iii. 568.

[1] For Themon see Duhem, *Léonard de Vinci*, i. 159 sqq.; Birkenmajer, 'Études sur Witelo, i, *BIAPSL*, 1918, pp. 4 sqq.; Thorndike, *History of Magic*, iii. 587; Sarton, *Introduction*, iii. 1539–40. Birkenmajer, op. cit., has discussed the relations between Themon's treatise and Oresme's *Quaestiones Meteororum* (Erfurt Stadtbücherei, Amplonian Collection, MS Q. 299, 14 c., ff. 51–103ᵛ). The incipits of these two treatises are the same as that of Simon Tunsted's *Quaestiones Meteorologicarum*; see above, p. 187, n. 2. The sixteenth-century Italian scholar Agostino Nifo thought that Themon's treatise had been written by Albert of Saxony: see Duhem, *Léonard de Vinci*, i, note B, p. 345; ii. 330.

[2] The references given below are to *Questiones* Thimonis *super Quatuor Lib. Metheor.* Venetiis, 1522. I have used also MS Vat. Lat. 2177, 14 c., ff. 1–92ᵛ, of the same work.

[3] e.g. 'multiplicare radium' (*Questiones* Thimonis, .iii. 2, f. 107ᵛ); 'multiplicatione virtutis', 'species vel forma directe multiplicata'. Ibid. 3, f. 108ᵛ.

[4] 'auctoritate Aristotelis primo posteriorum . . . et idem vult Linconiensis ibidem' (ibid. ii. 9, f. 105ʳ); 'Linconiensem in libro de radiorum refractione dicit quod luna . . . mittit radios. . . .' (Ibid. ii. 2, f. 102ᵛ: the reference must be to *De Nat. Loc.*, cf. above, p. 112); 'per Linconiensem in tractatu de radiis' (ibid. iii. 3, f. 108ᵛᵇ: this evidently refers to *De Lineis*); below, p. 263, nn. 2, 8.

[5] *Questiones* Thimonis, iii. 12, f. 116ᵛ; 13, f. 117ʳᵇ; below, p. 264, n. 1.

[6] 'Beatus Thomas de Aquino'. Ibid. i. 7, f. 93ʳ.

[7] 'magister Rogerius Alhacen in perspectiva sua'. Ibid. iii: 10, f. 115ʳ. See also below, p. 263, n. 2.

[8] There are many references to 'Vitulonis in quinto perspective', &c. Ibid. iii. 3, f. 109ʳᵇ; 9, f. 114ʳᵇ; 10, f. 115ʳ; 20, f. 121ʳᵇ, &c. See other notes below.

[9] Ibid. iii. 10, f. 114ᵛᵇ. Robertus Anglicus was an English astronomer who flourished in Paris (?) and Montpellier *c.* 1271. He wrote treatises on the astrolabe and quadrant, which he improved. See Sarton, *Introduction*, ii. 993–4.

Henry (of Mondeville?)[1] among medieval Latin writers; Plato,[2] Aristotle,[3] Euclid,[4] Archimedes,[5] Theodosius,[6] and Ptolemy,[7] and Seneca[8] among Classical writers; and Alkindi[9] and Alhazen[10] among the Arabs. He cited also the perpetual-motion device described by Petrus Peregrinus 'in tractatu de magnete'.[11] To Theodoric of Freiberg he made no reference by name, and the suggestion that he knew of his work on the rainbow would have to rest only on the points of similarity between the *Questiones* and *De Iride*. On the other hand there are also points of considerable difference[12] and, in the only oblique reference that could be to Theodoric, measurements are given different from those in Theodoric's *De Iride*.[13] Moreover, since Themon was so lavish with his citations of other authors, it would be strange if he had omitted all reference to the author of the most important treatise on the rainbow had he known his work. Thus it is possible that Themon reached identical conclusions about the rainbow independently of Theodoric.

Of the effects of 'species' propagated through space Themon gave

---

[1] '. . . et utilitatis pro medicis dicit Henricus'. *Questiones* Thimonis, iv. 3, f. 134ʳ. On Henry of Mondeville see Sarton, *Introduction*, iii. 865–73.

[2] *Questiones* Thimonis, i. 10, f. 94ᵛᵇ.

[3] 'auctoritate Aristotelis in textu veteris translationis. . . . Aristoteles in translatione nova' (ibid. iii. 23, f. 123ʳᵇ); '. . . nove translationis que fuit medicus regis Philippi filii Ludovici regis illustrissimi francorum' (ibid. 24, f. 124ʳ). The last reference is to William of Moerbeke's translation.

[4] 'primo libro Euclidis de aspectibus'. Ibid. iii. 10, f. 115ʳ.

[5] 'Archimidis de curvis superficiebus'. Ibid. iii. 21, f. 122ʳᵇ.

[6] 'Theodosi de spheris'. Ibid. iii. 20, f. 121ʳ.

[7] Ibid. iii. 1, f. 106ᵛᵇ; see above, p. 215, n. 3.   [8] Ibid. i. 10, f. 95ʳ.

[9] 'in tractatu Jacob Alchindi de umbris'. Ibid. iii. 3, f. 108ᵛᵇ; see also C. 4, f. 109ᵛ.

[10] Several references; e.g. see below, p. 263, n. 8; p. 267, n. 1.

[11] 'Item per aliam experientiam de magnete quia dicitur in tractatu de magnete. . . .' Ibid. i. 2, f. 88ʳ. See above, p. 210.

[12] e.g. he said there were only three species of colour in the rainbow while Theodoric said there were four (below, p. 266, n. 1; above, p. 244); and he gave a different explanation of the order of colours in the rainbow (below, p. 266, n. 4).

[13] 'arguitur per experientias quas ponit Auctor in tractatu de yride, qui dicit cum expertum sit per astrolabium vel per armillas quod diameter halo habet 42 gradus de circulo altitudinis et semidiameter yridis tantundem, ex quo patet quod semidiameter yridis est equalis toti diametro halo. . . .' (Ibid. iii. 21, f. 122ʳᵇ.) '. . . Ex istis patet quod auctores illi non sunt intelligendi pro omni tempore sed solum quandoque, et hoc est de yride circa solem; sed de aliis yridibus lune et halo per consimiles experientias instrumentorum poterit unusquisque investigare proportiones diversis temporibus.' (f. 122ᵛ. This question is numbered 19 in MS Vat. Lat. 2177, f. 68.) There is another reference 'in quodam tractatu de yride' in iii. 20, f. 121ʳᵇ. Both Theodoric (above, p. 252, n. 5) and Roger Bacon (above, p. 161) said that the diameter of the rainbow was twice that of the halo, but the figures given by Themon are those of Bacon. See above, p. 161, n. 4; p. 259; below, p. 265, n. 5.

several examples, including those produced by visible light. He gave an account of Grosseteste's theory of the tides which, he said, were produced by rays emitted from the moon 'sicut multiplicatur species coloris vel luminis'.[1] He discussed also the propagation of heat[2] and the problem of action at a distance and the 'multiplication of species' of different kinds, for example heat, magnetism, and light, through different media.[3] Of the laws of light he gave a summary based on the writings of earlier optical writers,[4] and he seems to have made some experiments on refraction.[5] He repeated the explanation of refraction given by Alhazen and Witelo[6] and mentioned Witelo's tables.[7] He asserted his adherence to the intramission theory of vision,[8] and he discussed also the question whether 'luminosum uniforme facit lumen uniformiter difformem in medio'.[9] Under suitable conditions, he said, light produced 'impressiones metheorologice'[10] such as the halo[11] and the rainbow, and most of the third book of the *Questiones* is devoted to these phenomena.

[1] *Questiones* Thimonis, i. 2, f. 88^r. On the tides see ibid. ii. 2, f. 102^v; cf. above, p. 261, n. 4.

[2] He referred to '. . . perspectivi sicut Auctor in libro de speciebus et Linconiensis in libro de radiis . . .' (ibid. i. 9, f. 94$^{rb, v}$; cf. above, p. 149, p. 87, n. 1). The first reference is evidently to Roger Bacon's *De Mult. Spec.* i. 1, ed. Bridges, p. 414, v. 1, p. 530.

[3] 'quedam sunt virtutes alterative que valde impediuntur a densitate medii vel passi, et alie non, exemplum primi sicut lumen, exemplum secundi . . . magnes enim per influentiam faceret ferrum moveri si lignum esset intermedium inter ferrum et magnetem sicut si solus aer esset in medio, dummodo densitas ligni non impediret motum ferri. Item alique virtutes agunt bene remote aliis virtutibus secum coextensis non potentibus eque remote agere, sicut unus ignis ageret bene in nocte speciem lucis valde remote, et tamen non potest per tantam distantiam agere calorem quamvis calor et lux in eodem igne extendantur.' (*Questiones* Thimonis, iii. 3, f. 108vb; MS Vat. Lat. 2177, f. 46^r.) Cf. Ockham, above, p. 176, n. 2, p. 212, n. 2.

[4] *Questiones* Thimonis, iii. 1–4, ff. 106^v–110^v.

[5] e.g. 'si in vase ponetur florenus et recedat quis videns. . .'. Ibid. iii. 1, f. 107^r; using a 'denarius' see C. 2, f. 107^v–108^r. Cf. C. 3, f. 108^r. [6] Cf. above, p. 219, n. 5.

[7] 'Vitulo in quarto perspective ordinat tabulas ad inveniendum diversitatem angulorum refractionis secundum diversitatem densitatum mediorum in quibus fit refractio.' Ibid. iii. 9, f. 113rb. See also C. 1, f. 106vb–107^r.

[8] 'et hinc concordat Alacen et Vitulo . . . sed . . . Linconiensis . . . dicit visum fieri extramittendo. . . .' (Ibid. iii. 1, f. 106vb.) The last reference is to Grosseteste's *De Iride*, above, p. 118; cf. p. 114, n. 1.

[9] *Questiones* Thimonis, iii. 3, f. 108rb. 'Ad aliam confirmationem quoniam dicebatur de luminosis quod agerent: potest dici quod dato quod radii diversi componerent unum tamen adhuc non esset eque intensum lumen in quolibet puncto medii, quia ista lumina sic extensa non possunt eque agere ad omnem differentiam positionis . . . sicut velocitas qua aliquid a non gradu inciperet intendere motum uniformiter difformiter esset uniformiter difformiter . . . radius non est solum linea indivisibilis secundum longitudinem et profunditatem, sed est multum divisibilis.' Ibid. f. 109^r. Cf. Dumbleton, above, p. 186.

[10] *Questiones* Thimonis, i. 1, f. 87^r.   [11] Ibid. iii. 5–9, ff. 110^v–114^r.

Before putting forward what he regarded as the true explanation of the rainbow, Themon tried to give experimental answers to a number of preliminary questions which had become an essential part of the discussion of the subject. First he asked whether the colours were truly where they appeared.[1] He answered in the affirmative because the colours produced when 'rays are differentially refracted' by hexagonal crystals could be seen in a determinate position in a mirror, just like other objects. Moreover, the colours of a spectrum produced by passing sunlight through a spherical glass flask of water could be seen either on the hand, when this was held in the right position, or by reflection in a second flask held in the same position. In what was evidently a reference to Grosseteste and Albertus Magnus, he said that this phenomenon had in fact led some writers to think that the rainbow was produced by sunlight which was refracted by spherical drops of water in a cloud between the observer and the sun, and projected on to a second cloud, where the bow was seen.[2] But he would show that this theory was false.[3] He went on to point out that although the colours of the rainbow were real colours they were not a real thing *on* the cloud, because if that were so it would be possible to see them from behind, and this was not the case.[4]

After agreeing with Albertus Magnus and Witelo that the rainbow was produced by both reflection and refraction,[5] Themon next asked whether the reflection took place from a continuous cloud or from a collection of discontinuous drops.[6] The former hypothesis he falsi-

---

[1] 'Queritur undecimo utrum colores apparentes in yride sint ibi ubi apparent esse et sint veri colores.' (*Questiones* Thimonis, iii. 11, f. 115rb.) '. . . Item etiam apparet in crystallo angulari et exagono . . . et causa est quia radii refranguntur diversimode et sic incorporati precedentes per tale corpus vel per tale causant talem apparentiam coloris. . . . Et est satis antiqua opinio quam recitat Albertus super isto tertio commento suo [on *Meteor.*] et adducit multas particulares experientias. . . . Et confirmant conclusionem hanc alio experimento posito quod sint duo vasa vitrea spherica plena aqua, sicut essent duo urinalia. . . .' (f. 115^v.)

[2] Cf. above, pp. 125–6, 196–8.   [3] 'falsum reputo. . . .' Ibid., ff. 115^v–116^r.

[4] 'si esset res realis tunc videretur ad omnem differentiam positionis: hoc est falsum, quia stans retro nubem nihil videret de yride quamvis nubes rorida esset diaphana, sicut experientia docet; et stans a latere non videret, ut patet in yridibus artificialibus.' Ibid. 12, f. 116^r.   [5] Ibid. 13, f. 116vb. See f. 117^r.

[6] Ibid. 14, f. 117rb. '. . . si esset unum continuum tunc . . .; hoc autem est falsum et inconveniens, ut experientia docet: consequentia tenet; . . . sint plura discontinua . . . Et ex isto patet quod ubi est defectus talium guttularum quod ibi non apparet yris nec portio eius quamvis omnia alia requisita essent sufficientia, et potest probari conclusio quia sicut reflexio yridis artificialis fit super plures guttulas discontinuas superficierum prope invicem cadentes sic etiam fit yris naturalis. . . .' (f. 117^v.)

fied[1] by pointing out that if it were true a simple reflection of the sun would be seen, which was not the case; he concluded that the rainbow was produced by discontinuous drops close together. This conclusion he reached by the use of the method of agreement and difference:[2] 'for where such drops are absent there no rainbow or part of it appears, although all the other requisite conditions be sufficient'; and this, he said, could be tested by experiments with rainbows in artificial sprays.[3]

In later Questions in Book III Themon simply resumed the main facts about the rainbow that had become known by the end of the thirteenth century. He repeated Witelo's statement that the maximum altitude of the rainbow was 42°, when it appeared as a semicircle,[4] and he said that the lunar rainbow had the same radius.[5] He said that the centres of the sun, the eye, the rainbow, and the circle of the horizon were always in a straight line,[6] and that each observer saw a different bow which followed him when he moved.[7] The last characteristic distinguished rainbows from the colours seen round a candle at night; these did not move when the observer did.[8] On these facts he based a discussion along the usual lines about the relationship between the appearance of the rainbow at different places and times and the altitude of the sun.[9]

His most original work Themon described in Questions 15 and 16 of the third book of his treatise. In Question 15 he tried to show that the colours seen in refracted light were not the result of differences in the density of the medium through which the light passed,

---

[1] Other references to falsification occur ibid. iii 2–4, ff. 107^v–108^r, 109vb.

[2] Cf. Ockham, above, p. 173.

[3] In *Questiones* Thimonis, iii. 14, f. 117^v, an experiment is described in which a small rainbow was made to appear in winter when a man with his back turned to the sun breathed out into the cold, clear air. This experiment was described by Leonardo da Vinci: see Duhem, *Léonard de Vinci*, i. 174.

[4] *Questiones* Thimonis, iii. 16, f. 118^v; cf. C. 17, 22. Cf. above, pp. 158, 228.

[5] Ibid. 23, f. 123^v; above, p. 262, n. 13. He also said that the lunar bow was never coloured: 'Sexto yris lune que apparet de nocte non apparet tricolor, ergo questio falsa, consequentia patet et antecedens patet etiam per experientiam, quia solum alba apparet sicut apparet de yridibus artificialibus factis in radiis lune.' Ibid. 15, f. 117vb.

[6] Ibid. 20, f. 121^r. He went on to describe an experiment with an artificial rainbow in which he showed that those four points remained always in a straight line however the observer moved his head about (f. 121^v). Cf. Duhem, *Léonard de Vinci*, i. 173.

[7] *Questiones* Thimonis, iii. 22, f. 123^r. Cf. ibid. 16, f. 118vb.

[8] Of the assertion that the two phenomena were the same he said: 'falsitas per experientiam patet, quia sive recedamus sive accedamus recte circa candelam apparet yris, et non accedit ad nos nec recedit licet maior et minor appareat extra eandem.' Ibid. 25, f. 124$^{rb, v}$.   [9] Ibid. CC. 19, 22, 24.

but were 'due to the nature of the rays'.[1] To prove this theory he described an experiment in which the observer held a spherical glass flask full of water in front of his face, which he turned away from a candle behind his head. His eye was thus between the candle and the flask, and light from the candle fell on the flask. He saw in the flask a coloured reversed image of the flame: the upper part of the image showed red, in the middle was green, and at the bottom of the image was the top of the flame (*suprema pars flamme*) showing blue.[2] In the water in this flask, he said, there were no differences in density, and the same was true of 'recently made spider's webs' in which the same colours could be seen. In fact, he held that the different colours were the result of differential refraction of the rays,[3] and that there were three species of colour and no more.

In Question 16 Themon tried to explain the order of the colours seen in the rainbow.[4] He criticized Witelo's explanation and asserted,

[1] 'Queritur utrum omnis yris debeat esse tricolor. Et arguitur quod non . . . quia infinitis modis contingit radium debilitari cum remittatur a certo gradu usque ad non gradum. Secundo ad idem aliquis est quatuor colorum . . . xanctos.' (*Questiones* Thimonis, iii. 15, f. 117vb.) 'Ad hoc dicitur quod hoc est propter naturam lucis reflexe vel refracte que sic apta nata est agere nec aliter. Nec videtur mihi posse dari melior ratio, sicut nec habemus quare celum non movetur ab occidente in oriens et quare equi non generant elephantes nisi quia natura eorum non est apta nata facere nisi equos. Istud tamen potest declarari per experientias, nam si urinale plenum aqua munda vel semiplenum illuminatum a candela . . . non tamen est aliqua diversitas mediorum et ergo hoc est propter naturam radiorum . . . sed tamen non diversis specie nisi istis tribus quia magis et minus non diversificant speciem.' (f. 118^r.) This passage occurs in MS Vat. Lat. 2177, f. 61rb, where the question is numbered Q. 14. Cf. above, pp. 111, 199, 229–32, 244, 247. He was attacking the theories of Aristotle (374^a) and Albertus Magnus; above, p. 199, n. 4.

[2] For the colours to be observed in the order described light would have had to have undergone two internal reflections, as in the secondary rainbow; above, pp. 250, 255–8, Figs. 14, 15. But Themon's account of a similar experiment in Question 16 (below, n. 4) shows that he believed that this order would be observed in the light that produced the primary bow. He has, in fact, confused the two cases: below, p. 268. Alternatively Themon might have been influenced by Theodoric's erroneous account of the order of colours with a large sphere; above, p. 249, Fig. 9.

[3] 'Et etiam dato quod media non sic colorata adhuc possunt propter diversitatem refractionis colores diversi apparere, sicut apparet si sol radiet super urinali pleno aqua ex alia parte radii incidente ad parietem quandoque apparent per modum colorum yridis.' *Questiones* Thimonis, iii. 11, f. 115^v. Cf. Witelo, above, pp. 164, 231.

[4] 'Sextodecimo queritur utrum solum duplex et non multiplicior yris possit apparere.' (Ibid. iii. 16, f. 118rb.) 'Sed quia magna difficultas est in hoc, ideo puto probabiliter tenendo quod hoc fit propter naturam radiorum sic diversimode ostendentium colores. Unde imaginandum est de guttulis inferioris yridis quod pars superior que apparet rubea causetur a radiis minus penetrantibus et reflexis; hec pars que apparet viridis fit a radiis transeuntibus per longius medium, puta magis propinquum ad centrum spherale roride; sed pars yridis que superior [inferior?] apparet alurga vel azurea causatur a radiis longissime medium transeuntibus et reflexis et refractis. Unde imaginor quod non

like Theodoric of Freiberg, that the rays by which the primary rainbow was seen were not those which had been reflected from the convex *external* surface of the drops of water in the atmosphere, but those which had been refracted into each drop, and reflected at the concave *internal* surface.[1] He also correctly described the intersection of the rays after reflection at the concave internal surface of each drop. But he thought that the order in which the colours were seen in the rainbow was the same as the order in which they emerged from the individual drops, and the order he described in his alleged observations with a spherical glass flask are in fact precisely the

solum convexa superficies spherule roride reflectit radium ad oculum, sed imo postquam incidit super convexam superficiem oblique refrangetur et ulterius penetrabit usque ad aliam superficiem ex opposita parte concava in comparatione ad centrum spherule; et sic in illa reflectitur secundum equalem angulum incidentie vel reflexionis; et quia oculus est ultra radiorum confluentiam que fit ex concavo speculo, ideo apparet reverse imago, puta radius inferior ad speculum incidens vel ad spherulam et ad minus spissum medium transiens apparebit superius, et adhuc superius inciditur quo ad visum nostrum reflecteret ista apparebit inferius, et sic in inferiori yride rubeum apparet superius sed alurgum in fine. Et istud quilibet potest experiri in urinali pleno munda aqua, posita candela retro caput radiante super urinale ante faciem, fiet talis reversio sive intensio colorum vel apparitionis eorum recte sicut contingit in speculo concavo, de quo dicit Auctor de speculis in questione undecima quod altitudines et profunditates a speculis concavis quemcumque sunt inter confluentiam visuum, id est antequam radii visuales reflexi coincidant et concurrant ista reversa apparent, sicut in speculis planis et convexis quecumque sunt extra confluentiam, quemadmodum sunt et apparent; et sic videmus in speculis concavis et sphericis, quod homo stans aliquantulum a remotis ultra confluentiam radiorum apparebit habere caput inferius et mentum vel corpus et pedes versus celum; et similiter imaginandum est de yride inferiori, quod superius apparet puniceus color et inferius alurgus. Et econverso imaginandum est de yride superiori, nam ibi sunt guttule intantum elevate quod radius transiens per maiorem spissitudinem medii vel aque, iste licet sit inferius tamen ostendit apparitionem rei superioris; et alius radius qui est superius transiens per minus medium vel minorem latitudinem, iste apparet inferius vel modo econverso. Et hoc iterum contingit propter concavitatem superficierum guttularum versus centrum, et ideo colores superiores apparebunt econverso modo positi coloribus inferioribus yridis. Et istud possumus experiri circa eandem candelam quiescentem, quia magis elevando urinale apparebit superior pars candele versa sursum et alurga, sed media apparebit viridis, et infima rubea, et hoc eque bene convenit a latere sicut superius, dummodo sit equalitas angulorum incidentie et reflexionis utrobique, alias non oporteret.' (f. 119ʳ.) The beginning of this passage suggests Theodoric's explanation of colour (above, p. 247, n. 2). The apparent mistake indicated by the suggested emendation in square brackets occurs also in MS Vat. Lat. 2177, f. 62ᵛᵇ–63. Cf. above, p. 266. In the last passage it would be the 'suprema pars flamme' that would appear at the bottom of the reversed image, looking red; actually, in this experiment, this would look blue: see *Questiones* Thimonis, iii. 15, f. 118ʳ; above, p. 266, n. 2, below, p. 268. Themon repeated the same theory ibid. iii. 17, f. 119ᵛ.

[1] Cf. 'ex septimo perspective Alacen et ex tractatu eiusdem de crepusculis . . . vult quod in superficie reflectatur radius, et hoc est verum si non multiplicetur usque ad profundum. Et si multiplicetur ad profundum tunc partim in superficie et partim in profundo reflectetur.' Ibid. 3, f. 108ᵛ.

reverse of what would be the case. In the primary rainbow red is above and blue below, but in the rays that have undergone a single internal reflection in a spherical flask or drop of water the colours emerge with blue above and red below.[1] Themon failed to grasp the essential fact pointed out by Theodoric, that the order of the colours seen in the rainbow was determined by the order of the different drops, from each of which a single colour came to the eye.[2]

The secondary rainbow Themon correctly understood to be seen in raindrops at a higher altitude than those in which the primary bow was seen, and he pointed out that when the flask of water in the experiment was held higher, a second set of colours was seen in the reverse order to the first set. But these again he described in the reverse of the true order[3] and, moreover, he did not recognize that the rays producing this upper bow had undergone a double internal reflection.[4]

(2)

In the transmission to the seventeenth century of this explanation of the rainbow by refraction and internal reflection in individual raindrops, both Theodoric's and Themon's treatises played their part.[5] Theodoric's De Iride was known to Regiomontanus (1436–76),

---

[1] Above, pp. 250, 254, and Fig. 10.

[2] Above, p. 254, Fig. 13. Duhem (Léonard de Vinci, i. 171–2) seems to have overlooked this point.

[3] Above, pp. 257–8.

[4] There are two special questions on the secondary rainbow: 'Queritur utrum semper apparentibus duabus yridibus superior debeat habere duos colores conversim positos' (Questiones Thimonis, iii. 17, f. 119rb); 'Queritur utrum yris superior vel secundaria necessario debeat apparere remissior in coloribus quam yris principalis.' Ibid. iii. 18, f. 119vb.

[5] Among later fourteenth-century writers who discussed the rainbow without mentioning these treatises are Simon Tunsted (see above, p. 187, n. 2 and p. 261, n. 1) and the author of the Questiones super Perspectivam ascribed to Henry of Hesse (d. 1397). This was a commentary on Pecham's Perspectiva Communis: see A. A. Björnbo, 'Die mathematischen S. Marcohandschriften in Florenz', BM, xii (1912) 203–4; Thorndike, History of Magic, iii. 509–10, 747; Sarton, Introduction, iii. 1123–4, 1502–10. The influence of Grosseteste or Roger Bacon is shown in the opening question: 'Utrum lux multiplicetur per radios; argumentatur quod non, quia multiplicatur per pyramides, igitur questio fallacia. . . .' MS S. Marci Florent. 202 (Bibl. Naz. convent. soppr. J.X.19) f. 56^r. In the fifteenth century Giovanni da Fontana referred to a student of optics who said that the maximum radius of the rainbow was 44° (Thorndike, op. cit., iv. 168–9). Another fifteenth-century writer, the Venetian Dominican Joannes Cronisbenus, in a commentary on the Meteorology asserted that the rainbow was produced by light from the sun refracted by raindrops and that the primary and secondary bows were produced by different modes of refraction, but he did not mention the theories of Theodoric or Themon. See Philosophia . . . Joannis Cronisbeni, cum Metaphysica, MS

who thought of publishing it, and his theory was taught in the
University of Erfurt at the beginning of the sixteenth century by a
certain Jodocus Trutfetter of Eisenach.[1] Jodocus Trutfetter was a
man of enormous learning and nominalist inclinations.[2] In a work
on logic he cited most of the leading thirteenth- and fourteenth-
century writers on method, including Grosseteste, Albertus Magnus,
Petrus Hispanus, Giles of Rome, Thomas Aquinas, Duns Scotus,
William of Ockham, and Buridan.[3] Of these Grosseteste, through his
commentary on the *Posterior Analytics*, seems particularly to have
influenced him, and he devoted considerable space to a discussion
of Grosseteste's views on formal and material definitions, *demonstratio quia* and *propter quid*, resolution and composition,[4] and
mathematical explanations.[5] Of Theodoric's *De Iride* he gave a
summary in another work, *Summa in Totam Physicam: hoc est
Philosophiam Naturalem*, first published in Erfurt in 1514. This
contains a brief account of the main features of Theodoric's theory
of the primary rainbow[6] and of some of his supporting observations
and experiments,[7] and a very perfunctory account of his explanation
of the reversed order of the colours of the secondary rainbow. But,
most important of all, it contains a series of woodcuts, including
two of the diagrams from Theodoric's treatise.[8]

Bibl. Marc. Lat. vi. 99, 15 c., ff. 53ʳ–56ᵛ; J. Valentinelli, *Bibl. Manuscr. ad S. Marci
Venet.* v. 26.

[1] G. Hellmann, *Meteorol. Optik*, pp. (8), (13); above, p. 233, n. 1. For knowledge of
Theodoric in Spain in the sixteenth century see Krebs, *Meister Dietrich*, pp. 13–14.

[2] For Jodocus see G. L. Plitt, *Jodokus Trutfetter von Eisenach*.

[3] *Summule Totius Logice* . . . per Jodocum Trutfetter Isennachcensem, 1501, ff.
A iiiᵛ sqq.

[4] Ibid. iii. 2, ff. eee iiʳ sqq.; verso of folio before kkk i (the foliation is eccentric). On
f. kkk i he referred to 'Linconiensis'.

[5] Ibid. iii. 3. After referring to 'Linco.' on f. lll iiiʳ he went on (verso) to discuss the
use of mathematics, including epicycles and eccentrics.

[6] Jodocus Eysennacensis, *Tocius Philosophie Naturalis Summa*, iv. 2, 1517, ff. 59ᵛ–
60ᵛ. '. . . quemadmodum de utraque experientiis et mathematicis rationibus deducere
nititur quidam Theodoricus Theologie Mgr. ordinis predicatorum in speciali tractatu de
huiusmodi impressionibus edito.' Jodocus referred several times to Albertus Magnus:
e.g. above, p. 199, n. 4. There is a reference also: '. . . specierum de se diffusionem
et multiplicationem ad oculum' (f. 58ʳ).

[7] e.g. the observation to show that four colours, each at a fixed angle from the incident
rays, were seen in light refracted and internally reflected in dewdrops on grass and on
spiders' webs (ibid. f. 59ʳ); cf. above, p. 244.

[8] These woodcuts occur only in the edition of 1514, of which there is a copy in the
Universitätsbibliothek Erlangen, from which the Director has kindly supplied me with
microfilms. Those of chief interest for the present discussion correspond to my Figs.
13 and 15. I have been unable to find a copy of this edition in Great Britain. There
are no diagrams in the edition of 1517, of which there is a copy in the British Museum.

Themon's *Questiones* had the advantage of being printed in four editions between *c.* 1480 and 1518,[1] two in Italy and two at Paris, one Italian edition being reprinted at Venice in 1522.[2] In Italy it was known to Leonardo da Vinci, who summarized passages from it in his notebooks in 1508,[3] and to the well-known commentators, Agostino Nifo (d. 1538 or 1545),[4] and Alessandro Piccolomini. In his *Tractatus de Iride* published in 1540 Piccolomini cited the Venetian edition of the *Questiones*[5], but did not describe Themon's explanation of the rainbow,[6] though he did assert that colours were produced by differential refraction.[7] The Paris editions of the *Questiones* were edited on both occasions (1516, 1518) by George Lokert, a Scots teacher at the Collège de Montaigu (1516) and at the Sorbonne (1518), who played a prominent part in the early sixteenth-century revival of interest in the work of the fourteenth-century Parisian 'nominalist' physicists.[8] Themon's work became part of that revival.

[1] Sarton, *Introduction*, iii. 1540.   [2] See above, p. 261, n. 2.

[3] Duhem, *Léonard de Vinci*, i. 160, 171–7. For Leonardo's MSS see *Literary Works*, ed. J. P. and I. A. Richter, 2nd ed., London, 1939, 2 vols.

[4] Sarton, *Introduction*, iii. 1539; above, p. 261, n. 1. In his *Comm. Meteor.*, Venetiis, 1560, there is no reference to Themon or Theodoric but only to 'iuniores perspectivi, ut halacen atque Vitellio... Robertus tamen linconiensis in eo libro quem de perspectiva scripsit...' (p. 442) and to Albertus Magnus (p. 441). The work by Grosseteste is *De Iride* (see Baur, 1912, p. 73).

[5] '... Gaetanus et Thimon et quamplurimi ex Latinis....' Alex. Piccolominei *Tr. de Iride*, f. 60ʳ. This treatise was published with Piccolomini's edition of the commentary by Alexander of Aphrodisias (above, p. 227, n. 2). The date of composition was 1539.

[6] Cf. Duhem, 'Physics—History of', in *Cath. Encyc.* xii. 50. Piccolomini's treatment of the rainbow was based mainly on Albertus Magnus (Piccolominei *Tr. de Iride*, f. 61ʳ) and 'Vitellio' (f. 60, on the production of different colours by different degrees of weakening of rays by refraction), 'doctor Suessanus' (f. 60ʳᵇ), 'Joan de Regio Monte in primo de triangulis' (f. 59ᵛᵇ), and 'fratre Luca' (f. 62ᵛᵇ, i.e. Pacioli). He mentioned the main facts established in the thirteenth century, including measurements with an astrolabe showing that the maximum elevation was 42° (f. 63ᵛᵇ).

[7] 'Nam si radius visualis ad fulgidum refractus satis fortiter refrangetur, puniceus color apparebit, si debilius aliquantulum viridis spectabitur, et sic de aliis. Semper enim quanto minus vel ex fortitudine visus, vel ex debilitate refractionis, ex parva ad modum mixtione ab albedine deficiet fulgidum, tanto minus ad nigredinem accedere videbitur, et e contra. Dixi autem vel ex fortitudine visus vel ex debilitate refractionis, quam quanto fortior est radius visualis tanto debilior sive ad minorem angulum est refractio, ut habetur in prima parte perspectivae: quicquid dicat Albertus in hoc.' Piccolominei *Tr. de Iride*, f. 61ʳ. Cf. above, pp. 164, 231; p. 266, n. 3.

[8] Duhem, *Léonard de Vinci*, i. 161–2. Lokert also published works by Buridan and Albert of Saxony. A number of prominent sixteenth-century writers on the rainbow did not mention the work of Themon or Theodoric. These include G. Reisch, *Margarita Philosophica* (1504); Simon Porta, *De Coloribus* (1548), and *Meteor.*, in Aristotelis ... *Opera Omnia* (1563); Girolamo Cardano, *De Subtilitate* (1554); Francesco Vico-

Of the original writers on the rainbow who took part in the revival of science that began in the sixteenth century, two who published before Descartes included part of the fourteenth-century theory in their works. These were the Italian mathematician Francesco Maurolyco (1494–1575), who gave an explanation of the rainbow in his *Diaphaneon* (1553) and *Problemata ad Perspectivam et Iridem Pertinentia* (1567), and his compatriot Marc Antonio de Dominis (1566–1624), who did the same in *De Radiis Visus* (1611). It seems probable that both writers, and also Descartes himself, knew something of the work of Theodoric and Themon. Maurolyco cited by name Roger Bacon, John Pecham and Witelo[1], and summarized much of the knowledge of reflection and refraction[2] and of the rainbow[3] found in their writings. All previous work on the rainbow, he said, was vitiated by the neglect of 'the size of the angle of reflection under which the rainbow is seen'. But, he continued, 'I hear certain books to have been discovered in Germany' in which this matter was treated, books 'which I have not yet seen'.[4] Certain passages in his own explanation of the rainbow suggest that he might have been referring to Theodoric's *De Iride*. He wrote, in fact, as though he had heard of part of Theodoric's theory and tried to work out the details himself. He said that the primary bow was produced by internal reflection within individual raindrops,[5] and that the secondary rainbow was not a reflection of the primary bow but was

mercato, *Meteor. Comm.* (1556); Johann Fleischer, *De Iridibus Doctrina Aristotelis et Vitellionis, certa methodo comprehensa, explicata et tam necessariis demonstrationibus, quam physicis et opticis causis* (1571); Bernardo Telesio, *Varii de Naturalibus Rebus Libelli* (1590); Giambattista della Porta, *De Refractione* (1593). The most commonly cited medieval authors were Albertus Magnus and Witelo. Giambattista della Porta (*De Refract.* ix. 4, 11) essentially accepted the two-cloud theory of Albertus Magnus (and Grosseteste), which Cardano criticized. Fleischer made a competent but unsuccessful attempt to account for the facts by means of Witelo's theory that the rays were refracted through one drop and reflected from the convex surface of another drop, whence they went to the eye. The title of his work shows his interest in method.

[1] 'Rogerio Bacchoni et Joan. Petsan.' (*Diaph.* iii, in *Photismi de Lumine et Umbra . . . Diaphanorum Partes . . . Problemata . . .*, p. 76); 'Plinius, Averroes, Jo. Petsan, multique expositores et opticorum Auctores' (*Probl.* § 6, p. 81; see also p. 84). 'Hinc Vitellio . . . laborem auget lectoribus ac nihil demonstrat' (ibid., § 24, p. 84) was his ungracious comment on Witelo. The other authors cited were Aristotle (*Meteor.*), Apollonius, Cardano, and Scaliger.

[2] *Diaph.* i. 10–24.   [3] Ibid. ii. 25–30; *Probl.*

[4] *Diaph.* ii. 30, p. 68; *Probl.* § 24, p. 84. In *Libellus* Linconiensis *de Phisicis Lineis . . .* (Nurenberge, 1503, preface) there is a reference to 'magister Andreas Stiborius Boius Collegiatus vinnensis atque professor mathematice . . .'. Maurolyco referred in these passages to 'Andreas Stibonius Canonicus Viennensis'.

[5] *Diaph.* ii. 25, pp. 50–51; *Probl.* § 9, p. 81.

produced by a variation of the same cause.[1] But he did not mention the refraction of the rays entering and leaving each drop, and he thought that in both the primary and secondary bows rays were reflected several times round the inside of each drop.[2] These passages could have been inspired also by Themon's *Questiones*, but another passage, unless it was quite original, could have come only from Theodoric's *De Iride* or from Jodocus Trutfetter's summary. In this Maurolyco described how in drops of water on the leaves of plants each colour was seen only at a particular angle from the incident rays of the sun, and at no other.[3] He pointed out also that the colours of the rainbow were generated at a fixed angle to the incident sunlight.[4] He said that this angle was 45 degrees for the primary rainbow and $56\frac{1}{4}$ degrees for the secondary rainbow.[5] This, he concluded, was in fact the angle between the incident and emergent rays at each raindrop.[6]

The account of the rainbow given by de Dominis[7] also contains parallel passages which suggest a partial knowledge of Theodoric's *De Iride*, though he did not cite this work among his acknowledged sources. These included Albertus Magnus, Witelo, and Piccolomini,[8] the last of whom could have led him to Themon. De Dominis understood that the primary rainbow was produced by rays from the sun that were refracted into each raindrop and reflected internally once,[9] that the angle between the incident and emergent rays was fixed,[10] and that the different colours were seen in drops at

---

[1] *Diaph.* ii. 30, pp. 58–61; *Probl.* § 13, p. 82.

[2] *Diaph.* ii. 25, 30, pp. 50, 59, and the diagram on p. 51.

[3] Ibid. ii. 25, Scholium, p. 51; cf. above, p. 244, p. 269, n. 7. Maurolyco said that there were four main colours in the rainbow: *Diaph.* ii. 29, pp. 54–55. See also *Probl.* § 24, p. 84.

[4] *Diaph.* ii. 30, Epilogus, p. 66. He pointed out also that the colours were real and that each observer saw a bow in different drops (ibid. ii. 28, p. 53; cf. Theodoric's *De Iride*; above, p. 254). But he did not realize that each of the colours of a particular bow came from different drops.

[5] *Diaph.* ii. 30, Coroll. 1, p. 60. See above, p. 228; below, p. 275, n. 2.

[6] *Probl.* § 9, p. 81. Maurolyco seems to have been the first explicitly to give a numerical value for this angle, though Theodoric had equated it with the angle between the incident sunlight and the rays coming from the rainbow to the eye; above, p. 251, n. 7.

[7] For de Dominis see R. E. Ockenden, 'Marco Antonio de Dominis and his explanation of the rainbow', *Isis*, xxvi (1936) 40 sqq.

[8] *De Radiis Visus*, e.g. pp. 7, 8, 10, 39, 42, 44, and 48–49 (where he discussed the two-cloud theory which Albertus Magnus derived from Grosseteste), 45 ('Alex. Piccolomineus qui tractatum edidit de Iride'), 46, 47, 50, 53, 58, 59, 61, 70–72. He cited also Aristotle, Euclid, Alexander of Aphrodisias (Piccolomini's edition), Alhazen, Averroës, Cardano, and Vicomercato.

[9] Ibid., C. 4, pp. 13–14.   [10] See above, p. 228; below, p. 275, n. 2.

different altitudes.[1] His book contains diagrams illustrating these points. But he overlooked the fact that the rays would have a second refraction on emerging from each drop,[2] and although he said that the secondary rainbow was produced by two internal reflections, he failed to realize that these rays went round the inside of each drop in the reverse direction to those producing the primary bow.[3] Other parallel passages which suggest some knowledge of Theodoric's work are those referring to the experiment in which two streams of coloured rays were seen to emerge from a spherical glass flask full of water held in suitable positions in relation to the sun and the eye;[4] to the proof that the rainbow could not be an image projected on to a cloud, where it was seen, because it moved with the observer;[5] to *species seu formae*;[6] and to the matter and form of the rainbow.[7]

Descartes was the first writer after Theodoric to publish[8] an explanation of the rainbow comparable in completeness with that in *De Iride*, though the only evidence of derivation from this work is once again from parallel passages. The only writer Descartes cited by name in *Les Météores* was Maurolyco,[9] though he cited Witelo elsewhere[10] and the arrangement of his treatise corresponds closely to that of the scholastic commentaries on Aristotle's *Meteorology*.[11] Certainly his presentation of his explanation of the rainbow as an exercise in scientific method is strictly in the tradition of

---

[1] Ibid., C. 13, pp. 54–9; C. 16, p. 68.

[2] Jodocus also omitted this point; see above, p. 269, n. 6.

[3] *De Radiis Visus*, C. 4, p. 14; CC. 14–15, pp. 59–63. Ockenden (op. cit., p. 45) misunderstood the nature of de Dominis's mistake.

[4] *De Radiis Visus*, C. 4, p. 14. Cf. above, pp. 250, 266.

[5] Ibid., C. 11, p. 47; C. 14, p. 59. Cf. above, p. 241; also pp. 158, 227, n. 2.

[6] 'Species seu formae huiusmodi, sicut et lumen ceteraque agentia naturalia. . . .' Ibid., C. 3, p. 8; cf. above, p. 239.

[7] 'Materia itaque Iridis est vapor. . . . Forma . . . lux solis . . . ex fundo ipsarum concavo . . . guttulis. . . .' (Ibid., C. 13, p. 54; cf. above, p. 251.) See also the discussions of why the rainbow has width: ibid., C. 13, pp. 58–9; cf. above, p. 246.

[8] See below, p. 275, n. 1, on Thomas Harriot (1560–1621).

[9] *Les Météores*, viii, 'De Iride', p. 266 in *Discours de la Méthode pour bien conduire sa raison, et chercher la vérité dans les sciences. Plus la Dioptrique, les Météores et la Géométrie, Qui sont des essais de cete Méthode*, Leyde, 1637. These treatises have been reprinted in *Œuvres de* Descartes, vi, but in this chapter I give page references to the 1637 edition. Ockenden (op. cit.) has discussed the relations between Descartes and de Dominis. On these see also Boscovich's account in C. Noceti, *De Iride et Aurora Boreali Carmina . . . cum notis* J. R. Boscovich, pp. 39–45; Libri, *Sciences mathématiques en Italie*, iv. 436–54.

[10] Below, p. 283, n. 5; p. 311, n. 2.

[11] See E. Gilson, *Pensée médiévale dans la formation du système cartésien*, pp. 102 sqq.

Grosseteste and Roger Bacon and the other thirteenth-and fourteenth-century optical writers.[1] Himself a Neoplatonist in philosophy, his kinship with these philosophers is emphasized by his decision to illustrate his method by an investigation into the geometry of light.[2] Apart from his giving similar explanations of the primary and secondary rainbows, the most striking parallel with Theodoric's *De Iride* is Descartes's account of the experiment with a spherical glass flask full of water held up in the sunlight and raised and lowered so that the two streams of coloured rays could be seen emerging from it.[3] Descartes pointed out that the rays that would produce the primary bow were seen at angles between approximately 42 (red) and 41 (blue) degrees from the incident light, and the rays that would produce the secondary bow between approximately 51 (red) and 52 (blue) degrees. Other parallels with thirteenth- and four-teenth-century work are the references to rainbows in sprays,[4] to a tertiary rainbow,[5] and to the production of colours by refraction through a prism.[6] The most important improvement that Descartes introduced into the theory of the rainbow was, after considering the incident sunlight to consist of parallel rays, to calculate by means of the newly formulated law of refraction[7] a table of angles of deviation with different angles of incidence upon a spherical raindrop, and to point out that there was an angle of minimum deviation at which the rays emerged almost parallel and therefore reached the eye of the observer in the greatest concentration. He calculated that for the red

[1] 'L'arc-en-ciel est une merueille de la nature si remarquable, et sa cause a esté de tout tems si curieusement recherchée par les bons esprits, et si peu connuë, que ie ne sçaurois choisir de matière plus propre à faire voir comment par la méthode dont ie me sers on peut venir à des connoissances, que ceux dont nous auons les escrits n'ont point euës.' *Météores*, viii, p. 250.

[2] Cf. also *Le Monde, ou Traité de la lumière* (first published posthumously in 1662); *Œuvres*, xi. *L'Homme*, his attempt to reduce physiology to mathematical principles, was originally part of this work.

[3] *Météores*, viii, pp. 250-4, 260-2, 266-7; above, p. 250, n. 4. The diagrams on pp. 251 and 253 improve on Theodoric's by showing the sun's rays parallel (cf. Figs. 13, 15). In Maurolyco's (*Diaph.* ii. 25, p. 51) diagram of the rainbow the sun's rays are shown parallel. Cf. Roger Bacon's views on this, above, p. 150, n. 2, p. 161.

[4] *Météores*, viii, p. 250.   [5] Ibid., p. 269. Cf. Theodoric, *De Iride*, iii, pp. 175-6.

[6] *Météores*, pp. 254-60. He said of his explanation of the colours by globules rotating at different velocities: 'Et en tout cecy la raison s'accorde si parfaitement auec l'expéri-ence, que ie ne croy pas qu'il soit possible, après auoir bien conneu l'vne et l'autre, de douter que la chose ne soit telle que ie viens de l'expliquer.' (p. 260.)

[7] See below, p. 283, n. 1. The modern law of refraction known as 'Snell's law' states that the sines of the angles of incidence and refraction are to each other in a ratio depend-ing on the media; i.e. $\sin i = \mu \sin r$, where μ is the *refractive index*, which is determined by the two media forming the interface. See below, p. 275, n. 1, on Harriot.

rays this angle would be 41° 47' for the primary bow and 51° 37' for the secondary bow.[1]

All that remained to complete the theory of Theodoric, Themon, Harriot, and Descartes[2] was for Newton to show finally how colours were formed by a prism. Of the two basic facts upon which Newton built his theory of colour, pseudo-Grosseteste, Witelo, Theodoric, and Themon had already suggested that in their experiments with prisms and hexagonal crystals the 'simple' colours were produced by the refraction of different species of rays through different angles.[3] This conclusion had been repeated by Alessandro Piccolomini,[4] though all these writers had supposed that there were only three or four simple colours, and had not clearly distinguished them from compound colours. The first to determine the actual amount of dispersion between red and blue rays was Harriot, followed by Descartes (in the rainbow), who also asserted definitely (after his experiments with prisms) that only refraction and not reflection produced these colours.[5] His diagrams show the rays diverging after leaving the prism. Newton's second basic fact, that the mono-chromatic rays kept their colours unaltered with further refraction, was first discovered by Johann Marcus Marci of Kronland in his study of the rainbow,[6] by means of experiments with prisms which

[1] *Météores*, p. 266. Modern measurements show a dispersion of colours of the primary bow between 42° 20' (red) and 40° 24' (violet) from the incident sunlight; cf. n. 2. For Harriot's discovery of the law of refraction, possibly about 1601, experimental measurements of the dispersion of sunlight into colours by a glass prism and other media, and quantitative analysis of the rainbow before Descartes, see Shirley and Lohne, references below, pp. 354–5.

[2] Above, pp. 234–7. The variations in the radius of the bow with the size of the raindrops led this theory to be questioned and replaced in the nineteenth century by an explanation based on the wave theory of light; above, p. 228; Boyer, *Isis*, xliii (1952) 97–8; Pernter–Exner, *Meteorol. Optik*, pp. 531, 549 sqq.

[3] Above, pp. 164, 231, 246–7, 264, n. 1, p. 266, nn. 1, 4; cf. pp. 111, 127, 159, 199.

[4] Above, p. 270, n. 7. The experimental production of colours by prisms was well known in the sixteenth and seventeenth centuries: e.g. see G. della Porta, *De Refract.* ix. 3, pp. 191–4, C. 26, pp. 222–4; and R. Boyle, *Experiments and Considerations Touching Colours*, iii. 4–6, 1664, pp. 191–5. In a review of current explanations of colour Boyle said that the atomists' theory that 'corpuscles of colour' issued from coloured bodies could be reconciled with the '. . . principal Opinion of the *Modern* Philosophers . . . which derives Colours from the Mixture of Light and Darkness, or rather Light and Shadows . . .' (ibid. i. 5, pp. 84–5). Colour was 'a Modification of Light . . .' (p. 90).

[5] *Météores*, pp. 255–9. Both had been thought to weaken light and produce colours.

[6] *Thaumantias*, Theorema viii–xii, xviii–xx, 1648, pp. 69 sqq., 99 sqq. For Marci's experiments see L. Rosenfeld, 'Marcus Marcis Untersuchungen über das Prisma und ihr Verhältnis zu Newtons Farbentheorie', *Isis*, xvii (1932) 325 sqq.; E. Hoppe, 'Marcus Marci de Kronland . . .', *AGNT*, x (1927) 282 sqq. Marci did not know the sine-law of refraction though he knew the correct explanation of the rainbow (see *Thaumantias*, 'Operis argumentum', p. 1; Theorema x, pp. 69–70; xlii, p. 184; lviii–xciv, pp. 193–221;

had apparently been suggested to him by the work of Witelo[1] and Roger Bacon.[2] These authors in fact provided him with his basic conception of light as a form of 'multiplication of species'[3] and he explained the production of colours from white light by the scholastic theory that refraction altered the degree of 'intension and remission' of the light.[4] The same explanation of colour was put forward by another pre-Newtonian writer on the rainbow, Francesco Maria Grimaldi, though he entirely overlooked the fact of differential refraction.[5]

Newton's contribution was to grasp clearly the significance of facts which his predecessors had not treated as of special importance[6] and, in his classical experimental study, unequivocally 'By the discovered properties of light to explain the colours of the rainbow.'[7] Reasserting that white 'light is not similar, or homogeneal, but consists of *difform* Rays, some of which are more refrangible than others',[8] he showed that each species of ray obeyed the common law of refraction but had a different refractive index, and that each had its own immutable colour which he called a 'simple' colour; that between the refractive indices and the colours there was a single, fixed order producing a continuous spectrum;[9] and that all

see also down to p. 249). The chief writers on the rainbow whom he cited were Roger Bacon, Witelo, and Maurolyco.

[1] By these experiments colours were produced 'quales se observasse Vitellio testatur'. *Thaumantias*, xii, p. 87.

[2] 'Rogerius Baccon cap. 5 de Speculis Mathem.' (ibid. x, p. 70); 'Rogerius Bacco parte 3 perspectivae cap. 4' (ibid. xxxvi, p. 148). These refer to the 1614 edition of Roger Bacon's writings.   [3] Ibid. xxxvi, p. 153.

[4] Ibid. ii, p. 7. In this Theorema he cited Scotus, 'Nominales', St. Thomas Aquinas, Burley, Durandus (pp. 11–16). Marci held that there were only four 'simple' colours. Cf. above, pp. 111, 247, n. 4, 266, n. 1.

[5] *Physico-mathesis de Lumine*, Prop. xxxiv–xxxv, 1665, pp. 253–4. Grimaldi gave the correct explanation of the rainbow (Prop. xlvi–lx, pp. 420–68), basing his calculations on 'Snell's law': 'de constanti proportione inter sinus angulorum Inclinationis et Refracti, et accipiendo pro vera quantitatem angulorum, quos assumpsimus ex Vitellione.' (lii, p. 438.) Grimaldi's book was summarized by Oldenburg in the *PT*, vi (1671–2) 3068 sqq. (22 Jan. 1672).

[6] He may not have known Marci's work, which he did not cite.

[7] *Opticks*, i. ii. ix. 4, 4th ed., 1730, p. 147.

[8] 'New Theory about Light and Colours', *PT*, vi (1671–2) 3081 (19 Feb. 1672). This paper, which is a model example of the experimental method, has been reprinted by G. Sarton in *Isis*, xiv (1930) 326 sqq., and by Michael Roberts and E. R. Thomas, *Newton and the Origin of Colours*, pp. 71 sqq. See also L. Rosenfeld, 'La Théorie des couleurs de Newton et ses adversaires', *Isis*, ix (1927) 44 sqq.; A. R. Hall, 'Sir Isaac Newton's Note-Book, 1661–65', *CHJ*, ix (1949) 239 sqq.

[9] This, with his *Experimentum Crucis* whereby he showed that the passing of any part of the spectrum through a second prism produced no further colours, enabled Newton

the prism did was to separate (or recombine) the different species of rays constituting white light. In the rainbow each species of coloured ray produced its own bow at a determinate angle from the incident sunlight, though there was a partial overlap between neighbouring bows. Among his predecessors in the study of the rainbow Newton cited de Dominis, Descartes, and Grimaldi, and of the work of the first two he mentioned in particular the experiments deriving from Theodoric of Freiberg in which the two streams of coloured rays were seen emerging from a glass globe full of water held at different heights.[1]

(3)

The long history of the work done on the rainbow from Grosseteste to Newton is a striking example of how a persistent attempt to explain a particular phenomenon, by bringing it within the reach of experiment and mathematics, could lead to a theory with much wider applications. In fact, the explanation of the colours of the rainbow had from the beginning been associated with the whole problem of the nature of light and its propagation in a homogeneous medium and at the interface between two different media. For their work on this problem, and on the practical applications of the laws of refraction and reflection, the men who revived optics in the sixteenth and early seventeenth centuries again took the thirteenth- and fourteenth-century writings as a point of departure.

For the continuous influence of those writings from the end of the fourteenth century there is ample evidence from citations in later writings, from catalogues of libraries of scholars, and from the number of manuscripts[2] and printed editions. For example, the well-known late fourteenth-century physicist Biagio Pelacani of Parma, or Blasius Parmensis (d. 1416),[3] wrote an elaborate set of questions on Pecham's *Perspectiva Communis*. A younger German contemporary, Nicholas of Dinkelsbühl (*c.* 1360–1433),[4] apparently used the same work as a basis for lectures on optics at Vienna. A work in a late fifteenth- or early sixteenth-century manuscript which

definitively to distinguish between simple and compound colours. Cf. Grosseteste, above, p. 111.

[1] *Opticks*, i. ii. ix. 4, 4th ed., pp. 147, 154.

[2] For these see L. Thorndike and P. Kibre, *Catalogue of Incipits of Mediaeval Scientific Writings in Latin*, and Thorndike's addenda published in *Speculum*, xiv (1939) 935 sqq., and ibid. xvii (1942) 342 sqq.

[3] Sarton, *Introduction*, iii. 1564–7; Thorndike, *History of Magic*, iv. 65 sqq., 652–62.

[4] Sarton, op. cit. iii. 1432–3.

is perhaps by the early fifteenth-century Italian mechanical inventor, Giovanni da Fontana, contains an attempt to improve on Witelo's theory of burning-mirrors.[1] Another Italian, the Florentine Neoplatonist Pico della Mirandola (1463–1494), had, in his library, copies of Grosseteste's *Commentaria in Libros Posteriorum*, Roger Bacon's *Perspectiva*,[2] and Blasius of Parma's *Quaestiones in Perspectiva*, and also some of Ockham's logical works and the treatises on mechanics, proportions, and latitudes by Jordanus Nemorarius, Bradwardine, Oresme, and Marliani.[3]

Of the titles issued by the early printing presses, a high proportion consisted of thirteenth- and fourteenth-century scientific works.[4] Those concerned with optics included six editions of Grosseteste's *Commentaria in Libros Posteriorum* between 1475(?) and 1537, an edition of his *Libellus de Phisicis Lineis Angulis et Figuris per quas Omnes Actiones Naturales Complentur* (Nurenberge, 1503), and an edition of his principal smaller treatises, *Opuscula Quaedam Philosophica* (Venetiis, 1514).[5] Roger Bacon's *De Multiplicatione Specierum* and *De Speculis Comburentibus* were published in Frankfort in 1614 under the title *Specula Mathematica* along with his *Perspectiva*.[6] His *Epistola de Secretis Operibus* was published in Dr. John Dee's works in 1618.[7] Albertus Magnus's scientific writings went through several separate editions between the end of the fifteenth century and the collected edition of 1651.[8] Witelo's *Perspectiva* was printed in 1535, 1551, and 1572.[9] Pecham's *Perspectiva* was published in as many as nine editions, one in Italian, between 1482 and 1627.[10] Themon Judaei's *Questiones* went through four editions between *c.* 1480 and 1518.[11]

In sixteenth-century England the most eminent mathematicians prized especially manuscripts of Roger Bacon's writings, and they seem in fact to have regarded their own work as a revival of his

---

[1] Thorndike, op. cit. iv. 178. The same manuscript, Biblioteca Medicea Laurenziana (Florence), Ashburnham 957 (888), contains Roger Bacon's *De Mult. Spec.*

[2] *Opus Maius*, v.

[3] Pearl Kibre, *Library of Pico della Mirandola*. Cf. Duhem, *Léonard de Vinci*, iii. 115 sqq.; Durand, *JHI*, iv (1943) 15–16; Kibre, ibid. vii (1946) 257–97.

[4] See A. C. Klebs, 'Incunabula scientifica et medica', *Osiris*, iv (1938) 1–359; G. Sarton, 'The scientific literature transmitted through the incunabula', ibid. v (1938) 41–245.   [5] Above, p. 45, n. 1; Sarton, *Introduction*, ii. 585.

[6] Above, p. 150, n. 3; Sarton, op. cit. ii. 963.   [7] *Opera*, J. Dee. . . .

[8] Above, p. 191, n. 4; Sarton, op. cit. ii. 941–3.

[9] Above, p. 213, n. 3; Sarton, op. cit. ii. 1028. Petrus Apianus (Bienewitz) assisted in publishing the 1535 ed.

[10] Above, p. 165, n. 2; Sarton, op. cit. ii. 1029–30.   [11] Above, p. 270.

experimental and mathematical methods.[1] Dr. John Dee in 1583 had in his library more manuscripts of Roger Bacon's *Opus Maius*, *De Multiplicatione Specierum*, and other works than of works by any other writer, and a high proportion of the rest of the collection was composed of manuscripts of Grosseteste's *De Iride*, *De Luce*, and other tracts,[2] of the *Perspectivae* of Pecham and Witelo, and of works by Bradwardine and other fourteenth-century mathematicians and astronomers. Dee and Leonard Digges (d. *c.* 1571) were pioneers in the construction of telescopes, of which they described a form with lenses set up in frames without a tube, and both referred to Roger Bacon's manuscripts as the principal source of their knowledge of the properties of lenses and of mirrors.[3] Leonard Digges's son Thomas wrote of his father's early experiments:

. . . he was able by *Perspective Glasses* duely scituate vpon conuenient *Angles*, in such sorte to discouer euery particularitie in the Countrey rounde aboute, wheresoeuer the *Sunne* beames mighte pearse: As sithence *Archimedes*, (*Bakon* of *Oxforde* only excepted) I haue not read of any in *Action* euer able by meanes natural to performe the like. Which partly grew by the aide he had by one old written booke of the same *Bakons Experiments*, that by straunge aduenture, or rather *Destinie*, came to his hands, though chiefelye by conioyning continual laborious *Practise* with his *Mathematical* studies.[4]

---

[1] F. R. Johnson, *Astronomical Thought in Renaissance England*, pp. 76–81, 178. Since the heyday of the Merton mathematicians in the fourteenth century science had declined in Oxford as in northern Europe generally.

[2] 'Roberti Lincoln. ep. de luce, de iride cum multis aliorum tract. circiter 34, perg. 4°. A thik boke with a labell', M. R. James, *Lists of Manuscripts formerly owned by Dr. John Dee*, p. 33. The astronomer Robert Recorde, who with Dee and Thomas Digges was among the first to support the Copernican theory in England, gave a list of astronomical books recommended to the student: 'Dyuers Englyshe menne haue written right well in that argument: as Grostehed, Michell Scotte, Batecombe, Baconthorpe, and other dyuers, but fewe of their bookes are printed as yet, therefore I will staye at these three for this tyme' (*Castle of Knowledge*, iii, 1556, pp. 98–99). Recorde helped to establish in England an important school of practical mathematics, with particular reference to navigation; see F. R. Johnson and S. V. Larkey, 'Robert Recorde's mathematical teaching and the anti-Aristotelian movement', *Huntington Lib. Bull.* vii (1935) 59 sqq.; F. R. Johnson, 'Thomas Hood's inaugural address as mathematical lecturer of the city of London (1588)', *JHI*, iii (1942) 94. Grosseteste, Roger Bacon, and Richard Suisseth (Swineshead) were included in a list of English astronomers also in a poem by John Seldon which was printed in the beginning of Arthur Hopton's *Concordancy of Yeares* (1612). See Johnson, *Astronomical Thought*, p. 253; cf. Pacchi (1965), below p. 353.

[3] Ibid., p. 178; F. R. Johnson and S. V. Larkey, 'Thomas Digges, the Copernican system, and the idea of the infinity of the universe', *Huntington Lib. Bull.* v (1934) 106–7; Singer, *SHMS*, ii. 405–6. Digges used a concave and a convex lens in combination, as Galileo did.

[4] Leonard and Thomas Digges, *Stratioticos*, 1579, pp. 189–90. In the preface Thomas

Later writers who contributed towards the invention of the telescope and compound microscope also show the influence of the
thirteenth-century opticians. Giambattista della Porta, who seems
to have been the first to try combinations of lenses to form a microscope,[1] based his optical work almost entirely on that of Roger
Bacon, Witelo, and Pecham.[2] The effective inventor of the telescope
and compound microscope was Galileo (1609),[3] though his own
work was suggested by the empirical discovery of suitable combinations of lenses in Holland between 1591 and 1608.[4] Galileo's account
of the path of the rays through the concave eye-piece and convex
objective which he used was not satisfactory and was considerably
improved by Kepler, who suggested the use of the two convex
lenses which became the basis of later instruments. Kepler had
already written an important optical treatise in the form of a commentary on Witelo's *Perspectiva* and used Witelo's table of refractive
angles in astronomical work.[5] His improvements to the telescope
may be regarded as a development of what he had learned from the
thirteenth-century writer.[6]

Of scarcely less importance than the invention of the telescope
and microscope, as a practical application of optics, was the improvement of spectacles, which itself depended on an improved knowledge
of the operation of the eye in vision. The main problem was to

Digges said that he would try to reform navigation by the use of mathematics, and that
experiment also disclosed errors.

[1] In *Magiae Naturalis*, xvii. 10, 1589, p. 269. The first edition of this work was
published in Naples in 1558 but the passages on the microscope first occur in that of
1589; cf. Singer, op. cit., p. 407.

[2] *De Refract.* i. 11, 12, pp. 19, 24; ii. 22, pp. 63–64; iii. 6, 9, pp. 76, 79; iv. 10, p. 104.
An account of experimental measurements of angles of refraction with an astrolabe
adapted for the purpose contains such phrases as: 'id quemadmodum fiat ratione et
experientia demonstrabimus' (i. 4, p. 12). The book on lenses begins 'Lux diaphanum
corpus pervadens multiplicatur in corpore ipso' (viii. 1, p. 174) and goes on to refer to
Witelo's experiment with a spherical burning-flask. In this work della Porta made
extensive use also of Alhazen. In *Magiae Naturalis* (iv. 15, 1558, p. 151; cf. iv, Prooemium, p. 141) he gave an account of Witelo's work on burning-mirrors. According to
Joseph Priestley (*History and Present State of Discoveries relating to Vision, Light, and
Colours*, 1772, i. 23) della Porta praised Roger Bacon as 'a man of an almost universal
genius'. Priestley accepted this judgement.

[3] Galileo was the first to use it for astronomical observations, which he published in
Sidereus Nuntius (1610). He described the use of the same instrument as a compound
microscope in 1614 (*Opere*, ed. naz., xix. 598).

[4] Singer, op. cit., pp. 408 sqq.; Rosen, *Centaurus*, ii (1951) 44–51.

[5] He used Risner's edition: Johann Kepler, *Ad Vitellionem Paralipomena*, 1604,
p. 150. See below, p. 283, n. 3.

[6] Ioannis Kepleri *Dioptrice*, 1611, p. 7.

understand how the eye formed an image. Roger Bacon,[1] Witelo,[2] and Pecham,[3] following Alhazen[4] and Avicenna,[5] had recognized the function of the lens as an organ focusing the light or 'visible species' entering the eye, and, although all had supposed that the lens was also the sensitive organ, they had recognized that vision was completed only in the optic nerve and brain.[6] Roger Bacon had, in fact, tried to show how the visible species were focused on to the end of the optic nerve without producing an inverted image. The same difficulties over the true sensitive organ and the inversion of the image were found in the sixteenth century. Leonardo da Vinci, who knew Witelo's *Perspectiva*[7] and some of Roger Bacon's writings,[8] discussed whether 'the visual faculty resides in it [crystalline humour or lens] or at the extremity of the optic nerve, which extremity catches these images and transmits them to the common sense as do the nerves of the sense of smell',[9] but he decided in favour of the lens. He thought that the eye acted as a kind of camera obscura in which the inversion of the image was prevented by the double crossing of the rays passing through the refracting bodies inside.[10] The first to show correctly how the lens focused the rays on to the retina was Maurolyco, another follower of Roger Bacon, Pecham, and Witelo, and as a result he was able to explain long- and short-sightedness and the use of convex and concave spectacles.[11] But Maurolyco could not understand that this focused light formed a real image on the retina, because he could not understand the inverted image. The anatomist Felix Plater was the first to recognize the retina as the visual receptor of images 'spread' by the lens, but without understanding the dioptics involved.[12] Hieronymo Fabrizio

---

[1] Above, pp. 151–5.
[2] Above, p. 217.
[3] Above, p. 166, n. 10.
[4] Above, p. 147, n. 2; p. 153, n. 3.
[5] Above, p. 151, n. 4.
[6] Cf. above, p. 153, n. 3; p. 217.
[7] Leonardo da Vinci, *Literary Works*, ed. Richter, 2nd ed., ii. 349, 361, 376.
[8] Ibid. ii. 371.
[9] *Notebooks* of Leonardo da Vinci, arranged by E. MacCurdy, i. 241; cf. *Literary Works*, ed. Richter, ii. 414. Cf. Roger Bacon, *Opus Maius*, v. i. v. 2, ed. Bridges, ii. 32–33; above, p. 154.
[10] *Literary Works*, ed. Richter, i. 140–6; note Leonardo's use of the word 'spetie' for light (p. 146); cf. 'le forme delli obietti' (ibid. ii. 99); see Singer, op. cit. pp. 401 sqq.; cf. Roger Bacon, above, pp. 154–5. G. della Porta (*De Refract.* iv. 1, p. 91) also thought that the eye acted as a camera obscura.
[11] *Diaph.* iii, pp. 73 sqq. He cited here 'Rogerius Bacchon' (p. 74) and 'Joan. Petsan' (p. 76). Cf. J. E. Montucla, *Histoire des mathématiques*, i. 625–6.
[12] *De Corporis Humani Structura et Usu*, 'De Capite', 1583, p. 187; see Crombie, op. cit. above, p. 153, n. 3.

of Aquapendente published accurate drawings showing the position of the lens and other parts of the eye.[1] Finally Kepler, after discussing Witelo's argument about the union of the 'species' from each eye,[2] asserted that the rays focused by the cornea and the lens formed a real inverted image on the retina.[3] After Kepler further aspects of the physiology of vision were developed by the Jesuit Father Christopher Scheiner, who also drew inspiration from Roger Bacon and Witelo.[4] Some of his experiments were included by Descartes in *La Dioptrique*,[5] in the admirable study of vision which preceded his attempt to generalize the methods of grinding lenses on the basis of the sine-law of refraction.

Between the seventeenth century attempt to construct an adequate theory of rectilinear propagation from which the laws of reflection and refraction and the production of colours could be deduced, and the thirteenth-century discussion of the 'multiplication of species', there is again a striking parallel.[6] Both before and after the sine-law itself had been formulated by Harriot, Snell,

---

[1] *De Oculo Visis Organo*, Venetiis, 1600.

[2] Cf. Roger Bacon, Witelo; above, pp. 154, 217.

[3] *Paralipomena*, v. 2, pp. 168–71. He based his ocular anatomy on Plater and, indirectly, Fabrizio; see Crombie, *Proc. Roy. Microscopical Soc.*, ii (1967) 52 sqq.

[4] Christophorus Scheiner, *Oculus*, 1619. In this work he discussed the 'communis specierum concursus' (ii. ii. 9, p. 106) and, after falsifying the hypothesis that 'Vitreus est formale visus organum' by deducing a conclusion from it 'quod est contra manifestissimam experientiam' (p. 107), he concluded: 'Radius in retinam receptus approbatur' (C. 14, p. 114). Then he cited the views of 'Alhazen enim et Vitellio' (C. 15, p. 116) and 'Rogerius Bacco, Anglus, ex antiquis Vir non tantum in Mathematicis, sed in aliis omnibus scientiis sua aetate eminentissimus in sua Perspectiva cap. 4' (p. 119). The main concern of the book was in fact with 'Proprietates erectarum specierum earumque causa' (iii. i. 24, p. 188) and 'Specierum erectarum applicatio ad oculum' (C. 26, p. 191). An impression of his use of experimental falsification and verification in the structure of the argument by which 'Ex dictis demonstratur Visionem in Retine fieri, non autem in humore Crystallino' can be gained from the *Index Capitum* at the beginning (C. 26, p. 193). See pp. 4, 20–1, 60, 84, 120, 134, 140, 237, for other references to Witelo and to Vesalius, Kepler, and other later writers.

[5] *Dioptrique*, v, pp. 35 sqq. contains an experiment in which the back of an eye was removed and the retina covered by a piece of paper on which the image was observed. This is described in Scheiner's *Rosa Ursina*, 1630, ii. 23. For further work on vision by Descartes see *L'Homme*. The geometrical theory of vision was completed by Huygens, who made an artificial model of the eye and with it demonstrated the phenomena of vision, the application of spectacles, &c. See Christian Huygens, *Dioptrica*, Prop. xxxi, in *Opera Posthuma*, 1703, pp. 112 sqq.; H. von Helmholz, *Treatise on Physiological Optics*, transl. from 3rd German ed., i. 116; S. L. Polyak, *The Retina*, pp. 136–9.

[6] For a general account of seventeenth-century theories see Whittaker, *History of the Theories of Aether and Electricity*; E. Mach, *Principles of Physical Optics*; Wolf, *Science, Technology, and Philosophy in the 16th and 17th Centuries*, pp. 244 sqq.; and references below, pp. 354–5.

and Descartes,[1] empirical knowledge of refraction was widely taken from Witelo's tables;[2] for example, by Kepler,[3] Scheiner,[4] Descartes himself,[5] Marci,[6] Emanuel Maignan,[7] James Gregory,[8] Grimaldi,[9] and C. F. Milliet De Chales.[10] Snell's interest in the formulation of an accurate law of refraction seems to have been stimulated by Risner's work and by Witelo and Alhazen.[11] Descartes presented the law of refraction as a deduction from his theory that light was an instantaneous[12] propagation of mechanical pressure through a medium consisting of globules in contact, and to derive the law he

[1] Snell first formulated the law before his death in 1626 but did not publish it. Descartes probably reached it independently and published it for the first time in *La Dioptrique* in 1637, but without the sine notation. On the problem of precedence and Descartes's possible borrowing see P. Kramer, 'Descartes und das Brechungsgesetz des Lichtes', *Abh. Gesch. Math.* iv (1882) 233 sqq.; D. J. Korteweg, 'Descartes et les manuscrits de Snellius', *Rev. métaph. et morale*, iv (1896) 489 sqq.; J. F. Scott, *The Scientific Work of René Descartes*, pp. 36–9; cf. pp. 71–82. See above, p. 274, n. 7; p. 275, n. 1.

[2] Omitting the impossible values; above, p. 225.

[3] Kepler also made independent measurements to correct Witelo: *Paralipomena*, iv, pp. 77 sqq., 114–16; *Dioptrice*, p. 7. In these two works he also tried, after criticizing Ptolemy's 'law' (*Paralip.*, p. 111; see above, p. 120, p. 225, n. 4), to work out an adequate geometrical expression for the relation between the angles of incidence and amounts of refraction. In *Dioptrice* he described the phenomenon of total reflection which had been recognized by Theodoric of Freiberg; above, p. 236.

[4] *Refractiones Coelestes*, CC. 35, 45, 1617, pp. 74, 100.

[5] See *Inventaire succinct des écrits . . . 1650* (*Œuvres*, x) 8; cf. *Excerpta ex Cartesio MS. de Leibniz* (*Œuvres*, xi) 646.

[6] *Thaumantias*, xi, p. 80. Among seventeenth-century writers he referred to Kepler, Scheiner, Gassendi, and Roberval.

[7] *Perspectiva Horaria*, 1648, pp. 555, 646–8 (describes the use of an astrolabe to measure angles of refraction; mentions Kepler's corrections of Witelo), 653 ('Tabula refractionum . . . a Vitellione factis experimentis').

[8] 'Cujus refractionis causas et elementa non nostrum est hic explicare, abunde enim de his disputarunt Alhazenus, Vittellio, Kepler, et multi alii.' (*Optica Promota*, 1663, p. 5.) He referred to Kepler's corrections and the measurements 'ab Athanasio Kerchero observatae' and gave a table of 'Refractiones a Vitellione observatae et earum a nostro Calculo Discrepantia' (pp. 11–13). Of the parabolic mirror he said 'Hanc pulcherrimam conclusionem, primus quod sciam invenit Vitellio' (p. 19). See also pp. 29, 36, on lenses.

[9] *Physico-mathesis de Lumine*, lii, p. 436: he gave a table of sines of refractive angles 'a Vitellione assignati'.

[10] *Cursus seu Mundus Mathematicus*, 1674, ii, pp. 619–21. Cf. N. G. Poudra, *Histoire de la perspective*, p. 70.

[11] G. Sarton, 'The tradition of the optics of Ibn al-Haitham', *Isis*, xxix (1938) 403 sqq., xxxiv (1942–3) 217. Cf. *Opticae ex voto Petri Rami novissimo per Fridericum Risnerum conscripti*, Cassellis, 1606; *Risneri Optica cum annotationibus* Willebrordi Snellii, ed. J. A. Wollgraff; Boyer, *Isis*, xliii (1952) 96.

[12] *Dioptrique*, i, p. 7. Descartes said the propagation of light was a tendency to movement rather than a movement. Some of his contemporaries explicitly refuted the theory that the propagation was instantaneous; e.g. Maignan, Hooke, below, p. 286. For a discussion of the mechanical idea on which Descartes based this theory see Koyré, *Études galiléennes*, iii. 158 sqq.

made use of the analogy of the behaviour of a ball thrown on to a
stretched cloth.[1] He supposed that light was refracted at an interface
because it travelled more easily in a dense than in a rare medium.
Witelo, following Alhazen, had already tried to explain refraction on
the assumption that the motion of light falling obliquely on an interface could be considered as consisting of two motions at right angles
which were differently affected on crossing the interface,[2] and Kepler had tried to put this explanation into stricter geometrical form.[3]
Kepler pointed out the analogy between light and local motion and
described a model with a ball which may well have been the parent
of Descartes's model.[4] Later, Fermat attempted to improve on
Descartes's explanation of the law of refraction by assuming (like
Witelo[5] and Kepler) that light travelled more easily in a *rarer*
medium; he derived the law from the principle on which Grosseteste himself had based his discussion of the subject, 'ce principe si
commun et si établi, que *la nature agit toujours par les voies les plus
courtes*'.[6]

---

[1] *Dioptrique*, i–ii: this amounted to a different model; cf. below, p. 311, n. 2.

[2] Above, p. 219, n. 5. Cf. Grosseteste, above, p. 119.

[3] *Paralipomena*, iv, p. 84. Another fundamental contribution to optics which seems
to have owed something to thirteenth-century work was Kepler's formulation of the
inverse square law of the change in intensity of light with distance: 'Sicut se habent
sphaericae superficies, quibus origo lucis pro centro est, amplior ad angustiam: ita se
habet fortitudo seu densitas lucis radiorum in angustiori, ad illam in laxiori sphaerica
superficie, hoc est, conversim.' *Paralipomena*, i. 9, p. 10; cf. above, p. 216; also pp. 106–
9, 112, 185–6.

[4] Ibid. i, pp. 7–17. Kepler held that light was an emission of 'species' which were
propagated instantaneously (ibid., p. 36; cf. pp. 28–29). On p. 17 there is a reference to
the work of Jordanus on the balance. This had been published by Tartaglia in 1565.

[5] Above, p. 219, n. 5.

[6] Epist. cxii, to M. de la Chambre, Jan. 1, 1662, in P. de Fermat, *Correspondance*
(*Œuvres*, ii) 457–8. For the same principle in reflection see Epist. lxxxvi, 1657, in ibid.,
p. 254. Cf. above, pp. 86, 96, 118, 123. Fermat referred to Witelo's work on refraction in
a letter to Mersenne in 1637, Epist. xxii, ibid., p. 107. See Whittaker, op. cit., p. 10;
Dugas, *Histoire de la mécanique*, pp. 244 sqq. Marci also used the principle of economy
as a basic principle: 'Pronuntiatum III. *Omne agens lucidum non impeditum, agit per
lineam rectam; estque idem terminus virtutis et hujus lineae rectae*. Ita Aristoteles lib. 5
Metaphy. ubi dicit *naturam operari breviori modo, quo potest*: linea autem recta omnium
est brevissima per 20.1 Elem: Eucl: Alhazen 2 n. 7. Vitell: lib. 2 theor. 1. Roger:
Baccon: de Specul. Mathem: cap: 1 quod experientia luculenta demonstratur locis jam
citatis Vitellione et Alhazene.' (*Thaumantias*, p. 3.) Maignan, on the other hand, rejected
this principle, which he associated with Witelo, as an explanation of the equality of the
angles of incidence and reflection, because the angles of incidence and refraction were
not equal (*Philos. Sacra*, i, Appendix, xiv. 10–13, 1661, pp. 44–46). He offered another
explanation of these phenomena in *Perspectiva Horaria*, iv. xxxii–xlv, pp. 631–47;
Fermat referred to this in his letter of 1662. For the use of the principle of economy by
other sixteenth- and seventeenth-century scientists, e.g. Copernicus, Kepler, Galileo,

The chief methodological principle on the basis of which the seventeenth-century theories of the nature of light were developed was that the 'subjective' sensations of colour should be represented in the language of science by concepts amenable to mathematical treatment. This is, of course, the well-known distinction between so-called 'primary' and 'secondary' qualities made by Galileo and Descartes.[1] As Galileo put it in a famous passage in *Il Saggiatore*:

> Philosophy is written in that vast book which stands forever open before our eyes, I mean the universe; but it cannot be read until we have learnt the language and become familiar with the characters in which it is written. It is written in mathematical language, and the letters are triangles, circles and other geometrical figures, without which means it is humanly impossible to comprehend a single word.[2]

Later in the same work he concluded, at the end of a discussion of 'what we call heat':

> I hold that there exists nothing in external bodies for exciting in us tastes, odours and sounds but sizes, shapes, multitudes and slow or swift motions. And I conclude that if the ears, tongues and noses were removed, shape, number and motion would remain, but there would be no odours, tastes or sounds, which apart from living animals I believe to be mere words.[3]

This principle was, however, already implied by the estimation of the role of mathematics made by Grosseteste and Roger Bacon. The beginning of its application to the problem of the nature of light is found in the distinction made by these two writers between the sensation produced by 'species' in sentient beings and the physical activity which carried the 'visible species' to the eye, and in their attempt to conceive of this physical activity as a succession of pulses or waves analogous to sound.[4] The conception of light as a propagation of 'species' was widely held during the sixteenth century, and the analogy with sound was, for example, the main burden of Francis Bacon's investigation of the 'Form of Light'.[5] The first

---

and Newton, see E. A. Burtt, *Metaphysical Foundations of Modern Physical Science*, 2nd ed., pp. 26 sqq., 46, 70, 214. Cf. P. Smith, *History of Modern Culture*, i. 76 sqq.

[1] *Prin. Philos.* i. 53, p. 16, in *Opera Philosophica*, Amsterdami, 1664. (Reprinted in *Œuvres*, viii.) For this point in both Galileo and Descartes see E. Cassirer, *Erkenntnisproblem in der Philosophie und Wissenschaft der neueren Zeit*, i. 289 sqq., 375 sqq.; Burtt, *Metaphysical Foundations*, pp. 73 sqq., 97 sqq.; Collingwood, *Idea of Nature*, pp. 102 sqq.

[2] *Il Saggiatore*, Q. 6 (*Opere*, vi) 232. The first edition was published in Rome in 1623.

[3] Ibid., Q. 48, pp. 347–8, 350; cf. Burtt, op. cit., pp. 75–76.

[4] Above, pp. 110, 115, 118, 144–7; also Witelo, above, p. 215.

[5] *De Augmentis*, iv. 3, in *Works*, i. 612, and iv. 403–4; *Topics of Inquiry respecting Light and Luminous Matter*, in *Works*, v. 409–14. The last contains Tables of Presence,

attempts to relate the motion of light to known mechanics were those made by Kepler[1] and Descartes. There seems to be no evidence that the writings of Grosseteste or Roger Bacon had any direct influence on the men who transformed Descartes's rotating globules, whose different angular velocities produced the different colours when they struck the retina,[2] into the waves or pulses of Hooke, Huygens, and Newton. But haunting the increasingly powerful mathematical technique that was the great strength of the seventeenth century and that made this transformation possible, are many reminiscences of thirteenth- and fourteenth-century ideas. For example, the word 'species' was retained, but from Descartes onwards its use was restricted to designate the activity that accounted for physical light producing sensation;[3] physical light was often described as the 'vehicle' of such 'species'. Maignan, who used the word 'species' in this way,[4] put forward the theory that physical light was not, as Descartes and Witelo had said,[5] an instantaneous

Absence, and Degree showing the analogy between light and sound. In *Natural History*, iii. 256 (*Works*, ii) 429, Bacon said that 'visibles and audibles' both 'have the whole species in every small portion of the air, or medium', and that 'The beams of light, when they are multiplied and conglomerate, generate heat' (§ 267, p. 430). Cf. his celebrated investigation of the 'Form of Heat' in *Novum Organum*, ii. 11 sqq.; below, pp. 301–2. Of Roger Bacon's writings Francis Bacon knew *De Mirabili Potestate Artis et Naturae*, of which an English translation by Dr. John Dee was published in 1618; see *Works*, ii. 97–98.

[1] Kepler's 'Lucis encomium' shows his Neoplatonic affiliations. Light was 'vinculum corporei et spiritualis mundi. . . .' *Paralipomena*, i, p. 7. Cf. above, p. 284, n. 4.

[2] Descartes ruled out 'espèces intentionelles' distinct from light as a connecting link between physical light and the sensation it produced (*Dioptrique*, i, p. 5; cf. above, Roger Bacon, p. 152, Witelo, p. 217). He compared the transmission of pressure along the globules from the object to the eye with the transmission of mechanical pressure along the stick with which a blind man finds his way. The sensation of red was produced by the globules with the greatest speed of rotation (*Météores*, viii, p. 259; *Princ. Philos.* iv. 195, p. 190). He connected physical light with sensation by means of the pineal gland (*L'Homme*, v, pp. 62 sqq.).

[3] e.g. 'Is not the sensory of Animals that place to which the sensitive Substance is present, and into which the sensible Species of Things are carried through the Nerves and Brain, that there they may be perceived by their immediate presence to that Substance?' Newton, *Opticks*, iii. i, Q. 28, 4th ed., pp. 344–5. Cf. Roger Bacon, above, p. 144, n. 6.

[4] *Philos. Sacra*, ii, Append. v. i. 17, 1672, p. 393; *Cursus Philosophicus*, iii. xxxv. xiii. 101, 2nd ed., 1673, p. 671 [1st ed. 1653]. Cf. Theodoric of Freiberg, above, p. 243. Marci, in a section entitled 'De Specierum multiplicatione in eodem medio', said like Grosseteste that 'Lux est agens necessarium. . . . Est itaque una forma communis, quae tam in aëre, quam in solo lucem ex se fundit . . .' (*Thaumantias*, xxxvi, pp. 153, 155–6). For Marci's contribution towards the formulation of 'Huygen's Principle' see Hoppe, *AGNT*, x (1927) 288.

[5] *Cursus Philos.* iii. xv. xiv, 2nd ed., pp. 422–3; iii. xxxiv, p. 622; xxxv, p. 634; iii. xxxv. xii, pp. 670 sqq. In refuting Descartes's theory Maignan used the method of

transmission, but a motion of undulation at different speeds in rectilinear rays of a substance[1] akin to the purest fire. The rays could be made more intense or remiss, that is concentrated or dispersed in space,[2] by a lens, and their substance could be 'modified' by refraction through a prism so that the light 'moves in different ways, tickles and affects the organ of vision, and so represents the various colours'.[3] This form of modification replaced the weakening of light by refraction to which Witelo and other writers had attributed the production of colours.[4]

Grimaldi also held that light was the vehicle of 'visual species'.[5] He had discovered the phenomenon of diffraction and added it to direct, reflected, and refracted rays as a fourth 'mode of propagation of light'.[6] He described light as a very subtle corporeal fluid substance which diffused itself by very rapid motion, and his book contains a figure showing the rectilinear propagation of light by minute transverse vibrations.[7] Arguing that the differences between some species of physical things depended on differences of quantity, as for example occurred with pulses of sound,[8] he maintained that the different sensations of colour were produced by the modification of the minute undulations that accompanied the diffusion of light. He asserted that no other entity was involved besides light in motion,

---

falsification. An essential part of 'mea methodus' was 'vulgatum illud, *nihil est in intellectu, quin prius fuerit in sensu*'. (Ibid. iii, 'Philosophia Naturae', Praef., pp. 125, 127.) Maignan knew his scholastics and cited, for example, Aquinas, Scotus, and Durandus (ibid. iii. iv, pp. 179, 190–1). He cited also Grimaldi and Gassendi (ibid. iii. xxxiii, Append. 2, pp. 590–1).

[1] But he argued that it was not 'aliquid substantiale fluens v.g. a sole' because then 'quatenus defluxu lucis continuo, dilaberetur etiam continue solis substantia.' (*Philos. Sacra*, i, Append. xiv. 30, p. 52.) The idea he was refuting was the Neoplatonic theory of emission; above, p. 105. Cf. Roger Bacon, above, pp. 146–7.

[2] *Cursus Philos.* iii. ix. vii. 13, p. 256; ibid., § 6, p. 255. Cf. above, p. 87, n. 1; p. 196.

[3] 'particulae cuiuslibet radii diversimode agitatae singulae et omnes . . . motum omnino rectum mutent in undulatum, crispulum sive alio modo etiam secundum gradus celeritatis diversum . . . diversimode moveat, titillet, afficiat organum visus, et ita varios repraesentet colores tum simul cum fulgore, tum etiam sine illo . . . ut in iride, trigono vitreo, etc. . . . in collo columbae, et in quibusdam villosis holosericis. . . . Igitur coloris nomen tribuendum . . . est modificare luci. . . .' *Cursus Philos.* iii. xv. xiii, 2nd ed., pp. 420–1. Apart from a reference to St. Thomas Aquinas this is the same as the passage in the 1553 edition, pp. 1553 sqq.

[4] Above, p. 231; cf. pp. 111, 199, 246, 266, n. 1.

[5] *Physico-mathesis de Lumine*, i. xl, pp. 283, 286.

[6] Ibid. i. i. 5, p. 2. Cf. above, p. 120, n. 5; Whittaker, op. cit., p. 11.

[7] *Physico-mathesis de Lumine*, i. xliii, p. 342; cf. i. xiii, p. 153.

[8] 'species physicas variari per magis ac minus. . . .' Ibid. i. xliii, p. 347. Cf. pp. 111, 182 sqq., 247.

and that the theory of undulations was the only means of 'saving' and explaining the experiments.[1]

Of the three later seventeenth-century physicists who between them did most to give mathematical exactitude to the idea that the propagation of light was a form of periodic motion, Hooke[2] and Newton's master, Isaac Barrow,[3] knew the work of Maignan, Huygens had Grimaldi's *Physico-mathesis de Lumine* among his books when he died,[4] and Newton cited this work.[5] As if further to emphasize the continuity of ideas, Huygens cited, as proof of the assertion that light was essentially a mode of motion, the example of the burning-glass which, he said, produced its effect because the rays dissociated the molecules of bodies on which they were focused.[6] Grosseteste, whose 'wave' theory is so suggestive of that of Huygens, might well have suggested this example too.[7]

The seventeenth century closed with the problem still undecided as to whether light should be conceived of as a train of vibrations propagated in an all-pervading aether, or as a stream of corpuscles emitted into the aether.[8] Optics since that time has made use of both conceptions. It has become so successful a branch of mathematical physics not only because 'students of optics' have had at their disposal a group of hypotheses so fruitful in suggesting forms of the mathematical 'superior science' which 'provides the reason for that thing of which the inferior science provides the fact'; but also because they have in practice always sacrificed the 'physical' aspects of the hypothesis to the success of the mathematical correlation. 'The superior science does not speak of the causes of the thing' as Grosseteste put it, and the student of optics 'does not care whether'

---

[1] 'Luminis Modificatio . . . quam . . . apparenter coloratur . . . non improbabiliter dici potest esse determinata ipsius Undulatio minutissime crispata, et quidam velut tremor diffusionis, cum certa fluitatione subtilissima, qua fiat ut illud propria, ac determinata applicatione afficiat sensorium visionis . . . et nullam superimportat entitatem praeter substantiam luminis sic motam . . . ac denique per eam solam salvari potest quidquid experimenta salvandum praescribunt.' (*Physico-mathesis de Lumine*, i. xliii, p. 341.) 'Posita Luminis Undulatione, et non aliter, salvantur atque explicantur Experimenta, quae habemus de Coloratione Luminis.' Ibid., p. 344.

[2] Hooke cited Maignan's *Perspectiva Horaria*; see Roberts and Thomas, *Newton and the Origin of Colours*, p. 38. For Hooke's theory of propagation see *Micrographia*, ix, 1665, pp. 54 sqq. See also his 'Lectures on Light', in *Posthumous Works*, 1705, pp. 71 sqq.

[3] *Lectiones Opticorum Phaenomenon*, ii, 1669, pp. 21, 27. Barrow cited also Alhazen (pp. 45, 65), Kepler, and Scheiner (p. 125).

[4] A. E. Bell, *Christian Huygens*, pp. 176 sqq.

[5] *Opticks*, iii. i, 4th ed., p. 292.

[6] *Traité de la lumière*, i, 1690, pp. 9–10.   [7] Above, p. 87, n. 1; pp. 122–3.

[8] Cf. Roberts and Thomas, op. cit., pp. 109 sqq.; Whittaker, op. cit.

a particular characteristic of radiant energy postulated by this or that hypothesis 'belongs by nature or not'.[1]

This last fundamental point of scientific method was well put by Newton in reply to the criticism made by 'an ingenious person from Paris'[2] that in his theory of colour he had not taken account of 'an *Hypothesis* by Motion. . . . And till he hath found this *Hypothesis*, he hath not taught us, what it is wherein consists the nature and difference of Colours, but only this accident (which certainly is very considerable) of their *different Refrangibility*'.[3] Newton replied that he had 'never intended to shew, wherein consists the Nature and Difference of colours, but only to shew . . . that different Refrangibility conduces to their production . . . by separating the Rays whose qualities they are'.[4] Newton was quite prepared to make use of physical or 'mechanical' hypotheses, though he considered that none of those which had been so far put forward to account for the experimental facts of light was wholly satisfactory.[5] But he rejected all criticisms of his theory taken from the belief that such hypotheses literally showed the nature of light. 'And therefore', he concluded, 'I could wish all objections were suspended, taken from *Hypotheses* or any other heads than these two; Of showing the insufficiency of Experiments to determine these *Quaere's* or prove any other parts of my Theory, by assigning the flaws and defects in my conclusions drawn from them; Or of producing other Experiments which directly contradict me, if any such may seem to occur. For if the Experiments, which I urge, be defective, it cannot be difficult to show the defects; but if valid, then by proving the Theory they must render all Objections invalid.'[6]

---

[1] Above, pp. 92, 93, 94.

[2] This was 'Huygens'; see Rosenfeld, *Isis*, ix (1927) 65.

[3] *PT*, viii (1673) 6086.

[4] Ibid., p. 6109; cf. below, p. 311, n. 2; pp. 315 sqq.

[5] See his reply to Hooke, ibid. vii (1672) 5084 sqq.; Roberts and Thomas, op. cit., pp. 95 sqq.

[6] *PT*, vii (1672) 5004, 5005. He gave a clear account of his method in another passage in a reply to J. Pardies. (Ibid., p. 5014.) See also his reply to Anthony Lucas, ibid. xi (1676) 698 sqq. Cf. the similar remarks by Descartes, below, p. 314; and by Theodoric of Freiberg, above, p. 239.

XI

The Historical Foundations of the Modern Theory of Experimental Science

(1)

THE evidence presented in the foregoing pages shows that as a result of their attempts to answer the Greek question: How is it possible to reach with the greatest possible certainty true premisses for demonstrated knowledge of the world of experience? the natural philosophers of Latin Christendom in the thirteenth and fourteenth centuries created the experimental science characteristic of modern times. This new method was both a guide to practical research and a means of defining accurately the type of explanation such research could provide. Devised in a society interested in both the applications and the philosophical meaning of science, the knowledge it gave was both useful[1] and enlightening.

As a practical guide the essential features of the new theory of experimental science are seen in the research into the cause of the rainbow. The object of the inquiry was to provide 'demonstrated knowledge' (*scientia propter quid*), as distinct from bare empirical knowledge (*scientia quia*), of the facts. Demonstrated knowledge of a fact was had when it was deduced from a theory which related it

---

[1] For the utilitarian motive in sixteenth- and seventeenth-century science see Libri, *Sciences math. en Italie*; M. Leroy, *Descartes social*; F. Borkenau, *Übergang vom feudalen zum bürgerlichen Weltbild*; H. Brown, *Scientific Organizations in Seventeenth Century France (1620–80)*, 'The utilitarian motive in the age of Descartes', *AS*, i (1936) 182 sqq.; J. U. Nef, 'The progress of technology and the growth of large scale industry in Great Britain, 1540–1640', *Econ. Hist. R.*, v (1934–5) 3 sqq.; H. Grossmann, 'Die gesellschaftlichen Grundlagen der mechanistischen Philosophie und die Manufaktur', *Zeitschr. f. Sozialforsch.* iv (1935) 161 sqq.; Wolf, *Science, Technology, and Philosophy in the 16th and 17th Centuries*; G. N. Clark, *Science and Social Welfare in the Age of Newton*; R. K. Merton, 'Science, technology and society in seventeenth century England', *Osiris*, iv (1938) 360 sqq.; M. Ornstein [Bronfenbrenner], *The Rôle of Scientific Societies in the Seventeenth Century*, 3rd ed.; E. Zilsel, 'The origins of William Gilbert's scientific method', *JHI*, ii (1941) 1 sqq., 'The sociological roots of science', *Amer. J. Sociol.* xlvii (1942) 544 sqq.; W. E. Houghton, 'The history of trades: its relation to 17th-century thought', *JHI*, ii (1941) 33 sqq.; L. Olschki, *Gesch. d. neusprach. wissensch. Literatur*; Baron, *JHI*, iv (1943) 21–49; H. Weisinger, *Lychnos*, 1946–7, pp. 11 sqq.

to other facts and showed its cause. Avoiding Aristotle's assumption that causal essences could be grasped simply by intuition from repeated instances, and accepting Plato's assertion that in natural science all theories were tentative and at best only probable, the methodologists of the thirteenth and fourteenth centuries tried to show how the most probable theories could be constructed and tested. The basis of their method was the double procedure described by Aristotle and related to experimental research by Grosseteste and his followers, who showed how the argument must alternate between inductive 'resolution' and deductive 'composition'. Research into a problem began with the collecting and classifying of facts relevant to the problem, as in Roger Bacon's survey of instances of phenomena similar to the rainbow. This led to an empirical generalization, namely that colours identical with those seen in the rainbow were seen whenever sunlight shone in a particular manner into a collection of water-drops; and it also isolated these instances from other instances, for example the colours seen in individual crystals, which were not in all respects identical with those seen in the rainbow: for example, they did not form part of a circle. This classification of instances could suggest a more abstract type of theory which asserted essentially that from the relations between a limited and usually small number of defined factors, all the facts in the empirical generalization and new facts not included in it could be deduced. The composite thing of observation was thus broken up into its parts or principles, which were reconstituted into a theoretical model. A theory of this kind was often mathematical in character. Examples are the different theories that asserted that the rainbow was caused by the reflection or refraction of light in a particular manner by raindrops.

Grosseteste and his successors clearly recognized that such theories could not be strictly inferred from the empirical generalization, but that they required a leap of intuition or scientific imagination acting on the empirical 'signs'. But they held that theories could be verified or falsified by arranging experiments in which the consequences of varying the relations between the different factors they postulated could be tested under controlled conditions, varying one factor at a time. In this way false theories could be eliminated and a true theory recognized which correctly described the conditions both necessary and sufficient to produce the events observed. All the writers on the rainbow from Grosseteste to Themon described

such experiments, much the best conceived being those of Theodoric of Freiberg. The experiments were usually arranged so that
false theories could be eliminated by the method of agreement and
difference, which was explicitly formulated by William of Ockham.
In accordance with this method measurements were often made
simply to establish equality or inequality, as for example those
which showed that the maximum elevation of 42° for the rainbow
was determined by the angle between the incident and emergent
rays at each raindrop. But recognition also of the method of concomitant variations was implied, for example, by the theory that the
colours of the rainbow were produced by a glass globe full of water
by the progressive weakening of the rays by increasing amounts of
refraction. Examples of series of measurements showing how one
factor varied with progressive variations in another are Witelo's
measurements of the amounts of refraction with different angles of
incidence, and the observations which showed how the respective
elevations of the rainbow and the sun varied from place to place
and season to season. The actual formulation of the method of concomitant variations seems to have been made first by Francis Bacon
and Galileo.

By ringing the changes upon induction, deduction from
theory, and experimental testing, the natural philosophers of the
thirteenth and fourteenth centuries showed how a system of theories
could be built up, with a range of application ever extending beyond
the original problem with which the research began. The work
undertaken to explain the rainbow became linked with other work
on originally independent problems. The most outstanding contributions made to optics during this period were the attempts to
apply the principle of minimum path to the laws of reflection and
refraction, the use of conic sections in the theory of mirrors and
particularly of parabolic mirrors, the attempts to work out a theory
of lenses and the invention of spectacles, Witelo's measurements of
angles of refraction and adaptation of Alhazen's explanation of
refraction by the composition of motions, the theory of propagation
of light by pulses or waves put forward by Grosseteste and Roger
Bacon, Theodoric's discovery of total reflection, and the statements
that the colours seen in light passing through a hexagonal crystal
or a globe of water were caused by differential refraction and
that each colour was a different species of ray. To the eventually
accepted theory of the rainbow nearly all this work contributed.

Each separate contributor saw as the goal of contemporary optics as a whole the building up of a general theory of light and colour by means of which all the separate problems would be related in a single system.

The type of relationship obtaining between a scientific theory and the facts it served to explain Grosseteste and his followers distinguished from those found in the other main divisions of philosophy principally by what they held to be the degrees of certainty involved. All members of the Oxford school and their colleagues in Paris agreed that in the nature of the case scientific demonstrations were always only probable and mathematical ones always certain, and most of them held for various reasons that metaphysical knowledge could also be certain. As compared with mathematical demonstrations they held that those in natural science were in a weaker position because, whereas in mathematics the premisses could be as immediately and completely known to us as the conclusion, in natural science the premisses of a demonstration could be reached only by argument from the observed facts which were to form the conclusion. This inductive argument they held to be weakened by two sources of uncertainty. First, except in the trivial case where a complete enumeration was possible, induction had to rely on a sample. Experimental models were, in fact, a special kind of sample. This weakness could be overcome by assuming the principle of uniformity, which allowed the results of induction to be extended into an empirical generalization. But the unavoidable weakness remained that from a bare empirical generalization there was no strictly logical inference to a theory of greater generality, capable of providing new knowledge. Moreover, very often the same facts could be deduced from more than one such theory, and it was impossible to exhaust all the possible theories. Therefore the experimental verification of a particular theory did not exclude the possibility that another theory might be true in the same sense. The experimental method could show in fact only that some theories were false and others *sufficient to save the appearances*; it could not show that a theory was *necessarily true* in the sense of being a necessary conclusion from the analysis of the experimental facts, and therefore a unique and final statement of how Nature was actually composed and constructed.

This conclusion led to the further principle seen, for example, in Ockham's use of the principle of economy; namely, that apart from experimental verification and logical coherence the choice between different scientific theories was entirely a matter of convenience or convention.

A far-reaching result of the foregoing analysis of the type of explanation found in science was to throw into prominence questions about relations, which could be described by mathematics, as opposed to questions about causes in the sense of Aristotle's 'physics', which were expressed in the language of attributes inhering in substances. Undoubtedly the Neoplatonic affiliations, found especially in Oxford, encouraged an emphasis on mathematics as a means of explaining the world of experience, though Aristotle's theory of the subordination of physical to mathematical sciences was more useful in practice. An important step towards establishing questions about relations as the proper questions for science was taken by Ockham and the 'nominalists', when they pointed out that 'substance' in Aristotle's 'physics' was in fact simply a definition, a concept, or even just a name. These writers thus disposed of substance and cause as means of scientific explanation, and reduced science to a description of the relations between individual observable entities. The first attempts to improve on the geometrical methods provided by Euclid and Apollonius for describing relations were made contemporaneously. Bradwardine tried for the first time to devise algebraic functions that would express rates of change; other fourteenth-century mathematicians associated the study of all kinds of change with representation by co-ordinates. This work was a prelude to the most fundamental contribution to scientific method made in the seventeenth century, the construction of an adequate mathematics of motion. The sources of seventeenth-century co-ordinate geometry and infinitesimal calculus were in fact the fourteenth-century speculations on the 'latitude of forms' and on the generation of magnitudes by the summation of infinitesimals, guided from the fifteenth century by principles derived from a renewed study of Archimedes's geometry. The sound mathematical basis which Archimedes provided for these procedures made it possible for the seventeenth-century mathematicians to develop from them a technical power beyond anything conceived of by the scholastics.[1]

[1] Some of Archimedes' geometrical treatises were used in the thirteenth century; renewed interest is seen with Blasius of Parma and Nicholas of Cusa. For the influence of fourteenth-century writers and of Cusa on Stevin, Kepler, Galileo, Descartes, Leibniz, and other seventeenth-century mathematicians see Boyer, *Concepts of the Calculus*,

That their conception of the functions of induction and experiment, and their insight into the possibilities of new mathematical methods of describing relations, gave to the creators of the thirteenth- and fourteenth-century theory of science the means of acquiring new experimental knowledge is amply shown by the research made during that period, not only into optics, but also into astronomy, mechanics, magnetics, zoology, botany, and medicine.[1] The main interest of the thirteenth- and fourteenth-century natural philosophers was, however, less in the particular questions about the world of experience which their new method enabled them to answer, than in the method itself and in the *type of knowledge* of which it showed natural science to consist. From the twelfth century the most distinctive feature of the intellectual life of the West had been its logical culture. In the thirteenth and fourteenth centuries, the principal object of the authors of the new experimental method was to enable them as precisely as possible to distinguish the logical character of natural science, and to show how it was related to that of the other main divisions of philosophy. The elegant experimental studies that they carried out were to a large extent simply illustrations of what could be done with the new method, and they were few in number compared with the writings on the logical foundations of the method itself.

After the middle of the fourteenth century there seems to have been a shift in the balance of interests towards an ever greater concentration on methodology.[2] Even in Italy and the Germanies, to which the leadership in Western science then passed, the wayward stream of systematic experimentation that ran through such writers as Blasius of Parma,[3] Giovanni Marliani,[4] Nicholas of Cusa,[5]

---

pp. 87–95, 112–15, and in general pp. 61–223. For an account of the new mathematics see especially Brunschvicg, *Étapes de la philos. math.* 3rd ed. Cf. Clagett, *J. Hist. Med.* vi (1951) 424; *Isis,* xliii (1952) 236–42.   [1] See above, p. 8, n. 3.

[2] Cf. Michalski's papers in *BIAPSL*; G. Ritter, *Studien zur Spätscholastik.* But in technology there was no slackening in progress: see Sarton, *Introduction,* iii and Thorndike, *History of Magic,* iv–vi, *passim*; Crombie, *Augustine to Galileo,* i, Ch. 4. Cf. E. F. Jacob, *Study of the Later Middle Ages.*   [3] Above, p. 277, n. 3.   [4] Above, p. 180, n. 3.

[5] See especially Nicolai de Cusa *Idiota de Staticis Experimentis,* ed. L. Baur (English transl., London, 1650); *De Docta Ignorantia,* ed. E. Hoffmann et R. Klibansky. For Cusanus see E. Cassirer, *Das Erkenntnisproblem,* i. 52 sqq., *Individuum und Kosmos in der Philosophie der Renaissance*; E. Vansteenberghe, *Le Cardinal Nicolas de Cues*; Thorndike, *Science and Thought in the Fifteenth Century,* pp. 133 sqq., *History of Magic,* iv. 387 sqq.; H. Bett, *Nicholas of Cusa*; M. Patronnier de Gandillac, *Philos. de Nicolas de Cues*; Markus, *Dominican Studies,* ii (1949) 358 sqq. See also E. F. Jacob, *Cusanus the Theologian.*

Regiomontanus,[1] and Leonardo da Vinci[2] scarcely fulfilled the promise of its Oxford-Parisian source. Outside those countries it seems practically to have dried up altogether. Undoubtedly this state of affairs must have been one reason why sixteenth- and seventeenth-century science could be felt as a revival, and it is significant that, apart from the mathematical physics of Archimedes, what it revived was the ordered and rational experimentation that had flourished two or three centuries before.[3] The methodological theory directing the use of experiment had in fact never ceased to be a subject of discussion. The most important difference between the original and the revived experimental science was that the natural philosophers of this second wave of the 'scientific revolution' were interested quite as much in the particular questions they could answer by experiment, as in the method itself.

(2)

It is interesting, in conclusion, briefly to trace the later history of the theory of experimental science from the end of the fourteenth century, when original writing in Oxford and Paris seems practically to have ceased for nearly 200 years, down to its classical formulation by Newton. As in the thirteenth and fourteenth centuries, so in the later period, scientific method had two main aspects, the experimental and the mathematical; and besides the problems strictly related to the procedure of science there was also the question of the type of knowledge the method provided, that is, the ontological status of scientific theories.[4]

---

[1] See R. Wolf, *Gesch. der Astronomie*, pp. 87 sqq.; Thorndike, *Science and Thought in the Fifteenth Century*, pp. 142 sqq., *History of Magic*, iv. 440 sqq.

[2] See the selections from Leonardo's notebooks published by Richter and MacCurdy, respectively: above, p. 281, nn. 7, 9; Duhem, *Léonard de Vinci*; E. Solmi, 'Leonardo da Vinci e il metodo sperimentale nelle ricerche fisiche', *Atti e Mem. della r. Accad. Virgiliana di Mantova*, 1905; O. Werner, *Zur Physik Leonardo da Vincis*; H. Hopstock, 'Leonardo as anatomist', in *SHMS*, ii; I. B. Hart, *Mechanical Investigations of Leonardo da Vinci*; Thorndike, *History of Magic*, v. 16 sqq.; Dugas, *Histoire de la mécanique*, pp. 71 sqq.

[3] Above, pp. 277 sqq. For complacent nonsense about this subject perhaps the prize should go to the following: 'What the antients, and the philosophers of the middle ages, have written concerning the rainbow has been recited. Their observations were such as could not have escaped the notice of the most illiterate husbandman who gazed at the sky, and their hypotheses were such as I have mentioned for the amusement, and not the instruction of my reader.' J. Priestley, *History and Present State of Discoveries relating to Vision, Light and Colours*, i. 48. Cf. Weisinger, *Lychnos*, 1946–7, pp. 11 sqq.

[4] For the general intellectual background to science in the fifteenth, sixteenth, and seventeenth centuries see H. Höffding, *History of Modern Philosophy*, i; Cassirer, *Das*

To the theory of experiment the main contribution in the fifteenth and sixteenth centuries was made by the Paduan school.[1] From the time of Pietro d'Abano,[2] at the end of the thirteenth century, Padua had been a stronghold of Aristotelianism and a leading medical university. Oxford methodology seems to have reached Padua at the end of the fourteenth century,[3] and in the fifteenth century the university began to attract many of the leading scientists: Cusanus, Puerbach, Regiomontanus, Copernicus, Fracastoro; and later Vesalius, Fabrizio, Galileo, and Harvey all belonged to it, either as students or professors. In a series of commentaries made during two centuries on Aristotle and Galen, the Averroist medical philosophers of Padua developed the 'double procedure' of resolution and composition that had formed the basis of the Oxford theory of experimental science, a procedure to which they gave the Averroist name *regressus*, into the form in which it was taken over by Galileo. The conception reached of this 'regress' was clearly described by the two sixteenth-century writers with whom the series culminated, Agostino Nifo (*c.* 1473–1545) and Jacopo Zabarella (1533–89).[4] The object of natural science was to discover the cause of a given observed effect, that is, a theory which could give demonstrated knowledge of the effect.[5] As Nifo put it: 'of the effect, or of the proposition signifying

---

Erkenntnisproblem, i–ii; H. O. Taylor, *Thought and Expression in the Sixteenth Century*; Ueberweg, *Gesch. der Philosophie*, iii, 'Die Philosophie der Neuzeit bis zum Ende des xviii. Jahrhunderts', 12. Aufl. neubearbeitet von M. Frischeisen-Köhler und W. Moog; Preserved Smith, *Hist. of Modern Culture*; Burtt, *Metaphysical Foundations*; B. Willey, *Seventeenth Century Background*; Thorndike, *Science and Thought in the Fifteenth Century*, *History of Magic*, iv–vi; E. W. Strong, *Procedures and Metaphysics*; E. Bréhier, *Hist. philos.* i–ii; J. N. D. Bush, *English Literature in the Earlier Seventeenth Century, 1600–60*; E. Cassirer, P. O. Kristeller and J. H. Randall, Jr. (ed.), *Renaissance Philosophy of Man*; W. K. Ferguson, *Renaissance in Historical Thought*.

[1] For an account of this school see Randall, *JHI*, i (1940) 177 sqq.

[2] Above, p. 202, n. 3.

[3] According to Randall (op. cit., p. 181) the Paduan teacher Paulus Venetus was sent by his Order to Oxford in 1390 and remained there for three years, after which he taught for two more years in Paris 'at the time of the last great Ockhamite, Pierre d'Ailly'. In his various encyclopaedic writings he fully though critically expounded Oxford ideas on logic and dynamics: see his *Summa Philosophie Naturalis*, Parisiis, 1514, *Logica*, 1546, *Expos. in Lib. Post.*, 1518. In the last work there is a reference to 'Linconiensis primo posteriorum' (i, f. 1rb). In ii, f. 100vb there is an interesting discussion of the possibility of acquiring universal knowledge by experiment.

[4] See Randall, op. cit., pp. 192 sqq.

[5] Augustini Niphi *Expos. Phys.* i, Expo. Commen. 4, 1552, ff. 5vb, 6^{r}; *Comm. Resol. Post.* ii, Comm. 100, 1540, f. 187^{r}. In this work he cited 'commentariis Linconiensis Grossetestae' (ibid. ii, Comm. 5, f. 7rb) and gave an account of nominal and real definitions (ibid. ii, Comm. 67, f. 166^{v}).

the effect, there are two kinds of knowledge: the one, that it is true, and this is clear to sense; the other, why it is so, and this is known to us through the discovery of the cause.'[1]

Against the charge of circularity both Nifo[2] and Zabarella[3] pointed out that this second kind of knowledge of the effect was very different from the initial observation. Nifo went on to show that the cause discovered by the first part of the regress was always only conjectural or hypothetical.

When I more diligently consider the words of Aristotle, and the commentaries of Alexander and Themistius, of Philoponus and Simplicius, it seems to me that in the regress made in demonstrations in natural science the first process, by which the discovery of the cause is put into syllogistic form, is a mere hypothetical (*coniecturalis*) syllogism.[4] . . . But the second process, by which is syllogised the reason why the effect is so through the discovered cause, is demonstration *propter quid*—not that it makes us know *simpliciter*, but conditionally (*ex conditione*), provided that that really is the cause, or provided that the propositions are true that represent it to be the cause, and that nothing else can be the cause. . . . Alexander . . . asserts that the discovery of the circles of epicycles and eccentrics from the appearances which we see is conjectural. . . . The opposite process he says to be a demonstration, not because it makes us know *simpliciter*, but conditionally, provided that those really are the cause and that nothing else can be the cause: for if those exist, then so do the appearances, but whether anything else can be the cause is not known to us *simpliciter*. . . . But you object that in that case the science of nature is not a science at all. To that it can be replied that the science of nature is not a science *simpliciter*, like mathematics.[5] Yet it is a science *propter quid*, because the discovered cause, gained through a conjectural syllogism, is the reason why the effect is so. . . . That something is a cause can never be so certain as that an effect exists (*quia est*); for the existence of an effect is known to the senses. That it is the cause remains conjectural . . .[6]

In another work Nifo expounded even more specifically the view, with regard to astronomical hypotheses, that 'those men are mistaken who, taking a natural phenomenon which might follow from

[1] *Expos. Phys.* i, Expo. Commen. 4, Recognitio, f. 6rb.
[2] See Randall, op. cit., p. 192.
[3] Ibid., p. 200; Markus, *Dominican Studies*, ii (1949) 372; below, pp. 299–300.
[4] Cf. Nicholas of Cusa's doctrine of 'Conjectura', expounded in *De Conjecturis*, in *Opera*, 1665, pp. 75 sqq.
[5] This is Averroës's distinction; above, p. 56, n. 1.
[6] Niphi *Expos. Phys.* i, Expo. Commen. 4, Recognitio, f. 6^v; Randall, op. cit., pp. 193–4. At the end of this passage Nifo cited Aristotle's *Meteor*.

many causes, conclude in favour of one cause. For these appearances can be saved . . . possibly by others which have not yet been discovered.'[1]

Zabarella summed up the whole of the pre-Galilean tradition of scientific logic at Padua. 'Method', he said, 'is an intellectual instrument which produces knowledge of what is unknown from what is known. . . . Method has the force of inference, and connects one thing with another.'[2] He held that there were only two scientific methods, resolution or inductive analysis of empirical phenomena to exhibit causal relations,[3] and composition or demonstration which, from the discovered cause, provided demonstrated knowledge of the effect.[4] Scientific induction necessarily began with things between which there was 'an essential and necessary connection'. It assumed the uniformity of nature and so could discover that connexion in a sample of instances, without having to follow the chimaera of complete enumeration.[5] The 'regress' by which the cause of an effect was discovered then proceeded by stages, in each of which a hypothesis was postulated and tested by a 'compositive' return to the facts. In this the investigator was constructing a theory from which he could demonstrate the facts, rather than revealing the order of nature; as Zabarella put it, 'both demonstrations are made by us and for us ourselves, not for nature'.[6] The end of the process was to isolate and define as accurately as possible the conditions capable of producing the effect.

There are, I judge, two things that help us to know the cause distinctly. One is the knowledge that it is, which prepares us to discover what it is. For when we form some hypothesis about the matter we are able to search out and discover something else in it; where we form no hypothesis at all,

---

[1] Niphi *De Coelo et Mundo Comm.* ii, Venetiis, 1553, f. 90vb. Ibid., ff. 80 sqq., 84 sqq. he discussed the problem of the earth's motion, quoting the opinions of 'Albertilla' (Albert of Saxony) and others. Cf. Simplicius, above, p. 5, n. 3; also Grosseteste, Aquinas, Oresme, &c., above, pp. 96–98, 202–4. For a full account of opinions about the ontological status of astronomical theories see Duhem, *Annal. philos. chrétienne*, vi (1908), especially pp. 137, 354 sqq.

[2] Jacobi Zabarellae *De Methodis*, iii. 2, in *Opera Logica*, 1594, cols. 224–5; ibid. iii. 1, col. 223. See Randall, op. cit., pp. 196 sqq.; Markus, op. cit., p. 370 sqq.

[3] *De Methodis*, iii. 17, cols. 264, 266; ibid. iii. 18, col. 268; ibid. iii. 16, cols. 260, 264. In his *Post. Anal. Comm.* i. 1, Context. 4, C. 19, 156, C. 26, 201, in *Opera Logica*, cols. 635, 933, 1027, there are references to 'Linconiensis'.

[4] *De Regressu*, C. 5, in *Opera Logica*, col. 486.

[5] *De Regressu*, C. 4, col. 485.

[6] Ibid. C. 2, col. 481. Cf. *De Speciebus Demonstrationis*, C. 10, in *Opera Logica*, col. 429.

we shall never discover anything. . . . Hence when we find that cause to be suggested, we are in a position to seek out and discover what it is. The other help, without which this first would not suffice, is the comparison of the cause discovered with the effect through which it was discovered, not indeed with the full knowledge that this is the cause and that the effect, but just comparing this thing with that. Thus it comes about that we are led gradually to the knowledge of the conditions of that thing; and when one of the conditions has been discovered we are helped to the discovery of another, until we finally know this to be the cause of that effect. . . . The regress thus consists necessarily of three parts. The first in a 'demonstration that', by which we are led from a confused knowledge of the effect to a confused knowledge of the cause. The second is this 'mental consideration' by which, from a confused knowledge of the cause, we acquire a distinct knowledge of it. The third is demonstration in the strictest sense, by which we are at length led from the cause distinctly known to the distinct knowledge of the effect. . . . From what we have said it can be clear that it is impossible to know fully that this is the cause of this effect, unless we know the nature and conditions of this cause, by which it is capable of producing such an effect.[1]

The most complete account of the non-mathematical side of the theory of experimental science that has been traced in these pages from thirteenth-century Oxford was given early in the seventeenth century by Francis Bacon. Like his thirteenth-century namesake, Francis Bacon held that the object of natural science was to provide both knowledge and power and that these were inseparable.[2] 'Human knowledge and human power meet in one; for where the cause is not known the effect cannot be produced. Nature to be commanded must be obeyed; and that which in contemplation is as the cause is in operation as the rule.'[3] Such causes or, as he also called them, 'forms', he conceived of as the laws according to which things behaved.

---

[1] *De Regressu*, C. 5, cols. 487, 489; Randall, op. cit., p. 201.

[2] Cf. C. D. Broad, *Philos. of Francis Bacon*. Francis Bacon insisted that the study of 'natural philosophy' was a full-time occupation which 'has scarcely ever possessed, especially in these later times, a disengaged and whole man (unless it were some monk studying in his cell, or some gentleman in his country house)'. (*Novum Organum*, i. 80, *Works*, i, pp. 187–8, iv, pp. 78–79; first ed. London, 1620.) He went on to insist that it must be carried on in particular sciences. It was, he said, because it had not in the past been based on particular experiments that natural philosophy had been stagnant while the mechanical arts had advanced: cf. *Advancement of Learning* (*Works*, iii; first ed. London, 1605).

[3] *Novum Organum*, i. 3; cf. i. 70, 73, 81, 124, ii. 4. For Roger Bacon on this point cf. above, pp. 23, 141–2; Thorndike, *History of Magic*, ii. 630 sqq.; Crombie, *Augustine to*

For though in nature nothing really exists beside individual bodies, performing pure individual acts according to a fixed law, yet in philosophy this very law, and the investigation, discovery, and explanation of it, is the foundation as well of knowledge as of operation. And it is this law, with its clauses, that I mean when I speak of *Forms*.[1] For the Form of a nature[2] is such, that given the Form the nature infallibly follows.[3]

Francis Bacon's method of discovering the form was precisely the 'double procedure' worked out during the preceding four centuries. Like the bee in his famous analogy,[4] the true philosopher must rely entirely neither upon experiments nor upon reasoning, but must use the two in combination:

my directions for the interpretation of nature embrace two generic divisions; the one how to educe and form axioms from experience; the other how to deduce and derive new experiments from axioms;[5] from the new light of axioms, which, having been educed from those particulars by a certain method and rule, shall in their turn point out the way again to new particulars, greater things may be looked for. For our road does not lie on a level, but ascends and descends; first ascending to axioms, then descending to works.[6]

The investigator began by making a collection of instances of the phenomenon or 'nature' under consideration: 'we must prepare a *Natural and Experimental History*.'[7] The next stage was not, as he was careful to point out, an 'induction which proceeds by simple enumeration', but an analysis of 'nature by proper rejections and exclusions; and then, after a sufficient number of negatives, come to a conclusion on the affirmative instances'.[8] To prepare for this 'true and legitimate induction' the investigator classified his observations into three *Tables and Arrangements of Instances*.[9] The first, as he described in his well-known investigation of the 'form of heat',

---

Galileo, ii. 38 sqq., 289–91. The resemblance of Francis Bacon's four Idols (*Nov. Org.* i. 38–71, *Works*, i. 163 sqq.) to Roger Bacon's four 'causae erroris' (*Opus Maius*, i, ed. Bridges, i. 2 sqq.) is very striking. Cf. above, p. 285, n. 5.

[1] *Nov. Org.* ii. 2; cf. ii. 17.

[2] By a 'nature' he meant a type of observed occurrence, e.g. heat, light, &c.: ibid. ii. 5, 11 sqq., 17.

[3] Ibid. ii. 4; cf. ii. 1, 5, 6, 7 on the 'latent process' and 'latent configuration'.

[4] Ibid. i. 95; cf. i. 64.   [5] Ibid. ii. 10.

[6] Ibid. i. 103; cf. 104–5.   [7] Ibid. ii. 10.

[8] Ibid. i. 105. He said that Plato had used this form of induction but no one else. Cf. ibid. i. 69.

[9] Ibid. ii. 10–14.

was the *Table of Essence and Presence*, which included all instances in which the form sought was present. The second was the *Table of Deviation, or of Absence in Proximity*, which included all instances in which the form sought was absent. The third was the *Table of Degrees or Table of Comparison*, in connexion with which he made what seems to be the first explicit published statement of what became known as the method of concomitant variations.[1] Induction consisted simply in an inspection of these tables:

for the problem is, upon a review of the instances, all and each, to find such a nature as is always [2] present or absent with the given nature, and always increases and decreases with it; and which is, as I have said, a particular case of a more general nature.[3] The first work therefore of true induction (as far as regards the discovery of Forms) is the rejection or exclusion of the several natures which are not found in some instance where the given nature is present, or are found in some instance where the given nature is absent, or are found to increase in some instance where the given nature decreases, or to decrease in some instance where the given nature increases. Then indeed after the rejection and exclusion has been duly made, there will remain at the bottom, all light opinions vanishing in smoke, a Form affirmative, solid and true and well defined.[4]

On the basis of this un-eliminated residue the investigator then embarked upon 'an essay of the Interpretation of Nature in the affirmative way',[5] a *First Vintage* or working hypothesis as to the 'laws and determinations' which governed the nature under consideration and constituted its Form.[6] So, Bacon concluded, 'From a survey of the instances, all and each, the nature of which Heat is a particular case appears to be Motion. . . . Heat itself, its essence and quiddity, is Motion and nothing else.'[7] From this hypothesis the process of repeated deduction, experiment, and elimination went on once more until the 'true definition' was discovered and the law of heat was known in all its clauses.

Francis Bacon's account of 'exclusion' is the classic statement of the method of elimination or falsification. His method was mentioned and used by more than one seventeenth-century scientist, particu-

---

[1] *Nov. Org.* ii. 13; cf. J. S. Mill, *System of Logic*, ii, Ch. 8, § 6.
[2] As he said: 'not only each table suffices for the rejection of any nature, but even any one of the particular instances contained in any of the tables'. Ibid. ii. 18.
[3] Ibid. ii. 15.   [4] Ibid. ii. 16.
[5] Ibid. ii. 20.   [6] Ibid. ii. 17.
[7] Ibid. ii. 20; cf. above, p. 87, n. 1, p. 149.

larly in England. For example, Harvey,[1] Hooke,[2] and Boyle[3] all referred to it in the midst of their investigations. What was chiefly lacking, however, both in Bacon's method and in that described by the Paduan logicians, was mathematics.[4] In fact the mathematical tradition that had existed in Western methodology since the time of Grosseteste and, of course, before him since the Greeks, seems largely to have by-passed these writers. Of the two aspects of that tradition,[5] the Platonic or Pythagorean evaluation of the ontological status of mathematical entities is found, among fifteenth-century scientists, predominantly in Nicholas of Cusa,[6] whom it links, through Copernicus, with Kepler;[7] Aristotle's strictly operational view of mathematics predominated with the Italian physicists of the sixteenth century.[8] Galileo was influenced by both views, which he united, in a manner never before achieved, with that experimental method which four centuries of thought and trial in Oxford, Paris, and Padua had prepared for him.

The originality of Galileo's method lay precisely in his effective combination of mathematics with experiment, a combination to which the new mathematics of motion inspired by Archimedes

---

[1] *Exer. de Gen. Animal.* Exer. 25, 1651, p. 75. For Bacon's possible influence on Harvey's researches into the circulation of the blood see Sir William Hale White, *Bacon, Gilbert and Harvey*; cf. J. Pelseneer, 'Gilbert, Bacon, Galilée, Kepler, Harvey et Descartes: leurs relations', *Isis*, xvii (1932) 171 sqq. The most likely source of Harvey's method is Padua, where he was a pupil of Fabrizio. This appears very strongly in the logical structure of his *De Motu Cordis*; cf. Crombie, *Augustine to Galileo*, ii. 228–38.

[2] R. Hooke, *Micrographia*, p. 54. See also Hooke's account of method in the preface, especially pp. 1, 6–8, 13, 18; and in the text, p. 1. There is another reference to Bacon in 'A General Scheme, or Idea of the Present State of Natural Philosophy, and How its Defects may be Remedied By a Methodical Proceeding in the making Experiments and Collecting Observations Whereby to Compile a Natural History, as the Solid Basis for the Superstructure of True Philosophy', in *Posthumous Works*, pp. 6–7.

[3] *Works*, ed. Thomas Birch, i. 196[b], iii. 154[b].

[4] Though Bacon did say: 'inquiries into nature have the best result, when they begin with physics and end in mathematics'. *Nov. Org.* ii. 8.

[5] For the history of the 'ontological' and the 'operational' views of mathematics and the influence of 'Platonism' and 'Aristotelianism' see L. Brunschvicg, *Conscience dans la philos. occidentale, Étapes de philos. math., Rôle du pythagorisme dans l'évolution des idées*; E. Cassirer, 'Mathematische Mystik und mathematische Naturwissenschaft', *Lychnos*, 1940, pp. 248 sqq.; also Cassirer, *Das Erkenntnisproblem*, i. 86 sqq.; Burtt, *Metaphysical Foundations*; Strong, *Procedures and Metaphysics*; Boyer, *Concepts of the Calculus*.

[6] Above, p. 294, n. 1, p. 295, n. 5.

[7] For Kepler's scientific method see Cassirer, *Das Erkenntnisproblem*, i. 253 sqq.; Burtt, op. cit., pp. 44 sqq.; Strong, op. cit., pp. 168 sqq.

[8] See Strong, *Procedures and Metaphysics*; Boyer, *Concepts of the Calculus*, pp. 88–89; Dugas, *Histoire de la mécanique*, pp. 68 sqq.

enabled him to give a power and range far beyond anything possible at an earlier period.[1] In fact his method was justified for him by its success in solving concrete problems. That success enabled him to overcome the hesitations even of his most enlightened predecessors[2] and to show unequivocally what science was about.

Galileo's mature conception of science was that it was a mathematical description of the relations between bodies in space. In the sixteenth century, as in the thirteenth, mathematical physicists had still accepted Aristotle's doctrine not only that mathematical theories were abstractions from a real world of substance, but also that a complete scientific explanation must give an account of that substance and of how it caused the events observed.[3] Galileo followed Ockham[4] in declaring that to introduce such substances and causes into the language of science was to introduce nothing but names. The Aristotelian 'substantial form' was simply a definition, a name for certain observed regularities, and as such it explained nothing. 'I do not question you about the name,' as he said in the famous answer to the statement that gravity was the *cause* of bodies falling, 'but the essence of the thing, of which essence you know not a tittle more than you know the essence of the mover of the stars in gyration; unless it be the name that hath been put to this, and made familiar, and domestical, by the many experiences which we see thereof every hour in the day.'[5]

[1] For Galileo's method see R. Caverni, *Metodo sperimentale in Italia*, iv; Cassirer, *Das Erkenntnisproblem*, i. 289 sqq., 'Galileo's Platonism', in *Studies and Essays offered to George Sarton*; Duhem, *Annal. philos. chrétienne*, vi (1908) 561 sqq.; F. Wieser, *Galileo als Philosoph*, pp. 51 sqq.; P. P. Wiener, 'The tradition behind Galileo's methodology', *Osiris*, i (1936) 733 sqq.; Burtt, *Metaphysical Foundations*, pp. 61 sqq.; Strong, *Procedures and Metaphysics*, pp. 141 sqq.; Boyer, *Concepts of the Calculus*, pp. 112 sqq.; Koyré, *Études galiléennes*, i–iii, 'Galileo and Plato', *JHI*, iv (1943) 400 sqq.; I. B. Cohen, 'Galileo', *Scientific American*, 1949, August, pp. 40 sqq.; Crombie, *Dominican Studies*, iii (1950) 105 sqq. See also A. Favaro, *Galileo e lo Studio di Padova*; J. J. Fahie, *Galileo; his Life and Work*, 'The scientific works of Galileo (1564–1642)', *SHMS*, ii. 206 sqq.; L. Olschki, *Gesch. d. neusprach. wissensch. Literatur*, iii; E. Mach, *Science of Mechanics*; F. Sherwood Taylor, *Galileo and the Freedom of Thought*; Mieli, *Archeion*, xxi (1938) 193–297; Dugas, op. cit., pp. 125 sqq. See also below, p. 310, n. 6, pp. 353–5.

[2] Galileo was well read in scholastic literature and in his 'Iuvenilia' he cited, for example, Scotus, Ockham, Burley, Calculator, Heytesbury, Paulus Venetus, Marliani, and Nifo: see *Opere*, i. 421–3 (index); Duhem, *Léonard de Vinci*, iii. 480 sqq., 513, 562 sqq.; Boyer, *Concepts of the Calculus*, pp. 112–14. For his connexion with Zabarella at Padua see Randall, *JHI*, i (1940) 202 sqq.; cf. Wiener, op. cit., pp. 734 sqq.; Moody, *JHI*, xii (1951).   [3] Above, pp. 90–96; cf. Strong, op. cit.   [4] Above, pp. 172–7.

[5] *Due Massimi Sistemi*, ii (*Opere*, vii) 260–1; first published Florence, 1632; English translation in T. Salusbury's *Mathematical Collections*, p. 210. I have corrected this translation where necessary in the quotations given below.

By a scientific explanation of an observed relationship Galileo meant, in fact, deducing the relationship from a mathematical theory. The investigator must first establish the relationship experimentally, and 'that we may not proceed arbitrarily and at random, but with a logical method, we will first attempt to ascertain ourselves by experiments often repeated'[1] what the relationship is. To connect the observations with a theory Galileo then described precisely the double procedure of resolution and composition which his predecessors in Oxford and Padua had made familiar. In a passage referring to Aristotle's method,[2] he said:

I do believe for certain that he first procured, by the help of the senses, such experiments and observations as he could, to assure him as much as it was possible of the conclusion, and that he afterwards sought out the means how to demonstrate it; for this is the usual course in demonstrative sciences. And the reason thereof is, because when the conclusion is true, by the help of the resolutive method (*metodo resolutivo*) one may hit upon some proposition before demonstrated or come to some principle known *per se*; but if the conclusion be false, a man may proceed *in infinitum* and never meet with any truth already known, but very often he shall meet with some impossibility or manifest absurdity. Nor need you question but that Pythagoras, a long time before he found the demonstration for which he offered the hecatomb, had been certain that the square of the side subtending the right angle in a rectangle triangle was equal to the square of the other two sides; and the certainty of the conclusion conduced not a little to the investigating of the demonstration.[3]

The special contribution that Galileo's conception of science as a mathematical description of relations enabled him to make to methodology, was to free it from the tendency to excessive empiricisim which was the main defect of the Aristotelian tradition, and to give it a power of generality which was yet strictly related to experimental facts to a degree which previous Neoplatonists had seldom achieved. This Galileo did in the first place by not hesitating to use, in his mathematical theories, concepts of which no examples had been or could be observed. He required only that from such concepts

[1] *Due Massimi Sistemi*, ii (*Opere*, vii) 249; Salusbury, p. 199. He was referring to falling bodies.
[2] As Wiener (op. cit., p. 734) points out, Galileo did not attack Aristotle's own method but that used by some of 'the so-called Aristotelians of his day'.
[3] *Due Massimi Sistemi*, i (*Opere*, vii) 75–76; Salusbury, pp. 37–38. For the methods of analysis and synthesis as used by the Greek mathematicians see Heath, *Euclid's Elements*, pp. 18 sqq.; Brunschvicg, *Étapes de la philos. math.*, pp. 49 sqq.

it should be possible to deduce the observed facts. For example, there is no such thing as a perfectly frictionless plane or an isolated body moving in empty, infinite, Euclidean space, yet from these concepts Galileo first constructed the seventeenth-century theory of inertia.[1] And, he said, 'I cannot find any bounds for my admiration, how that reason was able, in Aristarchus and Copernicus, to commit such a rape upon their senses, as in despight thereof to make herself mistress of their credulity.'[2]

His freedom from naïve empiricism enabled Galileo to see that, in the 'resolution', or analysis, of any effect, certain essential features could usually be isolated, and he pursued his investigation by first establishing the relationship between these alone, excluding all the others.[3] This method enabled him to begin with simple and manageable mathematical theories, and then to complicate them step by step to accommodate each additional factor. By varying these one at a time, he could discover what effect they might have. A good example is his study of the pendulum in which, by ignoring 'the opposition of the air, and line, or other accidents'[4], he showed that the period of oscillation was independent of the arc of swing and simply proportional to the square-root of the length.[5] Then having established this relationship for an 'ideal pendulum', he reintroduced the excluded factors one by one. He argued, for example, that the reason why a real pendulum, in which the thread was not weightless, eventually came to rest, was not simply because of air-resistance, but also because each particle of the thread acted as a small pendulum, each with its own frequency, which interfered with the oscillation of the other particles.

Galileo's usual method of procedure, then, was by what he called

[1] *Due Massimi Sistemi*, ii (*Opere*, vii) 48 sqq., 171 sqq.; Salusbury, pp. 13 sqq., 127 sqq. See also *Due Nuove Scienze*, iv (*Opere*, vii) 268 sqq., 274 sqq.; English transl. by H. Crew and A. de Salvio. See Koyré, *Études galiléennes*, iii. 71 sqq. For another example of Galileo's freedom from naïve empiricism cf. his proof from a 'thought experiment' that a heavy body does not fall faster than a lighter one: Caverni, *Metodo sperimentale*, iv. 277 sqq.; Wiener, op. cit., p. 738; Lane Cooper, *Aristotle, Galileo, and the Tower of Pisa*, p. 99. For the comparable use to which fourteenth-century speculations on infinity and void space were put cf. above, p. 202, n. 5; also pp. 98–9.

[2] *Due Massimi Sistemi*, iii (*Opere*, vii) 355; Salusbury, p. 301.

[3] This was, of course, simply a refinement of the method of isolating factors used, e.g., by Roger Bacon, Theodoric of Freiberg, and Themon Judaei in their work on the rainbow.

[4] *Due Massimi Sistemi*, i, p. 47; Salusbury, p. 13. See also *Due Nuove Scienze*, iii (*Opere*, viii).

[5] For Mersenne's prior formulation of this proportionality see Crombie, 'Mathematics, music and medical science', *Proc. XII Int. Congress of the History of Science, Paris, 1968*.

the 'argomento *ex suppositione*'.[1] After a 'resolution' of the mathematical relations involved in a given effect, he set up a 'hypothetical
assumption' from which he deduced the consequences that must
follow. This second stage he called the *metodo compositivo*.[2] The
third stage, to which he also applied the term 'resolution', was to
analyse by experiment examples of the effect, in order to discover
whether the deduced consequences did in fact occur. For, as he
said, 'I know very well that one sole experiment or concludent
demonstration, produced on the contrary part, sufficeth to batter to
the ground these and a thousand other probable arguments.'[3] In
his arguments from experiments he often used the method of agreement and difference,[4] but his actual experiments he usually arranged
in accordance with the method of concomitant variations.[5] A good
example of his whole method is his establishment of the law of the
acceleration of freely falling bodies, in which the verification consisted in the series of measurements of concomitant variations between space travelled and time passed with the ball rolling down the
inclined plane.[6] Firmly putting aside any suggestion that he was

[1] For a full description see Galileo a Pietro Carcavy, 5 giugno, 1637, in *Carteggio* (*Opere*, xvii) 90–91. Cf. *Due Massimi Sistemi*, ii (*Opere*, vii) 149–50; Salusbury, p. 106.

[2] *Risposta alle Opposizioni del S. Lodovico delle Colombe e del S. Vincenzio di Grazia* (*Opere*, iv) 521; first published 1615. For a good example of the use of the double procedure by Galileo's first disciple, 'ordinando tutto il discorso prima col metodo risolutivo
e poi compositivo', see the letter by Benedetto Castelli a [Galileo], 15 agosto, 1637, in
Carteggio (*Opere*, xvii) 160 sqq. Cf. P. Smith, *History of Modern Culture*, i. 103–4, ii.
54; L. Strauss, *Political Philosophy of Hobbes*, pp. 2–6, 135–9, 150–1.

[3] *Due Massimi Sistemi*, ii (*Opere*, vii) 148; Salusbury, p. 105.

[4] Galileo described this method delightfully in his satirical discussion of the assertion
'that the Babylonians cooked eggs by whirling them swiftly in a sling. . . . If an effect,
which has succeeded with others at another time, does not take place with us, it necessarily follows that in our experiment there is something lacking which was the cause of the
success of the former attempt; and, if we lack but one thing, that one thing is alone the
true cause' (*Il Saggiatore*, Q. 45, ed. naz., *Opere*, vi. 340). Cf. his argument about celestial influence: '. . . it would be requisite to remove that body for some time; and then
whatsoever effect I should find wanting in me, I would say it depended on that star', in
Due Massimi Sistemi, iii (*Opere*, vii) 395–6; Salusbury, p. 334.

[5] 'I say, therefore, that if it be true that of one effect there is but one sole primary
cause, and that between cause and effect there is a firm and constant connection; it is
necessary that whensoever there is a firm and constant alteration in the effect, there be a
firm and constant alteration in the cause.' (*Due Massimi Sistemi*, iv, *Opere*, vii. 471;
Salusbury, p. 407.) He was trying to prove that the tides were caused by the movements
of the earth. 'Therefore we must (if we will retain the identity of the cause) find the
alteration in these additions and substractions that make them more or less potent in
producing those effects which depend thereupon.'

[6] See *Due Nuove Scienze*, iii (*Opere*, viii) 205 sqq., especially pp. 212 sqq.; see
also 373–4. For an account of these experiments and their results see F. Sherwood
Taylor, *Galileo and the Freedom of Thought*, pp. 38 sqq., 186 sqq.; Koyré, *Études*

going 'to investigate the cause of the acceleration of natural motion, concerning which various opinions have been expressed by various philosophers', he insisted that he intended simply 'to investigate and demonstrate some of the properties of accelerated motion, whatever the cause of this acceleration may be'.[1]

And, first of all, it seems desirable to find and explain a definition best fitting natural phenomena. For any one may invent an arbitrary type of motion and discuss its properties; thus, for instance, some have imagined helices and conchoids as described by certain motions, which are not met with in nature, and have very commendably established the properties which these curves possess in virtue of their definitions; but we have decided to consider the phenomena of bodies falling with an acceleration such as actually occurs in nature and to make this definition of accelerated motion exhibit the essential features of observed accelerated motions. And this, at last, after repeated efforts we trust we have succeeded in doing. In this belief we are confirmed mainly by the consideration that experimental results are seen to agree with and exactly correspond with those properties which have been, one after another, demonstrated by us. Finally, in the investigation of naturally accelerated motion we were led, by the hand as it were, in following the habit and custom of nature herself, in all her various other processes, to employ only those means which are most common, simple, and easy.[2]

The 'definition' so confirmed was a motion 'in which the momentum of its velocity goes on increasing after departure from rest in simple proportionality to time, which is the same as saying that in equal time-intervals the body receives equal increments of velocity'.[3]

Because a true theory revealed the order of nature, the investigator could then deduce from it, with perfect confidence, new knowledge beyond anything already known by experience. He could, in fact, carry the theory into regions beyond the reach of convenient experimentation. So, as Galileo said of his work on projectiles:

The knowledge of a single fact acquired through the discovery of its causes prepares the mind to ascertain and understand other facts without need of recourse to experiments, precisely as in the present case, where by argumentation alone the Author proves with certainty that the maximum range occurs when the elevation is 45°. He thus demonstrates what perhaps has never been observed in experience, namely, that of other shots

---

galiléennes, ii, iii. 89 sqq.; Mach, op. cit., pp. 154 sqq.; Dugas, op. cit., pp. 128 sqq. For his refutation of the theory that heavy bodies fall faster than lighter see above, p. 306, n. 1.

[1] Due Nuove Scienze, iii (Opere, viii) 202. Cf. above, pp. 175–7.

[2] Ibid., p. 197.   [3] Ibid., p. 202; cf. above, pp. 182, 183, n. 1.

those which exceed or fall short of 45° by equal amounts have equal ranges.[1]

Whereas in practice Galileo decided upon the truth of a 'hypothetical assumption' by the familiar criteria of experimental verification and simplicity, it is plain that he was aiming at something more than merely to construct a convenient means of 'saving the appearances'. In fact he was trying to discover the real structure of nature, to read the real book of the universe. It was quite true that 'the principal scope of astronomers is only to render reason for the appearances of the celestial bodies';[2] but a criticism he made of the Ptolemaic system was just that 'although it satisfied an Astronomer merely Arithmetical, yet it did not afford satisfaction or content to the Astronomer Philosophical'.[3] But, he said, Copernicus 'very well understood that if one might save the celestial appearances with false assumptions in Nature, it might with much more ease be done with true suppositions'.[4] So it was not merely because of a pragmatic use of the principle of economy[5] that the simpler hypothesis must be chosen. It was Nature herself that 'doth not that by many things, which may be done by few',[6] Nature herself that commanded assent to the Copernican system.[7] He refused to accept Osiander's statement that this was simply a mathematical device, a statement in keeping with Western astronomical opinion since the thirteenth century;[8] the heliostatic theory was a literally true account of nature.[9]

---

[1] Ibid. iv (*Opere*, viii) 296. Thus Galileo showed the same belief in a discoverable uniformity of nature as most of his scholastic predecessors, e.g. Grosseteste, Scotus, Ockham, Paulus Venetus, Zabarella. He did not share Nicholas of Autrecourt's doubts: above, p. 171, n. 1.

[2] *Due Massimi Sistemi*, iii (*Opere*, vii) 369; Salusbury, p. 308.

[3] Loc. cit.

[4] Loc. cit. Cf. 'Apply not I pray you this term of inconvenience to a thing which possibly may of necessity be so.' Ibid., p. 348; Salusbury, p. 294. Cf. also ibid. ii (*Opere*, vii) 298; Salusbury, p. 246.

[5] 'un verissimo assioma d'Aristotle che c'insegna che *Frustra fit per plura quod potest fieri per pauciora* ci rende più probabile, il moto diurno esser della Terra sola, che dell' universo, trattone la Terra.' Ibid. ii (*Opere*, vii) 149; Salusbury, p. 106. See also *Due Nuove Scienze*, iii (*Opere*, viii) 197. Cf. above, p. 85, n. 4, p. 203.

[6] *Due Massimi Sistemi*, ii (*Opere*, vii) 143; Salusbury, p. 99.

[7] Ibid. iii (*Opere*, vii) 372 sqq.; Salusbury, 312 sqq. Cf. Burtt, *Metaphysical Foundations*, pp. 26–27.

[8] Burtt, op. cit., pp. 38–39. See Duhem, *Annal. philos. chrétienne*, vii (1908) 482 sqq.; Cassirer, *Das Erkenntnisproblem*, i. 340 sqq.

[9] Cf. *Due Massimi Sistemi*, iii (*Opere*, vii) 298, Salusbury, p. 246; Giornata iv, pp. 442–3, Salusbury, pp. 379–80, 422–3. Cf. Burtt, pp. 68, 73.

The momentous change that Galileo, along with other platonizing mathematicians like Kepler,[1] introduced into scientific ontology was to identify the substance of the real world with the mathematical entities contained in the theories used to describe the 'appearances'.[2] The important practical result of this identification was to open the physical world to an unrestricted use of mathematics. Galileo had removed the worst inconveniences of Aristotle's notion that there was a science of 'physics' outside the range of mathematics,[3] by declaring the substances and causes postulated by that physics to be mere names.[4] The success of his mathematical method convinced him that he had shown how to read the language in which the book of the universe was truly written. In other words, he believed that the world of appearances was the product of an underlying mathematical structure, and that he could discover what that structure was.[6] What logical inconveniences this form of 'mathematical realism' could bring are shown by his unsuccessful attempts to prove that the heliostatic theory was necessarily true.[6]

The most extreme seventeenth-century form of this mathematical ontology was that advanced by Descartes. Equally with his scientific contemporaries, Descartes held that the investigator began with the observations which it was the object of his science to explain. His

---

[1] For Kepler see Cassirer, *Das Erkenntnisproblem*, i. 253 sqq.; Burtt, op. cit., pp. 44 sqq.; Strong, op. cit., pp. 168 sqq.

[2] Above, p. 285.

[3] e.g. in the sixteenth century Aristotle's theory of natural places and natural motions interfered with the mathematical study of projectiles and also produced some of the 'physical' objections to the Copernican system that were most difficult to answer.

[4] But cf. 'Forces, resistances, moments, figures, etc. may be considered either in the abstract, dissociated from matter, or in the concrete, associated with matter. Hence, the properties which belong to figures that are merely geometrical and non-material must be modified when we fill these figures with matter and therefore give them weight.' (*Due Nuove Scienze*, i, *Opere*, viii. 154.) Cf. Wiener, op. cit., p. 744. In fact, Galileo retained 'gravity' as a 'natural' property of bodies: cf. Crombie, *Dominican Studies*, iii (1950) 126 sqq.; Koyré, *Études galiléennes*, iii. 113 sqq.

[5] That is, he substituted a mathematical substance for the Aristotelian qualitative substance as the identity persisting through change.

[6] For Galileo's view of the relations between science and theology see his well-known *Lettera a Madama Cristina di Lorena* (*Opere*, v) 307 sqq. This was first published in 1615 and an English translation was published in Salusbury's *Mathematical Translations*, pp. 425 sqq. For the history of Galileo's controversy with the ecclesiastical authorities see K. von Gebler, *Galileo Galilei and the Roman Curia*; A. Favaro, *Galileo Galilei e l'Inquisizione*; E. Wohlwill, *Galilei und sein Kampf für die Kopernikanische Lehre*; J. Brodrick, *Life and Work of Blessed Robert Francis, Cardinal Bellarmine*, ii. 326 sqq.; Preserved Smith, *History of Modern Culture*, i. 32 sqq.; L. Pastor, *History of the Popes*, xxv. 285 sqq., xxix. 42 sqq.; Sherwood Taylor, *Galileo and the Freedom of Thought*.

method of finding an explanation was precisely the familiar double procedure worked out by the medieval commentators on Aristotle, a procedure to which Descartes applied the Greek terms 'analysis' and 'synthesis'.

The whole of method consists in the order and disposition of the objects to which the mind's attention must be turned, that we may discover some truth. And we shall exactly observe this method, if we reduce involved and obscure propositions step by step to simpler ones, and then, from an intuition of the simplest ones of all, try to ascend through the same steps to the knowledge of all the others.[1]

Descartes carefully preserved the distinction between physics and mathematics,[2] and he insisted that experimentation was an essential part of the application of the analytic method to the physical world. The sequence in the physical sciences was from 'natures' which were 'composite *a parte rei*' to 'simple natures', then back to natures which 'we ourselves compound' by deduction.[3] The investi-

---

[1] *Regulae ad Directionem Ingenii*, v (*Œuvres*, x) 379. The *Regulae* were published posthumously in Amsterdam in 1701; for the date of composition see *Œuvres* x. 351 sqq. 'Demonstrandi autem ratio duplex est, alia scilicet per analysim, alia per synthesim. . . .' (*Secundae Responsiones*, *Œuvres*, vii. 155–6.) For a full account of Descartes's scientific method see A. Gewirtz, 'Experience and the non-mathematical in the Cartesian method', *JHI*, ii (1941) 183 sqq. Referring to Leibniz's use of the same double procedure, Gewirtz says: 'like Hobbes, Leibniz conceives analysis as corresponding only to the reductive and divisive operations of Descartes's method, and synthesis as corresponding only to the 'ascent' or deduction; whereas for Descartes the analytic method consists in both of these operations, while synthesis is only a method of exposition beginning with principles and demonstrating conclusions without appealing to any of the heuristic devices employed in the analytic method's deduction' (p. 190, n. 29). For a further discussion of the difference between the meaning Descartes gave to these terms and that given to them by the scholastics (with whom Leibniz agreed) see Régis, *Studia Mediaevalia R. J. Martin*, pp. 303–4, 329–30. Régis shows how unhistorical were Descartes's strictures on the scholastics. See G. Leibniz, *Nouveaux Essais*, iv. ii. 7 (*Œuvres*, i) 290–2. For further discussions of Descartes see L. Liard, *Descartes*, pp. 111 sqq.; O. Hamelin, *Système de Descartes*, 2e éd., pp. 45 sqq., espec. pp. 54 sqq.; G. Milhaud, *Descartes savant*, Ch. 9; Brunschvicg, *Étapes de philos. math.*, pp. 105 sqq., 192–4; Gilson, *Formation du système cartésien*; Burtt, op. cit., pp. 96 sqq.. See above, pp. 28–29.

[2] 'Mais d'exiger de moy des démonstrations Géométriques en une matière qui dépend de la Physique, c'est vouloir que ie fasse des choses impossibles. Et si on ne veut nommer démonstrations que les preuves des Géomètres, il faut donc dire qu'Archimède n'a iamais rien démonstré dans les Méchaniques, ny Vitellion en l'Optique, ny Ptolémée en l'Astronomie, etc. . . .' Descartes à Mersenne, 27 mai, 1638, in *Correspondance* (*Œuvres*, ii) 142. See also Reg. iv, viii, xiv (*Œuvres*, x) 378–9, 393–4, 448; *Princ. Phil.* i. 59 (*Œuvres*, viii) 27–28; *Météores*, i (*Œuvres*, vi) 231 sqq.; Gilson, op. cit., pp. 127 sqq.; Gewirtz, op. cit., pp. 188, 196, 205 sqq., 210.

[3] *Reg.* vi sqq. (*Œuvres*, x) 381 sqq. Cf. above, pp. 54–57, 63–67.

gation began with a complex situation 'which we experience to be composite *a parte rei*'.[1] This was the subject of the 'involved and obscure propositions' which the investigator's first step was to 'reduce' to specific problems for quantitative solution.[2] Examples Descartes gave were his own attempts to discover the law of refraction of light through transparent bodies[3] and to explain the rainbow,[4] and the work of Gilbert on magnets[5], and of Harvey on the circulation of the blood.[6] In this stage of analysis his procedure was to enumerate and classify instances of the effect in order to display the possibilities.[7] He then set up 'conjectures'[8] or possible hypotheses from which he deduced the consequences that must follow. Among these he tried, by eliminating the hypotheses whose consequences were contradicted by experiment, to discover the true cause,[9] the conditions necessary and sufficient to produce the effect.[10] The bases of his experimental procedure were, in fact, the method of agreement and difference and the method of concomitant variations.[11] An excellent example is his discussion of Harvey's theory of the circulation of the blood, some aspects of which he rejected in favour of what he considered to be a more complete theory of his own. After mentioning 'une expérience fort apparente', which could confirm Harvey's theory, he said: 'Et toutesfois cela ne prouue autre chose, sinon que les expériences mesme nous donnent souuent occasion de nous tromper, lors que nous n'examinons pas assez toutes les causes qu'elles peuuent auoir.' Harvey's theory might account

[1] *Regulae*, viii (*Œuvres*, x) 399; cf. *Reg.* vi, xii, pp. 381 sqq., 410 sqq., espec. 422, 425–6. For Descartes's insistence that natural science begins with experience see also *Reg.* v, p. 380. Like Roger Bacon he said there were two kinds of experience, internal and external: *Reg.* xii, pp. 412–14, 422–3; cf. above, p. 141, n. 2.

[2] *Reg.* vi, xiii (*Œuvres*, x) 381 sqq., 430 sqq.

[3] *Reg.* viii (*Œuvres*, x) 393 sqq.; above, p. 283.

[4] Above, pp. 273–5.

[5] *Reg.* xii, xiii (*Œuvres*, x) 427, 431.

[6] *Corps humain*, xvii–xviii (*Œuvres*, xi) 239 sqq. First published 1664.

[7] *Reg.* vii, x, xiii (*Œuvres*, x) 387 sqq., 404–5, 431–2. Cf. *Reg.* iii, xi (*Œuvres*, x) 368, 407.

[8] *Reg.* xii, *Œuvres*, x. 424. Such conjectures had a definite scientific value even when they merely saved the appearances and had not been proved true; see above, p. 311, n. 2.

[9] *Reg.* xii, *Œuvres*, x. 427. Descartes's object was to discover the invariable cause, which meant showing the equality between the *datum* of experience and the *quaesitum* of the theory: *Reg.* vii, xii, xiv (*Œuvres*, x) 388, 429, 440–1. See Gewirtz, op. cit., pp. 198–200; cf. above, p. 83, n. 3.

[10] 'Cavendum est, ne plura et strictiora, quam data sint, supponamus. . . . Omissione vero peccamus, quoties aliqua conditio ad quaestionis determinationem requisita . . . .' *Reg.* xiii (*Œuvres*, x) 435–6.

[11] Cf. below, p. 314, n. 1.

for many of the phenomena, but 'cela n'empesche pas que tous ces mesmes effets ne puissent aussi procéder d'une autre cause, à sçauoir de la dilatation du sang que i'ay décrite. Mais afin de pouuoir remarquer laquelle de ces deux causes est la vraye, il faut considérer d'autres expériences qui ne puissent conuenir à l'une et à l'autre.'[1]

The ontological interpretation that Descartes put upon this familiar method of scientific procedure was to suppose that in the ultimate analysis he would be led to intuit 'simple natures', which constituted the essence of the real and from which all the particulars of observation could be shown deductively to follow. These 'simple natures' could not be reduced to anything simpler; they were known *per se*, that is self-evident, and they had no logical definitions.[2] They were of three classes: purely intellectual, such as knowledge and doubt; purely material, such as extension, figure, and motion; and those common to the first two classes, such as existence, unity, duration, and Euclid's axioms.[3] In the first two classes were the 'simple natures' that constituted the essence of the two ultimate substances into which the created world was divided, *res cogitans* and *res extensa*.[4] Descartes's philosophical aim was in fact to reduce the particular or 'relative' propositions of the case to a *maxime absolutum*, a proposition which was either self-evident (that is a 'simple nature') or which had been shown by previous investigation to follow from self-evident propositions and therefore could itself be the origin of a demonstration.[5] Such was to be the structure of the 'Universal Mathematics'[6] which was to embrace the whole science of the physical world and to which all the particular sciences were subordinate. Descartes characterized his own position very clearly in a judgement he passed on Galileo in a letter to Mersenne.[7] First commending him because he 'attempts to examine physical matters by the method of mathematics. . . . I believe that there is absolutely

---

[1] Cited by Gewirtz, op. cit., p. 199, from *Corps humain*, xviii (*Œuvres*, xi) 241–2. See Gilson, *Formation du système cartésien*, pp. 76 sqq. Descartes misunderstood the importance of Harvey's cardinal proposition that the heart was a pump and held to the old Galenic idea that it was the centre of vital heat. Cf. Descartes's work on the rainbow, *Météores*, viii (*Œuvres*, vi) 325 sqq.; above, pp. 273–5.

[2] *Reg.* vi, viii, xii (*Œuvres*, x) 381 sqq., 399, 422, 425–6.

[3] *Reg.* xii, xiv (*Œuvres*, x) 419 sqq., 439 sqq.

[4] *Princ. Phil.* i. 53 (*Œuvres*, viii) 25. Cf. Duhem, *Théorie physique*, pp. 48 sqq., 65 sqq.; Burtt, op. cit., pp. 96 sqq.

[5] *Reg.* vi (*Œuvres*, x) 382–3.

[6] *Reg.* iv (*Œuvres*, x) 378; cf. *Princ. Phil.* ii. 64 (*Œuvres*, viii) 78–79; *Meditationes de Prima Philosophia*, ii (*Œuvres*, vii), pp. 30–31; *Quartae Respons.* (*Œuvres*, vii) 226.

[7] Descartes à Mersenne, 11 octobre, 1638, in *Correspondance* (*Œuvres*, ii) 380.

no other way of discovering the truth'; he went on to complain: 'it seems to me that he has merely sought reasons for certain particular effects, without having considered the first causes of nature; and thus that he has built without a foundation'.

In natural science, then, the sequence of Descartes's argument was first from natures that were 'composite *a parte rei*' to 'simple natures', and afterwards by deduction to the reconstitution of the composite thing. This theoretical composite was then checked by experiment against the composite *a parte rei* from which the inquiry began. The 'composite' of theory showed the true cause when it corresponded perfectly with the 'composite' of things.[1] So the theory explained the facts, and the facts proved the theory. This double movement Descartes called a demonstration:

Que si quelques vnes de celles [sc. des choses] dont i'ay parlé, au commencement de la Dioptrique et des Météores, chocquent d'abord, à cause que ie les nomme des suppositions, et que ie ne semble pas auoir enuie de les prouuer, qu'on ait la patience de lire le tout auec attention, et i'espère qu'on s'en trouuera satisfait. Car il me semble que les raisons s'y entresuiuent en telle sorte que, comme les dernières sont démontrées par les premières, qui sont leurs causes, ces premières le sont réciproquement par les dernières, qui sont leurs effets. Et on ne doit pas imaginer que ie commette en cecy la faute que les Logiciens nomment vn cercle; car l'expérience rendant la plupart de ces effets très certains, les causes dont ie les déduits ne seruent pas tant à les prouuer qu'à les expliquer; mais, tout au contraire, ce sont elles qui sont prouuées par eux.[2]

In fact Descartes belonged to the Augustinian tradition in the same way as Grosseteste and Roger Bacon, and as they found certainty only in Divine illumination, so he found it only in the belief that the most perfect of all Beings would not deceive him.[3] Backed by that guarantee he asserted that 'il n'y a que deux voyes pour réfuter ce que i'ay écrit, dont l'vne est de prouuer par quelques expériences ou raisons que les choses que i'ay supposées sont fausses; et l'autre, que ce que i'en déduis ne sçauroit en estre déduit.'[4]

By his Universal Mathematics Descartes not only captivated his contemporaries and placed all subsequent physics and physiology in

---

[1] *Reg.* xiv (*Œuvres*, x) 460. He continued with an assertion of the necessity for the method of concomitant variations. Cf. above, p. 312, n. 9.

[2] *Discours de la Méthode* (*Œuvres*, vi) 76. Cf. Gilson, *Formation du système cartésien*, pp. 132–3.

[3] *Meditationes*, i (*Œuvres*, vii) 20–21.

[4] Descartes à Mersenne, 27 mai, 1638, in *Correspondance* (*Œuvres*, ii) 143.

his debt; he also made it quite plain that if taken to be the whole truth and nothing but the truth his position was philosophically ridiculous.[1] By identifying geometrical extension with the substance of the real world, Descartes committed himself to speaking of events as attributes inhering in that substance, that is to putting mathematical descriptions into the language of Aristotle's 'physics' or metaphysics. Thus space became a *plenum*, an aether, with real mechanical properties which provided the material and efficient causes of events. Descartes himself, of course, never lost faith in his assumptions[2] and he proceeded with full confidence to deduce conclusions wildly beyond the observations. But in a short time this new mathematical substance became as inconvenient to physical scientists as the old qualitative Aristotelian substance it had replaced. The outstanding example occurred in Newton's controversy with Huygens, Leibniz, and others over whether, in order to give a scientific explanation of the effects, he was required to show the 'nature' and 'cause' of colours[3] and of gravity.

In contrast with Descartes, Newton not only carefully preserved the distinction between mathematical descriptions and theories about the real essence of matter which purported to show the real causes of phenomena,[4] but also nearly always insisted that in practice experimental science provided only the former and that to do so was a proper conclusion of a scientific inquiry. Statements of this point of view are scattered throughout Newton's major scientific writings. For example, speaking of gravitational attraction, he said:

our purpose is only to trace out the quantity and properties of this force from the phenomena, and to apply what we discover in some simple cases as principles, by which, in a mathematical way, we may estimate the effects thereof in more involved cases; for it would be endless and impossible to bring every particular to direct and immediate observation. We said, *in a mathematical way*, to avoid all questions about the nature or quality of this force, which we would not be understood to determine by any hypothesis.[5]

---

[1] Cf. Broad, 'The new philosophy: Bruno to Descartes', *CHJ*, viii (1944) 54 sqq.

[2] e.g. see his cock-sure reply to Gassendi's crushing criticism, that his theory that in man mind and body met in the pineal gland was absurd because between an unextended thinking substance and an extended unthinking substance there could be no point of contact: *Objectiones Quintae, in Meditationem vi, Quintae Responsiones* (*Œuvres*, vii) 328 sqq., 384 sqq.   [3] Above, pp. 288–9; and cf. p. 311, n. 2.

[4] Cf. Duhem, *Théorie physique*, pp. 65 sqq.

[5] *System of the World*, § 2, in *Mathematical Principles*, ed. F. Cajori, p. 550. See also Newton's preface to the first edition of the *Principia*, ibid., pp. xvii–xviii; and the introduction to Book iii, ibid., p. 397. For accounts of Newton's method see Burtt,

'Hypotheses non fingo' was Newton's usual approach to questions of the real causes of phenomena; for 'to us it is enough that gravity does really exist, and act according to the laws which we have explained, and abundantly serves to account for all the motions of the celestial bodies, and of our sea'.[1] In fact he accepted the operational evaluation which Galileo gave to mathematics when Galileo was simply seeking 'reasons for certain particular effects' and keeping clear of ontology;[2] and like Galileo he showed that the 'substances' and 'causes' of Aristotle's 'physics' had no place in the language of science. 'But', he continued,

to derive two or three general Principles of Motion from Phænomena, and afterwards to tell us how the Properties and Actions of all corporeal Things follow from those manifest Principles, would be a very great step in Philosophy, though the Causes of those Principles were not yet discover'd: And therefore I scruple not to propose the Principles of Motion above-mention'd, they being of very general Extent, and leave their Causes to be found out.[3]

These quotations show that although Newton never doubted that it could be within the competence of science to discover the real causes of phenomena, yet he would hesitate to assert that he had made such a discovery in any particular case.[4] Most of his statements about method had special reference to his own particular discoveries and were made, often during controversy, to show plainly

Metaphysical Foundations, pp. 202 sqq.; Roberts and Thomas, *Newton and the Origin of Colours*; J. H. Randall, Jr., 'Newton's natural philosophy: Its problems and consequences', in *Philosophical Essays in Honor of Edgar Arthur Singer, Jr.*, pp. 334 sqq.; E. W. Strong, 'Newton's "Mathematical Way"', *JHI*, xii (1951) 90 sqq.

[1] *Principia*, iii, General Scholium to Prop. xlii, p. 547. See Cajori's valuable notes 55–56, pp. 671 sqq.

[2] e.g. above, p. 308.

[3] *Opticks*, iii. i, Q. 31, 4th ed., pp. 376–7.

[4] An outstanding exception was his belief, as he said in the *Principia*, that it was possible 'to discover, and effectually to distinguish, the true motions of particular bodies from the apparent. . . .' (*Principia*, Scholium to Definitions, p. 12.) See Cajori's notes 13 and 52, pp. 639 sqq., 668 sqq. (for criticisms by Berkeley and others); Strong, *JHI*, xii (1951) 100 sqq. Cf. Oresme, above, p. 202; and Berkeley's exclusion of efficient causes from the field of experimental inquiry: *De Motu*, §§ 35, 41. Newton's belief that science could give ontological knowledge came out plainly when he discussed theology. Not only did he say that 'to discourse of [God] from the appearances of things, does certainly belong to Natural Philosophy' (*Principia*, iii, General Scholium to Prop. xlii, p. 546), but also there is much evidence to show that he believed that the continuous operation of God was an essential part of the mechanical system of the world. Newton's theology was severely criticized by Hume and Kant. See Burtt, op. cit., pp. 223 sqq., and especially pp. 280 sqq.

what he was asserting about the subject in question.[1] In particular he took pains to dissociate his own work from the two most popular scientific ontologies of his time, those deriving from Aristotle and from Descartes, because they were 'not deduced from the phenomena'. For this purpose he found the instrument ready to his hand, though had he known how it got there he might have been surprised. His 'mathematical way' was in fact related to the observations in the same manner as the mathematical 'superior science' of Aristotle's Latin commentators, which 'provides the reason for that thing of which the inferior science provides the fact' but which 'does not speak of the causes of the thing'.[2] Of his 'Rules of Reasoning in Philosophy' the first, second, and fourth were, respectively, the well-established principles of economy, uniformity, and experimental verification and falsification, and the third was a derivative of these three.[3] And when he came to describe his method in full, he described precisely the double procedure that had been worked out since Grosseteste in the thirteenth century:

As in Mathematicks, so in Natural Philosophy, the Investigation of difficult Things by the Method of Analysis, ought ever to precede the Method of Composition. This Analysis consists in making Experiments

[1] In this connexion it is worth noting Newton's primary interest in mathematics as a practical tool for use in physics: 'The ancients considered mechanics in a twofold respect; as rational, which proceeds accurately by demonstration, and practical. To practical mechanics all the manual arts belong, from which mechanics took its name . . . geometry is founded in mechanical practice, and is nothing but that part of universal mechanics which accurately proposes and demonstrates the art of measuring.' *Principia*, Preface to First Edition, ed. Cajori, p. xvii. Cf. above, pp. 22, 39–40, 42.

[2] Above, pp. 92–93.

[3] 'Rule I. *We are to admit no more causes of natural things than such as are both true and sufficient to explain their appearances.* To this purpose the philosophers say that Nature does nothing in vain, and more is in vain when less will serve; for Nature is pleased with simplicity, and affects not the pomp of superfluous causes. Rule II. *Therefore to the same natural effects we must, as far as possible, assign the same causes.* . . . Rule III. *The qualities of bodies, which admit neither intensification nor remission of degrees, and which are found to belong to all bodies within the reach of our experiments, are to be esteemed the universal qualities of all bodies whatsoever.* . . . Rule IV. *In experimental philosophy we are to look upon propositions inferred by general induction from phenomena as accurately or very nearly true, notwithstanding any contrary hypotheses that may be imagined, till such time as other phenomena occur, by which they may either be made more accurate, or liable to exceptions.*' (*Principia*, iii, pp. 398 sqq.) For Newton's empirical attitude to the first rule see also his comment on the statement that light-rays of all the different colours obeyed the sine-law of refraction: 'That it should be so is very reasonable, Nature being ever conformable to her self; but an experimental Proof is desired.' *Opticks*, i. i, Prop. vi, Theor. 5, 4th ed., p. 66; cf. iii. i, Q. 28, p. 344, Q. 31, pp. 351, 372; Burtt, op. cit., p. 216; cf. Grosseteste, above, pp. 96, 123.

and Observations, and in drawing general Conclusions from them by Induction, and admitting of no Objections against the Conclusions, but such as are taken from Experiments, or other certain Truths. For Hypotheses are not to be regarded in experimental Philosophy. And although the arguing from Experiments and Observations by Induction be no Demonstration of general Conclusions; yet it is the best way of arguing which the Nature of Things admits of, and may be looked upon as so much the stronger, by how much the Induction is more general. And if no Exception occur from Phænomena, the Conclusion may be pronounced generally. But if at any time afterwards any Exception shall occur from Experiments, it may then begin to be pronounced with such Exceptions as occur. By this way of Analysis we may proceed from Compounds to Ingredients, and from Motions to the Forces producing them; and in general, from Effects to their Causes, and from particular Causes to more general ones, till the Argument end in the most general. This is the Method of Analysis: And the Synthesis consists in assuming the Causes discover'd, and establish'd as Principles, and by them explaining the Phænomena proceeding from them, and proving the Explanations.

In the two first Books of these Opticks, I proceeded by this Analysis to discover and prove the original Differences of the Rays of Light in respect of Refrangibility, Reflexibility, and Colour, and their alternate Fits of easy Reflexion and easy Transmission, and the Properties of Bodies, both opake and pellucid, on which their Reflexions and Colours depend. And these Discoveries being proved, may be assumed in the Method of Composition for explaining the Phænomena arising from them: An Instance of which Method I gave in the End of the first Book.[1]

We reach the conclusion that despite the enormous increase in power that the new mathematics brought in the seventeenth century, the logical structure and problems of experimental science had remained basically the same since the beginning of its modern history some four centuries earlier. The history of the theory of experimental science from Grosseteste to Newton is in fact a set of variations on Aristotle's theme, that the purpose of scientific inquiry was to discover true premisses for demonstrated knowledge of observations, bringing in the new instrument of experiment and transposing into the key of mathematics. The investigator tried to construct a verified system of propositions within which the more particular bore to the more general the relation of necessary consequence. The establishing of that relation was what he meant by an explanation.

[1] *Opticks*, iii. i, Q. 31, 4th ed., pp. 380-1.

Only by relating them to their own time can the ideas forming that tradition be truly understood; but because of that true understanding we can release from their time the philosophical and scientific truths that are independent of time, and release ourselves from those that are not. The philosophical truth that the whole history of experimental science since the thirteenth century has brought to light is that the experimental method, originally designed as a method of discovering the true causes of observed occurrences, or facts, turns out to be a method of constructing true descriptions of them. A scientific theory has provided the whole of the explanation that can be asked from it when it has correlated the facts of experience as accurately, completely, and conveniently as possible. Any further questions that may be asked about the facts cannot be asked in the language of science. Of its nature such a description is provisional, and the practical programme of research is to replace limited theories by others ever more comprehensive.

A scientific theory, then, tells us no more than it appears to tell us about the experimental facts, namely that they may be related in a particular manner. It can provide no grounds for the belief that the entities postulated for the purposes of the theory actually exist. So, whether or not science makes metaphysical assumptions, a scientific theory has no metaphysical implications. It can never be used either to support or contradict interpretations of experience written in another language or a different mood, and propositions in other languages and moods have nothing to do with science. Dives was separated from Lazarus no farther than science is from theology or ethics or a theory of beauty. To try to pass from one to the other is to land in the chaos between.

XII

Bibliography

THIS Bibliography includes all the sources mentioned in the footnotes.[1] Some works of general reference fall into more than one of the three main sections of the Bibliography, but I have mentioned them only once, usually in the last section. Published texts I have invariably given under the name of the original author, not of the editor, even when they occur in a work by the latter. The place of publication of a journal or collection I have given, unless it is indicated by the title, in the first reference to it in the Bibliography. For journals and collections mentioned several times I have used the following abbreviations in both the footnotes and the Bibliography:

AFH, Archivum Franciscanum Historicum (Florence).

AGM, Archiv für Geschichte der Medizin (Leipzig).

AGNT, Archiv für die Geschichte der Naturwissenschaften und der Technik (Berlin). Continued as *Quellen und Studien zur Geschichte der Naturwissenschaften und der Medizin.*

AHDLMA, Archives d'histoire doctrinale et littéraire du moyen âge (Paris).

APAW, Abhandlungen der preußischen Akademie der Wissenschaften (Berlin).

APC, Annalen der Physik und Chemie (Leipzig). Continued as *Annalen der Physik.*

AS, Annals of Science (London).

ASI, Actualités scientifiques et industrielles (Paris).

BGPM, Beiträge zur Geschichte der Philosophie des Mittelalters (Münster).

BIAPSL, Bulletin international de l'Académie polonaise des sciences et des lettres, Classe d'hist. et de philos. (Cracow).

BM, Bibliotheca Mathematica (Copenhagen).

CHJ, The Cambridge Historical Journal.

EHR, The English Historical Review (London).

ÉPM, Études de philosophie médiévale (Paris).

HJ, Historisches Jahrbuch der Görres-Gesellschaft (Bonn).

JHI, Journal of the History of Ideas (Lancaster, Pa., and New York).

MH, Mediaevalia et Humanistica (Boulder, Colorado).

MRS, Mediaeval and Renaissance Studies (London, Warburg Institute).

MS, Mediaeval Studies (New York, Toronto).

NS, The New Scholasticism (Baltimore).

NSKME, Neudrucke von Schriften und Karten über Meteorologie und Erdmagnetismus, ed. G. Hellmann, Berlin, 1893-1904, 15 nos.

PBA, The Proceedings of the British Academy (London).

PJ, Philosophisches Jahrbuch der Görres-Gesellschaft (Bonn).

PL, Patrologia Latina, ed. J. P. Migne, Paris, 1844-55, 221 vols.

[1] See also below, pp. 350-2.

PT, *Philosophical Transactions* (of the Royal Society of London).

RBE, *Roger Bacon, Essays contributed by various writers on the occasion of the com-memoration of his birth*, ed. A. G. Little, Oxford, 1914.

RNP, *Revue néoscolastique de philosophie* (Louvain).

RS, *Rolls Series, The Chronicles and Memorials of Great Britain and Ireland during the Middle Ages*, London, 1858–96, 99 vols.

RSPT, *Revue des sciences philosophiques et théologiques* (Paris).

RTAM, *Recherches de théologie ancienne et médiévale* (Louvain).

SHMS, *Studies in the History and Method of Science*, ed. C. Singer, Oxford, 1917–21, 2 vols.

SKBAW, *Sitzungsberichte der (königlich) bayerischen Akademie der Wissenschaften*, philos.-philolog. und hist. Klasse (München).

SPAWB, *Sitzungsberichte der (königlich) preußischen Akademie der Wissenschaften zu Berlin*, philos.-hist. Klasse.

SPMSE, *Sitzungsberichte der physikalisch-medizinischen Societät in Erlangen*.

I. Classical sources, Greek and Latin

1. Original sources

(a) Manuscripts

Euclidis *Elementa*, British Museum MS Royal 15. A. xxvii, 12 c., ff. 47 sqq.

(b) Printed sources

Alexandri Aphrodisiensis . . . *in Quatuor Libros Meteorologicorum Aristotelis Commentatio lucidissima*, quam Latinitate donavit Alexander Piccolomini, Venetiis, 1540.

Anonymus Londinensis, *The Medical Writings of*, by W. H. S. Jones, Cambridge, 1947.

Aristotelis *Opera*, ex recensione I. Bekkeri, Oxonii, 1837, 11 vols.

Aristotle, *The Complete Works of*. Translated into English under the editorship of J. A. Smith and W. D. Ross, Oxford, 1908–31, 11 vols.

Aristotle's *Prior and Posterior Analytics*. A revised text with introduction and commentary by W. D. Ross, Oxford, 1949.

Sancti Aurelii Augustini, Hipponensis Episcopi, *Opera Omnia*, [ed.] J. P. Migne (*PL*, xxxii–xlvii) Paris, 1841–9, 16 vols.

Anitii Manlii Severini Boethi, philosophorum et theologicorum principis, *Opera Omnia*, Basileae, 1570.

Anicii Manlii Severini Boetii *Opera Omnia*, [ed.] J. P. Migne (*PL*, lxiii–lxiv) Paris, 1847, 2 vols.

Anicii Manlii Severini Boethii *In Isagogen Porphyrii Commenta*, copiis a G. Schepss comparatis suisque usus recensuit S. Brandt (*Corpus Scriptorum Ecclesiasticorum Latinorum*, xlviii) Lipsiae, 1906. (Also in Migne, *PL*, lxiv.)

Cassiodori Senatoris *Institutiones*, ed. R. A. B. Mynors, Oxford, 1937.

Chalcidii *Timaeus ex Platonis Dialogo translatus et in eundem Commentarius*, [ed.] F. G. A. Mullachius [F. W. A. Mullach] (*Fragmenta Philosophorum Graecorum*, ii) Parisiis, 1867, pp. 147 sqq.

Diocles. Tideus *de Speculis*, in *Alkindi, Tideus und Pseudo-Euklid. Drei optische Werke*, hrg. von A. A. Björnbo und S. Vogl (*Abhandlungen zur Geschichte der mathematischen Wissenschaften*, xxvi. 3) Leipzig und Berlin, 1912, pp. 73 sqq.

Sancti Dionysii Areopagitae *De Divinis Nominibus*, in Joannis Scoti [Erigena] *Opera quae supersunt Omnia*, . . . ed. . . . H. J. Floss (*PL*, cxxii) Paris, 1853.

Euclidis perspicacissimi, *Praeclarissimus Liber Elementorum, in Artem Geometrie*, Venetiis, 1482 (see also Heath's ed., below, p. 323).

Euclidis *Optica et Catoptrica*, nunquam antehac graece aedita. Eadem Latine reddita per Joannem Penam Regium Mathematicum, Parisiis, 1557. (Greek and Latin text ed. J. L. Heiberg, Leipzig (Teubner) 1895.)

Claudii Galeni *Opera Omnia*, editionem curavit C. G. Kühn (*Medicorum Graecorum Opera quae existant*) Lipsiae, 1821–33, 20 vols.

Galen, *On Medical Experience*, first ed. of the Arabic version with English translation and notes by R. Walzer, Oxford, 1944.

Heronis Alexandrini *Opera quae supersunt Omnia*, Leipzig (Teubner) 1899–1900, 2 vols.

Plato, *Œuvres complètes*, texte établi et traduit par M. Croiset, &c. (Collection G. Budé), Paris, 1921–30, 13 vols. in 17.

Plinius Secundus (Gaius), *Naturalis Historia*; ed. as *Natural History*, with an English translation by H. Rackham, London (Loeb Classical Library), 1938–52, 9 vols.

Claudii Ptolemei, *Almagestum*, Venetiis, 1515.

Ptolemy. Claudio Tolomeo, *L'Ottica di*, da Eugenio Ammiraglio di Sicilia — Scrittore del Secolo xii — ridotta in Latino sovra la traduzione Araba di un testo Greco imperfetto, pubblicata da G. Govi, Torino, 1885.

Lucius Annaeus Seneca, *Quaestiones Naturales*; as *Questions naturelles*, texte établi et traduit par P. Oltramare (Collection G. Budé), Paris, 1929, 2 vols.

Simplicii Peripatetici acutissimi *Commentaria in Octo Libros Aristotelis de Physico Auditu*, Parisiis, 1544.

Simplicii philosophi acutissimi *Commentaria in Quatuor Libros de Coelo Aristotelis*, Venetiis, 1563. (Greek text ed. J. L. Heiberg in *Commentaria in Aristotelem Graeca*, vii, Berolini, 1894.)

Themistii, Peripatetici acutissimi, *Paraphrasis in Posteriora Analytica Aristotelis*, Basiliae, 1533.

2. Modern works

D. M. Balme, 'Greek science and mechanism. I. Aristotle on nature and chance', *The Classical Quarterly* (Oxford), xxxiii (1939) 129 sqq.; 'II. The atomists', ibid. xxxv (1941) 23 sqq.

J. I. Beare, *Greek Theories of Elementary Cognition from Alcmaeon to Aristotle*, Oxford, 1906.

E. W. Beth, 'Critical epochs in the development of the theory of science', *The British Journal for the Philosophy of Science* (Edinburgh), i (1950) 27 sqq.

E. W. Beth, 'The prehistory of research into foundations', *The British Journal for the Philosophy of Science*, iii (1952) 58 sqq.

I. M. Bocheński, *La Logique de Théophraste* (*Collectanea Friburgensia*, N.S. xxxii) Fribourg, 1947.

C. B. Boyer, 'Aristotelian references to the law of reflection', *Isis* (Cambridge, Mass.), xxxvi (1946) 92 sqq.

P. Brunet et A. Mieli, *Histoire de sciences: Antiquité*, Paris, 1935.

R. G. Collingwood, *The Idea of Nature*, Oxford, 1945.

F. M. Cornford, *The Laws of Motion in the Ancient World*, Cambridge, 1931.

F. M. Cornford, *Plato's Cosmology. The Timaeus of Plato translated with a running commentary*, London, 1937.

F. M. Cornford, 'Greek philosophy and modern science', in *Background to Modern Science*, ed. J. Needham and W. Pagel, Cambridge, 1938. (Reprinted in *The Unwritten Philosophy and other Essays*, Cambridge, 1950.)

H. Diels, 'Über das physikalische System des Straton', *SPAWB*, 1893, pp. 101 sqq.

H. Diels, *Antike Technik*, 3. Aufl., Leipzig, 1924.

A. Edel, *Aristotle's Theory of the Infinite*, New York, 1934.

F. Enriques e G. de Santillana, *Compendio di Storia del Pensiero scientifico*, Bologna, 1937.

B. Farrington, *Greek Science*, London, 1949, ii.

A. Favaro, 'L'Ottica di Tolomeo', *Bolletino di Bibliografia e di Storia delle Scienze matematiche e fisiche* (Roma), xix (1886) 115 sqq.

A. Haas, 'Antike Lichttheorien', *Archiv für Geschichte der Philosophie* (Berlin), xx (1907) 345 sqq.

A. Haas, 'Die ältesten Beobachtungen auf dem Gebiete der Dioptrik', *AGNT*, ix (1922) 108 sqq.

Sir Thomas L. Heath, *The Thirteen Books of Euclid's Elements*, translated from the text of Heiberg with introduction and commentary, Cambridge, 1926, 3 vols.

Sir Thomas L. Heath, *Mathematics in Aristotle*, Oxford, 1949.

W. H. S. Jones, *Philosophy and Method in Ancient Greece; with an edition of Περὶ ἀρχαίης ἰητρικῆς* (with English translation) (*Bulletin of the History of Medicine*, Suppl. viii) Baltimore, 1946.

L. O. Kattsoff, 'Ptolemy and scientific method', *Isis*, xxxviii (1947) 18 sqq.

A. Lejeune, *Euclide et Ptolémée. Deux stades de l'optique géométrique grecque* (*Université de Louvain. Recueil de travaux d'histoire et de philosophie*, iii. 31) Louvain, 1948.

R. McKeon, 'Aristotle's conception of the development and the nature of scientific method', *JHI*, viii (1947) 3 sqq.

H. Magnus, *Die Anatomie des Auges bei den Griechen und Römern*, Leipzig, 1878.

H. Magnus, *Die Augenheilkunde der Alten*, Breslau, 1901.

H. Magnus, *Die Anatomie des Auges in ihrer geschichtlichen Entwicklung*, Breslau, 1906.

H. I. Marrou, *St. Augustin et la fin de la culture antique* (*Bibliothèque des écoles françaises d'Athènes et de Rome*, cxlv) 2ᵉ éd., Paris, 1938.

A. Neuburger, *The Technical Arts and Sciences of the Ancients*, London, 1930.

A. Rey, *La Science dans l'antiquité*, Paris, 1933–48, 5 vols.

A. Reymond, *Histoire des sciences exactes et naturelles dans l'antiquité gréco-romaine*, Paris, 1924.

W. D. Ross, *Aristotle*, 3rd ed., London, 1937.

A. Sayili, 'The Aristotelian explanation of the rainbow', *Isis*, xxx (1939) 65 sqq.

G. Senn, 'Über Herkunft und Stil der Beschreibungen von Experimenten im Corpus Hippocraticum', *AGM*, xxii (1923) 217 sqq.

G. Senn, *Die Entwicklung der biologischen Forschungsmethode in der Antike und ihre grundsätzliche Förderung durch Theophrast von Eresos*, Aarau, 1933.

A. E. Taylor, *Platonism and Its Influence*, London, 1925.

S. Vogl, 'Über die (Pseudo-)Euclidische Schrift, "De Speculis" ', *AGNT*, i (1908–9) 419 sqq.

II. *Arabic and Hebrew sources in Latin translation*

1. *Original Sources*

(a) *Manuscripts*

'Ali ibn Ridwan. Galeni *Liber Tegni cum Commento* Hali, Vaticano Palatino Latino MS 1102, *c.* 1300, ff. 117^r-174^v.

(b) *Printed sources*

Alhazeni Arabis *Opticae Thesaurus Libri Septem, nunc primum editi. Eiusdem liber De Crepusculis et Nubium Ascensionibus. Item* Vitellonis Thuringopoloni *Libri X.* Omnes instaurati, figuris illustrati et aucti, adiectis etiam in Alhazenum commentariis, a Federico Risnero, Basiliae, 1572.

'Ali ibn 'Abbas. *Pars theorica* of the *Liber Regalis,* in Constantini Africani *Summi in Omni Philosophia, De Communibus Medico Cognitu Necessariis Locis,* Basiliae, 1539.

'Ali ibn Ridwan. Galieni principis medicorum *Microtegni cum Commento* Hali Rodoham *Liber,* Venetiis, 1487.

Al-Kindi, Ja'qub ben Ishaq, *Die philosophischen Abhandlungen des.* Zum ersten Male hrg. von A. Nagy (*BGPM*, ii. 5) Münster, 1897.

Alkindi, *De Aspectibus,* in *Alkindi, Tideus und Pseudo-Euklid. Drei optische Werke,* hrg. von A. A. Björnbo und S. Vogl (*Abhandlungen zur Geschichte der mathematischen Wissenschaften,* xxvi. 3) Leipzig und Berlin, 1912, pp. 3 sqq.

Alpharabii *Opera Omnia quae Latina lingua conscripta reperiri potuerunt, ex antiquissimis manuscriptis eruta.* Studio et opera G. Camerarii. . . . Parisiis, 1638.

Alpharabius, *De Ortu Scientiarum,* hrg. von C. Baeumker (*BGPM*, xix. 3) Münster, 1916.

Alpharabii Philosophi *Opusculum de Scientiis*; *Liber* Alfarabii *de Scientiis,* translato a Magistro Girardo Cremonense; ed. A. González Palencia, in *Alfarabi, Catálogo de las Ciencias* (*Publicaciones de la Facultad de Filosofia y Letras, Univ. de Madrid,* ii) Madrid, 1932.

Averroës. Aristotelis Stagiritae . . . *Omnia quae extant Opera* . . . Averrois Cordubensis *in ea opera . . . Commentarii . . .* Venetiis, 1550-2, 11 vols. in 6.

Averrois Cordubensis *Colliget Libri VII,* cum quibus etiam nunc primum in quinto libro impressimus translationem trium illorum . . . a Jacob Mantino . . . Addidimus itidem post antiquam translationem tres illas sectiones Collectaneorum tribus Colliget libris, Secundo scilicet, Sexto et Septimo respondentes, a Iohanne Bruyerino Campegio elegantissime latinitate donatas, Venetiis, 1553.

Avicebron. Avencebrolis (Ibn Gebirol), *Fons Vitae,* ex Arabico in Latinum translatus ab Johanne Hispano et Dominico Gundissalino, primum edidit C. Baeumker (*BGPM,* i. 2-4) Münster 1892-5.

Avicenne perhypatetici philosophi ac medicorum . . . primi *Opera in Lucem Redacta . . . Logyca. Sufficientia. De Caelo et Mundo. De Anima. De Animalibus. De Intelligentiis.* Alpharabius *de Intelligentiis. Philosophia Prima,* Venetiis, 1508.

Avicennae Arabum medicorum principis, *Canon Medicinae,* Ex Gerardi Cremonensis versione et Andreae Alpagi Belunensis castigatione, Venetiis, 1608, 2 vols.

Pseudo-Euclides, *De Speculis,* in *Alkindi, Tideus und Pseudo-Euklid. Drei optische Werke,* hrg. von A. A. Björnbo und S. Vogl (*Abhandlungen zur Geschichte der mathematischen Wissenschaften,* xxvi. 3) Leipzig und Berlin, 1912, pp. 97 sqq.

Ysaac, *Omnia Opera in hoc volumine contenta*: *cum quibusdam aliis opusculis*, Lugduni, 1515.

Isaaci Iudaei, Salomonis Arabiae Regis adoptivi filii, *De Diaetis Universalibus et Particularibus, Libri II*, Basileae, 1570.

Isaac Israeli *Liber de Definicionibus*, ed. J. T. Muckle in *AHDLMA*, xi (1938) 299 sqq.

Liber de Causis, ed. R. Steele (*Opera Hactenus Inedita* Rogeri Baconi, xii) Oxford, 1935.

2. *Modern works*

H. Bauer, *Die Psychologie Alhazens, auf Grund von Alhazens Optik dargestellt von*, (*BGPM*, x. 5) Münster, 1911.

K. Brockelmann, *Geschichte der arabischen Literatur*, Weimar und Berlin, 1898-1902, 2 vols.; Suppl., Leiden, 1937-42, 3 vols.

P. de Konig, *Trois traités d'anatomie arabe*, Leiden, 1903.

H. G. Farmer, *Al-Farabi's Arabic-Latin Writings on Music* (*A Collection of Oriental Writers on Music*, ii) Glasgow, 1934.

L. Gauthier, *Ibn Rochd* (*Averroës*), Paris, 1948.

A. M. Goichon, *La Philosophie d'Avicenne et son influence en Europe médiévale*, Paris, 1944.

J. L. Heiberg und E. Wiedemann, 'Ibn al Haitams Schrift über parabolische Hohlspiegel', *BM*, x (1910) 201 sqq.

J. L. Heiberg und E. Wiedemann, 'Eine arabische Schrift über die Parabel und parabolische Hohlspiegel', *BM*, xi (1911) 193 sqq.

M. Horten, *Die Metaphysik des Averroës* (*1198†*). *Nach dem Arabischen übersetzt und erläutert* (*Abhandlungen zur Philosophie und ihre Geschichte*, hrg. von B. Erdmann, xiv) Halle a. S., 1912.

M. Horten, 'Avicennas Lehre vom Regenbogen, nach seinem Werk al Schifâ' (mit Bemerkungen von E. Wiedemann), *Meteorologische Zeitschrift* (Wien), xxx (1913) 533 sqq.

M. Meyerhof, 'Von Alexandrien nach Bagdad', *SPAWB*, 1930, pp. 389-429.

M. Meyerhof und C. Prüfer, 'Die Augenanatomie des Hunain b. Ishāq', *AGM*, iv (1910) 163 sqq.

A. Mieli, *La Science arabe et son rôle dans l'évolution scientifique mondiale*, Leyden, 1938.

Mustafa Nazif bey, *Al-Hasan ibn al-Haitham. His optical studies and discoveries*, Cairo, 1942-3, 2 vols. (in Arabic).

S. Pines, 'Les Précurseurs musulmans de la théorie de l'impetus', *Archeion. Archivio di Storia della Scienza* (Roma), xxi (1938) 298 sqq.

G. Quadri, *La Philosophie arabe dans l'Europe médiévale des origines à Averroës*, Paris, 1947.

A. M. Sayili, 'Al-Qarafi and his explanation of the rainbow', *Isis*, xxxii (1940) 16 sqq.

H. J. Seemann, 'Eilhard Wiedemann', *Isis*, xiv (1930) 166 sqq.

F. M. Shuja, *Cause of Refraction as explained by the Moslem Scientists*, Delhi, 1936.

H. Suter, *Die Mathematiker und Astronomen der Araber und ihre Werke* (*Abhandlungen zur Geschichte der mathematischen Wissenschaften*, x) Leipzig, 1900.

H. Suter, 'Nachträge und Berichtigungen zu "Die Mathematiker und Astronomen der Araber und ihre Werke" ', ibid. xiv (1902) 155 sqq.

H. Suter, 'Die Abhandlung über die Ausmessung des Paraboloides von Ibn al Haitham', *BM*, xii (1912) 289 sqq.

G. Vajda, *Introduction a la pensée juive du moyen âge* (*ÉPM*, xxxv) Paris, 1947.

E. Wiedemann, 'Zur Geschichte der Brennspiegel', *APC*, Neue (Dritte) Folge, xxxix (1890) 110 sqq.

E. Wiedemann, 'Zur Geschichte der Lehre vom Sehen', *APC*, Neué (Dritte) Folge, xxxix (1890) 470 sqq.

E. Wiedemann, 'Eine Beobachtung aus der physiologischen Optik', *SPMSE*, xxxvi (1904) 333 sqq.

E. Wiedemann, 'Kleinere Arbeiten von Ibn al Haitam', *SPMSE*, xli (1909) 1 sqq.

E. Wiedemann, 'Über die Brechung des Lichtes in Kugeln nach Ibn al Haitam und Kamâl al Dîn al Fârisî', *SPMSE*, xlii (1910) 15 sqq.

E. Wiedemann, 'Theorie des Regenbogens', *SPMSE*, xlvi (1914) 39 sqq.

E. Wiedemann, 'Ibn al Haitam ein arabischer Gelehrter', in *Festschrift J. Rosenthal gewidmet*, Leipzig, 1906, pp. 147 sqq.

E. Wiedemann, 'Ibn al-Haitams Schrift über die sphärischen Hohlspiegel', *BM*, x (1910) 293 sqq.

E. Wiedemann, 'Zu Ibn al. Haitams Optik', *AGNT*, iii (1910–11) 1 sqq.

E. Wiedemann, 'Zur Optik von Kamâl al Dîn', *AGNT*, iii (1910–11) 161 sqq.

E. Wiedemann, 'Zu den optischen Kenntnissen von Qutb al Dîn al Schîrazî', *AGNT*, iii (1910–11) 187 sqq.

E. Wiedemann, 'Ibn Sînâs Anschauung vom Sehvorgang', *AGNT*, iv (1912–13) 239 sqq.

E. Wiedemann, 'Arabische Studien über den Regenbogen', *AGNT*, iv (1912–13) 453 sqq.

E. Widemann, 'Über al Kindî's Schrift über Ebbe und Flut', *APC*, Vierte Folge, lxvii (1922) 374 sqq.

H. J. J. Winter and W. 'Arafat, 'Ibn Al-Haitham on the paraboloidal focussing mirror', *Journal of the Royal Asiatic Society of Bengal* (Calcutta), xv (1949), Science, pp. 25 sqq.

H. J. J. Winter, 'The Arabic achievement in physics', *Endeavour* (London), ix (1950) 76 sqq.

III. Western sources, Latin and vernacular

1. Original sources

(a) Manuscripts

Roger Bacon, *Opus Maius*, British Museum MS Royal 7. F. vii, 13 c.

Roger Bacon, *Opus Maius*, British Museum MS Royal 7. F. viii, 13 c.

Fratris Joannis Cronisbeni, Ordinis Fratrum Praedicatorum, *Philosophia, cum Metaphysica*, Venice MS Biblioteca Marciana Latino vi. 99, 15 c.

De Commendatione Cleri, MS Vaticano Palatino Latino 1252, 15 c., ff. 99^r–109^v.

Joannis de Dumbleton, *Summa Logice et Philosophie Naturalis*, Cambridge MS Peterhouse 272, 14 c., ff. 1 sqq.; Oxford MS Merton 306, 14 c., ff. 9 sqq.

Robert Grosseteste, *De Lineis, Angulis et Figuris*, Oxford MS Bodleian Library, Laud Misc. 644, 13 c., ff. 207vb–208vb.

Robert Grosseteste, *De Natura Locorum*, Oxford MS Bodleian Library, Laud Misc. 644, 13 c., ff. 208vb–210rb.

Robert Grosseteste, *De Iride*, British Museum MS Royal 6. E. v, 14 c., ff. 241^{r-vb}; Oxford MSS Bodleian Library, Digby 98, *c.* 1400, ff. 154^r–155^r; Digby 104, 14 c., f. 110^v; Digby 190, 13 c., ff. 197^v–199^v; Merton 306, 14 c., f. 118^r.

Robert Grosseteste, *De Universitatis Machina*, Cambridge University Library MS Ff. 6. 13, 13 c., ff. 17^v-26^r, 37^v-43^v.

Robert Grosseteste, *Commentarius in VIII Libros Physicorum Aristotelis*, Oxford MSS Merton 295, c. 1325, ff. 120^r-145^r; Digby 220, 15 c., ff. 84^r-105^r.

Robert Grosseteste, *Hexaëmeron*, British Museum MS Royal 6.E.v, 14 c., ff. 136^r-184vb.

Herba a Grosthede, British Museum MS Sloane 3468, 14 c., ff. 43^v-64^r.

Henry of Hesse. Henricus de Langenstein (?), *Questiones super Perspectivam*, MS s. Marci Florent. 202 (Biblioteca Nazionale, convent. soppr. J.X.19.), c. 1400, ff. 56^r-85^v.

Henry of Southwark (?), *De Visu et Speculis*, British Museum MS Royal 7.F.vii, 13 c., ff. 64rb-67vb.

Robert Kilwardby, *De Ortu Scientiarum*, Oxford MS Merton 261, 1294.

Joannis Marliani Mediolanensis *Questio de Proportione Motuum in Velocitate*, MS Vaticano Latino 2225, 1444, ff. 11^r-37^r; British Museum MS Harley 3833, 1470, ff. 1 sqq. (Published Pavia, 1482.)

Nicole Oresme, *Quaestiones Meteororum*, Erfurt Stadtbücherei, Amplonian Collection, MS Q. 299, 14 c., ff. 51-103^v.

Nicole Oresme, *Quaestiones super Euclidis Elementa*, MSS Vaticano Latino 2225, 1444, ff. 90^r-98vb; Chisianus F.iv.66, 15 c., ff. 22vb-40rb.

Sacerdos ad Altare Accessurus, Cambridge MS Gonville and Caius 385 (605), 13 c., ff. 7-61.

Themonis Judaei, *Questiones super IV Libros Meteorologicarum Aristotelis*, MS Vaticano Latino 2177, 14 c., ff. 1-92^v.

Theodorici Teutonici de Vriburgo, *De Iride*, MS Öffentliche Bibliothek der Universität Basel, F.IV.30, 14 c.

Theodorici Teutonici de Vriburgo, *Tractatus Varii Philosophici*, MS Vaticano Latino 2183, 14-15 c.

Walter of Odington, *Tractatus de Multiplicatione Specierum in Visu secundum omnem modum probatus* per magistrum Walterum de Evesham, Cambridge University Library MS Ii.1.13, 14 c., ff. 44^v-51; *Icocedron*, ibid., ff. 51^v-55^v.

William of Alnwick, *Determinationes*, MS Vaticano Palatino Latino, 1805, ff. 7 sqq.

(b) *Printed sources*

Peter Abaelards *Philosophische Schriften*, zum ersten Male hrg. von B. Geyer (*BGPM*, xxi. 2-4) Münster, 1921, 1927, 1933.

Petri Abani *Conciliator Differentiarum Philosophorum et Precipue Medicorum*, Venetiis, 1504.

Adae de Marisco *Epistolae*, in *Monumenta Franciscana*, ii, ed. J. S. Brewer (*RS*) London, 1858.

Adelard von Bath, *Des, Traktat De Eodem et Diverso*, ... hrg. ... von H. Willner (*BGPM*, iv. 1) Münster, 1903.

Adelardus von Bath, *Die Quaestiones Naturales des*, hrg. ... von M. Müller (*BGPM*, xxxi. 2) Münster, 1923.

Alani de Insulis *Opera Omnia*, [ed.] J. P. Migne (*PL*, ccx) Paris, 1855.

Beati Alberti Magni Ratisbonensis Episcopi, Ordinis Praedicatorum, *Opera Omnia*, ed. Petri Jammy, Lugduni, 1681, 21 vols.

Alberti Magni ... *De Vegetabilibus Libri VII*, [ed.] E. Meyer ... C. Jessen, Berolini, 1867.

Albertus Magnus, *De Animalibus Libri XXVI*, nach der Cölner Urschrift hrg. von H. Stadler (*BGPM*, xv, xvi) Münster, 1916–21.

Alexander de Hales, *see* Hales.

Alfredus Anglicus [de Sareshel], *De Plantis Libri Duo Aristoteli vulgo adscripti*. Ex Isaac Ben Honain versione Arabica Latine vertit Alfredus. Recensuit E. H. F. Meyer, Lipsiae, 1841.

Alfred von Sareshel (Alfredus Anglicus), *Des, Schrift De Motu Cordis*, . . . hrg. . . . von C. Baeumker (*BGPM*, xxiii. 1–2) Münster, 1923.

Sancti Thome [Aquinatis] *Expositio, super Libros Physicorum Aristotelis*, Venetiis, 1500.

S. Thomae Aquinatis *Opera Omnia iussu impensaque Leonis XIII P.M. edita*, Romae, 1882–1930, 15 vols.

Nicholas of Autrecourt, *Exigit Ordo Executionis*, ed. J. R. O'Donnell, in 'Nicholas of Autrecourt', *MS*, i (1939) 179 sqq.

William of Auvergne. Guilielmi Alverni *Opera Omnia*, Venetiis, 1591.

Francis Bacon, *The Works of*, ed. J. Spedding, R. L. Ellis and D. D. Heath, London, 1857–9, 7 vols.

Francis Bacon, *The Letters and Life of, including all his occasional works*. Newly collected by . . . J. Spedding, London, 1861–4, 7 vols.

Rogerii Bacconis Angli viri eminentissimi *Specula Matematica, in qua De Specierum Multiplicatione Earumdemque in Inferioribus Virtute Agitur*. Liber omnium scientiarum studiosis apprime utilis, editus opera et studio Iohannis Combachii, Francofurti, 1614.

Rogerii Bacconis Angli, viri eminentissimi *Perspectiva* . . . Nunc primum in lucem edita opera et studio Iohannis Combachii Francofurti, 1614. (This is *Opus Maius*, v.)

Roger Bacon, *Epistolae* . . . *de Secretis Operibus Artis et Naturae, et de Nullitate Magiae*, in *Opera* J. Dee . . ., Hamburgi, 1618. (Also ed. Brewer, see below.)

Fr. Rogeri Bacon *Opera Quaedam Hactenus Inedita*, ed. J. S. Brewer (RS) London, 1859. (*Opus Minus, Opus Tertium*, and *De Secretis Operibus Artis et Naturae*.)

Roger Bacon, prefatory letter of the *Opus Minus*, ed. F. A. Gasquet as 'An unpublished fragment of Roger Bacon', *EHR*, xii (1897) 494 sqq.

Roger Bacon, *The 'Opus Majus' of*, ed. J. H. Bridges, Oxford, 1897, vols. i–ii; London, 1900, vol. iii. (Vols. ii and iii contain also *Tractatus* Rogeri Baconi *De Multiplicatione Specierum*.)

Roger Bacon, *Un Fragment inédit de l'Opus Tertium de, précédé d'une étude sur ce fragment*, (par) P. Duhem, Quaracchi, 1909.

Roger Baconi *Opera Hactenus Inedita nunc primum edidit* R. Steele (in collaboration with F. Delorme, A. G. Little, and E. Withington) Oxford, 1905–40, 16 fasciculi. (This edition contains most of the scientific writings not edited by Brewer and Bridges.)

Fr. Rogeri Baconi *Compendium Studii Theologiae*, ed. H. Rashdall (*British Society of Franciscan Studies*, iii) Aberdeen, 1911. (Appendix by A. G. Little, *De Operibus Rogeri Baconi*.)

Roger Bacon, *Part of the Opus Tertium of*, ed. A. G. Little (*Brit. Soc. of Franciscan Studies*, iv) Aberdeen, 1912.

Roger Bacon, *The Opus Majus of*, transl. by R. B. Burke, Philadelphia, 1928, 2 vols.

Richardi Monachi Bardeniensis *Liber de Vita Roberti Grosthed Episcopi Lincolniensis*, in Henry Wharton, *Anglia Sacra*, London, 1691, ii.

I. Barrow, *Lectiones XVIII, Cantabrigiae in Scholis publicis habitae; in quibus Opticorum Phaenomenon genuinae rationes investigantur, ac exponuntur*, Londini, 1669.

Bartholomaeus Anglicus, *De Proprietatibus Rerum*, Coloniae, c. 1472.

Bedae *Opera de Temporibus*, ed. C. W. Jones, Cambridge (Mass.), 1943.

George Berkeley, *De Motu*, in *The Works of*, ed. A. A. Luce and T. E. Jessop, iv, Edinburgh, 1951.

J. R. Boscovich, notes in C. Noceti *De Iride et Aurora Boreali Carmina . . . cum notis* J. R. Boscovich, Roma, 1747.

The Hon. R. Boyle, *Experiments and Considerations Touching Colours*, London, 1664.

The Hon. R. Boyle, *The Works of*, ed. Thomas Birch, London, 1744, 5 vols.

Thome Braduardini *Tractatus Proportionum*, Parisiis, 1512 (?).

Bradwardini, *Tractatus de Continuo*, ed. M. Curtze in 'Über die Handschrift R.4º.2, Problematum Euclidis explicatio der Königl. Gymnasialbibliothek zu Thorn', *Zeitschrift für Mathematik und Physik* (Leipzig) Suppl. xiii (1868) 85 sqq.

Acutissimi philosophi reverendi Magistri Johannis Buridani *Subtilissime Questiones super Octo Phisicorum Libros Aristotelis* diligenter recognite et revise a magistro Johanne Dullaert de Gandano antea nusquam impresse, Parhisiis, 1509.

Gualteri Burlei *In Physicam Aristotelis Expositio et Questiones*, Venetiis, 1501.

Excellentissimi Doctoris Magistri Gualteri Burlei, *Scriptum super Libros Posteriorum Aristotelis . . .*, Venetiis, 1514.

Hieronymus Cardanus, *De Subtilitate*, Lugduni, 1554.

Guillelmi de Conchis, *De Philosophia Mundi*, printed as Lib. iv of *Elementorum Philosophiae* in *Opera Bedae Venerabilis*, Basileae, 1563, ii. 335 sqq.

Constantinus Africanus (see p. 324, 'Ali ibn 'Abbas).

C. Cusanus, *The Idiot in Four Books*, London, 1650.

D. Nicolai Cusa Cardinalis . . . *Opera*, Basiliae, 1665.

Nicolai de Cusa *Opera Omnia iussu et auctoritate Academiae Litterarum Heidelbergensis*, i, v, Lipsiae, 1932, 1937. (Texts ed. by E. Hoffmann, R. Klibansky, L. Baur.)

C. F. Milliet De Chales, *Cursus seu Mundus Mathematicus*, Lugduni, 1674, 3 vols.

Marc Antonio de Dominis, *De Radiis Visus et Lucis in Vitris Perspectivis et Iride Tractatus*. Per Ioannem Bartolum in lucem editus, Venetiis, 1611.

John Dee, *The Castle of Knowledge*, London, 1556.

R. Descartes, *Discours de la Méthode pour bien conduire sa raison, et chercher la vérité dans les sciences. Plus la Dioptrique, les Météores et la Géométrie, Qui sont des essais de cete Méthode*, Leyde, 1637. (Also in *Œuvres*, publiées par C. Adam et P. Tannery, vi, Paris, 1902.)

Renati Des-Cartes *Opera Philosophica*, Editio Quarta, Amsterdami, 1664.

R. Descartes, *Œuvres de*, publiées par C. Adam et P. Tannery, Paris, 1897–1913, 12 vols.

Leonard and Thomas Digges, *An Arithmeticall Militare Treatise, named Stratioticos*, London, 1579.

Thomas of Eccleston, *Tractatus de Adventu Fratrum Minorum in Angliam*, ed. A. G. Little, Paris, 1909.

Hieronymi Fabricii ab Aquapendente *De Oculo Visus Organo*, Venetiis, 1600.

P. de Fermat, *Œuvres de*, publiées par les soins de MM. Paul Tannery et Charles Henry, Paris, 1891–1912, 4 vols.

Ioannes Fleischerus Vratislaviense, *De Iridibus Doctrina Aristotelis et Vitellionis certa methodo comprehensa, explicata et tam necessariis demonstrationibus, quam physicis et opticis causis*, Wittebergae, 1571. (The title-page is dated 1579, the colophon 1571.)

Galileus Galileus, *The System of the World, in Four Dialogues*, . . . Inglished . . . by Thomas Salusbury in *Mathematical Collections and Translations*, London, 1661.

Galilæo Galilæi, *The Ancient and Modern Doctrine of the Holy Fathers. . . . Concerning the Rash citation of the Testimony of Sacred Scripture, in Conclusions meerly Natural*, in Thomas Salusbury, *Mathematical Collections and Translations*, London, 1661.

Galileo Galilei, *Le Opere di*, ed. naz., Firenze, 1890–1909, 20 vols.

Galileo, *Dialogues Concerning Two New Sciences*, translated from the Italian and Latin into English by H. Crew and A. de Salvio, New York, 1914.

Gerbertus, Silvestri II Pontificis Romani. . . . *Opera Omnia*, [ed.] J. P. Migne (*PL*, cxxxix) Paris, 1853.

Gilberti Porretae *Commentaria in Librum Quomodo Substantiae Bonae Sint*, [ed.] J. P. Migne (*PL*, lxiv) Paris, 1847, cols. 1313 sqq.

William Gilbert, *De Magnete Magnetisque Corporibus et de Magno Magnete Tellure*, London, 1600. (English transl. by P. F. Mottelay as *On the Lodestone and Magnetic Bodies and on the Great Magnet the Earth*, London, 1893.)

Giles of Rome. *Expositio Egidii Romani Super Libros Posteriorum Aristotelis cum textu eiusdem*, Venetiis, 1495.

Giles of Rome. Egidii Romani *De Intentionibus in Medio*, in G. Bruni, *Le Opere di Egidio Romano*, Firenze, 1936, p. 214.

Giraldus Cambrensis, *Opera*, ed. J. S. Brewer (*RS*) London, 1861, i.

John Gower, *Confessio Amantis*, ed. G. C. Macaulay (*Complete Works*, ii–iii) Oxford, 1901.

J. Gregory, *Optica Promota*, Londini, 1663.

F. M. Grimaldi, *Physico-mathesis de Lumine, Coloribus, et Iride, aliisque annexis libri duo*, Bononiae, 1665.

Robert Grosseteste. *Roberti Linconiensis, Commentaria in Libros Posteriorum Aristotelis, cum textu seriatim inserto*, Venetiis, 1494. *Habes* Aristotelis *Posteriorum Opus ac eius luculentissimum interpretem* Linconiensem Burleumque . . . , Venetiis, 1514.

Robert Grosseteste. *Summa* Linconiensis *super Octo Libris Physicorum Aristotelis*, Venetiis, 1500.

Robert Grosseteste. *Libellus* Linconiensis *de Phisicis Lineis Angulis et Figuris per Quas Omnes Actiones Naturales Complentur*, Nurenberge, 1503.

Roberti Grossetestae Episcopi quondam Lincolniensis *Epistolae*, ed. H. R. Luard (*RS*) London, 1861.

Robert Grosseteste, Bischofs von Lincoln, *Die philosophischen Werke des*, zum erstenmal vollständig in kritischer Ausgabe besorgt von L. Baur (*BGPM*, ix) Münster, 1912.

Robert Grosseteste. *Canon in Kalendarium* Venerabilis Episcopi Linconiensis, ed. A. Lindhagen as 'Die Neumondtafel des Robertus Lincolniensis', *Arkiv för Matematik, Astronomi och Fysik* (Uppsala), xi. 2 (1916).

Venerabilis patris Domini et Sancti Roberti Grosse Capitis Lincolniensis Episcopi, *Compotus, factus ad correctionem communis Kalendarii nostri*, ed. R. Steele (*Opera Hactenus Inedita* Rogeri Baconi, vi) Oxford, 1926, pp. 217 sqq.

Robert Grosseteste, *De Cometis et Causis Ipsarum*, ed. S. H. Thomson in 'The text of Grosseteste's De Cometis', *Isis*, xix (1933) 19 sqq. (see below, p. 350.)

Dominicus Gundissalinus, *De Divisione Philosophiae*, hrg. . . . von L. Baur (*BGPM*, iv. 2–3) Münster, 1903.

Alexandri de Hales *Summa Theologica*, Quaracchi, 1924–8, 2 vols.

Guilielmi Harvei Angli, *Exercitatio Anatomica de Motu Cordis et Sanguinis in Animalibus*, Francofurti, 1628.

William Harvey, *Exercitationes de Generatione Animalium*, Londini, 1651.

Magistri Roberti Holkot *Super Quattuor Libros Sententiarum Questiones*, Lugduni, 1497.

R. Hooke, *Micrographia*, London, 1665.

R. Hooke, *The Posthumous Works of*, London, 1705.

Hugonis de S. Victore, *Opera Omnia*, [ed.] J. P. Migne (*PL*, clxxvi) Paris, 1854.

Hugo de Sancto Victore, *Didascalicon de Studio Legendi*, ed. C. H. Buttimer, Washington (D.C.), 1939.

David Hume, *An Enquiry Concerning the Human Understanding, and an Enquiry Concerning the Principles of Morals*. Reprinted from the posthumous edition of 1777 and edited . . . by L. A. Selby-Bigge, Oxford, 1894.

Christian Huygens, 'An Extract of a Letter lately written by an ingenious person from Paris, containing some considerations upon Mr. Newtons doctrine of Colors, and also upon the effects of the different Refractions of the Rays in Telescopical Glasses', *PT*, viii (1673) 6086-7.

Christian Huygens, *Traité de la lumière*, Leide, 1690.

Christian Huygens, *Dioptrica* and *Dissertatio de Coronis et Pareliis*, in *Opuscula Postuma*, Lugduni Batavorum, 1703, pp. 1-263 and 293-366.

Isidori Hispalensis Episcopi *Etymologiarum sive Originum Libri XX*, [ed.] W. M. Lindsay, Oxford, 1911, 2 vols.

Joannes de Sancto Amando, *see* Sanctus Amandus.

Ioannis Saresberaensis *Metalogicon*, ed. C. C. J. Webb, Oxford, 1929.

Iordani *Opusculum de Ponderositate* Nicolai Tartaleae studio correctum, Venetiis, 1565.

Ioanne Keplero . . . *Ad Vitellionem Paralipomena, quibus Astronomiæ pars Optica traditur*, Francofurti, 1604.

Ioannis Kepleri *Dioptrice*, Augustæ Vindelicorum, 1611.

G. Leibniz, *Nouveaux essais sur l'entendement humain*, ed. M. A. Jacques (*Œuvres*, i) Paris, 1842.

Leonardo da Vinci, *The Notebooks of*, arranged, rendered into English and introduced by E. MacCurdy, London, 1938, 2 vols. [2 vols.

Leonardo da Vinci, *Literary Works*, ed. J. P. and I. A. Richter, 2nd ed., London, 1939,

Emanuel Maignan, *Perspectiva Horaria*, Romae, 1648.

Emanuel Maignan, *Philosophia Sacra*, Tolosae, 1661, 1672, 2 parts.

Emanuelis Maignan Tolosatis Ordinis minimorum, philosophiae ac sacrae theologiae professoris, *Cursus Philosophicus*, Lugduni, 1673. (First ed. Tolosae, 1653.)

Ioanne Marco Marci [a Kronland], *Thaumantias, Liber de Arcu Coelesti deque Colorum Apparentium Natura Ortu et Causis*, Pragae, 1648.

E. Mariotte, *De la nature des couleurs*, in *Œuvres*, Leide, 1717, i. 195 sqq.

Abbatis Francisci Maurolyci Messanensis *Photismi de Lumine et Umbra ad perspectivam et radiorum incidentiam facientes. Diaphanorum Partes, seu Libri tres, in quorum primo de perspicuis corporibus, in secundo de Iride, in tertio de organi visualis structura et conspiciliorum formis agitur. Problemata ad Perspectivam et Iridem pertinentia*, Neapoli, 1611.

J. S. Mill, *A System of Logic, Ratiocinative and Inductive*, London, 1843.

Alexander Neckam, *De Utensilibus*, ed. T. Wright in *A Volume of Vocabularies*, Liverpool, 1857.

Alexander Neckam, *De Naturis Rerum, De Laudibus Divinae Sapientiae*, ed. T. Wright (*RS*) London, 1863.

I. Newton. 'A Letter of Mr. Isaac Newton, Mathematick Professor in the University of Cambridge; containing his New Theory about Light and Colours: Where Light is declared to be not Similar or Homogeneal, but consisting of difform rays, some of which are more refrangible than others: And Colours are affirm'd to be not

Qualifications of Light, deriv'd from Refractions of natural Bodies (as 'tis generally believed); but Original and Connate properties, which in divers rays are divers: Where several Observations and Experiments are alledged to prove the said theory', *PT*, vi (1671-2) 3075-87 (19 Feb. 1672).

I. Newton. 'A Serie's of Quere's propounded by Mr. Isaac Newton, to be determin'd by Experiments, positively and directly concluding his new Theory of Light and Colours; and here recommended to the Industry of the Lovers of Experimental Philosophy, as they were generously imparted to the Publisher in a Letter of the said Mr. Newtons of July 8. 1672.', *PT*, vii (1672) 5004-7.

'Mr. Newtons Answer to the foregoing Letter [by R. Patris J. Pardies]', *PT*, vii (1672) 5014-8.

'Mr. Isaac Newtons Answer to some Considerations upon his Doctrine of Light and Colors; which Doctrine was printed in Numb. 80 of these Tracts', *PT*, vii (1672) 5084-5103.

I. Newton. 'An Extract of Mr. Isaac Newton's Letter, written to the Publisher from Cambridge April 3. 1673. concerning the Number of Colors, and the Necessity of mixing them all for the production of White. . . .', *PT*, viii (1673) 6108-11.

'Mr. Newton's Answer to the Precedent Letter [by Anthony Lucas], sent to the Publisher', *PT*, xi (1676) 698-705.

Sir Isaac Newton's *Mathematical Principles of Natural Philosophy and his System of the World*, Motte's translation revised by F. Cajori, Berkeley, Calif., 1946. (First published as *Philosophiae Naturalis Principia Mathematica*, London, 1687.)

Sir Isaac Newton, *Opticks: or, a Treatise of the Reflections, Refractions, Inflections and Colours of Light*, 4th ed., London, 1730. (Reprinted London, 1931; 1st ed., 1704.)

Nicholas, *see* Autrecourt, Cusa, Oresme.

Eutychi Augustini Nyphi medices philosophi Suessani *Commentaria in Libros Ἀναλυτικῶν ὑστέρων, id est, Resolutionum Posteriorum Aristotelis*, Parisiis, 1540.

Augustini Niphi philosophi Suessani *Expositio super Octo Aristotelis Stagiritae Libros de Physico Auditu*, Venetiis, 1552.

Augustini Niphi philosophi Suessani *In Aristotelis Libros De Coelo et Mundo Commentaria*, Venetiis, 1553.

Augustini [Niphi] Suessani philosophi perspicacissimi *Subtilissima Commentaria in Libros Meteorologicorum*, Venetiis, 1560.

William of Ockham. *Quotlibeta* Guillermi Hokan, Parisiis, 1487.

Magistri Guilhelmi di Ockam, *Tabule ad Diversas huius Operis, super Quattuor Libros Sententiarum annotationes et ad Centilogii Theologici eiusdem conclusiones facile reperiendas apprime conducibiles*, Lugduni, 1495. (See below, p. 350.)

Venerabilis inceptoris fratris Guilielmi de villa Hoccham Anglie, Achademic Nominalium Principis, *Summule in Libros Physicorum*, Venetiis, 1506.

Magistri Guielmi Occham Anglici logicorum argutissimi, *Summa Totius Logice*, Venetiis, 1508.

William of Ockham, *The De Sacramento Altaris of*, ed. [with English translation] by T. B. Birch, Burlington, Iowa, 1930.

William of Ockham, *The Tractatus de Successivis attributed to*, ed. P. Boehner (*Franciscan Institute Publ.* i) New York, 1944.

William of Ockham, *The Tractatus de Praedestinatione et de Praescientia Dei et de Futuris Contingentibus of, edited with a study on the medieval problem of three-valued logic*, by P. Boehner (*Franciscan Institute Publ.* ii) New York, 1945.

H. Oldenburg, review of 'Physico Mathesis de Lumine, Coloribus et Iride, etc. Auth. Franc. Maria Grimaldo S.J., Bononiae, 1665. in 4°', *PT*, vi (1671-2) 3068-70.

Maistre Nicole Oresme, *Le Livre du ciel et du monde*. Text and Commentary by A. D. Menut and A. J. Denomy, *MS*, iii (1941) 185 sqq., iv (1942) 159 sqq., v (1943) 167 sqq.

Oxoniensis, Statuta Antiqua Universitatis, ed. S. Gibson, Oxford, 1931.

Matthaei Parisiensis, *Chronica Majora*, ed. H. R. Luard (*RS*) London, 1877-80, iv-v.

Matthew Paris, *Four Maps of Great Britain by, about 1250*, London, 1928.

Clarissimi philosophi Pauli Veneti, *Summa Philosophie Naturalis*, Parisiis, 1514.

Clarissimi artium et sacre theologie doctoris Pauli Veneti ordinis Heremitarum Divi Augustini *Expositio in Libros Posteriorum Aristotelis*, Impensis et mandato heredum nobilis viri quondam domini Octaviani Scoti Modoetiensis et sociorum, 1518.

Pauli Veneti, *Logica*, Venetiis, 1546.

Ioannis [Pecham] Archiepiscopi Cantuariensis *Perspectivae Communis Libri Tres*, Coloniae, 1592.

Petrus Abanus, *see* Abanus.

Petrus Hispanus, *Die Ophthalmologie des*, ... hrg. ... von A. M. Berger, München, 1899.

Petrus Hispanus. Peter of Spain, *The Summulae Logicales of*, ed. J. P. Mullally (*Publications in Medieval Studies*, viii) Notre Dame, Indiana, 1945. (Also ed. I. M. Bocheński, O.P., Torino, 1947.)

Petrus Peregrinus, *The Epistle of, Concerning the Magnet*, done into English by S. P. Thompson, London, 1902. (*See* Harradon, below, p. 351.)

Petri Peregrini Maricurtensis *De Magnete*, hrg. von G. Hellmann, in *Rara Magnetica* (*NSKME*, x) Berlin, 1898.

Alexander Piccolomini. Alexandri Aphrodisiensis ... *in Quatuor Libros Meteorologicorum Aristotelis Commentatio lucidissima*, quam Latinitate donavit Alexander Piccolomineus. Accedit ... Alexandri Piccolominei *Tractatus de Iride*, Venetiis, 1540.

Felix Platerus, *De Corporis Humani Structura et Usu*, Basiliae, 1583.

Giambattista della Porta, *Magiae Naturalis*, Neapoli, 1558. Also ibid., Neapoli, 1589.

Giambattista della Porta, *De Refractione Optices Parte Libri Novem*, Neapoli, 1593.

Simon Porta. *De Coloribus Libellus* a S. Portio Latinitate donatus et commentariis illustratus, una cum ejusdem praefatione, Florentiae, 1548.

Simon Porta. *Meteorologicorum Libri Quatuor*, in Aristotelis Stagiritae tripartitae philosophiae *Opera Omnia* ... ex ... interpretibus [S. Portius etc.] collecta ..., Basiliae, 1563, Pars iii, pp. 255 sqq.

Joseph Priestley, *The History and Present State of Discoveries relating to Vision, Light, and Colours*, London, 1772, 2 vols.

Robert Recorde, *The Castle of Knowledge*, London, 1556.

G. Reisch, *Margarita Philosophica*, Argentinae, 1504.

Richardus Bardeniensis, *see* Bardeniensis.

Fridericum Risnerum, *Opticae Libri Quatuor* ex voto Petri Rami novissimo per, ejusdem in mathematicis olim conscripti ..., Cassellis, 1606.

Risneri *Optica cum annotationibus* Willebrordi Snellii, edidit J. A. Wollgraff. Pars prima, librum primum continens, Ghent, 1918.

Rufinus, *The Herbal of*, ed. from the unique MS by L. Thorndike assisted by F. S. Benjamin Jr., Chicago, 1946.

Fratris Salimbene de Adam, *Cronica*, edidit O. Holder-Egger (*Monumenta Germaniae Historica*, Scriptorum tomus, xxxii) Hannoverae, Lipsiae, 1905-13.

Joannes de Sancto Amando, *Super Antidotarium Nicolai*, Venetiis, 1508.

Christophoro Scheiner, *Refractiones Coelestes, sive Solis Elliptici Phaenomenon Illustratum*, Ingolstadti, 1617.

Christophorus Scheiner, *Oculus, hoc est, Fundamentum Opticum* . . ., Oeniponti, 1619.

Ioannis Duns Scoti *Opera Omnia*, [ed.] Luke Wadding, Lugduni, 1639, 12 vols. in 13.

Joannis Duns Scoti *Commentaria Oxoniensia ad IV. Libros Magistri Sententiarum*, ed. Marianus Fernandez Garcia, Quaracchi, 1912, 2 vols.

Magistri Michaelis Scoti, *Phisionomia*, in *Mensa Philosophica*, Parrhisiis, 1515.

John Seldon, poem in Arthur Hopton, *A Concordancy of Yeares*, London, 1612.

William of Sherwood, *The Syncategoremata of*, ed. J. R. O'Donnell, *MS*, iii (1941) 46 sqq.

Wilhelm von Shyreswood, *Die Introductiones in Logicam des*, [ed.] M. Grabmann in *SKBAW*, 1937, No. 10.

Bernardo Telesio, *Varii de Naturalibus Rebus Libelli*, Venetiis, 1590.

Theodoric of Freiberg, *De Coloribus, De Elementiis Corporum Naturalium in quantum sunt Partes Mundi, De Intellectu et Intelligibli, De Intelligentiis et Motoribus Caelorum, De Luce et Eius Origine, De Magis et Minus, De Miscibilibus in Mixto, De Tribus Difficilibus Articulis*; extracts ed. Krebs in *Meister Dietrich*, below, p. 342.

Theodoricus Teutonicus de Vriberg, *De Iride et Radialibus Impressionibus* (Dietrich von Freiberg *Über den Regenbogen und die durch Strahlen erzeugten Eindrücke*), zum ersten Male nach den Handschriften herausgegeben und mit einer Einleitung versehen von J. Würschmidt (*BGPM*, xii. 5–6) Münster, 1914.

Theodoric of Friberg, *De Esse et Essentia*, ed. E. Krebs in 'Le Traité "De esse et essentia" de Thierry de Fribourg', *RNP*, xviii (1911) 516 sqq.

Theophilus Presbyter, *Schedula Diversarum Artium*, [ed.] Albert Ilg (*Quellenschriften für Kunstgeschichte*, vii) Wien, 1874 (Latin and English edition by C. R. Dodwell, London, 1961).

Thimonis, *Questiones super Quatuor Libros Metheororum*, Venetiis, 1522 (with *Libros Metheororum* Aristotelis . . . *cum Commentariis* . . . Gaietani de Thienis).

Thomas of Eccleston, *see* Eccleston.

F. Nicholai Triveti *De Ordine Frat. Praedicatorum, Annales Sex Regum Angliae*, ed. T. Hog, London, 1845.

Jodocum Trutuetter Isennachcensem, *Summule Totius Logice quod Opus Maius appellitare per*, Erphurdie, 1501.

Jodocus [Trutfetter] Eysennacensis philosophus et theologus, *Quam, Tocius Philosophie Naturalis Summam nuper elucubravit* . . ., Erffordie, 1517. (First ed. Erfurt, 1514.)

Simon Tunsted, *Quaestionum Meteorologicarum*, ed. Luke Wadding in Ioannis Duns Scoti *Opera Omnia*, iii, Lugduni, 1639.

Turisani monaci Cartusiensis *Plusquam Commentum in Microtegni Galieni*, Venetiis, 1498.

Franciscus Vicomercatus, *In Quatuor Libros Aristotelis Meteorologicorum Commentarii et eorundem librorum e Graeco in Latinum per eundem conversio*, Lutetiae Parisiorum, 1556.

Villard de Honnecourt, *Kritische Gesamtausgabe des Bauhüttenbuches MS. fr.* 19093 *der Pariser Nationalbibliothek* [by] H. R. Hahnloser, Wien, 1935.

Vitellonis Thuringopoloni *Opticae Libri Decem*, instaurati . . . a Federico Risnero, Basilae, 1572. (Sections re-edited by C. Baeumker in *Witelo*, below, p. 335.)

Ricardi Walynforde, *Quadripartitum de Sinibus Demonstratis*, ed. J. D. Bond, *Isis*, v (1923) 99 sqq.

William, *see* Conches, Ockham, Sherwood.

John Wyclyf, *De Ente Primo*, ed. S. H. Thomson, Oxford, 1930.

Jacobi Zabarellae Patavini *Opera Logica*, Basileae, 1594.

2. *Modern works*

(a) *Unpublished dissertation*

R. W. Hunt, *Alexander Neckham*, dissertation deposited in the Bodleian Library, Oxford.

(b) *Published works*

N. Abbagnano, *Guglielmo di Ockham*, Lanciano, 1931.

The Agrarian Life of the Middle Ages (*The Cambridge Economic History of Europe*, i) ed. J. H. Clapham and Eileen Power, Cambridge, 1941.

P. Aiken, 'The animal history of Albertus Magnus and Thomas of Cantimpré', *Speculum* (Cambridge, Mass.), xxii (1947) 205 sqq.

G. Albertotti, 'Lettera intorno alla invenzione degli occhiali, all' Onorev.^{mo} Senatore Isidoro del Lungo', *Annali di Ottalmologia e Clinica Oculistica* (Roma), l (1922), 85 sqq.

D. J. Allan, 'Mediaeval versions of Aristotle, *De Caelo*, and of the Commentary of Simplicius', *MRS*, ii (1950) 82 sqq.

Sir T. C. Allbutt, *The Historical Relations of Medicine and Surgery to the End of the Sixteenth Century*, London, 1905.

R. Almagia, 'Quelques questions au sujet des cartes nautiques et des portulans d'après les recherches récentes', *Actes du ve congrès international d'histoire des sciences, Lausanne, 1947* (*Collection de travaux de l'Académie internationale d'histoire des sciences*, ii) Paris, 1948, pp. 140 sqq.

M. Alonso Alonso, 'Notas sobre los traductores toledanos Domingo Gundisalvo y Juan Hispano', *Al-Andalus* (Madrid), viii (1943) 155 sqq.

M. Alonso Alonso, 'Las fuentes literarias de Domingo Gundisalvo', *Al-Andalus*, xi (1946) 159 sqq.

M. Alonso Alonso, 'Homenaje a Avicena en su milenario. Las traducciones de Juan González de Burgos y Salomón', *Al- Andalus*, xiv (1949) 291 sqq.

A. Arber, *The Natural Philosophy of Plant Form*, Cambridge, 1950.

C. Baeumker, 'Über die Lockesche Lehre von den primären und sekundären Qualitäten,' *PJ*, xxi (1908) 293 sqq.

C. Baeumker, 'Zur Vorgeschichte zweier Lockescher Begriffe', *Archiv für Geschichte der Philosophie*, xxi (1908) 493 sqq., xxii (1909) 380.

C. Baeumker, *Witelo, ein Philosoph und Naturforscher des XIII. Jahrhunderts* (*BGPM*, iii. 2) Münster, 1908.

C. Baeumker, 'Zur Biographie des Witelo', *HJ*, xxxiii (1912) 359 sqq.

C. Baeumker, 'Die Stellung des Alfredus von Sareshel (Alfredus Anglicus) und seiner Schrift De Motu Cordis in der Wissenschaft des Beginnenden xiii. Jahrhunderts', *SKBAW*, 1913, No. 9.

C. Baeumker, *Roger Bacons Naturphilosophie*, Münster, 1916.

C. Baeumker, 'Zur Frage nach Abfassungszeit und Verfasser des irrtümlich Witelo zugeschriebenen Liber de Intelligentiis', in *Miscellanea F. Ehrle* (*Studi e Testi*, xxxvii) Roma, 1924, i, 87 sqq.

C. Baeumker, 'Der Platonismus im Mittelalter', in *Studien und Charakteristiken zur Geschichte der Philosophie insbesondere des Mittelalters* (*BGPM*, xxv. 1–2) Münster, 1927, pp. 139 sqq.

H. Balss, *Albertus Magnus als Zoologe*, München, 1928.

L. Baudry, 'Les Rapports de Guillaume d'Occam et de Walter Burleigh', *AHDLMA*, ix (1934) 155 sqq.

M. Baumgartner, *Die Philosophie des Alanus de Insulis* (*BGPM*, ii. 4) Münster, 1896.

L. Baur, 'Das Licht in der Naturphilosophie des Robert Grosseteste', in *Festschrift Georg von Hertling*, Freiburg i. B., 1913.

L. Baur, 'Der Einfluss des Robert Grosseteste auf die wissenschaftliche Richtung des Roger Bacon', in *RBE*.

L. Baur, *Die Philosophie des Robert Grosseteste, Bischofs von Lincoln* (*BGPM*, xviii. 4–6) Münster, 1917.

C. R. Beazley, *The Dawn of Modern Geography*, London, 1897–1906, 3 vols.

A. Bednarski, 'Das anatomische Augenbild von J. Peckham', *AGM*, xxii (1929) 352 sqq.

A. Bednarski, 'Die anatomischen Augenbilder in den Handschriften des Roger Bacon, Johann Peckham und Witelo', *AGM*, xxiv (1931) 60 sqq.

H. Bédoret, 'Les Premières Traductions tolédanes de philosophie. Œuvres d'Alfarabi', *RNP*, xli (1938) 80 sqq.

H. Bédoret, 'Les Premières Versions tolédanes de philosophie. Œuvres d'Avicenne', *RNP*, xli (1938) 374 sqq.

H. Bédoret, 'L'Auteur et le traducteur du *Liber de Causis*', *RNP*, xli (1938) 519 sqq.

A. E. Bell, *Christian Huygens and the Development of Science in the Seventeenth Century*, London, 1947.

P. E. M. Berthelot, *La Chimie au moyen âge*, Paris, 1893, 3 vols.

H. Bett, *Nicholas of Cusa*, London, 1932.

T. B. Birch, 'The theory of continuity of William of Ockham', *Philosophy of Science* (Baltimore), iii (1936) 494 sqq.

A. Birkenmajer, 'Études sur Witelo, i–iv', *BIAPSL*, Année 1918, pp. 4–6, Année 1920, pp. 354–60, Année 1922, pp. 6–9.

A. Birkenmajer, 'Witelo e lo studio di Padova', *Ommagio dell' Accademia Polacca di Scienze e Lettere all' Università di Padova*, Cracovie, 1922, pp. 147 sqq. (Italian transl. of 'Études sur Witelo, iv'.)

A. Birkenmajer, 'Drei neue Handschriften der Werke Meister Dietrichs', in *Vermischte Untersuchungen* (*BGPM*, xx. 5) Münster, 1922, pp. 70 sqq.

A. Birkenmajer, 'Le Rôle joué par les médecins et les naturalistes dans la réception d'Aristote aux xiie et xiiie siècles', *La Pologne au vie congrès international des sciences historiques, Oslo, 1928*, Warsaw, 1930, pp. 1 sqq.

A. Birkenmajer, 'Robert Grosseteste and Richard Fournival', *MH*, v (1948) 36 sqq.

A. A. Björnbo, 'Die mathematischen S. Marcohandschriften in Florenz', *BM*, xii (1912) 193 sqq.

E. Bock, *Die Brille und ihre Geschichte*, Wien, 1903.

P. Boehner, 'The notitia intuitiva of non-existents according to William Ockham', *Traditio* (New York), i (1943) 223 sqq.

P. Boehner, 'The realistic conceptualism of William Ockham', *Traditio*, iv (1946) 307 sqq. (See below, pp. 350–1.)

P. Boehner, 'On a recent study of Ockham', *Franciscan Studies*, x (1950) 191 sqq.

J. D. Bond, 'Richard Wallingford (1292?–1335)', *Isis*, iv (1922) 458 sqq.

E. Borchert, *Die Lehre von der Bewegung bei Nicolaus Oresme* (*BGPM*, xxxi. 3) Münster, 1934.

F. Borkenau, *Der Übergang vom feudalen zum bürgerlichen Weltbild*, Paris, 1933.

C. B. Boyer, *The Concepts of the Calculus*, New York, 1939.

C. B. Boyer, 'The invention of analytic geometry', *The Scientific American* (New York), 1949, January, pp. 40 sqq.

E. Bréhier, *Histoire de la philosophie*, Paris, 1942–3, i–ii.

J. H. Bridges, *The Life and Work of Roger Bacon*, London, 1914.

C. D. Broad, *The Philosophy of Francis Bacon*, Cambridge, 1926.

C. D. Broad, 'The new philosophy: Bruno to Descartes', *CHJ*, viii (1944) 54 sqq.

J. Brodrick, *The Life and Work of Blessed Robert Francis, Cardinal Bellarmine, 1542–1621*, London, 1928, ii.

H. Brown, *Scientific Organizations in Seventeenth Century France (1620–1680)*, Baltimore, 1934.

H. Brown, 'The utilitarian motive in the age of Descartes', *AS*, i (1936) 182 sqq.

G. Bruni, *Le Opere di Egidio Romano*, Firenze, 1936.

L. Brunschvicg, *Le Progrès de la conscience dans la philosophie occidentale*, Paris, 1927, 2 vols.

L. Brunschvicg, *Les Étapes de la philosophie mathématique*, 3e éd., Paris, 1929.

L. Brunschvicg, *Le Rôle du pythagorisme dans l'évolution des idées* (*ASI*, No. 446) Paris, 1937.

Delisle Burns, 'William of Ockham on continuity', *Mind* (London), N.S. xxv (1916) 508 sqq.

E. A. Burtt, *The Metaphysical Foundations of Modern Physical Science*, 2nd ed., London, 1932.

J. N. D. Bush, *English Literature in the Earlier Seventeenth Century, 1600–60* (*Oxford History of English Literature*, v) Oxford, 1945.

D. A. Callus, 'Philip the Chancellor and the *De Anima* ascribed to Robert Grosseteste', *MRS*, i (1941–3) 105 sqq.

D. A. Callus, 'Introduction of Aristotelian learning to Oxford', *PBA*, xxix (1943) 229 sqq.

D. Callus, 'The Oxford career of Robert Grosseteste', *Oxoniensia* (Oxford), x (1945) 42 sqq.

D. A. Callus, 'The *Summa Duacensis* and the Pseudo-Grosseteste's *De Anima*', *RTAM*, xiii (1946) 225 sqq.

D. A. Callus, 'The date of Grosseteste's translations and commentaries on Pseudo-Dionysius and the Nicomachean Ethics', *RTAM*, xiv (1947) 186 sqq.

D. A. Callus, 'The *Summa Theologiae* of Robert Grosseteste', in *Studies in Mediaeval History presented to Frederick Maurice Powicke*, ed. R. W. Hunt, W. A. Pantin, and R. W. Southern, Oxford, 1948, pp. 180 sqq.

D. A. Callus, 'The "Tabulae super Originalia Patrum" of Robert Kilwardby, O.P.', in *Studia Mediaevalia in honorem admodum Reverendi Patris Raymundi Josephi Martin, O.P., S.T.M.*, Brugis Flandrorum, 1948, pp. 243 sqq.

M. Cantor, *Vorlesungen über Geschichte der Mathematik*, Leipzig, 1881–92, i–ii.

M. H. Carré, *Realists and Nominalists*, Oxford, 1946.

M. H. Carré, 'A medieval attack on metaphysics', *The Hibbert Journal* (London), xlvii (1949) 226 sqq.

R. Carton, *L'Expérience physique chez Roger Bacon* (*ÉPM*, ii) Paris, 1924.

R. Carton, *L'Expérience mystique de l'illumination intérieure chez Roger Bacon* (*ÉPM*, iii) Paris, 1924.

R. Carton, *La Synthèse doctrinale de Roger Bacon* (*ÉPM*, v) Paris, 1924.

E. M. Carus-Wilson, 'An industrial revolution in the 13th century', *Economic History Review* (London), xii (1941) 39 sqq.

E. Cassirer, *Das Erkenntnisproblem in der Philosophie und Wissenschaft der neueren Zeit*, Berlin, 1906–7, i–ii.

E. Cassirer, *Individuum und Kosmos in der Philosophie der Renaissance (Studien der Bibl. Warburg*, x) Leipzig, 1927.

E. Cassirer, 'Mathematische Mystik und mathematische Naturwissenschaft', *Lychnos* (Uppsala), 1940, pp. 248 sqq.

E. Cassirer, 'Galileo's Platonism', in *Studies and Essays . . . offered . . . to George Sarton*, ed. M. F. Ashley Montagu, New York, 1944.

E. Cassirer, P. O. Kristeller, and J. H. Randall, Jr. (ed.), *The Renaissance Philosophy of Man*, Chicago, 1948.

R. Caverni, *Storia del Metodo sperimentale in Italia*, Firenze, 1895, iv.

M. D. Chenu, 'Un Essai de méthode théologique au xiie siècle', *RSPT*, xxiv (1935) 258 sqq.

M. D. Chenu, 'Aux Origines de la "science moderne" ', *RSPT*, xxix (1940) 206 sqq.

M. D. Chenu, *La Théologie comme science au xiiie siècle*, 2e éd., Paris, 1943.

K. Chiu, 'The introduction of spectacles into China', *The Harvard Journal of Asiatic Studies* (Cambridge, Mass.), i (1936) 186 sqq.

M. Clagett, *Giovanni Marliani and the Late Medieval Physics (Columbia University Studies in History, Economics and Public Law*, cccclxxxiii) New York, 1941.

M. Clagett, 'Some general aspects of physics in the Middle Ages', *Isis*, xxxix (1948) 29 sqq.

M. Clagett, review of J. R. Weinberg, *Nicolaus of Autrecourt* (Princeton, 1948), *Isis*, xl (1949) 265 sqq.

G. N. Clark, *Science and Social Welfare in the Age of Newton*, Oxford, 1937.

A. Clerval, 'L'Enseignement des arts libéraux à Chartres et à Paris dans la première moitié du xiie siècle d'après l'*Heptateuchon* de Thierry de Chartres', *Congrès scientifique international des catholiques, Paris, 1888*, Paris, 1889, ii. 277 sqq.

A. Clerval, *Les Écoles de Chartres*, Paris, 1895.

I. B. Cohen, 'Galileo', *Scientific American*, 1949, August, pp. 40 sqq.

Lane Cooper, *Aristotle, Galileo, and the Tower of Pisa*, New York, 1935.

G. W. Corner, *Anatomical Texts of the Earlier Middle Ages*, Washington, 1927.

J. Cottiaux, 'La Conception de la théologie chez Abélard', *Revue d'histoire ecclésiastique* (Louvain), xxviii (1932) 247 sqq., 533 sqq., 788 sqq.

A. C. Crombie, 'Galileo's "Dialogues Concerning the Two Principal Systems of the World" ', *Dominican Studies* (Oxford), iii (1950) 105 sqq.

A. C. Crombie, *Augustine to Galileo*, 2nd, revised ed., 2 vols., London, 1961; reissued with further corrections 1970 (published as *Medieval and Early Modern Science*, New York, 1959; 1st ed., London, 1952).

T. Crowley, *Roger Bacon. The problem of the soul in his philosophical commentaries*, Louvain-Dublin, 1950.

F. Daujat, 'Note sur un fondateur de la physique du magnétisme au xiiie siècle: Pierre de Maricourt', *Thalès* (Paris), ii (1935) 58 sqq.

M. de Bouard, 'Encyclopédies médiévales', *Revue des questions historiques* (Paris), cxii (1930) 258 sqq.

J. de Ghellinck, 'Dialectique et dogme aux xe-xiie siècles', in *Studien zur Geschichte der Philosophie: Festgabe zum 60. Geburtstag Clemens Baeumker (BGPM*, Supplementband, i) Münster, 1913, pp. 79 sqq.

J. de Ghellinck, *Le Mouvement théologique du xiie siècles. . . . Études, recherches et documents (Mus. Lessianum, Section hist.*, x) 2e éd., Bruges, 1948.

A. Delorme, 'La Morphogenèse d'Albert le Grand dans l'embryologie scolastique', *Revue thomiste* (Paris), N.S. xiv (1931) 352 sqq.

F. Delorme, 'Le Prologue de Roger Bacon à son traité De Influentiis Agentium', *Antonianum* (Roma), xviii (1943) 81 sqq.

R. de Vaux, 'La Première Entrée d'Averroës chez les Latins', *RSPT*, xxii (1933) 193 sqq.

M. de Wulf, 'Un Scolastique inconnu de la fin du xiiie siècle', *RNP*, xiii (1906) 434 sqq.

M. de Wulf, *History of Mediæval Philosophy*, 3rd English ed., London, 1938, 2 vols. (6th French ed., vol. 3, Louvain et Paris, 1947.)

E. J. Dijksterhuis, *Val en Worp*, Groningen, 1924.

S. d'Irsay 'Les Sciences de la nature et les universités médiévales', *Archeion*, xv (1933) 216 sqq.

S. E. Dolan, 'Resolution and composition in speculative and practical discourse', *Laval théologique et philosophique* (Québec), vi (1950) 9 sqq.

V. Doucet, 'Notulae bibliographicae de quibusdam operibus fratris Iohannis Pecham O.F.M.', *Antonianum*, viii (1933) 307 sqq., 425 sqq.

J. Drecker, 'Hermannus Contractus über das Astrolab', *Isis*, xvi (1931) 200 sqq.

R. Dugas, *Histoire de la mécanique*, Neuchâtel, 1950.

P. Duhem, *Les Origines de la statique*, Paris 1905–6, 2 séries.

P. Duhem, *La Théorie physique*, Paris, 1906.

P. Duhem, *Études sur Léonard de Vinci, ceux qu'il a lus et ceux qui l'ont lu*, Paris, 1906–13, 3 séries.

P. Duhem, *Le Mouvement absolu et le mouvement relatif* (extrait de la *Revue de philosophie*, Paris, xi–xiv, 1907–9) Montligeon, 1909.

P. Duhem, 'Σῴζειν τὰ φαινόμενα. Essai sur la notion de théorie physique de Platon à Galilée', *Annales de philosophie chrétienne* (Paris), 4 série, vi (1908) 113 sqq., 277 sqq., 352 sqq., 482 sqq., 561 sqq.

P. Duhem, 'Un Précurseur français de Copernic. Nicole Oresme (1377)', *Revue générale des sciences pure et appliquées* (Paris), xx (1909) 866 sqq.

P. Duhem, 'Physics—History of', in *Catholic Encyclopedia*, New York, 1911, xii, 47–67.

P. Duhem, 'François de Meyronnes et la question de la rotation de la terre', *AFH*, vi (1913) 23–25.

P. Duhem, *Le Système du monde. Histoire des doctrines cosmologiques de Platon à Copernic*, Paris, 1913–17, 5 vols.

P. Duhem, 'Roger Bacon et l'horreur du vide', in *RBE*.

D. B. Durand, 'Nicole Oresme and the mediaeval origins of modern science', *Speculum*, xvi (1941) 167 sqq.

A. Dyroff, 'Über Heinrich und Dietrich von Freiberg', *PJ*, xxviii (1915) 55 sqq.

J. J. Fahie, *Galileo; his Life and Work*, London, 1903.

J. J. Fahie, 'The scientific works of Galileo (1564–1642)', in *SHMS*, ii.

E. Faral, 'Jean Buridan. Notes sur les manuscrits, les éditions et le contenu de ses ouvrages', *AHDLMA*, xv (1946) 1 sqq.

A. Favaro, *Galileo e lo Studio di Padova*, Firenze, 1883, 2 vols.

A. Favaro, *Galileo Galilei e l'Inquisizione. Documenti del processo Galileiano . . .*, Firenze, 1907.

H. Felder, *Geschichte der wissenschaftlichen Studien im Franziskanerorden*, Freiburg i. B., 1904.

F. M. Feldhaus, *Die Technik der Vorzeit, der geschichtlichen Zeit und der Naturvölker*, Leipzig und Berlin, 1914.

F. M. Feldhaus, *Die Technik der Antike und des Mittelalters*, Potsdam, 1931.

S. Fellner, *Albertus Magnus als Botaniker*, Wien, 1881.

J. Felten, *Robert Grosseteste, Bischof von Lincoln*, Freiburg i. B., 1887.

H. W. K. Fischer, *Mittelalterliche Pflanzenkunde*, München, 1929.

R. J. Forbes, *Short History of the Art of Distillation*, Leiden, 1948.

R. J. Forbes, *Man the Maker. A History of Technology and Engineering*, London, 1950.

M. B. Foster, 'The Christain doctrine of creation and the rise of modern natural science', *Mind*, N.S. xliii (1934) 446 sqq.; 'Christian theology and modern science of nature', ibid. xliv (1935) 439 sqq., xlv (1936) 1 sqq.

E. Franceschini, *Roberto Grossatesta, Vescovo di Lincoln, e le sue Traduzioni Latine* (*Atti del reale Istituto Veneto di Scienze, Lettere ed Arti*, xciii) Venezia, 1933.

E. Franceschini, 'Intorno ad alcune opere di Roberto Grossatesta, Vescovo di Lincoln', *Aevum, Revista di Scienze storiche, linguistiche e filologiche* (Milano), viii (1934) 529 sqq.

S. Gandz, 'The origin of the Ghūbar numerals, or the Arabian abacus and the articuli', *Isis*, xvi (1931) 393 sqq.

C. Gauthier, 'Un Psychologue de la fin du xiiie siècle, Thierry de Fribourg', *Revue augustinienne* (Paris), xv (1909) 657 sqq.; xvi (1910) 178 sqq., 541 sqq.

K. von Gebler, *Galileo Galilei and the Roman Curia*, English transl. by Mrs. G. Sturge, London, 1879.

A. Gewirtz, 'Experience and the non-mathematical in the Cartesian method', *JHI*, ii (1941) 183 sqq.

E. Gilson, *Index scolastico-cartésien*, Paris, 1912.

E. Gilson, *La Philosophie au moyen âge*, 2e éd., Paris, 1944.

E. Gilson, *Études sur le rôle de la pensée médiévale dans la formation du système cartésien* (*ÉPM*, xiii) Paris, 1930. (Section on *Météores* first published in *RNP*, xxii, 1920, pp. 358–84; xxiii, 1921, pp. 73–84.)

B. Ginzburg, 'Duhem and Jordanus Nemorarius', *Isis*, xxv (1936) 341 sqq.

M. Grabmann, 'Studien über Ulrich von Strassburg', *Zeitschrift für katholische Theologie* (Innsbruck), xxix (1905) 607 sqq.

M. Grabmann, *Die Geschichte der scholastischen Methode*, Freiburg i. B., 1909–11, 2 vols.

M. Grabmann, 'Der Neuplatonismus in der deutschen Hochscholastik', *PJ*, xxiii (1910) 38 sqq.

M. Grabmann, 'Die Metaphysik des Thomas von York († *ca.* 1260)', in *Studien zur Geschichte der Philosophie. Festgabe zum 60. Geburtstag Clemens Baeumker* (*BGPM*, Supplementband, i) Münster, 1913, pp. 181 sqq.

M. Grabmann, *Forschungen über die lateinischen Aristoteles-Übersetzungen des xiii. Jahrhunderts* (*BGPM*, xvii. 5–6) Münster, 1916.

M. Grabmann, 'Studien zu Johannes Quidort von Paris O.Pr.', *SKBAW*, 1922, No. 3.

M. Grabmann, *Mittelalterliches Geistesleben*, München, 1926–36, 2 vols.

M. Grabmann, *Der hl. Albert der Grosse*, München, 1932.

M. Grabmann, *Bearbeitungen und Auslegungen der Aristotelischen Logik aus der Zeit von Peter Abaelard bis Petrus Hispanus* (*APAW*, philos.-hist. Klasse, v) Berlin 1937.

H. Grossmann, 'Die gesellschaftlichen Grundlagen der mechanistischen Philosophie und die Manufaktur', *Zeitschrift für Sozialforschungen* (Leipzig), iv (1935) 161 sqq.

R. Guelluy, *Philosophie et théologie chez Guillaume d'Ockham*, Louvain, 1947.

R. T. Gunther, *Early Science in Oxford*, Oxford, 1923, ii.

A. R. Hall, 'Sir Isaac Newton's Note-Book 1661–5', *CHJ*, ix (1949) 239 sqq.

O. Hamelin, *Le Système de Descartes*, 2ᵉ éd., Paris, 1911.

K. Hammerle, *Von Ockham zu Milton*, Innsbruck, 1936.

H. Hankel, *Zur Geschichte der Mathematik in Altertum und Mittelalter*, Leipzig, 1874.

C. R. S. Harris, *Duns Scotus*, Oxford, 1927, 2 vols.

I. B. Hart, *The Mechanical Investigations of Leonardo da Vinci*, London, 1925.

C. H. Haskins, *Studies in the History of Mediaeval Science*, 2nd ed., Cambridge (Mass.), 1927.

C. H. Haskins, *The Renaissance of the Twelfth Century*, Cambridge (Mass.), 1928.

G. Hellmann, 'Die Anfänge der magnetischen Beobachtungen', *Zeitschrift der Gesellschaft für Erdkunde zu Berlin*, xxxii (1897) 126 sqq.

G. Hellmann, *Rara Magnetica* (*NSKME*, x) Berlin, 1898.

G. Hellmann, *Wetterprognosen und Wetterberichte des xv. und xvi. Jahrhunderts* (*NSKME*, xii) Berlin, 1899.

G. Hellmann, *Meteorologische Beobachtungen vom xiv. bis xvii. Jahrhundert* (*NSKME*, xiii) Berlin, 1901.

G. Hellmann, *Meteorologische Optik 1000–1836* (*NSKME*, xiv) Berlin, 1902.

G. Hellmann, *Denkmäler mittelalterlicher Meteorologie* (*NSKME*, xv) Berlin, 1904.

G. Hellmann, 'Zur Optik des Robertus Linconiensis', *BM*, ii (1901) 443–4.

G. Hellmann, *Die Wettervorhersage im ausgehenden Mittelalter (xii. bis xv. Jahrhundert) (Beiträge zur Geschichte der Meteorologie*, viii) Berlin, 1917.

H. von Helmholz, *Treatise on Physiological Optics*. Transl. from the 3rd German ed. Ed. J. P. C. Southall, Wisconsin, 1924–5, 3 vols.

F. M. Henquinet, 'Un Recueil de questions annoté par S. Bonaventura', *AFH*, xxv (1932) 553.

G. v. Hertling, *Albertus Magnus, Beiträge zu seiner Würdigung* (*BGPM*, xiv. 5–6) Münster, 1914.

S. A. Hirsch, 'Roger Bacon and philology', in *RBE*.

H. Höffding, *A History of Modern Philosophy*, transl. from the German edition by B. E. Meyer, London, 1900, i.

E. Hoppe, 'Marcus Marci de Kronland. Ein vergessener Physiker des 17. Jahrhunderts', *AGNT*, x (1927) 282 sqq.

H. Hopstock, 'Leonardo as anatomist', in *SHMS*, ii.

W. E. Houghton, 'The history of trades: its relation to seventeenth-century thought', *JHI*, ii (1941) 33 sqq.

R. W. Hunt, 'English learning in the late twelfth century', *Transactions of the Royal Historical Society* (London), 4th Series, xix (1936) 19 sqq.

R. W. Hunt, 'The Introductions to the "Artes" in the twelfth century', in *Studia Mediaevalia in honorem admodum Reverendi Patri Raymundi Josephi Martin, O.P., S.T.M.*, Brugis Flandrorum, 1948, pp. 85 sqq.

E. F. Jacob, *Cusanus the Theologian*, Manchester, 1937.

M. R. James, *A Descriptive Catalogue of the Manuscripts in the Library of Peterhouse*, Cambridge, 1899.

M. R. James, *Lists of Manuscripts formerly owned by Dr. John Dee* (*Bibliographical Society Transactions Suppl. i*) Oxford, 1921.

B. Jansen, 'Olivi, der älteste scholastische Vertreter des heutigen Bewegungsbegriffs', *PJ*, xxxiii (1920) 137 sqq.

F. R. Johnson, *Astronomical Thought in Renaissance England*, Baltimore, 1937.

F. R. Johnson, 'Thomas Hood's inaugural address as mathematical lecturer of the city of London (1588)', *JHI*, iii (1942) 94.

F. R. Johnson and S. V. Larkey, 'Thomas Digges, the Copernican system, and the idea of the infinity of the universe in 1576', *Huntington Library Bulletin* (San Marino, Calif.), v (1934) 69 sqq.

F. R. Johnson and S. V. Larkey, 'Robert Recorde's mathematical teaching and the anti-Aristotelian movement', *Huntington Library Bulletin*, vii (1935) 59 sqq.

R. P. Johnson, 'Compositiones variae from Codex 490, Biblioteca Capitolare, Lucca, Italy', *Illinois Studies in Language and Literature* (Urbana), xxiii (1939) 3 sqq.

F. Kaltenbrunner, *Die Vorgeschichte der Gregorianischen Kalenderreform (Sitzungsberichte der kaiserlichen Akademie der Wissenschaften*, philos.-hist. Klasse, lxxxii) Wien, 1876, pp. 289 sqq.

D. Kaufmann, *Die Sinne. Beiträge zur Geschichte der Physiologie und Psychologie im Mittelalter aus hebräischen und arabischen Quellen*, Leipzig, 1884.

P. Kibre, *The Library of Pico della Mirandola*, New York, 1936.

S. Killermann, *Die Vogelkunde des Albertus Magnus, 1207-80*, Regensburg, 1910.

A. C. Klebs, 'Incunabula scientifica et medica', *Osiris* (Brughes), iv (1937) 1 sqq.

R. Klibansky, *The Continuity of the Platonic Tradition during the Middle Ages: Outlines of a Corpus Platonicorum Medii Aevi*, London, 1939.

M. D. Knowles, 'Some recent advance in the history of medieval thought', *CHJ*, ix (1947) 22 sqq.

D. J. Korteweg, 'Descartes et les manuscrits de Snellius', *Revue de métaphysique et de morale* (Paris), iv (1897) 489 sqq.

A. Koyré, *Études galiléennes*. i. *A l'aube de la science classique*; ii. *La Loi de la chute des corps. Descartes et Galilée*; iii. *Galilée et la loi d'inertie* (*ASI*, Nos. 852-4) Paris, 1939.

A. Koyré, 'Galileo and Plato', *JHI*, iv (1943) 400 sqq.

A. Koyré, 'Le Vide et l'espace infini au xive siècle', *AHDLMA*, xxiv (1949) 45 sqq.

P. Kramer, 'Descartes und das Brechungsgesetz des Lichtes', *Abhandlungen zur Geschichte der Mathematik* (Leipzig), iv (1882) 233 sqq.

E. Krebs, *Meister Dietrich (Theodoricus Teutonicus de Vriberg). Sein Leben, seine Werke, seine Wissenschaft (BGPM*, v. 5-6) Münster, 1906.

K. Kretschmer, *Die italienischen Portolane des Mittelalters*, Berlin, 1909.

P. O. Kristeller, 'The scholastic background of Marsilio Ficino, with an edition of unpublished texts', *Traditio*, ii (1944) 257 sqq.

G. Lacombe, *Aristoteles Latinus*, Roma, 1939.

J. Lappe, *Nicolaus von Autrecourt. Sein Leben, seine Philosophie, seine Schriften (BGPM*, vi. 2) Münster, 1908.

H. P. Lattin, 'The eleventh century MS Munich 14436: Its contribution to the history of coordinates, of logic, of German studies in France', *Isis*, xxxviii (1948) 205 sqq.

M H. Laurent et M. J. Congar, 'Essai de bibliographie albertinienne', *Revue Thomiste*, N.S. xiv (1931) 422 sqq.

Lefebvre des Noëttes, 'La "Nuit" du moyen âge et son inventaire', *Mercure de France* (Paris), ccxxxv (1932) 572 sqq.

M. Leroy, *Descartes social*, Paris, 1931.

L. Liard, *Descartes*, Paris, 1882.

G. Libri, *Histoire des sciences mathématiques en Italie, depuis la renaissance des lettres*, Paris, 1838-41, 4 vols.

R. Liertz, *Der selige Albert der Grosse als Naturforscher und Lehrer*, München, 1931.

E. O. von Lippmann, *Geschichte der Magnetnadel bis zur Erfindung des Kompasses* [*gegen* 1300] (*Quellen und Studien zur Geschichte der Naturwissenschaften und der Medizin*, iii. 1) Berlin, 1932.

A. G. Little, *The Grey Friars in Oxford* (*Oxford Hist. Society*, xx) Oxford, 1892.

A. G. Little, 'On Roger Bacon's life and works', in *RBE*.

A. G. Little, *Studies in English Franciscan History*, Manchester and London, 1917.

A. G. Little, 'The Franciscan school at Oxford in the thirteenth century', *AFH*, xix (1926) 803 sqq.

A. G. Little, 'Thomas Docking and his relations to Roger Bacon', in *Essays presented to R. L. Poole*, Oxford, 1927.

A. G. Little, 'Roger Bacon', *PBA*, xiv (1928) 265 sqq.

A. G. Little, 'Chronological notes on the life of Duns Scotus', *EHR*, xlvii (1932) 568 sqq.

A. G. Little, *Franciscan Letters, Papers and Documents*, Manchester, 1943.

A. G. Little and F. Pelster, *Oxford Theology and Theologians, c. 1282–1302* (Oxford Historical Series), Oxford, 1934.

E. Longpré, 'Thomas d'York et Matthieu d'Aquasparta', *AHDLMA*, i (1926) 269 sqq.

E. Longpré, *La Philosophie du B. Duns Scot*, Paris, 1926.

E. Longpré, 'La Summa Dialectica de Roger Bacon', *AFH*, xiii (1938) 204 sqq.

H. R. L(uard), 'Grosseteste, Robert', in *Dictionary of National Biography*, ed. Leslie Stephen and Sidney Lee, London, 1890, xxiii. 275 sqq.

J. Łukasiewicz, 'Zur Geschichte der Aussagenlogik', *Erkenntnis* (Leipzig), v (1935–6) 111 sqq.

E. Mach, *The Principles of Physical Optics, an historical and philosophical treatment*, transl. by J. S. Anderson and A. F. A. Young, London, 1926.

E. Mach, *The Science of Mechanics*, 5th English ed., translated from the German by T. J. McCormack, La Salle, Ill., 1942.

C. K. McKeon, *A Study of the Summa Philosophiae of the Pseudo-Grosseteste*, New York, 1948.

R. McKeon, *Selections from Medieval Philosophers*, London, 1929–30, 2 vols.

L. C. MacKinney, *Early Medieval Medicine*, Baltimore, 1937.

A. Maier, *Das Problem der intensiven Grösse in der Scholastik*, Leipzig, 1939.

A. Maier, *Die Impetustheorie der Scholastik*, Wien, 1940. (Second ed. of this and previous item pub. as *Zwei Grundprobleme der scholastischen Naturphilosophie*, Roma, 1951.)

A. Maier, *An der Grenze von Scholastik und Naturwissenschaft*, Essen, 1943 (Roma, 1952).

A. Maier, 'La Doctrine de Nicolas d'Oresme sur les "configurationes intensionum"', *RSPT*, xxxii (1948) 52 sqq.

A. Maier, *Die Vorläufer Galileis im 14. Jahrhundert*, Roma, 1949.

A. Maier, 'Die Anfänge des physikalischen Denkens im 14. Jahrhundert', *Philosophia Naturalis* (Meisenheim am Glan), i (1950) 7 sqq.

P. Mandonnet, 'La Date de naissance d'Albert le Grand', *Revue thomiste*, N.S. xiv (1931) 233 sqq.

A Mansion, 'L'Induction chez Albert le Grand', *RNP*, xiii (1906) 115 sqq., 246 sqq.

A. Mansion, 'La Version médiévale de l'Éthique à Nicomaque. La "Translatio Lincolniensis" et la controverse autour de la révision attribuée à Guillaume de Moerbeke', *RNP*, xli (1938) 401 sqq.

R. I. Markus, 'Method and metaphysics: the origins of some Cartesian presuppositions in the philosophy of the Renaissance', *Dominican Studies*, ii (1949) 356 sqq.

R. S. Marx, 'A xiiith-century theory of heat as a form of motion', *Isis*, xxii (1934) 19 sqq.

R. K. Merton, 'Science, technology and society in seventeenth century England', *Osiris*, iv (1938) 360 sqq.

E. H. F. Meyer, *Geschichte der Botanik*, Königsberg, 1857, iv.

E. Meyerson, *Identity and Reality*, transl. by K. Loewenberg, London, 1930.

K. Michalski, 'Les Courants philosophiques à Oxford et à Paris pendant le xive siècle', *BIAPSL*, 1920, pp. 59 sqq.

K. Michalski, 'Les Sources du criticisme et du scepticisme dans la philosophie du xive siècle', *BIAPSL*, 1922, pp. 50 sqq.

K. Michalski, 'Le Criticisme et le scepticisme dans la philosophie du xive siècle', *BIAPSL*, 1925, pp. 41 sqq.

K. Michalski, 'Les Courants critiques et sceptiques dans la philosophie du xive siècle', *BIAPSL*, 1925, pp. 192 sqq.

K. Michalski, 'La Physique nouvelle et les différents courants philosophiques au xive siècle', *BIAPSL*, 1927, pp. 93 sqq.

G. Milhaud, *Descartes savant*, Paris, 1921.

P. Minges, 'Robert Grosseteste Übersetzer der Ethica Nicomachea', *PJ*, xxxii (1919) 230 sqq.

P. Minges, *Joannis Duns Scoti Doctrina Philosophica et Theologica*, Berlin, 1930, 2 vols.

A. C. Mitchell, 'Chapters in the history of terrestrial magnetism', *Terrestrial Magnetism and Atmospheric Electricity* (Baltimore), xxxvii (1932) 105 sqq., xlii (1937) 241 sqq., xlvi (1939) 77 sqq.

A. Mitterer, 'Der Wärmebegriff des hl. Thomas nach seinem physikalischen Weltbild und dem der Gegenwart', *Aus der Geisteswelt des Mittelalters. Studien und Texte Martin Grabmann . . . gewidmet*, hrg. von A. Lang, J. Lechner, M. Schmaus (*BGPM*, Supplement Band iii. 1) Münster, 1935, pp. 720 sqq.

J. E. Montucla, *Histoire des mathématiques*, Paris, 1758, 2 vols.

E. A. Moody, *The Logic of William of Ockham*, New York, 1935.

E. Moody, 'Ockham, Buridan, and Nicholas of Autrecourt', *Franciscan Studies* (St. Bonaventure), N.S. vii (1947) 113 sqq.

S. Moser, *Grundriss der Naturphilosophie bei Wilhelm von Occham* (*Philosophie und Grenzwissenschaften* iv. 2–3) Innsbruck, 1932.

P. F. Mottelay, *Bibliographical History of Electricity and Magnetism*, London, 1922.

J. T. Muckle, 'The Hexameron of Robert Grosseteste', *MS*, vi (1944) 151 sqq.

J. T. Muckle, 'Robert Grosseteste's use of Greek sources in his Hexameron', *MH*, iii (1945) 33 sqq.

L. Mumford, *Technics and Civilization*, London, 1934.

J. U. Nef, 'The progress of technology and the growth of large scale industry in Great Britain, 1540–1640', *Economic History Review*, v (1934–5) 3 sqq.

R. E. Ockenden, 'Marco Antonio de Dominis and his explanation of the rainbow', *Isis*, xxvi (1936) 40 sqq.

J. R. O'Donnell, 'The philosophy of Nicholas of Autrecourt and his appraisal of Aristotle', *MS*, iv (1942) 97 sqq.

G. H. Oliver, *History of the Invention and Discovery of Spectacles*, London, 1913.

L. Olschki, *Geschichte der neusprachlichen wissenschaftlichen Literatur:* i, *Die Literatur der Technik und der angewandten Wissenschaften vom Mittelalter bis zur Renaissaance*, Heidelberg, 1919; ii, *Bildung und Wissenschaft im Zeitalter der Renaissance in Italien*, Leipsig, 1922; iii, *Galilei und seine Zeit*, Halle a. S., 1927.

M. Ornstein [Bronfenbrenner], *The Rôle of Scientific Societies in the Seventeenth Century*, 3rd ed., Chicago, 1938.

G. Paré, A. Brunet et P. Tremblay, *La Renaissance du xiie siècle; les écoles et l'enseignement (Publ. de l'institut d'études médiévales d'Ottawa*, iii) Paris et Ottawa, 1933.

J. M. Parent, *La Doctrine de la création dans l'école de Chartres*, Paris et Ottawa, 1938.

J. R. Partington, 'Albertus Magnus on alchemy', *Ambix* (London), i (1937) 3 sqq.

L. von Pastor, *The History of the Popes, from the Close of the Middle Ages*, transl. and ed. by Dom E. Graf, London, 1937, xxv; 1938, xxix.

M. Patronnier de Gandillac, *La Philosophie de Nicolas de Cues*, Paris, 1941.

J. F. Payne, *English Medicine in the Anglo-Saxon Times*, Oxford, 1904.

S. Pegge, *The Life of Robert Grosseteste*, London, 1793.

A. C. Pegis, 'Concerning William of Ockham', *Traditio*, ii (1944) 465 sqq.

J. Pelseneer, 'Gilbert, Bacon, Galilée, Kepler, Harvey et Descartes: leurs relations', *Isis*, xvii (1932) 171 sqq.

F. Pelster, 'Heinrich von Harclay, Kanzler von Oxford, und seine Quaestionen', *Miscellanea F. Ehrle (Testi e Studi*, xxxvii) Roma, 1924, i. 307 sqq.

F. Pelster, 'Zwei unbekannte philosophische Traktate des Robert Grosseteste', *Scholastik* (Freiburg i. B.), i (1926) 572–3.

F. Pelster, 'Roger Marston O.F.M. (†1303), ein englischer Vertreter des Augustinismus', *Scholastik*, iii (1928) 526 sqq.

F. Pelster, 'Das Leben und die Schriften des Oxforder Dominikanerlehrers Richard Fishacre', *Zeitschrift für katholische Theologie*, liv (1930) 517 sqq.

F. Pelster, 'Les "Quaestiones" de Guiard de Laon dans "Assise Bibl. comm. 138" ', *RTAM*, v (1933) 369 sqq.

F. Pelster, 'Um die Datierung Alberts des Grossen Aristoteles-paraphrase', *PJ*, xlviii (1935) 443 sqq.

A. Pelzer, 'Une Source inconnue de Roger Bacon, Alfred de Sareshel, commentateur des Météorologiques d'Aristote', *AFH*, xii (1919) 44 sqq.

A. Pelzer, 'Les Versions latines des ouvrages de morale conservés sous le nom d'Aristote, en usage au xiiie siècle', *RNP*, xxiii (1921) 378 sqq.

A. Pelzer, 'Le Cours inédit d'Albert le Grand sur la Morale à Nicomaque', *RNP*, xxiv (1922) 333 sqq.

J. M. Pernter und F. M. Exner, *Meteorologische Optik*, 2. Aufl., Wien und Leipzig, 1922.

G. B. Phelan, 'An unedited text of Robert Grosseteste', in *Hommage . . . à M. De Wulf*, Louvain, 1934, pp. 172 sqq.

F. Picavet, *Esquisse d'une histoire générale et comparée des philosophies médiévales*, 2e éd., Paris, 1907.

F. Picavet, *Essais sur l'histoire générale et comparée des théologies et philosophies médiévales*, Paris, 1913.

M. H. Pirenne, *Vision and the Eye*, London, 1948.

T. Plassman, 'Bartholomaeus Anglicus', *AFH*, xii (1919) 67 sqq.

G. L. Plitt, *Jodokus Trutfetter von Eisenach, der Lehrer Luthers in seinem Wirken geschildert*, Erlangen, 1876.

F. A. Pouchet, *Histoire des sciences naturelles au moyen âge*, Paris, 1853.

N. G. Poudra, *Histoire de la perspective ancienne et moderne*, Paris, 1864.

F. M. Powicke, 'Robert Grosseteste and the Nicomachian Ethics', *PBA*, xvi (1930) 85 sqq.

F. M. Powicke, *The Medieval Books of Merton College*, Oxford, 1931.

C. von Prantl, *Geschichte der Logik im Abendlande*, Leipzig, 1861–7, ii–iii.

J. H. Randall, Jr., 'The development of scientific method in the school of Padua', *JHI*, i (1940) 177 sqq.

J. H. Randall, Jr., 'Newton's natural philosophy: Its problems and consequences', in *Philosophical Essays in Honor of Edgar Arthur Singer, Jr.*, ed. F. P. Clarke and M. C. Nahm, Philadelphia, 1942, pp. 334 sqq.

H. Rashdall, 'Nicholas de Ultricuria, a medieval Hume', *Proceedings of the Aristotelian Society* (London), N.S. vii (1907) 1 sqq.

H. Rashdall, *The Universities of Europe in the Middle Ages*, 2nd ed. by F. M. Powicke and A. B. Emden, Oxford, 1936, 3 vols.

G. Reese, *Music in the Middle Ages*, New York, 1940 (London, 1941).

L. M. Régis, 'Analyse et synthèse dans l'œuvre de Saint Thomas', in *Studia Mediaevalia in honorem admodum Reverendi Patri Raymundi Josephi Martin, O.P., S.T.C.*, Brugis Flandrorum, 1948, pp. 303 sqq.

G. Ritter, *Studien zur Spätscholastik* (*Situngsberichte der Heidelbergischer Akademie der Wissenschaften*, philos.-hist. Klasse, iv, vii) Heidelberg, 1921-2.

M. Roberts and E. R. Thomas, *Newton and the Origin of Colours*, London, 1934.

M. von Rohr, 'Aus der Geschichte der Brille', *Beiträge zur Geschichte der Technik und Industrie* (Berlin), xvii (1927) 30 sqq.; xviii (1928) 95 sqq.

M. von Rohr, 'Gedanken zur Geschichte der Brillenherstellung', *Forschungen zur Geschichte der Optik (Beilage-hefte zur Zeitschrift für Instrumentenkunde*, Berlin) ii (1937) 121 sqq.

V. Rose, *Aristoteles Pseudepigraphus*, Leipzig, 1863.

E. Rosen, 'When did Galileo make his first telescope', *Centaurus* (Copenhagen), ii (1951) 44 sqq.

L. Rosenfeld, 'La Théorie des couleurs de Newton et ses adversaires', *Isis*, ix (1927) 44 sqq.

L. Rosenfeld, 'Marcus Marcis Untersuchungen über das Prisma und ihr Verhältnis zu Newtons Farbentheorie', *Isis*, xvii (1932) 325 sqq.

J. C. Russell, 'Hereford and Arabic science in England about 1175-1200', *Isis*, xviii (1932) 14 sqq.

J. C. Russell, 'The preferments and "Adiutores" of Robert Grosseteste', *The Harvard Theological Review* (Cambridge, Mass.), xxvi (1933) 161 sqq.

J. C. Russell, *Dictionary of Writers of Thirteenth Century England* (*Bulletin of the Institute of Historical Research*, iii) London, 1936.

J. C. Russell, 'Richard of Bardney's account of Robert Grosseteste's early and middle life', *MH*, ii (1944) 45 sqq.

J. C. Russell, 'Phases of Grosseteste's intellectual Life', *The Harvard Theological Review*, xliii (1950) 93 sqq.

Sir J. E. Sandys, 'Roger Bacon in English literature', in *RBE*.

Sir J. E. Sandys, *A History of Classical Scholarship*, 3rd ed., Cambridge, 1921, i.

G. Sarton, 'Discovery of the dispersion of light and of the nature of colour (1672)', *Isis*, xiv (1930) 326 sqq.

G. Sarton, *Introduction to the History of Science*, Baltimore, 1927-47, 3 vols.

G. Sarton, 'The scientific literature transmitted through the incunabula', *Osiris*, v (1938) 41 sqq.

G. Sarton, 'The tradition of the Optics of Ibn al-Haitham', *Isis*, xxix (1938) 403-6; xxxiv (1942-3) 217.

N. Scalinci, 'A proposito de Alessandro della Spina e di storia della invenzione degli occhiali', *Rivista di Storia critica delle Scienze mediche e naturali* (Faenza), xv (1933) 139 sqq.

H. C. Scheeben, *Albert der Grosse. Zur Chronologie seines Lebens* (*Quellen und Forschungen zur Geschichte des Dominikanerordens in Deutschland*, xxvii) Leipzig, 1931.

H. C. Scheeben, 'Les Écrits d'Albert le Grand d'après les catalogues', *Revue thomiste*, N.S. xiv (1931) 260 sqq.

E. Schlund, 'Petrus Peregrinus von Maricourt: sein Leben und seine Schriften', *AFH*, iv (1911) 436 sqq., 633 sqq.; v (1912) 22 sqq.

H. Scholz, *Geschichte der Logik* (*Gesch. der Philosophie in Längsschnitten*, iv) Berlin, 1931.

L. Schütz, *Thomas-Lexikon*, 2te Aufl., Paderborn, 1895.

J. F. Scott, *The Scientific Work of René Descartes* (*1596-1650*), London, 1952.

D. E. Sharp, *Franciscan Philosophy at Oxford in the Thirteenth Century*, Oxford, 1930.

D. E. Sharp, 'The philosophy of Richard Fishacre', *NS*, vii (1933) 281 sqq.

D. E. Sharp, 'The *De Ortu Scientiarum* of Robert Kilwardby (d. 1279)', *NS*, viii (1934) 1 sqq.

C. Singer, 'Daniel of Morley, an English philosopher of the xiith century', *Isis*, iii (1920-1) 263 sqq.

C. Singer, 'Steps leading to the invention of the first optical apparatus', *SHMS*, ii.

C. and D. Singer, 'The origin of the medical school of Salerno, the first European university', in *Essays on the History of Medicine presented to Karl Sudhoff*, ed. C. Singer and H. E. Sigerist, Oxford and Zurich, 1924.

D. E. Smith, 'The place of Roger Bacon in the history of mathematics', in *RBE*.

Preserved Smith, *A History of Modern Culture*, London, 1930-4, 2 vols.

E. Solmi, 'Leonardo da Vinci e il metodo sperimentale nelle ricerche fisiche', *Atti e Memorie della r. Accademia Virgiliana di Mantova*, Mantova, 1905.

P. H. Spettmann, *Die Psychologie des Johannes Pecham* (*BGPM*, xx. 6) Münster, 1919.

E. Stamm, 'Tractatus de Continuo von Thomas Bradwardina' *Isis*, xxvi (1936-7) 13 sqq.

M. Steinschneider, *Die europäischen Übersetzungen aus dem Arabischen, bis Mitte des 17. Jahrhunderts* (*Sitzungsberichte der kaiserlichen Akademie der Wissenschaften*, philos.-hist. Klasse, cxlix. 4, cli. 1) Wien, 1905-6.

F. S. Stevenson, *Robert Grosseteste, Bishop of Lincoln*, London, 1899.

J. M. Stillman, *The Story of Early Chemistry*, New York, 1924.

E. W. Strong, *Procedures and Metaphysics, a study in the philosophy of mathematical-physical science in the sixteenth and seventeenth centuries*, Berkeley, Calif., 1936.

E. W. Strong, 'Newton's "Mathematical Way" ', *JHI*, xii (1951) 90 sqq.

F. Strunz, *Albertus Magnus. Weisheit und Naturforschung im Mittelalter*, Wien und Leipzig, 1926.

K. Sudhoff, 'Daniels von Morley *Liber de naturis inferiorum et superiorum*, nach der Handschrift Cod. Arundel 377 des Britischen Museums zum Abdruck Gebracht', *AGNT*, viii (1918) 14 sqq.

K. Sudhoff, *Kurzes Handbuch der Geschichte der Medizin*, Berlin, 1922.

H. Suter, 'Die Mathematik auf den Universitäten des Mittelalters', in *Festschrift der Kantonsschule in Zürich*, Zürich, 1887, pp. 39 sqq.

P. Tannery, *Mémoires scientifiques, V. Sciences exactes au moyen âge*, publiés par J. L. Heiberg, Toulouse et Paris, 1922.

F. Sherwood Taylor, *Galileo and the Freedom of Thought*, London, 1938.

F. Sherwood Taylor, *The Alchemists: Founders of Modern Chemistry*, New York, 1949.

F. Sherwood Taylor, 'Mediaeval scientific instruments', *Discovery* (London), xi (1950) 282 sqq.

H. O. Taylor, *Thought and Expression in the Sixteenth Century*, New York, 1920, 2 vols.

G. Théry, 'Notes indicatrices pour s'orienter dans l'étude des traductions médiévales', in *Mélanges Joseph Maréchal*, Bruxelles, 1950, ii. 296 sqq.

J. W. Thompson, 'The introduction of Arabic science into Lorraine in the tenth century', *Isis*, xii (1929) 184 sqq.

S. P. Thompson, 'Petrus Peregrinus de Maricourt and his Epistola de Magnete', *PBA*, ii (1905-6) 377 sqq.

S. H. Thomson, 'A note on Grosseteste's work of translation', *The Journal of Theological Studies* (London), xxxiv (1933) 48 sqq.

S. H. Thomson, 'The "Notule" of Grosseteste on the Nicomachean Ethics', *PBA*, xix (1933) 195 sqq.

S. H. Thomson, 'The *De Anima* of Robert Grosseteste', *NS*, vii (1933) 201 sqq.

S. H. Thomson, 'The *Summa in VIII Libros Physicorum* of Grosseteste', *Isis*, xxii (1934) 12 sqq.

S. H. Thomson, 'An unnoticed treatise of Roger Bacon on time and motion', *Isis*, xxvii (1937) 219 sqq.

S. H. Thomson, *The Writings of Robert Grosseteste, Bishop of Lincoln, 1235-1253*, Cambridge, 1940.

W. M. Thornburn, 'The myth of Occam's razor', *Mind*, N.S. xxvii (1918) 345 sqq. See also ibid. xxiv (1915) 287-8.

L. Thorndike, *A History of Magic and Experimental Science*, New York, 1923-43, 6 vols.

L. Thorndike, *Science and Thought in the Fifteenth Century*, New York, 1929.

L. Thorndike, 'A weather record for 1399-1406 A.D.', *Isis*, xxxii (1939) 304 sqq.

L. Thorndike, *University Records and Life in the Middle Ages*, New York, 1944.

L. Thorndike, 'John of St. Amand on the magnet', *Isis*, xxxvi (1946) 156-7.

L. Thorndike, 'Thomas Werkwoth on the motion of the eighth sphere', *Isis*, xxxix (1948) 212 sqq.

L. Thorndike, *The Sphere of Sacrobosco and Its Commentators*, Chicago, 1949.

L. Thorndike and P. Kibre, *A Catalogue of Incipits of Mediaeval Scientific Writings in Latin*, Cambridge (Mass.), 1937. Continued by Thorndike in 'Additional incipits of mediaeval scientific writings in Latin', *Speculum*, xiv (1939) 935 sqq.; 'More incipits of mediaeval scientific writings in Latin', ibid. xvii (1942) 342 sqq.

E. Turrière, 'Le Développement de l'industrie verrière d'art depuis l'époque vénitienne jusqu'à la fondation des verreries d'optique', *Isis*, vii (1925) 77 sqq.

A. Uccelli *et alii*, 'La Storia della tecnica', in *Enciclopedia storica delle Scienze e delle loro Applicazioni*, Milano, 1944, ii.

A. Uccelli, *Storia della Tecnica del Medio Evo ai nostri Giorni; Opera compilata con la collaborazione di eminenti specialisti*, 2a tiratura, Milano, 1945.

F. Ueberweg, *Grundriss der Geschichte der Philosophie*, ii, 'Die patristische und scholastische Philosophie', 11. neubearbeitete ... Aufl. hrg. von B. Geyer, Berlin, 1928.

F. Ueberweg, *Grundriss der Geschichte der Philosophie*, iii, 'Die Philosophie der Neuzeit bis zum Ende des xviii. Jahrhunderts', 12.... Aufl.... neubearbeitet von M. Frischeisen-Köhler und W. Moog, Berlin, 1924.

A. P. Usher, *A History of Mechanical Inventions*, New York, 1929.

J. Valentinelli, *Bibliotheca Manuscripta ad S. Marci Venetiarum*, Venice, 1868-76, 6 vols.

C. B. Vandewalle, *Roger Bacon dans l'histoire de la philologie*, Paris, 1929.

A. van der Vyver, 'Les Étapes du développement philosophique du haut moyen âge', *Revue belge de philologie et d'histoire* (Bruxelles), viii (1929) 425 sqq.

A. van der Vyver, 'Les Premières Traductions latines (x^e–xie siècles) de traités arabes sur l'astrolabe', *Ier Congrès international de géographie historique*, ii, *Mémoires*, Bruxelles, 1931, pp. 266 sqq.

A. van der Vyver, 'Les Plus Anciens Traductions latines médiévales (x^e–xie siècles) de traités d'astronomie et d'astrologie', *Osiris*, i (1936) 658 sqq.

A. van der Vyver, 'L'Évolution scientifique du haut moyen âge', *Archeion*, xix (1937) 12 sqq.

E. Vansteenberghe, *Le Cardinal Nicolas de Cues (1401–1464)*. *L'action, la pensée* (*Biblio-thèque du xve siècle*, xxiv) Paris, 1920.

F. Van Steenberghen, 'La Littérature albertino-thomiste (1930–1937)', *RNP*, xli (1938) 126 sqq.

F. Van Steenberghen, *Siger de Brabant d'après ses œuvres inédites*, ii, 'Siger dans l'histoire de l'aristotélisme' (*Les Philosophes belges*, xiii) Louvain, 1942.

F. Van Steenberghen, *Aristote en occident. Les origines de l'aristotélisme parisien*, Louvain, 1946.

Giambattista Venturi, *Commentari sopra la Storia e le Teorie dell' Ottica*, Bologna, 1814, i.

E. E. Viollet-le-Duc, *Dictionnaire raisonné de l'architecture française du xie au xve siècle*, Paris, 1868, ix.

S. Vogl, *Die Physik Roger Bacos*, Erlangen, 1906.

S. Vogl, 'Roger Bacons Lehre von der sinnlichen Spezies und vom Sehvorgange', in *RBE*.

J. J. Walsh, *Medieval Medicine*, London, 1920.

P. A. Walz, A. Pelzer *et alii*, 'Serta Albertina', *Angelicum* (Roma), xxi (1944).

J. R. Weinberg, *Nicolaus of Autrecourt. A study in 14th century thought*, Princeton, 1948.

H. Weisinger, 'The idea of the Renaissance and the rise of modern science', *Lychnos*, 1946-7, pp. 11 sqq.

M. C. Welborne, 'Lotharingia as a center of Arabic and scientific influence in the xi. century', *Isis*, xvi (1931) 188 sqq.

O. Werner, *Zur Physik Leonardo da Vincis*, Berlin, 1911.

Sir William Hale White, *Bacon, Gilbert and Harvey* (Harveian Oration), London, 1927.

Lynn White, Jr., 'Technology and invention in the Middle Ages', *Speculum*, xv (1940) 141 sqq.

A. N. Whitehead, *Science and the Modern World*, Cambridge, 1926.

Sir E. T. Whittaker, *A History of the Theories of Aether and Electricity*, i, 'The Classical Theories', 2nd ed., Edinburgh, 1951.

E. Wickersheimer, 'Robert Grosseteste et la médecine', *3e Congrès de l'histoire de l'art de guérir, Londres, 1922*, Anvers, 1923.

E. Wiedemann, 'Roger Bacon und seine Verdienste um die Optik', in *RBE*.

H. Wieleitner, 'Der "Tractatus de Latitudinibus Formarum" des Oresme', *BM*, xiii (1913) 115 sqq.

H. Wieleitner, 'Über den Funktionsbegriff und die graphische Darstellung bei Oresme', *BM*, xiv (1914) 193 sqq.

P. P. Wiener, 'The tradition behind Galileo's methodology', *Osiris*, i (1936) 733 sqq.

F. Wieser, *Galileo als Philosoph*, Basel, 1919.

B. Willey, *The Seventeenth Century Background; Studies in the thought of the age in relation to poetry and religion*, London, 1934.

J. Wimmer, *Deutsches Pflanzenleben nach Albertus Magnus*, Halle a. S., 1908.

S. D. Wingate, *The Mediaeval Latin Versions of the Aristotelian Scientific Corpus, with special reference to the biological works*, London, 1931.

E. Wohlwill, *Galilei und sein Kampf für die Kopernikanische Lehre*, Hamburg und Leipzig, 1909.

A. Wolf, *A History of Science, Technology, and Philosophy in the 16th and 17th Centuries*, 2nd ed. by D. McKie, London, 1950.

R. Wolf, *Geschichte der Astronomie* (*Geschichte der Wissenschaften in Deutschland*, xvi) München, 1877.

J. K. Wright, 'Notes on the knowledge of latitudes and longitudes in the Middle Ages', *Isis*, v (1923) 75 sqq.

J. Würschmidt, 'Roger Bacons Art des wissenschaftlichen Arbeitens, dargestellt nach seiner Schrift *De Speculis*', in *RBE*.

F. Wüstenfeld, *Die Übersetzungen arabischer Werke in das Lateinische seit dem xi. Jahrhundert* (*Abhandlungen der königlichen Gesellschaft der Wissenschaften zu Göttingen*, xxii. 3) Göttingen, 1877.

H. G. Zeuthen, *Geschichte der Mathematik im Altertum und Mittelalter*, Kopenhagen, 1896. (French translation, Paris, 1902.)

E. Zilsel, 'The origins of William Gilbert's scientific method', *JHI*, ii (1941) 1 sqq.

E. Zilsel, 'The sociological roots of science', *American Journal of Sociology* (Chicago), xlvii (1942) 544 sqq.

ADDENDA

Original Sources

Nicolao Cabeo, *Philosophia Magnetica*, Coloniae, 1629.

Robert Grosseteste, *On Light* (*De Luce*), translated from the Latin with an introduction by C. C. Riedl, Milwaukee, 1942.

Pseudo-Grosseteste, *Summa Philosophiae ad Roberto Grosseteste adscripta*, ed. L. Baur in *Die philosophischen Werke des Robert Grosseteste* (*BGPM*, ix) Münster, 1912, pp. 275 sqq.

William of Ockham, 'The *Centiloquium* attributed to', ed. P. Boehner, *Franciscan Studies*, N.S. i (1941) March, pp. 58 sqq., June, pp. 35 sqq., September, pp. 62 sqq.; ii (1942) 46 sqq., 146 sqq., 251 sqq.

Christopher Scheiner, *Rosa Ursina*, Bracciani, 1630.

Modern Works

A. Aliotta e C. Carbonara, *Galilei* (*Storia della Filosofia italiana*, xii) Milano, 1949.

H. Baron, 'Towards a more positive evaluation of the fifteenth-century renaissance', *JHI*, iv (1943) 21 sqq.

I. M. Bocheński, *Ancient Formal Logic* (*Studies in Logic and the Foundations of Mathematics*) Amsterdam, 1951.

P. Boehner, 'The medieval crisis of logic and the author of the *Centiloquium* attributed to Ockham', *Franciscan Studies*, N.S. iv (1944) 151 sqq.

—— 'Ockham's theory of truth', *Franciscan Studies*, N.S. v (1945) 138 sqq.

P. Boehner, 'Scotus's teaching according to Ockham', *Franciscan Studies*, N.S. vi (1946) 100 sqq., 362 sqq.

—— 'Ockham's theory of signification', *Franciscan Studies*, N.S. vi (1946) 143 sqq.

—— 'Ockham's theory of supposition and the notion of truth', *Franciscan Studies*, N.S. vi (1946) 261 sqq.

—— 'A first redaction of the *Exposito Aurea* of Ockham', *Franciscan Studies*, N.S. viii (1948) 69 sqq.

—— 'The critical value of quotations of Scotus's works found in Ockham's writings', *Franciscan Studies*, N.S. viii (1948) 192 sqq.

—— '*Notitia Intuitiva* of non-existents according to Peter Aureoli, O.F.M. (1322)', *Franciscan Studies*, N.S. viii (1948) 388 sqq.

—— *Medieval Logic. An outline of its development from 1250-c. 1400*, Manchester, 1952.

C. B. Boyer, 'Descartes and the radius of the rainbow', *Isis*, xliii (1952) 95–8.

E. Cassirer, 'Some remarks on the question of the originality of the renaissance', *JHI*, iv (1943) 49 sqq.

M. Clagett, 'Richard Swineshead and the late mediaeval physics', *Osiris*, ix (1950) 131 sqq.

—— review of Herbert Butterfield, *The Origin of Modern Science*, in *Journal of the History of Medicine* (New Haven, Conn.), vi (1951) 42 sqq.

—— 'The use of the Moerbeke translations of Archimedes in the Works of Johannes de Muris', *Isis*, xliii (1952) 236 sqq

A. C. Crombie, 'Avicenna's influence on the medieval scientific tradition', in *Avicenna, Scientist and Philosopher*, ed. G. M. Wickens, London, 1952.

D. L. Douie, *Archbishop Pecham*, Oxford, 1952.

D. B. Durand, 'Tradition and innovation fifteenth-century Italy', *JHI*, iv (1943) 1 sqq.

S. C. Easton, *Roger Bacon and his Search for a Universal Science*, Oxford 1952.

W. K. Ferguson, *The Renaissance in Historical Thought: Five centuries of interpretation*, Cambridge, Mass., 1948.

A. Forest, F. Van Steenberghen, M. de Gandillac, *Le Mouvement doctrinal du xie au xive siècle (Histoire de l'Église depuis les origines jusqu'à nos jours*, fondée par. A Fliche et V. Martin; dirigée par A. Fliche et E. Jarry, xiii) Paris, 1951.

V. Fukala, 'Der arabische Artz Averrhoës war der erste, welche die Netzhaut als den lichtempfindlichen Theil des Auges erkannte', *Archiv für Augenheilkunde*, xlii (1900) 203 sqq.

A. Garreau, *Saint Albert le Grand*, Paris 1932.

M. Grajewski, 'Scotistic bibliography of the last decade (1929–39)', *Franciscan Studies*, N.S. i (1941) May, pp. 73 sqq., June, pp. 55 sqq., September, pp. 71 sqq.; ii (1942) 61 sqq., 158 sqq.

Robert Grosseteste, Scholar and Bishop. Essays in commemoration of the seventh centenary of his death, ed. D. A. Callus, with an introduction by Sir Maurice Powicke, Oxford, 1955. (In an essay on his science, I have given an English translation of *De Calore Solis*, and an account of his work on the calendar.)

H. D. Harradon, 'Some early contributions to the history of geomagnetism—I', *Terrestrial Magnetism and Atmospheric Electricity*, xlviii (1943) 3 sqq.

W. A. Heidel, *The Heroic Age of Science: the conceptions, ideals, and methods of science among the Ancient Greeks*, Baltimore, 1933.

J. Hirschberg, *Geschichte der Augenheilkunde* (Graefe-Saemisch, *Handbuch der gesamten Augenheilkunde*, 2te Aufl., xii–xiv) Leipzig, 1899–1912.

E. Hochstetter, *Studien zur Metaphysik und Erkenntnislehre Wilhelms von Ockham*, Berlin, 1927.

E. F. Jacob, *Some Recent Contributions to the Study of the Middle Ages. An inaugural lecture*, Oxford, 1951.

P. Kibre, 'The intellectual interests reflected in libraries of the 14th and 15th centuries', *JHI*, vii (1946) 257 sqq.

V. Kraft, *Die Grundformen der wissenschaftlichen Methoden (Sitzb. d. Akad. d. Wissensch. in Wien*, philos.-hist. Klasse, cciii. 3) Wien und Leipzig, 1925.

P. O. Kristeller and J. H. Randall, Jr., 'The study of the philosophies of the renaissance', *JHI*, i (1941) 449 sqq.

A. Mansion, *Introduction à la physique aristotélicienne (Aristote: traductions et études,* Collection publiée par l'Institut Supérieur de Philosophie de l'Université de Louvain) 2e éd., Louvain et Paris, 1946.

A. Mieli, 'Il tricentenario dei "Discorsi e dimostrazioni matematiche" di Galileo Galilei', *Archeion*, xxi (1938) 193 sqq.

L. Minio-Paluello, 'Note sull' Aristotele latino medievale', *Rivista di Filosofia neoscolastica* (Milano), xlii (1951) 222 sqq.

G. E. Mohan, 'The prologue to Ockham's exposition of the physics of Aristotle', *Franciscan Studies*, N.S. v (1945) 235 sqq.

E. A. Moody, 'Ockham and Aegidius of Rome', *Franciscan Studies*, N.S. ix (1949) 417 sqq.

—— 'Galileo and Avempace. The dynamics of the Leaning Tower Experiment', *JHI*, xii (1951) 163 sqq., 375 sqq.

O. Neugebauer, *The Exact Sciences in Antiquity*, 2nd ed., Providence, R.I., 1957.

A. Pegis, 'Some recent interpretations of Ockham', *Speculum*, xxiii (1948) 452 sqq.

F. Pelster, 'Gilbert de la Porrée, Gilbertus Porretanus oder Gilbertus Porreta?' *Scholastik* (Freiburg i. B.), xx–xxiv (1949) 401–3.

S. L. Polyak, *The Retina*, Chicago, 1941 (with historical bibliography).

— 'The history of our knowledge of the structure and functioning of the eye', in P. C. Kronfeld, *The Human Eye in Anatomical Transparencies*, New York, 1944.

K. R. Popper, *The Logic of Scientific Discovery*, London, 1959 (1st ed., *Logic der Forschung*, Wien, 1935).

P. Rotta, 'La nozione di misura nella concezione metafisico-scientifica di Nicolo da Cusa', *Rivista di Filosofia neo-scolastica*, xxii (1931) 518 sqq.

H. Scholz und H. Schweitzer, *Die sogenannten Definitionen durch Abstraktion. Eine Theorie der Definitionen durch Bildung von Gleichheitsverwandtschaften (Forschungen zur Logistik und zur Grundlegung der exakten Wissenschaften*, iii) Leipzig, 1935.

R. Steele, 'Roger Bacon and the state of science in the thirteenth century', *SHMS*, ii.

L. Strauss, *The Political Philosophy of Hobbes, its Basis and Genesis*; transl. from the German MS by E. M. Sinclair, Oxford, 1936.

E. W. Strong, 'Newton and God', *JHI*, xiii (1952) 147 sqq.

Studia Albertina. Festschrift für Bernhard Geyer zum 70. Geburtstage, hrg. von H. Ostlender (*BGPM*, Supplementband iv) München, 1952.

L. Thorndike, 'Dates in intellectual history: the 14th century', *JHI*, vi (1945) Suppl. i.

— edited by, *Latin Treatises on Comets Between 1238 and 1368 A.D.*, Chicago, 1950.

E. Troilo, *Averroismo e Aristotelismo padovano*, Padova, 1939.

H. Weisinger, 'English treatment of the relationship between the rise of science and the Renaissance, 1740–1840', *AS*, vii (1951) 248 sqq.

William Whewell, *The Philosophy of the Inductive Sciences, founded upon their history*, 2nd ed., London, 1847, 2 vols.

H. J. J. Winter, *Eastern Science. An outline of its scope and contribution*, London, 1952.

G. H. von Wright, *A Treatise on Induction and Probability*, London, 1951.

Brief Additional Bibliography 1952–69

On Grosseteste himself: there is a useful bibliography in *Robert Grosseteste, Scholar and Bishop*, ed. D. A. Callus, Oxford, 1955; F. Alessio, 'Storia e teoria nel pensiero scientifico di R. Grossatesta', *Rivista critica di storia della filosofia*, xii (1957) 251 sqq.; R. C. Dales, 'Robert Grosseteste's *Commentarius in Octo Libros Physicorum Aristotelis*', *Medievalia et Humanistica*, xi (1957) 10 sqq., 'Robert Grosseteste's scientific works', *Isis*, lii (1961) 381 sqq. 'The text of Robert Grosseteste's *Questio de fluxu et refluxu maris* with an English translation', ibid., lvii (1966) 455 sqq.; B. S. Eastwood, 'Robert Grosseteste's theory of the rainbow', *Archives internationales d'histoire des sciences* (Paris), xix (1966) 313 sqq., 'Grosseteste's "quantitative" law of refraction', *Journal of the History of Ideas*, xxviii (1967) 403 sqq., 'Mediaeval empiricism: the case of Grosseteste's optics', *Speculum*, xliii (1968) 306 sqq.; P. Michaud-Quantin, 'La notion de loi naturelle chez Robert Grosseteste', *Proceedings of the XIth International Congress of Philosophy, Brussels 1953*, xii (Amsterdam & Louvain, 1953) 116 sqq.; A. Pacchi, 'Ruggero Bacone e Roberto Grossatesta in un inedito hobbesiano del 1634', *Rivista critica di storia della filosofia* (Firenze), xx (1965) 499 sqq.; S. H. Thomson, 'Two early portraits of Robert Grosseteste', *Medievalia et Humanistica*, viii (1954) 20 sqq., 'Grosseteste's *Questio De Calore, De Cometis* and *De Operacionibus Solis*', ibid., xi (1957) 34 sqq.; C. M. Turbayne, 'Grosseteste and an ancient optical principle', *Isis*, l (1959) 467 sqq. Also H. C. Plummer, 'Halley's comet and its importance', *Nature*, cl (1942) 249 sqq. (above p. 49).

On scientific methodology: F. Alessio, *Mito e Scienza in Ruggero Bacone*. Milano, 1957; R. M. Blake, C. J. Ducasse and E. H. Madden, *Theories of Scientific Method: the Renaissance through the Nineteenth Century*, Seattle, 1960; M. Clagett, *Archimedes in the Middle Ages*, i– , Madison, Wisc., 1964–, *Nicole Oresme and the Medieval Geometry of Qualities and Motions*, Madison, Wisc., 1968; A. C. Crombie, 'The significance of medieval discussions of scientific method for the scientific revolution', in *Critical Problems in the History of Science*, ed. M. Clagett, Madison., Wisc., 1959, 'Some aspects of Descartes' attitude to hypothesis and experiment', *Actes du 2ème Symposium International d'Histoire des Sciences, Pise-Vinci 16–18 juin 1958*, Paris, 1960, pp. 192 sqq., 'Quantification in medieval physics', *Isis*, lii (1961) 143 sqq., 'The relevance of the middle ages to the scientific movement', in *Perspectives in Medieval History*, ed. K. F. Drew and F. S. Lear, Chicago, 1963 pp., 35 sqq., 'The primary properties and secondary qualities in Galileo Galilei's natural philosophy', in *Saggi su Galileo Galilei*, Firenze, 1969, 'Mathematics, music and medical science', *Actes du XIIe Congrès International d'Histoire des Sciences, Paris 1968*, Paris (in press), with J. D. North, 'Bacon, Roger', *Dictionary of Scientific Biography*, ed. C. C. Gillispie, i, New York (1970); *Galilée. Aspects de sa vie et de son œuvre*, Centre international de Synthèse, Paris, 1968; Galileo Galilei, *Discorsi e dimostrazione matematiche intorno a due nuove scienze*, a cura di A. Carugo e L. Geymonat, Torino, 1958; E. Garin, 'Gli umanisti e la scienza', *Rivista di filosofia* (Milano), lii (1961) 259 sqq.; N. W. Gilbert, *Renaissance Concepts of Method*, New York, 1960, 'Galileo and the school of Padua', *Journal of the History of Philosophy* (Berkeley & Los Angeles), i (1963) 223 sqq.; E. Grant, 'Hypotheses in late medieval and early modern science', *Daedalus: Proceedings of the American Academy of Arts and Sciences* (Cambridge, Mass.), xci (1962) 599 sqq.; M. B. Hesse, 'Hooke's philosophical algebra', *Isis*, lvii (1966) 67 sqq.; A. Koyré, *Newtonian Studies*, London, 1965, *Metaphysics and Measurement: Essays in scientific revolution*, London, 1968; L. Laudan, 'Theories of scientific method from Plato to Mach: a bibliographical review', *History of Science* (Cambridge), vii (1968) 1 sqq.; E. McMullin (editor), *Galileo: Man of Science*, New York & London, 1967; G. Meyer, 'En quel sens peut-on parler de "methode scientifique" de Roger Bacon', *Bulletin de litterature ecclésiastique* (Toulouse), liii (1952) 3 sqq., 77 sqq.; J. H. Randall, Jr., *The School of Padua and the Emergence of Modern Science*, Padova, 1961; P. Rossi, *Clavis Universalis*, Milano & Napoli, 1960, *Francis Bacon: From Magic to Science*, translated by S. Rabinovitch, London, 1968; S. Sambursky, *Physics of the Stoics*, London, 1959, *The Physical World of Late Antiquity*, London, 1962; M. Schramm, 'Aristotelianism: basis and obstacle to scientific progress in the middle ages', *History of Science*, ii (1963) 91 sqq., 'Steps towards the idea of function: a comparison between Eastern and Western science in the middle ages', ibid., iv (1965) 70 sqq.; Norman Kemp Smith, *New Studies in the Philosophy of Descartes*, London, 1952; F. Solmsen, *Aristotle's System of the World*, Ithaca, N.Y., 1960; C. Vasoli, 'Il programma reformatore di Ruggero Bacone', *Rivista di filosofia*, ii (1956) 178 sqq.; W. A. Wallace, *The Scientific Methodology of Theodoric of Freiberg*, Fribourg, 1959; J. A. Weisheipl, 'The place of John Dumbleton in the Merton school', *Isis*, l (1959) 439 sqq., 'Curriculum of the Faculty of Arts at Oxford in the early fourteenth century', *Mediaeval Studies*, xxvi (1964) 143 sqq., 'Classification of the sciences in medieval thought', ibid., xxvii (1965) 54 sqq., 'Developments in the Arts curriculum at Oxford in the early fourteenth century', ibid., xxviii (1966) 151 sqq. See also the reviews by M. Clagett in *Isis*, xlvi (1955) 66 sqq.; A. Koyré, 'Les origines de la science moderne', *Diogène*, No. 16, October 1956; and S. H. Thomson in *Speculum*, xxix (1954) 545 sqq.

On the history of optics: F. Alessio, 'Per uno studio sull' ottica del trecento', *Studi medievali* (Spoleto), 3ª serie, ii. 2 (1961), 'Questioni inediti di ottica di Biagio Pelacani da Parma', *Rivista critica di storia della filosofia*, xvi (1961) 59 sqq., 188 sqq.; C. B. Boyer, 'The theory of the rainbow: medieval triumph and failure', *Isis*, xlix (1958) 378 sqq.; P. Costabel, 'Matière et lumière au xviiᵉ siècle', *Acta historiae rerum naturalium necnon technicarum*, Special Issue iii, Prague, 1967, pp. 115 sqq.; A. C. Crombie, 'The mechanistic hypothesis and the scientific study of vision', *Proceedings of the Royal Microscopical Society*, ii (1967) 3–112 (with extensive bibliography); B. S. Eastwood, 'Averroes' view of the retina—a reappraisal', *Journal of the History of Medicine* (New York), xxiv (1969) 77 sqq.; J. Itard, 'Les lois de la réfraction de la lumière chez Kepler', *Revue d'histoire des sciences* (Paris), x (1957) 59 sqq.; D. C. Lindberg, 'The "Perspectiva communis" of John Pecham: its influence, sources and content', *Archives internationales d'histoire des sciences*, xviii (1965) 37 sqq., 'Roger Bacon's theory of the rainbow: progress or regress?', *Isis*, lvii (1966) 235 sqq., 'The cause of refraction in medieval optics', *The British Journal for the History of Science* (London), iv (1968) 23 sqq., 'The theory of pinhole images from antiquity to the thirteenth century', *Archive for History of Exact Sciences* (Berlin, Göttingen & Hamburg), v (1968) 154 sqq., 'Alhazen's theory of vision and its reception in the West', *Isis*, lviii (1968) 321 sqq.; J. Lohne, 'Thomas Harriot (1560-1621): the Tycho Brahe of optics', *Centaurus* (Copenhagen), vi (1959) 113 sqq., 'The fair fame of Thomas Harriot', ibid., viii (1963) 69 sqq., 'Zur Geschichte des Brechungsgesetzes', *Sudhoffs Archiv für Geschichte der Medizin und der Naturwissenschaften* (Wiesbaden), xlvii (1963) 152 sqq., 'Regenbogen und Brechzahl', ibid., xlix (1965) 401 sqq.; S. L. Polyak, *The Vertebrate Visual System*, Chicago, 1957; *L' Optique de Claude Ptolémée dans la version latine d'après l'arabe de l'émir Eugène de Sicile*, édition critique et exégétique par A. Lejeune, Louvain, 1956 and A. Lejeune, *Recherches sur la catoptrique grecque d'après les sources antiques et médiévales*, Bruxelles, 1957; V. Ronchi, *Histoire de la lumière*, Paris, 1956 (1st, Italian ed., Bologna, 1952), 'L'optique au xviᵉ siècle', in *La science au xviᵉ siècle: Colloque international de Royaumont, 1-4 juillet 1957*, Paris, 1960, pp. 49 sqq.; E. Rosen, 'The invention of eye-glasses', *Journal of the History of Medicine*, xi (1956) 13 sqq., 183 sqq.; A. I. Sabra, *Theories of Light from Descartes to Newton*, London, 1967; M. Schramm, 'Zur Entwicklung der physiologischen Optik in der arabischen Literatur', *Sudhoffs Archiv*, xliii (1959) 289 sqq., *Ibn al-Haytham's Weg zur Physik*, Wiesbaden, 1962, 'Ibn Al-Haythams Stellung in der Geschichte der Wissenschaften', *Fikrun Wa Fann* (Hamburg), No. 6 (1965) 1 sqq.; J. W. Shirley, 'An early experimental determination of Snell's law', *American Journal of Physics* (Lancaster, Pa.), xix (1951) 507 sqq.; G. ten Doesschate, 'Oxford and the revival of optics in the thirteenth century', *Vision Research* (Oxford), i (1961) 313 sqq.; G. Federici Vescovini, 'Le Questioni di "Perspectiva" di Biagio Pelacani da Parma', *Rinascimento* (Firenze), xii (1961) 163 sqq., *Studi sulla prospettiva medievale*, Torino, 1965.

Further bibliography will be found in A. C. Crombie, *Augustine to Galileo*, 2nd, revised ed., 2 vols., reissued with further corrections, London, 1970. Special attention is drawn to M. Clagett, *The Science of Mechanics in the Middle Ages*, Madison, Wisc., 1959; A. C. Crombie (editor), *Scientific Change. Historical studies in the intellectual, social and technical conditions for scientific discovery and technical invention, from antiquity to the present*, London & New York, 1963 and, with the collaboration of A. Carugo, *Galileo's Natural Philosophy: Theories of science and the senses*, (in the press)—with extensive bibliography; E. J. Dijksterhuis, *The Mechanization of the World Picture*, Oxford, 1961; and A. Maier, *Metaphysische Hintergründe der spätscholastischen Naturphilosophie*, Roma, 1955, *Zwischen Philosophie und Mechanik*, Roma, 1958, *Ausgehendes Mittelalter: Gesammelte Aufsätze zur Geistesgeschichte des 14. Jahrhunderts*, 2 vols., Roma, 1964–7, and *Zwei Untersuchungen zur nachscholastischen Philosophie: i, Die Mechanisierung des Weltbilds im 17. Jahrhundert*; ii, *Kants Qualitätskategorien*, 2 Aufl., Roma, 1968.

Index

OTHER TITLES IN THIS HARDBACK REPRINT PROGRAMME
FROM OXBOW BOOKS (OXFORD) AND POWELLS BOOKS (CHICAGO) www.oxbowbooks.com
www.powellschicago.com

ISBN 0-19-	Author	Title
8264011	ALEXANDER Paul J.	The Patriarch Nicephorus of Constantinople
8143567	ALFÖLDI A.	The Conversion of Constantine and Pagan Rome
9241775	ALLEN T.W	Homeri Ilias (3 volumes)
6286409	ANDERSON George K.	The Literature of the Anglo-Saxons
8219601	ARNOLD Benjamin	German Knighthood
8208618	ARNOLD T.W.	The Caliphate
8142579	ASTIN A.E.	Scipio Aemilianus
8144059	BAILEY Cyril	Lucretius: De Rerum Natura (3 volumes)
814167X	BARRETT W.S.	Euripides: Hippolytos
8228813	BARTLETT & MacKAY	Medieval Frontier Societies
8219733	BARTLETT Robert	Trial by Fire and Water
8118856	BENTLEY G.E.	William Blake's Writings (2 volumes)
8111010	BETHURUM Dorothy	Homilies of Wulfstan
8142765	BOLLING G. M.	External Evidence for Interpolation in Homer
814332X	BOLTON J.D.P.	Aristeas of Proconnesus
9240132	BOYLAN Patrick	Thoth, the Hermes of Egypt
8114222	BROOKS Kenneth R.	Andreas and the Fates of the Apostles
8214715	BUCKLER Georgina	Anna Comnena
8203543	BULL Marcus	Knightly Piety & Lay Response to the First Crusade
8216785	BUTLER Alfred J.	Arab Conquest of Egypt
8148046	CAMERON Alan	Circus Factions
8143516	CAMERON Alan	Claudian
8148054	CAMERON Alan	Porphyrius the Charioteer
8148348	CAMPBELL J.B.	The Emperor and the Roman Army 31 BC to 235
826643X	CHADWICK Henry	Priscillian of Avila
826447X	CHADWICK Henry	Boethius
8222025	COLGRAVE B. & MYNORS R.A.B.	Bede's Ecclesiastical History of the English People
8131658	COOK J.M.	The Troad
8219393	COWDREY H.E.J.	The Age of Abbot Desiderius
8241895	CROMBIE A.C.	Robert Grosseteste and the Origins of Experimental Science 1100–1700
8644043	CRUM W.E.	Coptic Dictionary
8148992	DAVIES M.	Sophocles: Trachiniae
814153X	DODDS E.R.	Plato: Gorgias
825301X	DOWNER L.	Leges Henrici Primi
814346X	DRONKE Peter	Medieval Latin and the Rise of European Love-Lyric
8142749	DUNBABIN T.J.	The Western Greeks
8154372	FAULKNER R.O.	The Ancient Egyptian Pyramid Texts
8221541	FLANAGAN Marie Therese	Irish Society, Anglo-Norman Settlers, Angevin Kingship
8143109	FRAENKEL Edward	Horace
8142781	FRASER P.M.	Ptolemaic Alexandria (3 volumes)
8201540	GOLDBERG P.J.P.	Women, Work and Life Cycle in a Medieval Economy
8140215	GOTTSCHALK H.B.	Heraclides of Pontus
8266162	HANSON R.P.C.	Saint Patrick
8581351	HARRIS C.R.S	The Heart and Vascular System in Ancient Greek Medicine
8224354	HARRISS G.L.	King, Parliament and Public Finance in Medieval England to 1369
8581114	HEATH Sir Thomas	Aristarchus of Samos
8140444	HOLLIS A.S.	Callimachus: Hecale
8212968	HOLLISTER C. Warren	Anglo-Saxon Military Institutions
9244944	HOPKIN-JAMES L.J.	The Celtic Gospels
8226470	HOULDING J.A.	Fit for Service
2115480	HENRY Blanche	British Botanical and Horticultural Literature before 1800
8219523	HOUSLEY Norman	The Italian Crusades
8223129	HURNARD Naomi	The King's Pardon for Homicide – before AD 1307
9241783	HURRY Jamieson B.	Imhotep
8140401	HUTCHINSON G.O.	Hellenistic Poetry
9240140	JOACHIM H.H.	Aristotle: On Coming-to-be and Passing-away
9240094	JONES A.H.M	Cities of the Eastern Roman Provinces
8142560	JONES A.H.M.	The Greek City
8218354	JONES Michael	Ducal Brittany 1364–1399
8271484	KNOX & PELCZYNSKI	Hegel's Political Writings
8212755	LAWRENCE C.H.	St Edmund of Abingdon
8225253	LE PATOUREL John	The Norman Empire
8212720	LENNARD Reginald	Rural England 1086–1135
8212321	LEVISON W.	England and the Continent in the 8th century
8148224	LIEBESCHUETZ J.H.W.G.	Continuity and Change in Roman Religion
8143486	LINDSAY W.M.	Early Latin Verse
8141378	LOBEL Edgar & PAGE Sir Denys	Poetarum Lesbiorum Fragmenta
9240159	LOEW E.A.	The Beneventan Script
8115881	LOOMIS Roger Sherman	Arthurian Literature in the Middle Ages
8241445	LUKASIEWICZ, Jan	Aristotle's Syllogistic
8152442	MAAS P. & TRYPANIS C.A.	Sancti Romani Melodi Cantica

8113692	MANDEVILLE Bernard	The Fable of the Bees (2 volumes)
8142684	MARSDEN E.W.	Greek and Roman Artillery—Historical
8142692	MARSDEN E.W.	Greek and Roman Artillery—Technical
8148178	MATTHEWS John	Western Aristocracies and Imperial Court AD 364–425
9240205	MAVROGORDATO John	Digenes Akrites
8223447	McFARLANE K.B.	Lancastrian Kings and Lollard Knights
8226578	McFARLANE K.B.	The Nobility of Later Medieval England
814296X	MEIGGS Russell	The Athenian Empire
8148100	MEIGGS Russell	Roman Ostia
8148402	MEIGGS Russell	Trees and Timber in the Ancient Mediterranean World
8141718	MERKELBACH R. & WEST M.L.	Fragmenta Hesiodea
8143362	MILLAR F.G.B.	Cassius Dio
8142641	MILLER J. Innes	The Spice Trade of the Roman Empire
8147813	MOORHEAD John	Theoderic in Italy
8264259	MOORMAN John	A History of the Franciscan Order
8181469	MORISON Stanley	Politics and Script
8142218	MORITZ L.A.	Grain-Mills and Flour in Classical Antiquity
8274017	MURRAY H.J.R.	History of Board Games
8274033	MURRAY H.J.R.	History of Chess
9240582	MUSURILLO H.	Acts of the Pagan Martyrs & Christian Martyrs (2 volumes)
9240213	MYRES J.L.	Herodotus The Father of History
9241791	NEWMAN W.L.	The Politics of Aristotle (4 volumes)
8219512	OBOLENSKY Dimitri	Six Byzantine Portraits
8270259	O'DONNELL J.J.	Augustine: Confessions (3 volumes)
8144385	OGILVIE R.M. & RICHMOND I.A.	Tacitus: Agricola
263268X	OSLER Sir William	Bibliotheca Osleriana
8116020	OWEN A.L.	The Famous Druids
8131445	PALMER, L.R.	The Interpretation of Mycenaean Greek Texts
8143427	PFEIFFER R.	History of Classical Scholarship (volume 1)
8143648	PFEIFFER Rudolf	History of Classical Scholarship 1300–1850
8111649	PHEIFER J.D.	Old English Glosses in the Epinal-Erfurt Glossary
8142277	PICKARD–CAMBRIDGE A.W.	Dithyramb Tragedy and Comedy
8269765	PLATER & WHITE	Grammar of the Vulgate
9256497	PLATNER S.B. & ASHBY T.	A Topographical Dictionary of Ancient Rome
8213891	PLUMMER Charles	Lives of Irish Saints (2 volumes)
820695X	POWICKE Michael	Military Obligation in Medieval England
8269684	POWICKE Sir Maurice	Stephen Langton
821460X	POWICKE Sir Maurice	The Christian Life in the Middle Ages
8225369	PRAWER Joshua	Crusader Institutions
8225571	PRAWER Joshua	The History of The Jews in the Latin Kingdom of Jerusalem
8143249	RABY F.J.E.	A History of Christian Latin Poetry
8143257	RABY F.J.E.	A History of Secular Latin Poetry in the Middle Ages (2 volumes)
8214316	RASHDALL & POWICKE	The Universities of Europe in the Middle Ages (3 volumes)
8154488	REYMOND E.A.E & BARNS J.W.B.	Four Martyrdoms from the Pierpont Morgan Coptic Codices
8148380	RICKMAN Geoffrey	The Corn Supply of Ancient Rome
8141556	ROSS Sir David	Aristotle: De Anima
8141076	ROSS Sir David	Aristotle: Metaphysics (2 volumes)
8141084	ROSS Sir David	Aristotle: Parva Naturalia
8141092	ROSS Sir David	Aristotle: Physics
9244952	ROSS Sir David	Aristotle: Prior and Posterior Analytics
8142307	ROSTOVTZEFF M.	Social and Economic History of the Hellenistic World (3 volumes)
8142315	ROSTOVTZEFF M.	Social and Economic History of the Roman Empire (2 volumes)
8264178	RUNCIMAN Sir Steven	The Eastern Schism
814833X	SALMON J.B.	Wealthy Corinth
8171587	SALZMAN L.F.	Building in England Down to 1540
8218362	SAYERS Jane E.	Papal Judges Delegate in the Province of Canterbury 1198–1254
8221657	SCHEIN Sylvia	Fideles Crucis
8148135	SHERWIN WHITE A.N.	The Roman Citizenship
825153X	SHERWIN WHITE A.N.	Roman Society and Roman Law in the New Testament
9240167	SINGER Charles	Galen: On Anatomical Procedures
8113927	SISAM, Kenneth	Studies in the History of Old English_Literature
8113668	SKEAT Walter	Langland: The Vision of William Concerning Piers the Plowman (2 volumes)
8642040	SOUTER Alexander	A Glossary of Later Latin to 600 AD
8270011	SOUTER Alexander	Earliest Latin Commentaries on the Epistles of St Paul
8222254	SOUTHERN R.W.	Eadmer: Life of St. Anselm
8251408	SQUIBB G.	The High Court of Chivalry
8212011	STEVENSON & WHITELOCK	Asser's Life of King Alfred
8212011	SWEET Henry	A Second Anglo-Saxon Reader—Archaic and Dialectical
8143443	SYME Sir Ronald	Ammianus and the Historia Augusta
8148259	SYME Sir Ronald	History in Ovid
8143273	SYME Sir Ronald	Tacitus (2 volumes)
8142714	THOMPSON E.A.	The Goths in Spain
9256500	THOMPSON Sir E.Maunde	Introduction to Greek and Latin Palaeography
8200951	THOMPSON Sally	Women Religious
924023X	WALBANK F.W.	Historical Commentary on Polybius (3 volumes)
8201745	WALKER Simon	The Lancastrian Affinity 1361–1399
8161115	WELLESZ Egon	A History of Byzantine Music and Hymnography
8140185	WEST M.L.	Greek Metre